ORGANOTIN COMPOUNDS

VOLUME 3

ORGANOTIN COMPOUNDS

IN THREE VOLUMES

Edited by ALBERT K. SAWYER

Department of Chemistry
University of New Hampshire
Durham, New Hampshire

Volume 3

MARCEL DEKKER, INC., New York 1972

CHEMISTRY

MARCEL DEKKER, INC.
95 Madison Avenue, New York, New York 10016

LIBRARY OF CONGRESS CATALOG CARD NUMBER 71–142895
ISBN 0–8247–1604–3

PRINTED IN THE UNITED STATES OF AMERICA

DEDICATED TO HENRY G. KUIVILA

for whom I have the greatest respect, both as an individual and as a chemist, and who is responsible for my first contact with organotin chemistry.

and to

GREGORY

PREFACE

There has been a marked increase of activity in organotin chemistry in recent years. This work was undertaken to provide up-to-date, comprehensive coverage of this field, prepared by individuals who are well informed in their specialized areas. As editor I have been most fortunate to have such well-qualified authors for the individual chapters.

It is hoped that this book will be of value not only to active workers in organotin chemistry and related areas, but also to new workers in providing the present state of knowledge in the field. In addition to chapters on the chemistry of compounds containing tin bonded to the main group elements, there are chapters on tin- other element bonds, and on such specialized topics as organotin polymers, applications, biological effects and analyses. Complete referencing has not been attempted although such referencing has been attempted for publications since the comprehensive review article by Ingham, Rosenberg, and Gilman in *Chemical Reviews*, October, 1960.

I am particularly indebted to Drs. William Considine and Gerald Reifenberg for critical reviews of several chapters. In addition I wish to thank Dr. Paul Jones for translating the chapter on "Organotin Compounds with Sn–S, Sn–Se, and Sn–Te Bonds," and Mr. Ingo Hartmann for translating the chapter on "Organotin Compounds with Sn–P, Sn–As, Sn–Sb, and Sn–Bi Bonds." I wish also to express appreciation for the help, advice, and encouragement given by many friends too numerous to mention, but particularly for the reading of individual chapters by Drs. Henry Kuivila, Paul Jones, and John Uebel.

Durham, New Hampshire   A. K. SAWYER

FOREWORD

There can be little question of the usefulness of a book that brings together up-to-date material in an active area of organometallic chemistry. Professor Sawyer has done this with *Organotin Compounds*. Not only is there included his continuing, extensive studies but also the cooperative efforts of a group of eminent chemists distinguished for the breadth and depth of their researches in different aspects of this area.

Where does organotin chemistry stand relative to organometallic chemistry as a whole? This is a query that carries with it a relatively high degree of subjectivity. Organotin compounds were among the first organometallic species to be investigated. They have an increasing importance as synthetic agents. However, for a long period no organometallic group equaled the versatility of Grignard reagents as synthetic tools. What of industrial applications? On a tonnage basis, tetraethyllead and tetramethyllead (used primarily as antiknock agents) for many years have exceeded other organometallic groups. In this connection we wrote only about 35 years ago: "Undoubtedly the greatest value of organometallic compounds is their laboratory use for synthesis. It is doubtful that any other group of organic compounds combines at the same time an astonishingly high utility in the laboratory with an equally low usefulness in industry." However, the industrial picture of organometallic chemistry has changed markedly in the last two or three decades.

What shall be said of the use of organotin compounds in the investigation of bonding? Here studies with every type of organometallic compound are important with this most fundamental of all concepts. Some organometallic compounds currently lend themselves to a greater extent than others to the development and testing of new principles by a variety of kinetic and spectroscopic measurements and techniques. One that comes to mind with organotin compounds is the Mössbauer effect.

What of biological or physiological properties? One is aware of the expanding applications of organotin compounds as biocides. But how is one to compare tonnage use of some materials with the extraordinary importance of trace quantities of metal combinations in basically vital processes such as animal enzymatic transformations and photosynthesis? In an exercise of this kind, involved with some comparisons or correlations of similarities and differences, how shall one evaluate the relative impact of organometallic types in the effective interdisciplinary bridging of different branches of chemistry as well as currently disparate areas of science generally.

How much consideration should be given to the recent and current rate of growth of research interest, both academic and industrial? Here organotin chemistry has a highly distinguished record. Might this be ephemeral, or may there be great pauses or interruptions in activity? It is known that more than 100 years passed before the problem of dialkyltins was clarified, and that more than 40 years went by between the times when the structure of tetrakis-(triphenylstannyl)tin was suggested and confirmed. But interruptions in some developments are not atypical. With greater activity in the broad domain of organometallic chemistry, the prospects of fewer discontinuities will improve.

Whatever the prognosis may be, it is reasonably certain that the significant development of organotin chemistry will continue. This book will assist by providing a most helpful background; by suggesting new avenues of approach; by indicating useful correlations, particularly because of the special situation of tin in the periodic arrangement of the elements; and, by setting up research targets for those who hunt intentionally or unknowingly.

Iowa State University   HENRY GILMAN
Ames, Iowa

CONTRIBUTORS TO THIS VOLUME

M. GIELEN AND J. NASIELSKI, Faculté des Sciences, Université Libre de Bruxelles, Bruxelles, Belgium

ALBERT K. SAWYER, Department of Chemistry, College of Technology, University of New Hampshire, Durham, New Hampshire

MICHAEL J. NEWLANDS, Department of Chemistry, Memorial University of Newfoundland, St. John's, Newfoundland, Canada

J. G. A. LUIJTEN, Institute for Organic Chemistry TNO, Utrecht, Netherlands

MALCOLM C. HENRY AND WENZEL E. DAVIDSOHN, U.S. Army Natick Laboratories, Natick, Massachusetts

C. R. DILLARD, Department of Chemistry, Brooklyn College of the City University of New York, Brooklyn, New York

CONTENTS

PREFACE v
FOREWORD vii
CONTRIBUTORS TO THIS VOLUME ix
CONTENTS OF OTHER VOLUMES xiii

9. **Organotin Compounds with Sn–C Bonds without Sn–Sn Bonds** 625

M. Gielen and J. Nasielski

I. Symmetrical Organotin Compounds 626
II. Unsymmetrical (Mixed) Organotin Compounds 634
Appendices 663
References 809

10. **Organotin Compounds with Sn–Sn Bonds** 823

Albert K. Sawyer

I. Introduction 823
II. Preparation and Properties 826
III. Reactions 854

11. **Organotin Compounds with Tin–Other Metal Bonds** 881

M. J. Newlands

I. Introduction
II. Compounds Containing Tin-Typical Element Bonds
III. Compounds Containing Tin-Transition Metal Bonds
IV. Postscript
References

12. **Applications and Biological Effects of Organotin Compounds** 931

J. G. A. Luijten

I. Introduction 931
II. Use of Organotin in Compounds as Stabilizers in Polymers 933
III. Biological Effects of Organotin Compounds 940
IV. Use of Organotin Compounds as Biocides 953
V. Catalytic Uses of Organotin Compounds 961
VI. Miscellaneous Uses 964
References 966

13. **Organotin Polymers** 975

Malcolm C. Henry and Wenzel E. Davidsohn

    I. Introduction 975
   II. Tin Atoms Pendent to Polymer Chain 977
  III. Tin Atoms in Polymer Backbone 984
References 994

14. **Analysis of Organotin Compounds** 997

C. R. Dillard

    I. Introduction 997
   II. Wet Analyses 997
  III. Instrumental Methods 998
  IV. Infrared Spectroscopy 999
   V. Nuclear Magnetic Resonance Spectroscopy 1001
  VI. Mössbauer Spectroscopy 1004
References 1004

CUMULATIVE AUTHOR INDEX 1007
CUMULATIVE SUBJECT INDEX 1065

CONTENTS OF OTHER VOLUMES

VOLUME I

INTRODUCTION, G. J. M. Van der Kerk and J. G. A. Luijten, *Institute for Organic Chemistry TNO, Utrecht, The Netherlands*

ORGANOTIN HYDRIDES, Eugene J. Kupchik, *Department of Chemistry, St. John's University, Jamaica, New York*

ORGANOTIN HALIDES, G. P. Van der Kelen, E. V. Van den Berghe, and L. Verdonck, *Rijksuniversiteit Gent, Laboratorium voor Algemene en Anorganische Chemie-B, Gent, Belgium*

ORGANOTIN COMPOUNDS WITH SN–O BONDS. ORGANOTIN ALKOXIDES, OXIDES, AND RELATED COMPOUNDS, A. J. Bloodworth and Alwyn G. Davies, *University College, London, England*

VOLUME 2

ORGANOTIN COMPOUNDS WITH Sn–O BONDS. ORGANOTIN CARBOXYLATES, SALTS, AND COMPLEXES, R. Okawara and M. Ohara. *Osaka University, Osaka, Japan*

ORGANOTIN COMPOUNDS WITH Sn–S. Sn–Se, AND Sn–Te BONDS, Herbert Schumann, Ingeborg Schumann-Ruidisch, and Max Schmidt, *Institute for Inorganic Chemistry of the University of Würzburg, Germany*

ORGANOTIN COMPOUNDS WITH Sn–N BONDS, K. Jones, *Department of Chemistry, University of Manchester, Institute of Science and Technology*, and M. F. Lappert, *The Chemical Laboratory, University of Sussex, Brighton, England*

ORGANOTIN COMPOUNDS WITH Sn–P, Sn–As, Sn–Sb, and Sn–Bi BONDS, Herbert Schumann, Ingeborg Schumann–Ruidisch, and Max Schmidt. *Institute for Inorganic Chemistry of the University of Würzburg, Würzburg, Germany*

ORGANOTIN COMPOUNDS

VOLUME 3

9. ORGANOTIN COMPOUNDS WITH Sn–C BONDS WITHOUT Sn–Sn BONDS

M. GIELEN AND J. NASIELSKI

Faculté des Sciences
Université Libre de Bruxelles
Bruxelles, Belgium

I. Symmetrical Organotin Compounds	626
A. General	626
B. Preparation	626
C. Chemical Properties	629
II. Unsymmetrical (Mixed) Organotin Compounds	634
A. General	634
B. Preparation	634
C. Physical Properties	648
D. Chemical Properties	650
Appendices	663
References	809

The present chapter deals with compounds having four organic groups attached to tin through a carbon atom. Except for one notable case (*21, 26*), diorganotin(II) compounds are unstable and their structure is rather that of tin-tin polymer chains; they are not discussed here.

Progress has been appreciable in the field of mechanistic studies these last years, and this chapter includes some important generalizations deduced from kinetic and stereochemical results when they can be of some use in synthetic chemistry.

The guiding principle has been that of reactivity and mechanism. Since the behavior of a carbon-tin bond depends strongly on the hybridization of the carbon atom, the paragraphs discuss organotin compounds where this hybridization is sp_3, and sp_2 or sp in turn, aryltins being examined last.

The chapter has been divided, somewhat arbitrarily, into two main sections devoted to symmetrical tetraorganotins and nonsymmetrical tetraorganotins, respectively. Latest data on the synthesis of compounds having four different organic groups attached to tin have been added.

The literature search has been limited to June 1968. Reviews by Ingham et al. (*181*) and by Weiss (*443*) should be consulted for a more complete survey of the earlier literature.

I. Symmetrical Organotin Compounds

A. GENERAL

The symmetrical organotin compounds R_4Sn with four identical R groups are regarded as possessing typical covalent bonds. They can generally be distilled without decomposition and, besides this thermal stability, they do not react very quickly with air. A slow oxidation can nevertheless be observed for some aliphatic derivatives which mostly yields dialkyltin oxides among the reaction products (*7, 50*):

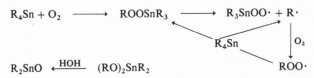

n-Alkyl derivatives are less sensitive to this oxidation than branched-chain containing compounds and, if this oxidation is autocatalytic, very pure compounds can be held in this state for a long time under nitrogen in the dark.

Water generally does not cleave carbon-tin bonds even in the presence of bases, but electrophiles [halogens, strong aqueous acids, or oxidants (*181*)] do this very readily.

Less active electrophiles (water, ketones, or acid chlorides) do react with activated carbon-tin bonds such as α-functionally substituted derivatives [see Sec. II, D, 1, a (*4*)].

B. PREPARATION

Tetraalkyltins are generally prepared by methods in which carbon-tin bonds are built, either by transforming Sn—X or Sn—H (or other Sn—hetero-element) bonds into Sn—C bonds or by transforming C—X bonds into C—Sn bonds by the action of tin or tin alloys.

Other methods of synthesis would include reactions of the alkyl chain without cleavage of the carbon-tin bonds. The sensitivity of these bonds toward electrophiles makes such methods rather inconvenient, except for certain functionally substituted derivatives, where side-chain reactions may proceed faster than carbon-tin cleavage reactions. One of the few examples of such transformations of symmetrical tetraalkyltins into other tetra-alkytins is the alkaline hydrolysis of tetrakis(2-cyanoethyl)tin (*332*):

$$(N{\equiv}C{-}CH_2{-}CH_2)_4Sn \xrightarrow{OH^-} (^{(-)}OOC{-}CH_2{-}CH_2)_4Sn$$

The carboxylic acid salt obtained can even be neutralized to the free acid if one uses for this proton transfer a weak acid which does not cleave the carbon-tin bonds at an appreciable rate:

$$(^{(-)}OOC{-}CH_2{-}CH_2)_4Sn \xrightarrow[\text{weak acid}]{H^+} (HOOC{-}CH_2{-}CH_2)_4Sn$$

1. Symmetrical Tetraalkyltins R₄Sn

a. Metal-Metal Exchange Reactions

$$4\,RM + SnX_4 = R_4Sn + 4\,MX$$

Organomagnesium (*265*) or organolithium compounds react with tin tetrahalide in ethers (diethyl ether, higher ethers, cyclic or special ethers) or in mixtures of ethers and hydrocarbons, frequently in an inert atmosphere (generally N_2). Aluminium alkyls have also been used with SnO_2 or SnS_2 instead of SnX_4.

An excess of RM is generally used in order to make the amount of un-reacted R_3SnX or R_2SnX_2 formed in the reaction as small as possible. The alkyltin halides can be separated by KF treatment, by extraction with a minimum of alcohol (this method is very convenient for the higher alkyl derivatives), or by column chromatography (alumina complexes alkyltin halides very strongly and the tetraalkyltins migrate with the solvent, generally a low boiling hydrocarbon); this last purification method is convenient for the separation of traces of alkyltin halides from tetraalkyltins: the halides are generally not recovered.

Organosodium derivatives are also used as are some other alkali-metals, and these Würtz syntheses (*47a*) are run in hydrocarbon solvents, frequently in an inert atmosphere.

b. Tin-Alloy Syntheses

$$Mg_2Sn + 4\,RX = R_4Sn + 2\,MgX_2$$

Alkyl halides react with Mg_2Sn or with tin alloys such as Na—K—Sn, Sn—Zn—Cu, Frequently, an inert atmosphere (N_2, Ar) is used. Organomercury compounds have been used instead of alkyl halides.

Methyl or benzyl halides react with tin in the presence of molten salts ($SnCl_2$, KCl) (*415*) to give very high yields of R_4Sn.

c. Electrolytic Syntheses

Electrolytic syntheses seem to have become more important than some twenty years ago.

Cyanoethyltin compounds have been made from acrylonitrile using a tin cathode (*187*). Other tetraalkyltins have been synthesized with excellent yields using a tin anode (*458*), and alkyl bromides or chlorides in esters in the presence of $ZnBr_2$. Aluminium alkyls have also been used instead of alkyl halides (*443*). Methyl chloride also reacts with tin halides in a molten non-oxidizing salt mixture with an electrode as the acceptor for halogen (*416*). This variation of the Würtz syntheses gives up to 95% yield.

d. Conversion of Alkyltin Halides to Tetraalkyltins

Tributyltin chloride and dibutyltin chloride can be converted into tetrabutyltin by using zinc and triethylamine (*401*). $(Bu_2SnCl)_2O$ reacts similarly with butyl chloride in the presence of zinc to give high yields of a mixture of tetrabutyltin and of tributyltin chloride.

As these starting organometallic derivatives may be made from butyl halide and tin (*111, 402*), this method might have some practical interest.

e. Addition to Unsaturated Compounds

Halomethyltin (*181*) derivatives can be made by the reaction of carbene (CH_2) with Sn—X bonds:

$$SnX_4 + 4\,CH_2 = Sn(CH_2X)_4$$

2. Symmetrical Vinylic Derivatives $(RR'C=CR'')_4Sn$

The first of the methods described for symmetrical tetraalkyltins has been used to make ethylenic tetraalkyltins: vinylic organomagnesium RMgX or organolithium RLi derivatives can be made in solvents such as THF for instance and react with tin tetrahalides to give the corresponding R_4Sn compounds.

3. Symmetrical Acetylenic Derivatives $(R—C\equiv C—)_4Sn$

Similarly (*85, 246*) acetylenic Grignard reagents or sodium derivatives in THF yield, with SnX_4, the expected organotin compound.

4. Symmetrical Tetraaryltins Ar_4Sn

Symmetrical tetraaryltins are usually made by the metal-metal interchange reaction, starting from $SnCl_4$ and the corresponding Grignard reagent (*171, 181, 252, 443*) or aryl lithium (*181, 214, 419, 443*) in ether or in tetrahydrofuran. There seems to be no general rule enabling one to select either reagent, both being used with equally variable results. Highly overcrowded tetraaryltins can only be made from ArLi (*19*). The hydrolysis of the Grignard reaction mixture is usually carried out with aqueous ammonium chloride, although dilute mineral acids should prove fairly harmless towards the rather unreactive tetraaryltins, and have indeed been used (*18, 19*). The work-up of lithium reaction mixtures is of course much easier.

Less usual methods include the reaction of bis(triphenyltin)oxide with triphenyl silane, yielding tetraphenyltin (*164*), and the direct interaction of tin metal with pentafluoroiodobenzene or 2,2′-diiodooctafluorobiphenyl to give the corresponding perfluorinated tetraaryltins (*72*).

The symmetrical tetraaryltins are poorly soluble solids, some of them melting with decomposition. They can be sublimed or crystallized to achieve a good degree of purity.

C. CHEMICAL PROPERTIES

1. *Symmetrical Tetraalkyltins*

a. General. Most of the reactions of R_4Sn derivatives involve the replacement of one or more of the R groups. These cleavage reactions of carbon-tin bonds can be realized by electrophiles (*181*) or radicals (*27, 28*). Among the electrophiles, one may use halogens, halogen acids, tin(IV) halides, and also reagents such as other inorganic halides (BX_3 (*293*), $HgCl_2$, $HGeCl_3$ (*262*), PF_5 (*424*)) for instance, organometallic halides ($RBCl_2$, R_3SnCl (*417*)), or oxidants (CrO_3 (*89*)). Alkyl halides react in the presence of $AlCl_3$ with tetraalkyltins to give trialkyltin halides (*84, 329*). Halogens can also be used as radical sources (*41*).

b. Electrophilic Substitution at a Saturated Carbon Atom. Kinetic studies have shown that tetraalkyltins react with electrophiles (I_2 (*131*), Br_2 (*40*), HgX_2 (*1, 2*), CrO_3 (*89*)) by a complex mechanism (*42*) which involves a predetermining equilibrium between the organotin substrate and a nucleophile. This step is then followed by the reaction of an electrophile with the activated carbon-tin bond.

Two different situations may arise:

(1) *Reaction in "nonpolar" solvents:* S_F2

The most nucleophilic species available in solution is the electrophile E—N itself (X—X (*42*), H—Cl (*132*), O_2Cr—O (*89*); this depends on the relative nucleophilicity of E—N and of the solvent or of any dissolved species present in the solution):

$$\text{C—Sn} + \text{N—E} \quad \rightleftharpoons \quad \overset{(-)}{\text{C—Sn}}\!\!-\!\!\overset{(+)}{\text{N}}\text{—E} \qquad\qquad \text{(I)}$$

The complex formed in this equilibrium contains activated carbon atoms (bound to a negatively charged tin atom) and an enhanced electrophilic species (E bound to a positively charged atom). An intramolecular reaction, which seems thus a reasonable way in which this complex might give reaction products, is observed when the structure of the complex allows such a cyclic transition state (four center mechanism $S_F 2$):

$$
\begin{array}{c}
\text{C}\!\!-\!\!\text{Sn}^{(-)} \\
\diagdown\!\!\diagup\;| \\
\text{E}\!\!-\!\!\text{N}^{(+)}
\end{array}
\quad\longrightarrow\quad
\left[
\begin{array}{c}
\text{C}\text{------}\text{Sn} \\
\vdots\qquad\vdots \\
\text{E}\text{------}\text{N}
\end{array}
\right]^{\ddagger}
\quad\longrightarrow\quad
\begin{array}{cc}
\text{C} & \text{Sn} \\
| & | \\
\text{E} & \text{N}
\end{array}
\qquad\text{(II)}
$$

This seems roughly to be the case for tetramethyl- and tetraethyltin.

This complex, which contains thus rather nucleophilic carbon atoms, may also react with another electrophile E—N to give the cleavage of a carbon-tin bond:

$$
\text{N}\!-\!\text{E} + \overset{(-)}{\text{C}}\!-\!\overset{(+)}{\text{Sn}}\!-\!\text{N}\!-\!\text{E} \longrightarrow \text{C}\!-\!\text{E} + \overset{(-)}{\text{N}}\!-\!\overset{(+)}{\text{Sn}}\!-\!\text{N}\!-\!\text{E} \qquad\text{(III)}
$$

A third possibility cannot be excluded: it is the reaction of the electrophilic part of this complex with another organotin molecule:

$$
\overset{(-)}{\text{C}}\!-\!\overset{(+)}{\text{Sn}}\!-\!\text{N}\!-\!\text{E} + \text{C}'\!-\!\text{Sn}' \longrightarrow \text{C}'\text{E} + \text{Sn}'\!-\!\text{N} + \text{C}\!-\!\text{Sn} \qquad\text{(IV)}
$$

This mechanistic picture explains a large number of findings such as:

The presence of a third-order term: the rate of the reaction between tetra-isopropyltin and bromine in chlorobenzene may roughly be described by:

$$
-d\,[\text{X}_2]/dt = k_2^{\text{exp}}\,[\text{R}_4\text{Sn}][\text{X}_2] + k_3^{\text{exp}}\,[\text{R}_4\text{Sn}][\text{X}_2]^2
$$

where the third-order term may be considered as due to the existence of reaction (III). For tetramethyl- and tetraethyltin, the contribution of the third-order term is rather small, but can be determined outside of experimental errors by an appropriate treatment of the kinetics results.

The mixing effect: tetraethyltin reacts 11.7 times faster than tetra-methyltin with bromine in chlorobenzene when these compounds are studied separately. A mixture of tetramethyl- and tetraethyltin, reacting with bromine in chlorobenzene, yields a ratio [EtBr]/[MeBr] = 4.3. It can be shown (*42*) that the presence of tetraethyltin influences the reaction of bromine with tetramethyltin.

This mixing effect may be explained by reaction (IV).

Jungers and co-workers (*186*) have shown that the polarizability of aromatic solvents plays an important role in the reactivity of tetrabutyltin toward iodine.

The kinetics of the reaction of tetramethyltin with tin tetrachloride in CCl_4:

$$
(\text{CH}_3)_4\text{Sn} + \text{SnCl}_4 = (\text{CH}_3)_3\text{SnCl} + \text{CH}_3\text{SnCl}_3
$$

have also been interpreted in terms of formation of association complexes undergoing rapid exchange (155). Besides this rather fast reaction, different slowly reached equilibria are to be considered:

$$(CH_3)_3SnCl + CH_3SnCl_3 \rightleftharpoons 2\,(CH_3)_2SnCl \qquad (K = 10^4)$$
$$(CH_3)_4Sn + (CH_3)_2SnCl_2 \rightleftharpoons 2\,(CH_3)_3SnCl \qquad (K = 330)$$
$$(CH_3)_2SnCl_2 + SnCl_4 \rightleftharpoons 2\,CH_3SnCl_3 \qquad (K = 14)$$

Similar reactions had been studied on tetraethyltin (282) and on tetrabutyltin (244). For the reaction of tetrabutyltin and germanium tetrachloride, butyl germanium trichloride, and tributyltin chloride are the only reaction products; on the contrary, equimolar amounts of tetramethyltin and germanium tetrachloride yield a mixture of dimethylgermanium dichloride and tetramethylgermanium, instead of the expected methylgermanium trichloride. The reaction of tetramethyltin with germanium tetrachloride is indeed complicated by the fact that methylgermanium trichloride and trimethylgermanium chloride are better electrophiles toward tetramethyltin and trimethyltin chloride than germanium tetrachloride.

(2) Reaction in "polar" solvents: $S_E 2$

The most nucleophilic species available in solution is not the electrophile, but the solvent

$$C—Sn + S \rightleftharpoons \overset{(-)\ (+)}{C—Sn—S}$$

In this case, the reaction of the organotin molecule with the solvent gives a "collision complex" whose carbon atoms are once more able to be attacked by an electrophile, yielding an open transition state whose existence has been fairly well established by Abraham and Spalding (2) ($S_E 2$):

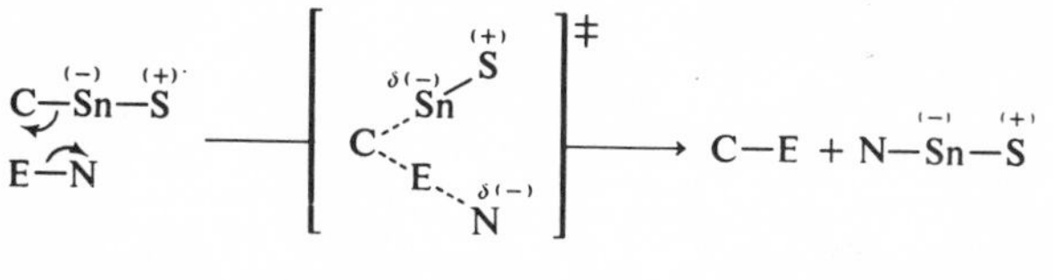

The nucleophilic solvent has not yet become electrophilic enough through the coordination with the metal to compete with the electrophile E—N and to react either intermolecularly or intramolecularly with a carbon-tin bond.

These two steps seem thus the only reasonably possible reactions and indeed, neither a third-order term nor any mixing effect could be detected in nucleophilic solvents such as methanol.

The nucleophilicity of the solvent toward tin (which seems to be the most important factor affecting the polarity of the solvents for electrophilic aliphatic substitutions (*131*)) may be estimated by the ability of this medium to complex the tin atom of trimethyltin chloride (*135, 136*). The following sequence has been found, using NMR spectroscopy in order to evaluate the equilibrium constant

$$HMPT > DMSO \simeq DMF > Py > MeOH \simeq iPrOH >$$
$$tBuOH \simeq MeCOMe \simeq MeCOOMe > Dioxane > MeCN > MeCOOH >$$
$$MeNO_2 > PhCl \simeq CCl_4 \simeq cyclohexane$$

(3) *Dibromination as a function of the nucleophilicity of the solvent*

Tetraalkyltins react some 1000 times faster (*129, 130*) with halogens than trialkyltin halides. Important quantities of dibromides (up to 50%) are however formed when tetrabutyltin for instance, reacts with bromine in a non-nucleophilic solvent (PhCl), even when stoichiometric amounts of halogen are used (*45*). This might be due to the fact that the transition state of a part of the reaction contains two halogen molecules for one tetralkyltin; this could give an intramolecular reaction yielding a dialkyltin dibromide. This is no longer true in nucleophilic solvents and no traces of dibromides can be found if the same reaction is run in methanol (*45*). This shows that the most convenient method to transform tetraalkyltins into trialkytin halides using bromine as the cleavage agent is to use a nucleophilic solvent such as methanol or isopropanol. This rule might even be more general, i.e., applicable to other electrophiles (SnX_4, HgX_2) or to other organometallic derivatives (R_4Pb).

c. Radical Substitution at a Saturated Carbon Atom. Symmetrical tetraalkyltins may also be attacked by radicals. For the reaction of these organometallic molecules with halogens in PhCl in an inert atmosphere (N_2) under illumination, the following mechanistic picture has been proposed to account for a mixing effect (*42*):

$$Br_2 \xrightarrow{h\nu \,(410\,nm)} 2\,Br^{\cdot}$$

$$Br^{\cdot} + R_4Sn \longrightarrow \overset{(-)}{R_4}\overset{(+)}{Sn} - Br^{\cdot}$$

$$\overset{(+)}{R_4}\overset{(-)}{Sn} - Br^{\cdot} \longrightarrow R_3SnBr + R^{\cdot}$$

and

$$\overset{(-)}{R_4}\overset{(+)}{Sn} - Br + R'_4Sn' \longrightarrow R_4Sn + R'_3Sn'Br + R'^{\cdot}$$

forming a chain with

$$R^{\cdot} + Br_2 \longrightarrow R - Br + Br^{\cdot}$$

Oxygen seems to modify the stoichiometry, the reaction products and thus the mechanism of the analogous reaction of tetraethyltin with iodine (*339a*):

$$I_2 \xrightarrow{\text{hv (430 nm)}} 2 \, I\cdot$$

$$I\cdot + Et_4Sn \longrightarrow EtI + Et_3Sn\cdot$$

in the absence of oxygen $\quad Et_3Sn\cdot + I_2 \longrightarrow Et_3SnI + I\cdot$

chain reaction: $\Phi \gg 1$

in the presence of oxygen $\quad Et_3Sn\cdot + O_2 \longrightarrow Et_3Sn-O-O\cdot$

$$Et_3Sn-O-O\cdot \longrightarrow \text{stable products}$$

These results seem to be contradictory, although there is no reason at all that the photo-induced reaction of bromine or iodine with tetraalkyltins must follow the same kinetic scheme.

Razuvaev and co-workers (*327–329*) have obtained a considerable body of evidence for the participation of trialkyltin radicals in the photolysis of tetraalkyltins and in the reactions of these derivatives with carbon tetrachloride, initiated by oxygen or by peroxides:

$$R_4Sn \longrightarrow R_3Sn\cdot + R\cdot$$

The organotin radicals can for instance take part in halogen abstractions:

$$R_3Sn\cdot + X-C{\textstyle\leqq} \longrightarrow R_3SnX + \cdot C{\textstyle\leqq}$$

An alternative route to the triethyltin radicals produces ethylene (*438*):

$$R\cdot + (C_2H_5)_4Sn \longrightarrow RH + (C_2H_5)_4Sn-C_2H_4\cdot \longrightarrow (C_2H_5)_3Sn\cdot + C_2H_4$$

2. Symmetrical Vinylic and Acetylenic Derivatives

Tetravinyltin reacts more than 20 times faster with iodine than tetraethyltin, but is less reactive than vinyltrialkyltins (*17*).

The mechanism, which has been elucidated by the study of mixed tetraalkyltins ($(RR'C{=}CR'')SnMe_3$), will be described in the section devoted to these derivatives (Sec. II.D.2.a.(2)).

Little is known about the more reactive symmetrical acetylenic organotin compounds (*246*).

3. Symmetrical Tetraaryltins

Tetraaryltins are usually more prone to cleavage than tetraalkyltins; they react with electrophiles, and one or two aryl groups are cleaved off the tin atom according to experimental conditions. In carbon tetrachloride, bromine gives Ar_2SnBr_2, whereas iodination in chloroform at $-40°C$ is limited to monosubstitution (*181, 225a, 443*).

The most widely used reaction is the disproportionation (or redistribution) with $SnCl_4$; selecting the proper conditions, one obtains good yields of the triaryltin chloride, diaryltin dichloride, or aryltin trichloride (*171, 181, 214,*

252, 440, 441, 443). These aryltin halides have found use in the synthesis of various aryl derivatives of tin.

Sulfur reacts with tetraphenyltin to yield phenyltin-sulfur polymer chains and diphenyl sulfide; selenium yields only a monoinsertion product (342–344).

Tetraphenyltin has been included in a Ziegler-type catalyst (92) and an addition compound between tetraphenyltin and hexaphenylditin has been described briefly (257).

There are no mechanistic nor kinetic studies on the behavior of symmetrical tetraaryltins; our knowledge about the mechanisms of aryl-tin cleavages comes from the field of mixed aryl-alkyltins (see Sec. II.D.3).

II. Unsymmetrical (Mixed) Organotin Compounds

A. GENERAL

Since convenient methods are presently available for the synthesis of pure trialkyltin halides, and as dialkyltin halides can also be made, it is now very easy to prepare mixed tetraalkyltins. Fast high yield syntheses of organotin compounds with four different alkyl (aryl) groups linked to tin, have been described (45, 144a, 225a).

B. PREPARATION

1. Methods where no Carbon-Tin Bonds are Made

The availability of functionally substituted organotin compounds has made these methods possible when nucleophilic or radical species are able to react faster with these functional groups than with the carbon-tin bonds.

Among these reactions, one finds:

a. Radical Addition Reactions. Trialkylvinyltins react with a series of compounds to give the addition products:

$$R_3Sn-CH{=}CH_2 + A-B \xrightarrow{\text{Bz}_2\text{O}_2 \text{ or } h\nu} R_3Sn-\underset{A}{\overset{\mid}{C}H}-\underset{B}{\overset{\mid}{C}H_2}$$

$(A-B = Br-CCl_3, H-CCl_3, H-SH, H-SCOCH_3, H-SiCl_3, Cl-CCl_3)$

The same reaction is possible for alkenyl derivatives; these carbon-tin bonds are indeed less sensitive to *electrophilic* species than vinyl-tin bonds (286):

$$Et_3Sn-CH_2-CH_2-CH{=}CH_2 + HSnEt_3 = Et_3Sn-(CH_2)_4SnEt_3$$

Even allyltrialkyltins can be reduced by H_2S_x (349):

$$2\,R_3Sn-CH_2-CH{=}CH_2 + H_2S_x = (R_3Sn-CH_2-\underset{CH_3}{\overset{\mid}{C}H}-)_2S_x$$

Double bonds seem to be more suitable for these reactions than triple bonds:

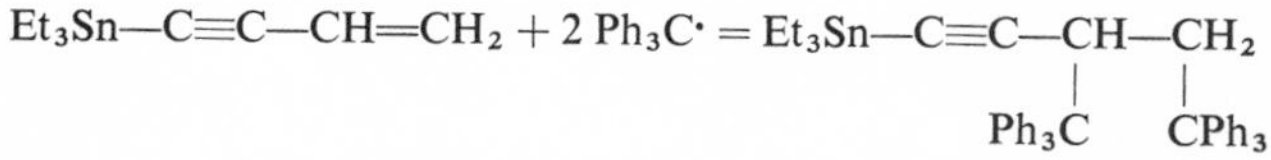

$$Et_3Sn-C\equiv C-CH=CH_2 + 2\ Ph_3C\cdot = Et_3Sn-C\equiv C-\underset{\underset{Ph_3C}{|}}{CH}-\underset{\underset{CPh_3}{|}}{CH_2}$$

although 1–4 addition has been observed when more hindered double bonds are used (*246*):

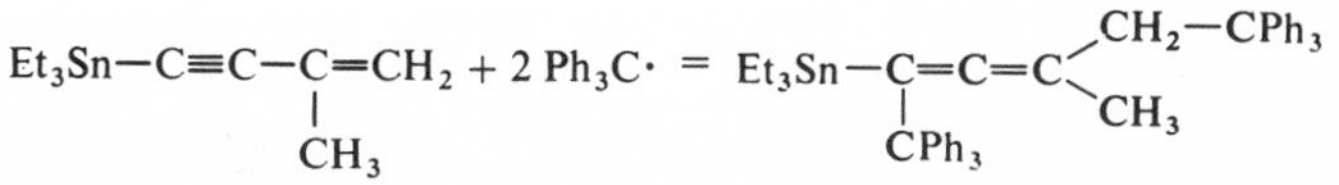

$$Et_3Sn-C\equiv C-\underset{\underset{CH_3}{|}}{C}=CH_2 + 2\ Ph_3C\cdot = Et_3Sn-\underset{\underset{CPh_3}{|}}{C}=C=C\underset{CH_3}{\overset{CH_2-CPh_3}{<}}$$

Addition reactions have been made on acetylenic polymers although the same reactions on the analogous monomers seem to be impossible leading to a very rapid cleavage reaction of the acetylenic-tin bond (*246a*):

$$(R_2Sn-C\equiv C-R'-C\equiv C)_n \xrightarrow{2n\ Br_2} (R_2Sn-CBr=CBr-R'-CBr=CBr)_n$$

$$(R_2Sn-C\equiv C)_n \xrightarrow{n\ Br_2} (R_2Sn-CBr=CBr)_n$$

b. Dipolar 1–3 Additions. Trimethylstannyldiazomethane reacts with phenylisocyanate, yielding a five-membered ring derivative (*218*):

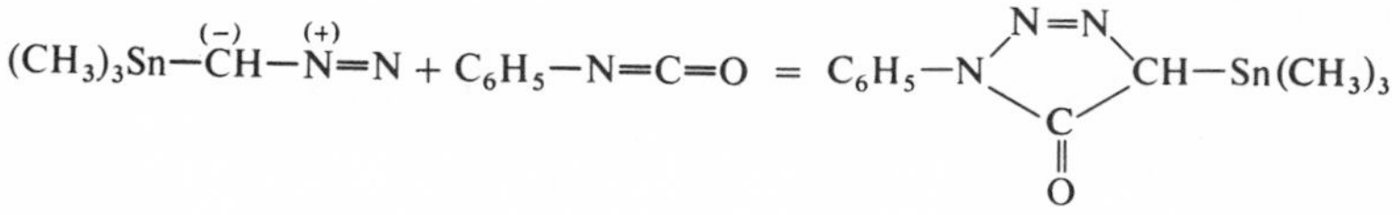

$$(CH_3)_3Sn-\overset{(-)}{C}H-\overset{(+)}{N}=N + C_6H_5-N=C=O = C_6H_5-N\overset{N=N}{\underset{\underset{\overset{\|}{O}}{C}}{<}}CH-Sn(CH_3)_3$$

For this type of addition reaction, a double bond seems also to be more reactive than a triple bond (*85, 290*):

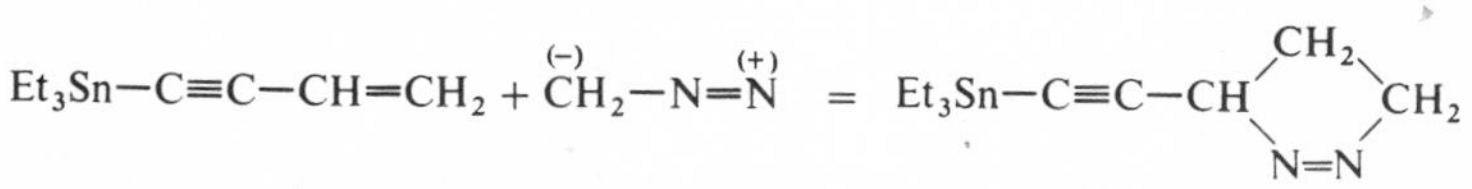

$$Et_3Sn-C\equiv C-CH=CH_2 + \overset{(-)}{C}H_2-N=\overset{(+)}{N} = Et_3Sn-C\equiv C-CH\overset{CH_2}{\underset{N=N}{<}}CH_2$$

c. Diels-Alder Addition Reactions. Komarow and Misyunas (*198*) have studied the reaction of vinylacetylenic compounds with hexachlorocyclopentadiene yielding tin acetylenic hexachlorobicycloheptenes:

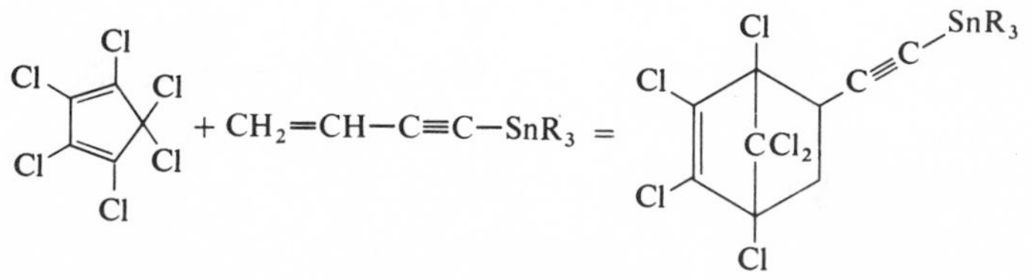

Hexachloropentadiene reacts similarly with acetylenic organotin compounds (*369*) to give hexachloronorbornadienyltin derivatives:

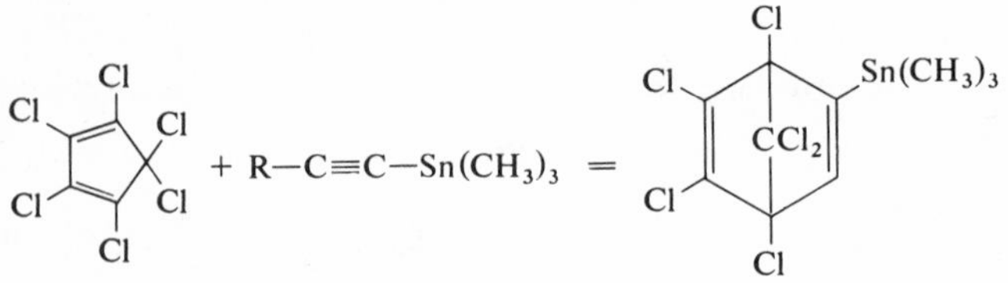

$$R = CH_3, C_6H_5, Sn(CH_3)_3$$

d. Carbene Addition or Insertion Reactions. Carbenes have also been found to add to carbon-carbon double bonds, yielding cyclic derivatives, either on reactions with allyltin compounds (*369, 425*):

$$R_3Sn-CH_2-CH=CH-R + CCl_2 = R_3Sn-CH_2-\underset{\underset{CCl_2}{\diagdown\diagup}}{CH}-CH-R$$

with vinyl derivatives (*366, 371*):

$$R_3Sn-CH=CH_2 + Y = R_3Sn-\underset{\underset{Y}{\diagdown\diagup}}{CH}-CH_2$$

$$(Y = CH_2, CF_2, O)$$

or with other alkenyl compounds (*369*):

$$(CH_3)_3Sn-CH_2-CH_2-CH=CH_2 + CCl_2 = (CH_3)_3Sn-CH_2-CH_2-\underset{\underset{CCl_2}{\diagdown\diagup}}{CH}-CH_2$$

The following reaction might perhaps also be considered as an addition of a carbene to a triple bond (*77*):

$$(CH_3)_3Sn-C\equiv C-CF_3 + (CH_3)_3Sn-CF_3 = (CH_3)_3Sn-\underset{\underset{CF_2}{\diagdown\diagup}}{C}=C-CF_3 + (CH_3)_3SnF$$

Carbenes may also react with organotin molecules by insertion reactions (*359, 366*):

$$R_3Sn-CH_2-CH_2-COOH + CH_2 = R_3Sn-CH_2-CH_2-COOCH_3$$

$$R_3Sn-\overset{|}{\underset{|}{C}}-\overset{|}{\underset{H}{C}}- + CCl_2 = R_3Sn-\overset{|}{\underset{|}{C}}-\overset{|}{\underset{CCl_2H}{C}}-$$

The β-selectivity has been explained by a participation of the tin atom in a cyclic transition state.

e. *Addition or Addition-Elimination Reactions on Carbon-Heteroelement Multiple Bonds.* Trialkyltin esters or nitriles such as $R_3Sn(CH_2)_n$—Y (Y = CN or COOR'; $n \geq 2$) are reduced by $LiAlH_4$, react with hydroxyl ions (*333*), or with organomagnesium compounds, giving the expected reaction of the —CN or —COOR' group.

α-Functionally substituted derivatives with $n = 1$ behave differently (*292*) (this will be discussed later [see Sec. II.D.1.a.(4)].

Characteristic derivatives have been made from organotin ketones (*443*):

$$R_3Sn—(CH_2)_2—\underset{\underset{R'}{|}}{C}{=}O + R''NH_2 = R_3Sn—(CH_2)_2—\underset{\underset{R'}{|}}{C}{=}NH—R''$$

$$R'' = NHCONH_2, \text{ OH or } (NO_2)_2C_6H_3—NH$$

Acetoxyethyl and thioacetoxyethyltrialkyltins react with hydroxide ions to give the corresponding organotin alcohol or sulfide (*443*):

$$R_3Sn—CH_2—CH_2—Y—COCH_3 + OH^{(-)}/ROH$$
$$\longrightarrow R_3Sn—CH_2—CH_2YH \quad (Y = O, S)$$

f. *Nucleophilic and Electrophilic Substitutions.* Nucleophilic substitutions at a saturated carbon atom are possible on organotin molecules:

$$R_3Sn—CH_2Cl + N^{(-)} = R_3Sn—CH_2N + Cl^{(-)}$$
$$N^{(-)} = I^-, SCN^- \text{ or } EtO^- (39) \text{ or } R'R''NH (203)$$
$$(CH_3)_3Sn—CBrCl—Sn(CH_3)_3 + I^- = (CH_3)_3Sn—CICl—Sn(CH_3)_3$$

Analogous reactions have been used on propargyl derivatives (*389*):

$$R'—O—C{\equiv}C—\overset{|}{\underset{|}{C}}—SnR_3 + R''X = R''O—C{\equiv}C—\overset{|}{\underset{|}{C}}—SnR_3 + R'X$$

$$R' = Et_3Sn; R'' = Ac, CH_3OCH_2, (CH_3)_3Si, CH_3, Bz$$

A methyltin group linked to oxygen can be replaced by an alkyl or a trimethylsilicon group (*389*) and a reasonable mechanism could be:

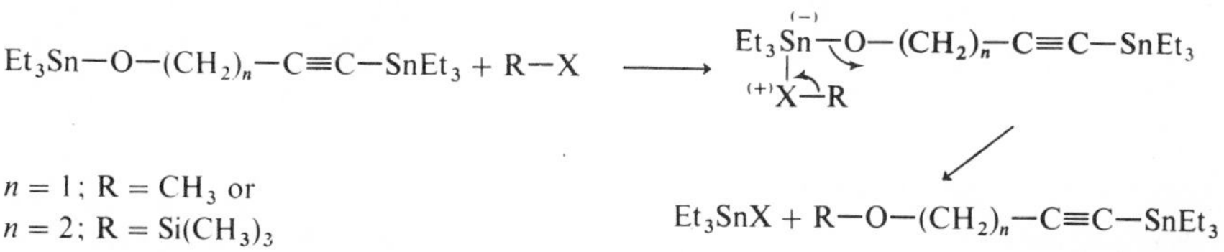

$$Et_3Sn—O—(CH_2)_n—C{\equiv}C—SnEt_3 + R—X \longrightarrow \underset{(+)X^-R}{\overset{(-)}{Et_3Sn^-O}—(CH_2)_n—C{\equiv}C—SnEt_3}$$

$n = 1; R = CH_3$ or
$n = 2; R = Si(CH_3)_3$

$$Et_3SnX + R—O—(CH_2)_n—C{\equiv}C—SnEt_3$$

The same reaction is possible for acetylenic derivatives (*454*):

$$R_3Sn—C{\equiv}C—X + N^{(-)} = R_3Sn—C{\equiv}C—N + X^{(-)}; X = R_3Sn \text{ or } EtS$$

Some other reactions are possible on acetylenic organotin compounds such as (*455*):

$$R_3Sn-C{\equiv}C-X + P(OR')_3 \longrightarrow R_3Sn-C{\equiv}C-\underset{\underset{X}{|}}{P}(OR')_3$$

$$\longrightarrow R_3Sn-C{\equiv}C-\underset{\underset{O}{\|}}{P}(OR')_2$$

Boron containing organotin compounds react with electrophiles through the cleavage of carbon-boron bonds (*443*):

$$(Me_3Sn-CH_2)_3B \xrightarrow{H_2O_2/OH^{(-)}} Me_3Sn-CH_2OH$$

$$(R_3Sn-CH_2-CH_2-B-NPh) \xrightarrow{H_2O_2/OH^{(-)}} R_3Sn-CH_2-CH_2OH$$

The same is, of course, true for lithium containing organotins (*362*):

$$Me_3Sn-CCl_2-Li + HCl = Me_3Sn-CCl_2-H + LiCl$$

and for selected silicon containing compounds (*102*):

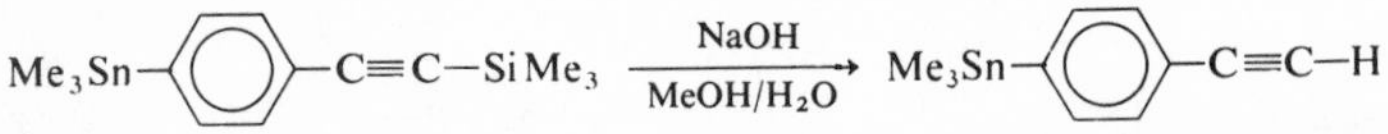

$$Me_3Sn-\!\!\left\langle\bigcirc\right\rangle\!\!-C{\equiv}C-SiMe_3 \xrightarrow[MeOH/H_2O]{NaOH} Me_3Sn-\!\!\left\langle\bigcirc\right\rangle\!\!-C{\equiv}C-H$$

g. Grignard Reactions and Analogs. Chloroalkyltins can be transformed into the corresponding Grignard derivatives which react with electrophiles such as BF_3, allyl chloride or acetaldehyde (*286*):

$$R_3Sn-CH_2Cl \begin{array}{l} \xrightarrow{Mg,\ BF_3} (R_3Sn-CH_2)_3B \\ \xrightarrow{Mg,\ ClCH_2-CH=CH_2} R_3Sn-CH_2-CH_2-CH=CH_2 \end{array}$$

$$R_3Sn-(CH_2)_nX \xrightarrow{Mg,\ CH_3CHO} R\ Sn-(CH_2)_n-\underset{\underset{OH}{|}}{CH}-CH_3$$

with only minor C—Sn cleavage.

The same is true for the analogous reaction on an aromatic ring:

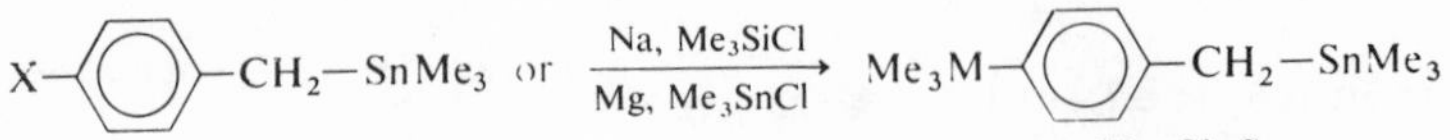

$$X-\!\!\left\langle\bigcirc\right\rangle\!\!-CH_2-SnMe_3 \text{ or } \xrightarrow[Mg,\ Me_3SnCl]{Na,\ Me_3SiCl} Me_3M-\!\!\left\langle\bigcirc\right\rangle\!\!-CH_2-SnMe_3$$

$$M=Si,\ Sn$$

and for tin containing organolithium or organosodium reagents:

$$Me_3Sn-CCl_2Li + CH_3I \longrightarrow \text{ a mixture containing } Me_3Sn-CCl_2-CH_3$$

$$+ Me_3SiCl \longrightarrow Me_3Sn-CCl_2-SiMe_3 \ (362)$$

$$Et_3Sn-C{\equiv}C-SnEt_3 \xrightarrow{NaC{\equiv}CH} Et_3Sn-C{\equiv}C-Na \xrightarrow{RBr} Et_3Sn-C{\equiv}C-R$$

$$(456)$$

h. Organotin Compounds as Nucleophiles. Organotin alcohols have been transformed into the corresponding ethers, for instance, using sodium and alkyl halides:

$$R_3Sn-(CH_2)_nOH \xrightarrow{\text{Na, R'X}} R_3Sn-(CH_2)_nOR'$$

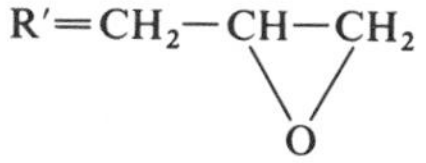

$$R'=CH_2-CH-CH_2$$
$$\diagdown O \diagup$$

and organotin amines can be protonated, or quaternized by alkyl halides (*203*):

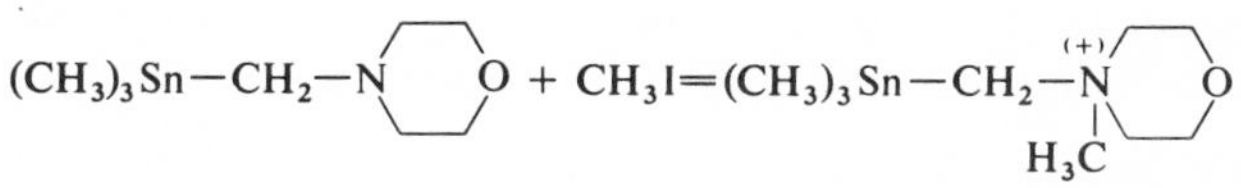

$$(CH_3)_3Sn-CH_2-N\!\!\!\bigcirc\!\!\!O + CH_3I = (CH_3)_3Sn-CH_2-\overset{(+)}{N}\!\!\!\bigcirc\!\!\!O$$
$$\underset{H_3C}{|}$$

i. Photochemical Reactions. Seyferth (*364*) describes the photochemical isomerization of hexachloronorbornadienyltin compounds:

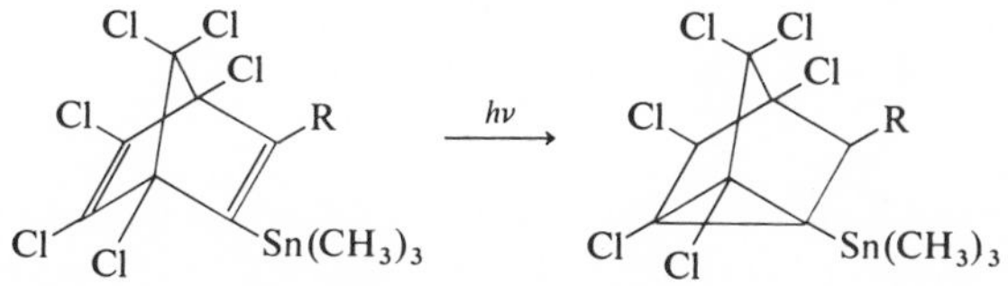

$$R = CH_3, Sn(CH_3)_3$$

j. Decompositions, Oxidations and other Reactions. The pyrazoline obtained by the addition of diazomethane to $Et_3Sn-C\equiv C-CH=CH_2$ is transformed into the cyclopropylethynyl derivative which is the expected product of the addition of CH_2 to the starting organotin alkenyne (*85, 443*):

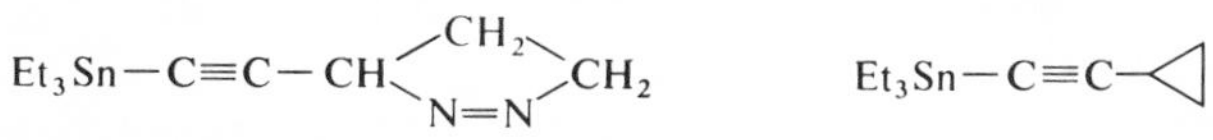

Organotin alcohols have been oxidized into the corresponding acids by permanganate solutions; the same acids have also been made by the catalyzed oxidation of a methyl group by oxygen (*443*).

2. Methods Where Carbon-Tin Bonds Are Made

a. Unsymmetrical (Mixed) Tetraalkyltins $R_nSnR'_{4-n}$

(1) Metal-metal exchange

One finds of course the same methods as for the synthesis of symmetrical tetraalkyltins, plus certain specific ones.

Organotin halides, hydroxides and alkoxides (390) react with organo-magnesium or organolithium reagents in ethers or in mixtures of ethers with hydrocarbons, frequently in an inert atmosphere:

$$R_{4-n}SnX_n + n\,R'M = R_{4-n}SnR'_n + 4\,MX \qquad (M = Li\ or\ MgX)$$

Organomercury and organoaluminium compounds (290) have been used as R'M and organotin oxides or carboxylates instead of $R_{4-n}SnX_n$. More frequently than these last organometallic derivatives, organosodium or potassium derivatives are used and react with organotin halides in hydro-carbons or in liquid ammonia.

Pollard (313) has made mixed organotin derivatives using tin tetrachloride and a mixture of organomagnesium derivatives. This gives essentially the expected product, which has, however, to be separated from a mixture:

$$SnX_4 + n\,RMgX + (4\text{-}n)\,R'MgX = essentially\ R_nSnR_{4-n}$$

Et_3Sn-CH_2COOR have been made by the reaction of hexaethylditin with $Hg(CH_2-COOR)_2$ (249).

Triethyltin hydride gives the same reaction:

$$Et_3Sn-Y + Hg(CH_2-COOR)_2 = Et_3Sn-CH_2-COOR + Hg + Y-CH_2-COOR$$
$$Y = H, SnEt_3$$

Some examples of redistribution reactions between tetraorganometals have been studied by Pollard (311, 312). These redistribution reactions:

$$R_4M + R'_4M' \xrightarrow{\ AlCl_3\ (catal.)\ } R_nMR'_{4-n} + R_{4-n}MR'_n$$

seem to occur only when the central atoms are adjacent members of the fourth group (Ge, Sn; Sn, Sn or Sn, Pb); the following mechanism has been suggested:

$$R_3Sn-R + Al_2Cl_6 \longrightarrow R_3SnCl + RAl_2Cl_5$$
$$R_3SnCl + R'_4Sn \rightleftharpoons R_3SnR' + R'_3SnCl$$

and so on.

The complexity of the reaction mixture after this random exchange makes this method practically unusable for large scale syntheses.

This also seems to be the case for the reaction of R_3SnX or R_2SnX_2 with R'X in the presence of zinc and triethylamine, the reaction mixture generally containing the five possible derivatives: two symmetrical and three mixed ones (401).

Seyferth (362) used another metal-metal exchange reaction to make $Me_3SnCCl_2SnMe_3$, which also gives $BuSnMe_3$:

$$Me_3SnCCl_2SnMe + BuLi = BuSnMe_3 + Me_3SnCCl_2Li$$

Pereyre (303) studied the reactions of mixed tetraalkylsilicons with methoxy-tributyltin, giving excellent yields of mixed tetraalkyltins:

$$R\text{---}Si(CH_3)_3 + CH_3O\text{---}SnBu_3 = R\text{---}SnBu_3 + CH_3O\text{---}Si(CH_3)_3$$
$$R = CH_2CN, (CH_2)_3CN \text{ or } CH_2COOEt$$

(2) Metal-hydrogen exchange

Compounds which contain active hydrogen atoms bound to carbon react with alkyltin alkoxides $R_nSn(OR')_{4-n}$ or with the analogous nitrogen derivatives $R_nSn(NR'_2)_{4-n}$ giving mixed tetraalkyltins (443):

$$Sn\text{---}Y + R''\text{---}H = Sn\text{---}R'' + Y\text{---}H$$

$Y = OR', NR_2 \qquad R''H = CH_3NO_2, Ac_2CH_2, AcCH_2COOR', AcCH_2\text{---}SO_2Ph,$
$$CH_2(COOR')_2, NC\text{---}CH_2COOCH_3, RR'CH\text{---}C\equiv N,$$
$$\text{indene, cyclopentadiene, } H\text{---}C\equiv N.$$

e.g.,

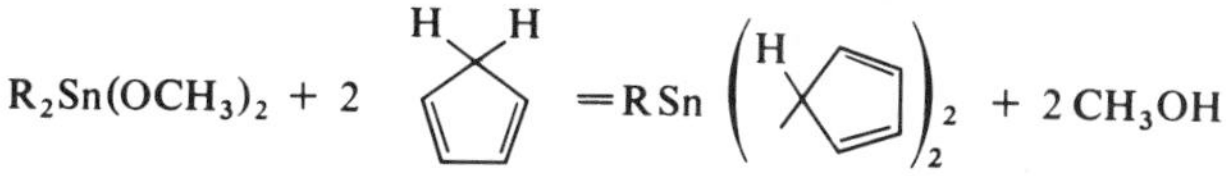

$$R_3Sn\text{---}NR'_2 + H\text{---}C\equiv N = R_3Sn\text{---}C\equiv N + HNR'_2$$

(3) Metal-halogen exchange

Metal-halogen exchange reactions can also be used to make mixed tetraalkyltins.

Tin-metal bonds react with alkyl halides to give such derivatives (181):

$$R_3SnLi + R'X = R_3SnR' + LiX$$
$$R_3Sn\text{---}SnR_3 + I\text{---}CF_3 = R_3Sn\text{---}CF_3 + I\text{---}SnR_3$$

(4) Addition of organotin hydrides to alkenes

Organotin hydrides add to carbon-carbon double bonds, the reaction being schematically described (47):

$$\gtrdot Sn\text{---}H + \gtrdot C=C\lessdot = \gtrdot Sn\text{---}\overset{|}{C}\text{---}\overset{|}{C}\text{---}H$$

e.g.,

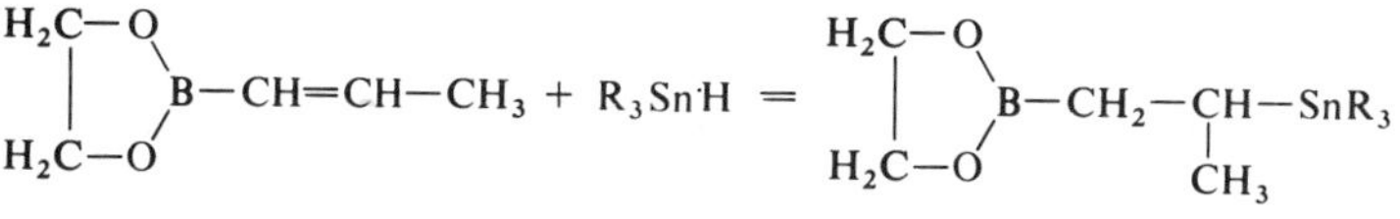

$$R_3Sn\text{---}CH=CH\text{---}COOCH_3 + R'_3SnH = \underset{R'_3Sn}{\overset{R_3Sn}{\diagdown}}CH\text{---}CH_2\text{---}COOCH_3$$

Addition reactions to cycloalkenes seem to occur less readily but are nevertheless possible (409).

1,2- and 1,4-additions occur on conjugated dienes (286):

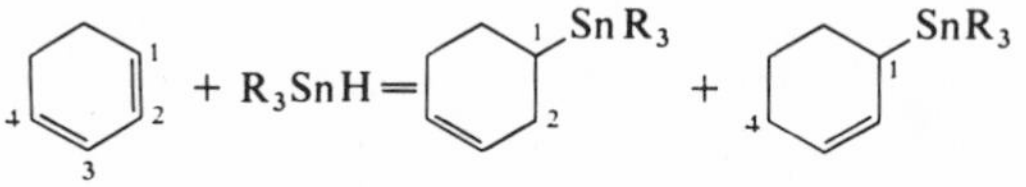

Addition to monosubstituted C=C double bonds seems to occur faster than on C=O (300):

$$R_3SnH + CH_2=CH-CH_2-CH_2-C=O \quad\longrightarrow\quad Mostly\ R_3Sn-(CH_2)_4-COCH_3$$
$$|$$
$$CH_3$$

but the replacement of one or two hydrogen atoms on this C=C bond by one or two methyl groups causes a very important decrease in the amount of this reaction product.

Dichlorocarbene also inserts in the tin-hydrogen bond, and this reaction is then formally analogous to that of alkenes (362, 425):

$$R_3Sn-H + CCl_2 = R_3Sn-CCl_2-H$$

Addition reactions to vinylcyclopropanes are followed by a ring opening which results in the formation of n-alkenyltin compounds (369):

$$R_3SnH + CH_2=CH-CH-CH_2 = R_3Sn-CH_2-CH=CH-CH_2-CCl_2H$$
$$\diagdown\diagup$$
$$CCl_2$$

(5) Other addition reactions

Numerous addition reactions (86) can be used to make carbon-tin bonds.

Trialkyltin hydrides react with carbon-nitrogen double bonds of isocyanates to give an organotin amide:

$$C_6H_{11}-N=C=O + Et_3SnH = Et_3Sn-C-NH-C_6H_{11}$$
$$\parallel$$
$$O$$

Organotin alkoxides add to the carbon-carbon double bond of ketene:

$$CH_2=C=O + R_3SnOR' = R_3Sn-CH_2-C=O$$
$$|$$
$$OR'$$

Metal-metal bonds can also be used in an addition reaction to double bonds (68):

$$CF_2=CF_2 + R_3Sn-SnR_3 = R_3Sn-CF_2-CF_2-SnR_3$$

and the analogous reaction with carbene as "ethylenic" reagent is also possible (362):

$$CCl_2 + Me_3Sn-SnMe_3 = Me_3Sn-CCl_2-SnMe_3$$

Other dimetallic compounds can be used instead of the symmetrical ditins (*30, 31, 69*):

$$CF_2{=}CF_2 + R_3Sn{-}M(CO)_n = R_3Sn{-}CF_2{-}CF_2{-}M(CO)_n$$

$$M(CO)_n = Mn(CO)_5\,,\ Co(CO)_4\,,\ \text{etc.}\ldots$$

Hexafluoro-2-butyne has been added to tin–tin and tin–iron bonds, giving the expected ethylenic addition product (vide infra), but tin–manganese bonds yield, with the same acetylenic hydrocarbon, the formal addition product to the dimer tetrakis(trifluoromethyl)cyclobutadiene:

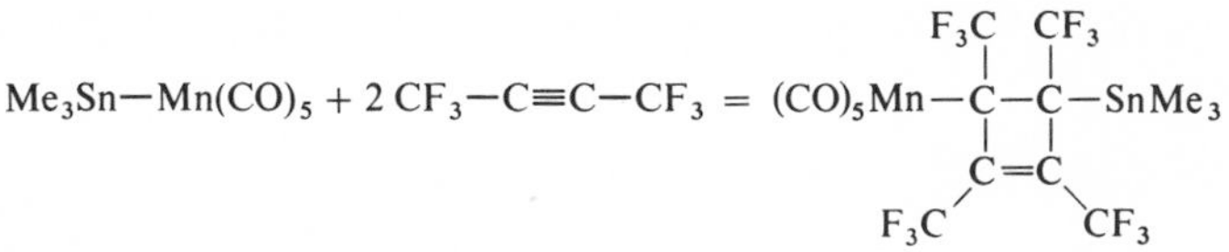

$$Me_3Sn{-}Mn(CO)_5 + 2\ CF_3{-}C{\equiv}C{-}CF_3 = \underset{\underset{\displaystyle F_3C \diagup\ \diagdown CF_3}{\overset{\displaystyle \ \ \ C{=}C}{\ }}}{\overset{\displaystyle F_3C\ \ \ CF_3}{(CO)_5Mn{-}\underset{|}{\overset{|}{C}}{-}\underset{|}{\overset{|}{C}}{-}SnMe_3}}$$

(6) *Addition-elimination reactions on enol acetates*

Addition of R_3SnOR' to an enol acetate (*305*) is sometimes followed by an elimination reaction yielding an α-stannyl ketone:

$$CH_2{=}\underset{\underset{\displaystyle OCOCH_3}{|}}{C}{-}CH_3 + Bu_3Sn{-}OCH_3 = Bu_3Sn{-}CH_2{-}\underset{\overset{\displaystyle ||}{O}}{C}{-}CH_3 + CH_3COOMe$$

but gives sometimes the stannyl-enol (this result is different from that described by Nesmeyanov (*277*)).

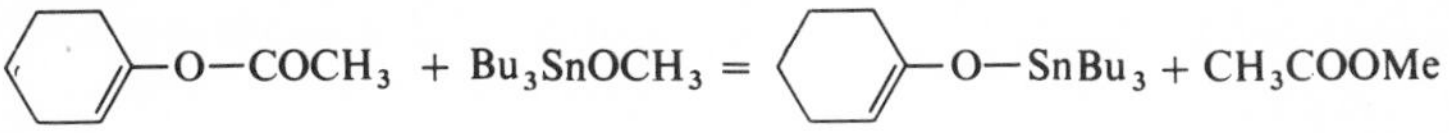

$$\text{⟨ ⟩}{-}O{-}COCH_3 + Bu_3SnOCH_3 = \text{⟨ ⟩}{-}O{-}SnBu_3 + CH_3COOMe$$

Generally, a mixture of both isomers is obtained and the proportion of these isomers seems to depend essentially on steric effects (*305*):

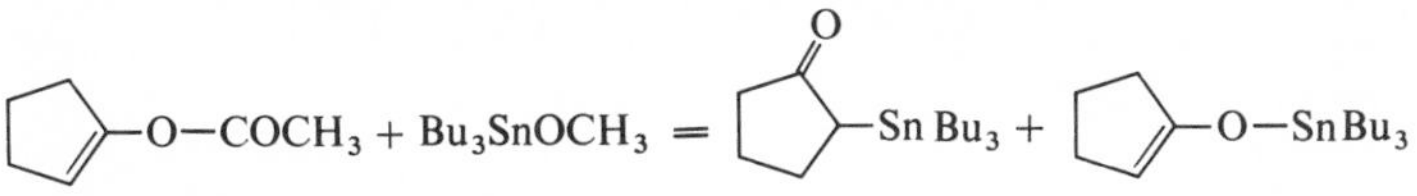

$$\text{⟨ ⟩}{-}O{-}COCH_3 + Bu_3SnOCH_3 = \overset{\displaystyle O}{\text{⟨ ⟩}}{-}Sn\,Bu_3 + \text{⟨ ⟩}{-}O{-}SnBu_3$$

(7) *Thermal decompositions*

Trialkyltin carboxylates may lose carbondioxide, yielding mixed organotin compounds (*243*):

$$Bu_3Sn{-}O{-}COCH_2{-}CN \xrightarrow{\ \Delta\ } Bu_3Sn{-}CH_2{-}CN + CO_2$$

$Bu_3Sn{-}O{-}\underset{\underset{\displaystyle OR}{|}}{CH}{-}CX_3$, formed by the addition of Bu_3SnOR to $CX_3{-}CHO$,

yields Bu_3SnCX_3 (*87*) on heating.

b. Unsymmetrical (Mixed) Alkenyl Organotin Compounds

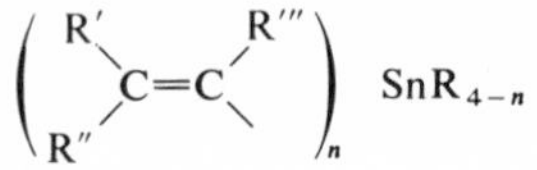

$$\left(\begin{array}{c} \text{R}' \\ \text{R}'' \end{array} \text{C}=\text{C} \begin{array}{c} \text{R}''' \\ \text{R}''' \end{array} \right)_n \text{SnR}_{4-n}$$

(1) *Metal-metal exchange*

Alkenyl Grignard reagents made in a suitable solvent (a cyclic ether for instance) react with organotin halides or oxides to give excellent yields of the expected mixed alkenyl organotin compound.

Alkali-metal organic synthesis has also been used (Li, Na), giving comparable results.

(2) *Metal-halogen exchange*

Triakyltin halides can be converted into trialkyltin alkali metals (R_3Sn-Na for instance), which react with alkenyl halides in ammonia to give the mixed organotin derivatives.

(3) *Hydrostannylation*

Alkyltin hydrides react with substituted acetylenes:

$$\text{Bu}_2\text{Sb}-\text{C}\equiv\text{CH} + \text{Me}_3\text{SnH} = \text{Bu}_2\text{Sb}-\text{CH}=\text{CH}-\text{SnMe}_3 \quad (280)$$
$$\text{HC}\equiv\text{C}-\text{CH}_2-\text{CH}_2\text{OH} + \text{Et}_3\text{SnH} = \text{Et}_3\text{Sn}-\text{CH}=\text{CH}-\text{CH}_2-\text{CH}_2\text{OH} \quad (435)$$

but this reaction gives generally a mixture of three addition products: the α-adduct (polar mechanism) and the two possible *cis-* and *trans-*isomers (free-radical mechanism), when an asymmetric acetylenic compound is used (229):

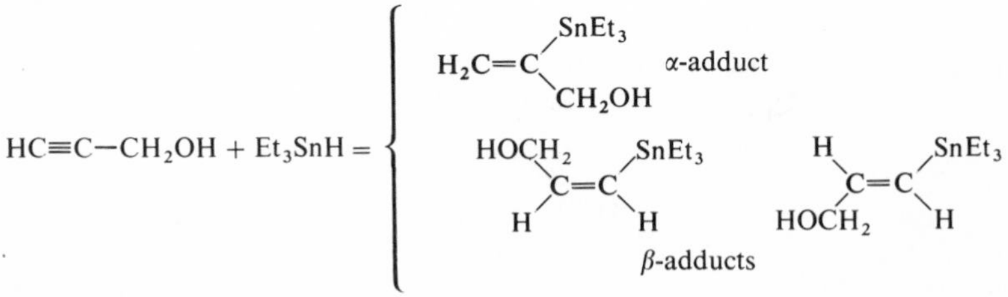

$$\text{HC}\equiv\text{C}-\text{CH}_2\text{OH} + \text{Et}_3\text{SnH} = \left\{ \begin{array}{c} \text{H}_2\text{C}=\text{C} \begin{array}{c} \text{SnEt}_3 \\ \text{CH}_2\text{OH} \end{array} \quad \alpha\text{-adduct} \\ \\ \begin{array}{c} \text{HOCH}_2 \\ \text{H} \end{array} \text{C}=\text{C} \begin{array}{c} \text{SnEt}_3 \\ \text{H} \end{array} \qquad \begin{array}{c} \text{H} \\ \text{HOCH}_2 \end{array} \text{C}=\text{C} \begin{array}{c} \text{SnEt}_3 \\ \text{H} \end{array} \\ \beta\text{-adducts} \end{array} \right.$$

The addition has been shown (234) to be stereospecifically *trans*, but $R_3Sn\cdot$ causes an isomerization by an addition-elimination mechanism (235).

Alkyltin hydrides react with allenes giving a mixture of the substituted allyl derivatives and of the expected alkenyl-tin compound (208).

(4) *Other addition reactions*

Dimetals with tin-tin or tin-iron bonds have also been used to give similar addition reactions (32):

$(CO)_2(\pi\text{-}C_5H_5)Fe\text{—}SnMe_3 + CF_3\text{—}C\equiv C\text{—}CF_3 = (CO)_2(\pi\text{-}C_5H_5)Fe\text{—}C\text{=}C\text{—}SnMe_3$
$$\qquad\qquad\qquad\qquad\qquad\qquad\qquad\qquad\qquad\qquad\quad \underset{F_3C\ \ CF_3}{\mid\ \ \mid}$$

(5) *Addition-elimination reactions*

Vinylic organotin molecules react with triorganotin hydrides to give the substitution product by an addition-elimination mechanism (*235*):

$$R_3Sn\text{—}CH\text{=}CH\text{—}OC_2H_5 + R'_3SnH = R'_3Sn\text{—}CH\text{=}CH\text{—}OC_2H_5 + R_3SnH$$

c. Unsymmetrical (Mixed) Alkynyl Organotin Compounds $(R'\text{—}C\equiv C\text{—})_n$ SnR_{4-n}. Among the most important methods which can be used to make alkynyl organotin compounds one finds (*85, 246*):

(1) *Metal-metal exchange*

Alkynyl Grignard reagents can be used to transform organotin halides or oxides into the mixed alkynyltin derivatives. Group I metal acetylides (lithium or sodium derivatives in ether, sodium derivatives in ammonia or silver compounds in acetone) can be used instead of the Grignard reagents. Organolithium compounds have also been used (*156*).

(2) *Metal-halogen exchange*

Trialkyltin sodium react with acetylenic halides in ammonia or ether.

(3) *Metal-hydrogen exchange*

Substituted acetylenes react with organotin alkoxides, oxides or hydroxides or with dialkylaminotin derivatives, presumably by an addition-elimination mechanism, to give substituted organotin acetylenes:

$$Sn\text{—}Y + R'\text{—}C\equiv C\text{—}H = H\text{—}Y + R'\text{—}C\equiv C\text{—}Sn$$
$$Y = NR''_2, OR'', O\text{—}SnR_3, OH$$

Mixed tetraalkynyltins with an activated carbon-tin bond may be used instead of $\overset{\mid}{-Sn-Y}$ (*320*):

$$Et_3Sn\text{—}CH_2\text{—}CO\text{—}NMe_2 + EtO\text{—}C\equiv C\text{—}H = EtO\text{—}C\equiv C\text{—}SnEt_3 + \underset{\overset{\|}{O}}{CH_3C\text{—}NMe_2}$$

(4) *Thermal decompositions*

Thermal decompositions of trialkyltin carboxylates gives, as for the analogous saturated compounds, mixed tetrasubstituted organotin derivatives (*243, 246*):

$$R_3Sn\text{—}O\text{—}CO\text{—}C\equiv C\text{—}R' \xrightarrow{\Delta} R_3Sn\text{—}C\equiv C\text{—}R'; R' = C_6H_5 \text{ or } SnR_3$$

d. Unsymmetrical (Mixed) Aryltins

(1) Metal-metal exchange

As with the symmetrical tetraaryltins, lithium (*48, 71, 145a, 181, 213, 214, 442, 443*) and magnesium (*145, 181, 443*) derivatives are the most popular reagents for the synthesis of mixed tetraaryltins.

2,2'-Dilithio-biphenyl gives the expected stannafluorenes when reacted with appropriate diaryltin dichlorides (*124, 125*). The reactants should, however, not be left in contact too long, because lithium reagents are effective in inducing redistributions (*125, 214*):

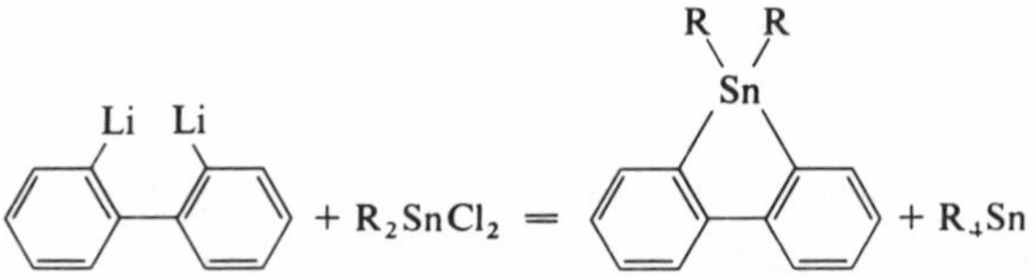

Mixed arylalkyltins are made (*181, 443*) by reacting appropriate aryltin halides with alkylmetals (*23, 445*), a trialkylstannyllithium with an aryl iodide (*103*), or arylmetals with alkyltin halides. Here again, aryl lithium (*38, 52, 54, 81, 213, 326, 374*) and aryl magnesium (*38, 99, 102, 103, 183, 337*) reagents have been used with variable success. Both have been used in the synthesis of perhalophenyltin derivatives:

$$C_6Cl_5MgCl + (C_6H_5)_3SnCl = C_6Cl_5Sn(C_6H_5)_3 \quad (145)$$

$$C_6Cl_5Li + (CH_3)_3SnCl = C_6Cl_5Sn(CH_3)_3 \quad (65, 66)$$

$$C_6F_5MgBr + (CH_3)_3SnF = C_6F_5Sn(CH_3)_3 \quad (103, 310)$$

The lithium reagent obtained from tolane and butyllithium gives a mixed aryl-alkenyl spiro-stannaindene with $SnCl_4$ (*326*):

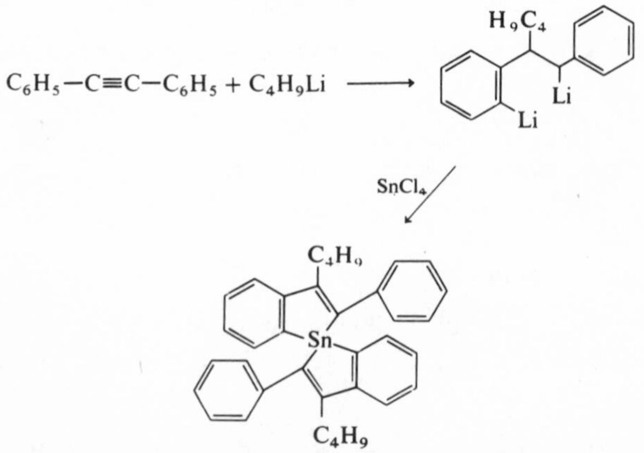

The same spiro-stannaindene is also formed when the dilithio-butyl-styrene is reacted with divinyltin dichloride, showing here again the ability of lithium derivatives to induce redistributions (*326*). These side reactions have been examined by Zuckerman (*457*), who showed the importance of the order in which the reactants are added to each other (see also (*80*)).

The interesting "aromatic" groups carborane (*450*) and ferrocene (*299*) are also introduced by way of their lithium derivatives.

Diphenyltin (II) polymers insert in the C—X bond of alkyl halides to give mixtures of arylalkyltin halides which are useful starting materials for the synthesis of unsymmetrical arylalkyltins (*400*).

(2) Addition reactions

The addition of aryltin hydrides to multiple carbon-carbon bonds has been used in some cases. The reaction is spontaneous (*231, 331*) or has to be induced by free-radical initiators (AIBN) or by uv light (*90, 433, 443*):

$$(C_6H_5)_2SnH_2 + 2\ CH_2{=}CH{-}CN = (C_6H_5)_2Sn(CH_2{-}CH_2{-}CN)_2 \quad (331)$$

$$(C_6H_5)_3SnH + C_6H_5{-}C{\equiv}C{-}H = (C_6H_5)_3Sn{-}CH{=}CH{-}C_6H_5 \quad (231)$$

The addition to terminal olefins is practically quantitative (*90*), but cyclohexene failed to react. The mechanism of the addition to activated multiple bonds has been carefully examined (*237*).

Triphenyltin hydride reduces the carbon-carbon double bond of α,β-unsaturated ketones, instead of adding to it (*230, 304*).

The unusual addition of triphenyltin bromide to allyl bromide in the presence of pyridine has been reported (*259*):

$$(C_6H_5)_3SnBr + Br{-}CH_2{-}CH{=}CH_2 = (C_6H_5)_3Sn{-}CH_2{-}CHBr{-}CH_2Br \quad \text{or}$$

$$CH_2Br{-}CH{-}CH_2Br$$
$$|$$
$$Sn(C_6H_5)_3$$

Aromatic rings have also been attached to tin by Diels-Alder reactions, in a series of interesting experiments, by Seyferth and Evnin:

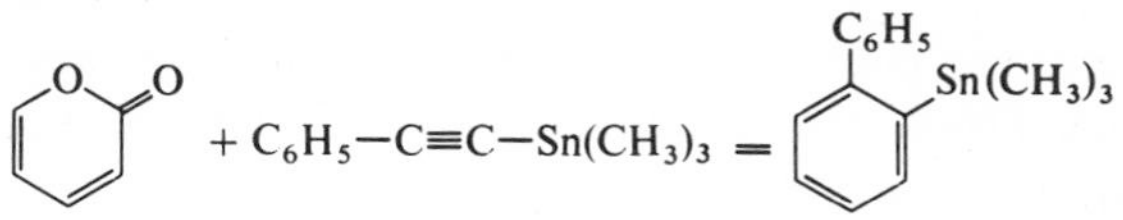

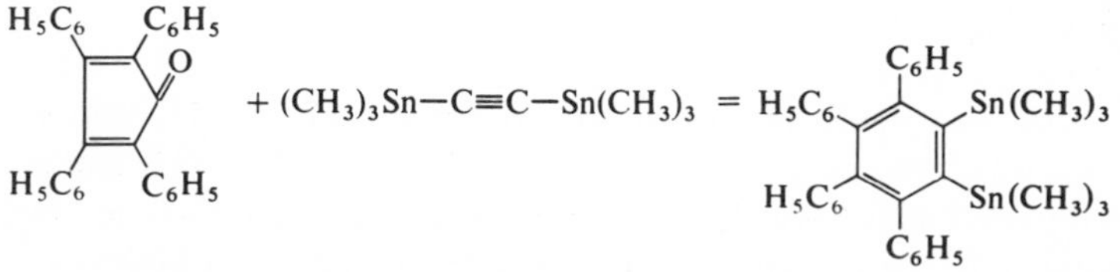

(3) *Insertion*

Diazomethane inserts methylene groups between the metal and halogen atoms of phenyltin trichloride (*206*):

$$C_6H_5SnCl_3 + CH_2N_2 = C_6H_5Sn(CH_2Cl)_3$$

Diphenyltin dichloride yields only a monoinsertion product.

C. PHYSICAL PROPERTIES

1. *UV Spectra*

Saturated tetraalkyltins show only featureless absorption, extending up to 250 nm or even to longer wavelength.

Aryltins display the usual spectrum of the aromatic moiety with a slight bathochromic shift. The analysis of the uv absorption has led many authors to infer the importance of $(p$-$d)\pi$ conjugation in the excited states (*82, 157, 267*). It should however be recalled that discussions on uv spectra should be restricted to 0—0 bands, rather than on λ_{max}; most conclusions drawn from simple inspection of the absorption curves might be very misleading.

The absence of any spectroscopic shift on going from pentachlorobenzene to pentachlorophenyl-trimethyltin has been used by Chivers and David (*66*) to demonstrate the lack of distortion of the organotin compound, whereas the corresponding silicon derivative does show distortion and a red shift.

In this connection, it is interesting to mention that dipole moments of aryltins (*174, 175, 240, 267*) and aryltin chlorides (*150*) also show the participation of $(p$-$d)\pi$ bonding, and that EPR measurements on the highly labile radical anion of 4,4'-bis-(trimethylstannyl)biphenyl (*81*) seems to confirm the possibility of such an interaction.

2. *Raman and IR Spectra*

Raman and ir spectra of tetraorganotin molecules have generally not been studied systematically (*86, 290*) although routine ir spectra are in most cases recorded and published in condensed form when new derivatives are synthesized. These spectra are then used for analytical purpose rather than for critical discussion.

3. *NMR Spectra*

Apart from the PMR spectra of methyl derivatives (*43, 51, 89a, 97, 98, 256a, 397*), which are very simple, those of ethyl (*242, 430, 432*) and propyl compounds (*194, 433*) have also been studied, although a zero-order analysis is not possible in these cases, even by using ^{119}Sn and ^{117}Sn satellites.

The J_{Sn-CH_3} coupling constant seems to correlate with the hybridization (or percentage s character) of the carbon-tin bond in R_3Sn-CH_3 (*89a*). In olefinic organotin systems such as $R-CH=CR'Sn$ the $J_{Sn-C=C-H}$ coupling constant has been used to determine the stereochemistry around the double bond, J being larger for two nuclides in *trans* than in *cis* position (*17, 228*).

The PMR spectra of aryltrimethyltins show that the chemical shift of the aliphatic protons is influenced by the ring currents of the aryl moiety (*43*); large coupling constants between the ^{117}Sn or ^{119}Sn isotopes and *ortho* or *meta* protons are reported for ring-substituted phenyltrimethyltins (*212*). Other arylalkyltins and aryltin hydrides have been examined (*8, 66, 400, 433*).

^{19}F spectra of fluorophenyltins are also reported (*112, 252*).

4. *Mössbauer Spectra (MB)*

Most of the symmetrical tetraalkyltins have an isomeric shift IS (*410*) of about -0.8 mm/sec relative to α-Sn (*149*) and show no quadrupole splitting. Tin compounds exhibit resolvable QS only when the symmetry of Sn is lower than tetrahedral so long as at least one bond to tin is from an atom possessing a lone pair of electrons (*463*).

A quadrupole splitting, QS, is for instance observed when some of the carbon atoms bound to the tin have a sp hybridization; $Et_3Sn-C\equiv C-SnEt_3$ gives two lines centered at -0.70 mm/sec and 1 mm/sec apart.

The trialkylstannylacetones show a quadrupole splitting which has been explained by an intramolecular coordination of the carbonyl on the tin atom.

For $R_3Sn-C\equiv N$, both factors could be responsible for the observed large quadrupole splitting (*149, 413*), the structure of the compound is indeed that of a polymer (*340*) with planar R_3Sn groups and fairly loose $Sn\cdots C\equiv N\cdots Sn$ bonds.

5. *Mass Spectra*

Mass spectrometry may give very useful information about bond energies in excited positively charged ions (*216, 449*), but the behavior of organotin derivatives under electron impact has also been used to obtain some evidence for the structure of new organotin molecules (*45*).

Mass spectrometry might therefore become a very important tool for the analysis of organometallic compounds and fragmentation rules have already been obtained (*44, 137, 138*) which can be applied to such analytical determinations.

Negative ion mass spectrometry of tetramethyltin has been studied recently (*205*) and might become a useful structural method for organic compounds containing tin atoms.

D. CHEMICAL PROPERTIES

1. *Unsymmetrical (Mixed) Tetraalkyltins*

   a. *Electrophilic Substitution at a Saturated Carbon Atom.* The kinetic scheme which describes the reaction of symmetrical tetraalkyltins with electrophiles E—N is also valid for the same reaction on mixed tetraalkyltins and can be used to explain a lot of experimental facts. The only important difference between this case and the former one is the non-equivalence of the alkyl groups bound to the metal atom in mixed derivatives; this introduces a new parameter: the selectivity, which depends dramatically on the experimental conditions.

   (1) *Reactions in "nonpolar" solvents: low selectivity*

   A mixing effect (42) can also be seen on the selectivity of the reaction; the reaction of bromine with propyltrimethyltin in chlorobenzene is described by a ratio $k_2^{exp}(Me)/k_2^{exp}(Pr) = 6.0$, showing a rather low selectivity. However, this ratio becomes even smaller in the presence of tetraethyltin (4.3), although it remains unaltered when changing the concentration of propyltrimethyltin itself.

   The mixing effect may be ascribed to the following reactions:

$$RSnMe_3 + X_2 \rightleftharpoons RMe_3\overset{-}{Sn}-\overset{+}{X}_2 \begin{cases} RX + XSnMe_3 \\ MeX + XSnMe_2R \end{cases}$$

$$R'_4Sn + X_2 \rightleftharpoons R'_4\overset{-}{Sn}-\overset{+}{X}_2 \longrightarrow R'-X + R'_3SnX$$

$$RSnMe_3 + R'_4\overset{-}{Sn}-\overset{+}{X}_2 \begin{cases} RX + XSnMe_3 + R'_4Sn \\ MeX + XSnMe_2R + R'_4Sn \end{cases}$$

the selectivity being decreased when X_2 [Eq. (1)] is replaced by the more electrophilic species $R'_4\overset{-}{Sn}-\overset{+}{X}_2$ [Eq. (3)].

   On the contrary, the presence of trialkyltin halides has two important effects on the reaction of tetraalkyltins with halogens:

   (i) a decrease of the relative importance of the third-order term;

   (ii) an increase of the selectivity (from 6.0 to 7.1 for propyltrimethyltin when triethyltin bromide is added to the chlorobenzene solution).

This can also be due to the competition of reactions (4) and (5) with the normal mechanism (1):

$$RSnMe_3 + R'_3SnX \; \rightleftharpoons \; RMe_3\overset{-}{Sn}-X-\overset{+}{Sn}R'_3$$

$$RMe_3\overset{-}{Sn}-\overset{+}{X}-SnR'_3 + X_2 \Big\langle \begin{array}{c} RX + Me_3\overset{-}{Sn}-\overset{+}{X}-SnR_3' \\ \quad X \\ \\ MeX + Me_2R\overset{-}{Sn}-\overset{+}{X}-SnR'_3 \\ \quad X \end{array}$$

Evidence for such an association is found in the heat of solution of about 3 kcal/mole for trace amounts of trimethyltin bromide dissolved in tetramethyltin (*155*).

Such a pentacoordinate tin atom has also independently been suggested by Eaborn in order to explain the increased reactivity of chloromethyltrimethyltin toward nucleophiles, compared to that of the analogous neopentyl chloride:

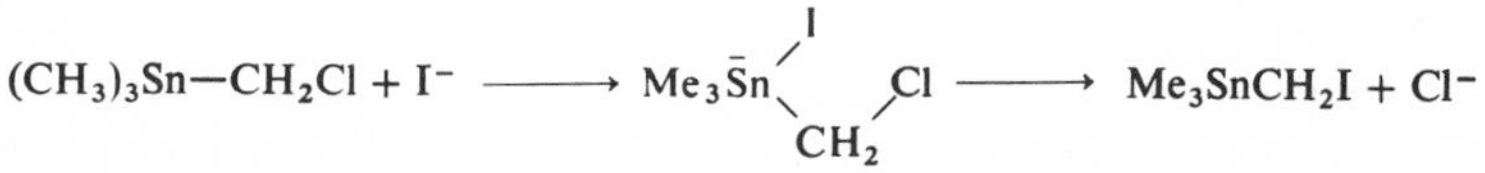

$$(CH_3)_3Sn-CH_2Cl + I^- \longrightarrow Me_3\overset{-}{Sn} \underset{CH_2}{\overset{I}{\Big\langle}} Cl \longrightarrow Me_3SnCH_2I + Cl^-$$

van der Kerk (*333*) suggests an intramolecular nucleophilic assistance for the base-catalyzed hydrolysis of tin-containing esters:

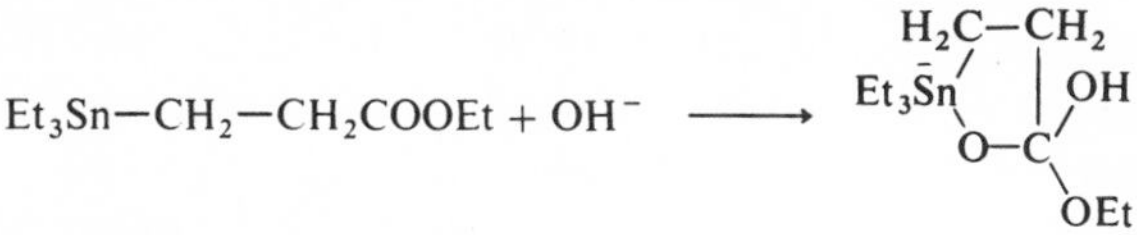

$$Et_3Sn-CH_2-CH_2COOEt + OH^- \longrightarrow Et_3\overset{-}{Sn} \begin{array}{c} H_2C-CH_2 \\ \diagup \quad \big| \diagup OH \\ O-C \\ \qquad \diagdown OEt \end{array}$$

and Seyferth (*366*) adopts a five coordinate tin atom for the reaction of dichlorocarbene with tetraalkyltins:

$$R_4Sn + CCl_2 \longrightarrow R_4\overset{-}{Sn}-\overset{+}{C}Cl_2 \longrightarrow \text{products}$$

The low selectivity observed for the reaction of halogens with mixed tetraalkyltins in nonpolar solvents can be used for the analysis of these organometallic derivatives, the formed alkyl halides showing qualitatively which radicals were bound to the tin atom in the initial derivative (*45*).

(2) *Reactions in polar solvents: high selectivity*

When the same reaction is run in a polar solvent (methanol for instance), the selectivity becomes much higher which is a reasonable extrapolation of the influence of trialkyltin halides on this reaction. For the iododemetallation of propyltrimethyltin in methanol or in acetic acid, the ratio $k_2^{exp}(Me)/k_2^{exp}(Pr)$ is equal to 35. For isopropyltrimethyltin, $k_2^{exp}(Me)/k_2^{exp}(iPr) = 150$; (the same ratio was equal to 2.7 for the bromodemetallation in chlorobenzene).

The use of polar solvents such as methanol (or isopropanol, when the solubility of the organotin compound is not sufficient in methand) is thus strongly recommended for the synthesis of mixed tetraalkyltins, not only in order to avoid dibromination but also to take advantage of the increased selectivity in those polar solvents. Bromination of isopropyltrimethyltin in chlorobenzene yields a mixture of 11 % Me_3SnBr and 88 % $iPrSnMe_2Br$. In methanol, the same reaction gives less than 0.2 % of trimethyltin bromide and very high yields of pure $iPrSnMe_2Br$ (45).

The use of an alcohol as a solvent for the bromination of mixed tetra-alkyltins made it possible to synthesize racemic tetraalkyltins containing *four different alkyl groups* (see Appendix 40) attached to the tin atom. These easily available potentially asymmetrical tetraalkyltins open a way to the study of the stereochemistry of substitution reactions on the tin atom.

(3) *Stereochemistry of bimolecular electrophilic substitution at a saturated carbon atom: S_E2o with inversion, S_E2e with retention of configuration*

Only a few studies have been devoted to the stereochemistry of S_E2 re-actions on organotin compounds, but the results obtained so far are in agree-ment with the following hypothesis: S_E2o reactions seem to proceed with complete inversion of configuration (464) as shown by Jensen (465) on the bromodemetallation of *sec*-butyltrineopentyltin in methanol. On the con-trary, S_E2c reactions, which go through a cyclic transition state, should occur with retention of configuration (16). Of course, substrates for which the inver-sion of configuration is unfavorable, such as *cis*- or *trans*-2-methyl-cyclopro-pyltrimethyltins, or $(+)$—(1-methyl-2,2-diphenylcyclopropyl)-trimethyltin (398) for instance react with retention of configuration even in polar solvents.

$$\bigvee\!\!\bigwedge_{Sn(CH_3)_3} + E\!-\!N = \bigvee\!\!\bigwedge_{E} + N\!-\!Sn(CH_3)_3$$

$$E\!-\!N = I\!-\!I,\ Br\!-\!Br,\ H\!-\!Cl$$

This general hypothesis seems also to be valid for S_E2 reactions on other organometallic substrates, as shown by H. C. Brown, (466) who studied the bromodemetallation of tri-*exo*-norbornyl-boron, which occurs with full re-tention of configuration in THF (and which might be described as a S_E2c

reaction) whereas the same reaction occurs with full inversion of configuration in the same solvent in the presence of methoxide ions (and which may now be described as following a S_E2o mechanism).

(4) *The reactivity sequence and the S_E1 mechanism*

The reactivity sequence for the bimolecular replacement of a constant R_3Sn group by an electrophile (I_2 or Br_2 in methanol or in acetic acid (*40*), HgX_2 in methanol (*2*), or Br_2 in chlorobenzene (*40*)):

$$R'—SnR_3 + E—N = R'—E + N—SnR_3$$

can be described by:

$$R' = C_6H_5—CH_2 > CH_3 > CH_3—CH_2 > (CH_3)_2CH > (CH_3)_3C$$

i.e., the sequence one would expect for a S_E1 reaction. This shows that the stablization of the partial negative charge appearing on the different carbon atoms after this first complexation step

$$N + R_3SnR' \rightleftharpoons R_3R'\overset{-}{Sn}—\overset{+}{N}$$

plays a very important role. Electron-attracting substituents accelerate the substitution reaction and it is reasonable to admit that strong electron-attracting substituents could sufficiently stabilize the incipient carbanion so that this complexation would be no longer dependent on the attack of the electrophile on the carbon-atom, giving then a monomolecular electrophilic substitution.

It has not yet been possible to find an aliphatic electrophilic substitution which could be studied kinetically and would give a first-order rate equation.

The reaction of benzyltrimethyltin with iodine in methanol is a second-order reaction, but poorly electrophilic reagents do not react with this organotin molecule if a strong nucleophile is present. Eaborn (*37*) has indeed shown that the reaction of *m*-chlorobenzyltrimethyltin with water in ethanol yields *m*-chlorotoluene and is catalyzed by hydroxyl ions. The electrophile is unfortunately present in large excess and it is thus impossible to determine whether it has to be included in the transition state or not. Nevertheless, the nucleophilic catalysis is once more important and the kinetic results suggest that there is a considerable negative charge on the separating benzyl group in the transition state. It is thus reasonable to assume that this reaction might be an example of a monomolecular electrophilic substitution S_E1 at a saturated carbon atom.

Triethylstannylacetone (*141*) reacts very fast indeed with iodine, giving an instantaneous discoloration in polar solvents (methanol, DMSO), which is probably an S_E1 reaction, but which cannot be followed by spectrophoto-metric techniques, so that this has not yet actually been demonstrated:

$$\text{Et}_3\text{Sn—CH}_2\text{—COCH}_3 + \text{S} \rightarrow \underset{\underset{\text{S}^{(+)}}{|}}{\text{Et}_3\overset{(-)}{\text{Sn}}\text{—CH}_2\text{COCH}_3}$$

$$\xrightarrow[\text{det.}]{\text{rate}} \text{Et}_3\text{SnS}^+ + {}^-\text{CH}_2\text{COCH}_3$$

The high reactivity of α-functionally substituted organotin compounds could be ascribed also to a possible monomolecular mechanism. Trialkyl-stannylacetone or the corresponding ester or nitrile react with poorly electro-philic reagents such as benzyl halides

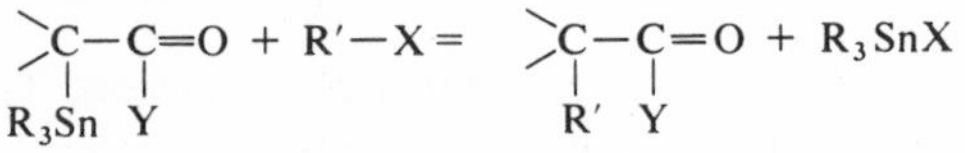

$$\underset{\underset{\text{R}_3\text{Sn} \quad \text{Y}}{| \quad |}}{\text{C—C=O}} + \text{R'—X} = \underset{\underset{\text{R'} \quad \text{Y}}{| \quad |}}{\text{C—C=O}} + \text{R}_3\text{SnX}$$

$$\text{Y} = \text{CH}_3 \text{ or } \text{OR''}$$

or with trimethylsilicon chloride (*302*):

$$\underset{\underset{\text{SnBu}_3}{|}}{(\text{CH}_3)_2\text{CH—CH—CN}} + \text{Me}_3\text{SiCl} = \underset{\underset{\text{SiMe}_3}{|}}{(\text{CH}_3)_2\text{CH—CH—CN}} + \text{Bu}_3\text{SnCl}$$

Reformatsky-type reactions can also be made with those derivatives showing that aldehydes or ketones are electrophilic enough to cleave the carbon-tin bonds of those α-functionally substituted organotin derivatives. The formation of the corresponding β-triorganostannoxy derivatives:

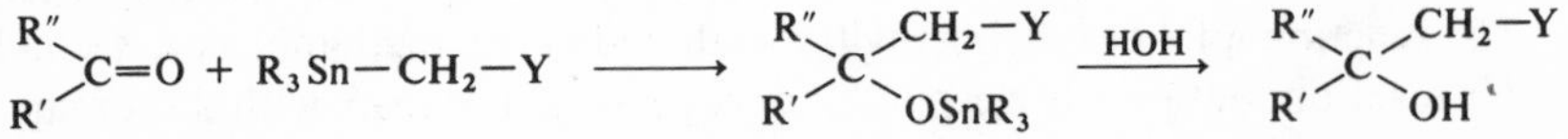

$$\underset{\text{R'}}{\overset{\text{R''}}{>}}\text{C=O} + \text{R}_3\text{Sn—CH}_2\text{—Y} \longrightarrow \underset{\text{R'}}{\overset{\text{R''}}{>}}\text{C}\underset{\text{OSnR}_3}{\overset{\text{CH}_2\text{—Y}}{<}} \xrightarrow{\text{HOH}} \underset{\text{R'}}{\overset{\text{R''}}{>}}\text{C}\underset{\text{OH}}{\overset{\text{CH}_2\text{—Y}}{<}}$$

is almost quantitative and the products formed are over 98 % pure. This is thus an especially facile organometallic method of functional chain ex-tension (*292*).

(5) Reactions of allyl derivatives: the S_E2' mechanism

Allyl derivatives are α-functionally substituted organotin compounds, and might therefore undergo S_E1 substitutions. Allyltriethyltin reacts indeed with weak electrophiles such as aldehydes (*201*):

$$\text{R—CHO} + \text{CH}_2\text{=CH—CH}_2\text{—SnEt}_3 = \underset{\underset{\text{O—SnEt}_3}{|}}{\text{R—CH—CH}_2\text{—CH=CH}_2}$$

and 9-triethylstannylfluorene is rapidly cleaved by anhydrous methanol, yielding fluorene (*37*):

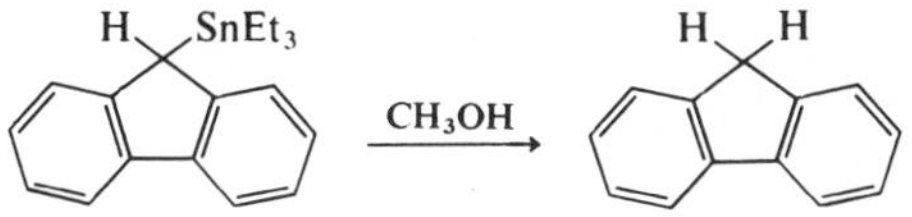

Nevertheless, it has been shown that the high reactivity of allylic derivatives of tin has sometimes to be attributed to an S_E2' mechanism (*130*):

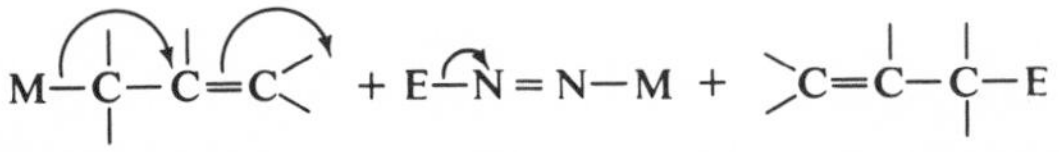

Kuivila (*207*) has reported evidence for a S_E2' mechanism in the cleavage of allyltin compounds by HCl in methanol, trimethylcrotyltin yielding mostly 1-butene:

$$(CH_3)_3Sn-CH_2-CH=CH-CH_3 + HCl = (CH_3)_3SnCl + CH_2=CH-CH_2-CH_3$$

This preferred S_E2' mechanism seems to be quite general in organometallic chemistry (*136*) and this might be attributed to the fact that electrophiles will attack the most nucleophilic part of the molecule, i.e., the γ-carbon atom of an allyl-metal molecule, rather than the α-carbon atom, the former possessing very polarizable π-electrons.

When a tin-substituted allene molecule is used, the S_E2' occurs in methanol at about the same rate as the S_E2, which is now also a reaction at an olefinic center:

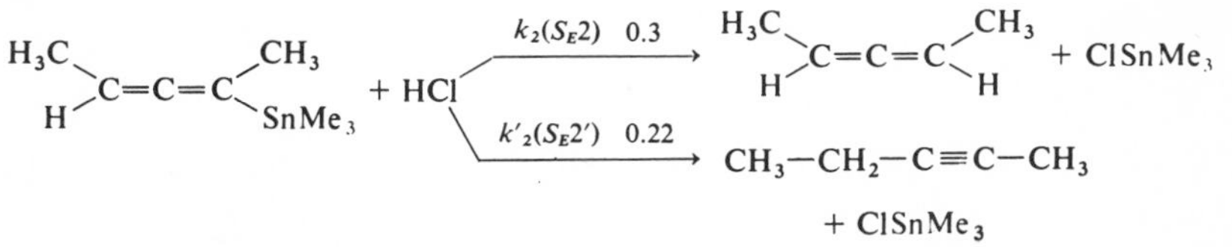

The analogous reaction of penta-2,3-dien-2-yltrimethyltin with 2,4-dinitrobenzenesulfonyl chloride in methylene chloride yields, on the contrary, only the reaction product originating from the S_E2' reaction (*211*).

b. Radical Substitutions at a Saturated Carbon Atom

(1) *Light-induced bromodemetallation of mixed tetraalkyltins: reversed low selectivity*

The mechanistic description of the reaction of symmetrical tetraalkyltins with bromine atoms is also valid for mixed tetraalkyltins. The ease of cleavage of carbon-tin bonds follows the sequence (*41*):

$$(CH_3)_2CH > C_4H_9 \simeq C_3H_7 \simeq C_2H_5 > CH_3$$

which might correspond to the stabilization by hyperconjugation of the radical R·:

$$Br· + R_3SnR' \nearrow R_3SnBr + R''·$$
$$\searrow R_2R'SnBr + R·$$

$$R· \text{ (or } R''·) + Br_2 \longrightarrow RBr \text{ (or } R'Br) + Br·$$

There is a small, but noticeable influence of the other three tin substituents. The relationship between structure and reactivity of the tetraalkyltins suggests that the carbon-tin bond is only slightly loosened in the transition state.

The same mixing-effect as for S_E2 reactions is found for these S_R2 reactions (*42*). The ratio $k(nPr)/k(Me)$ is equal to 3.23 for the reaction of Br· with propyltrimethyltin, but drops to 2.4 in the presence of tetraethyltin in chlorobenzene.

This shows a third effect which might be put forward as preferring polar solvents rather than less polar ones for the synthesis of mixed trialkyltin halides: for the S_F2, $k(Me)/k(iPr)$ was equal to 2.7; for the S_R2, the same ratio for the reaction in the same solvent (chlorobenzene) is equal to 0.14. As S_F2 reactions are rather slow, daylight may perturb the selectivity, competition between S_F2 and S_R2 being possible. This is no longer the case for the much faster S_E2 reactions and the reaction of halogens with tetraalkyltins in polar solvents does not seem to be affected by the presence of light.

(2) Stereochemistry of the radical substitutions: racemization

Sisido (*398*) has observed a racemization for the reaction of (+)-(1-methyl-2,2-diphenylcyclopropyl)trimethyltin with bromine in carbon tetrachloride. This result could be considered as due to the fact that the authors did not take any precaution in order to avoid a rapid radical reaction and one might thus suppose that the stereochemical course of radical substitution reactions is a racemization. This is reasonable if a radical R· is formed, as suggested formerly (*41*):

$$R'_3SnR + Br· \rightleftharpoons R'_3\bar{Sn}\underset{+Br·}{\overset{R}{\diagup}} \longrightarrow R_3SnBr + R'$$

(3) Photochemistry

Maxfield (*256*) has examined the reaction products after the photolysis in hydrocarbon solvents of acyclic ketones containing a tin atom (Me_3Sn

$(CH_2)_nCOR$; $n = 2$ or 3; $R = CH_3$ or C_6H_5). He observed cleavage reactions of carbon-tin bonds getting always dimethyltin (always more than
34% and even up to 70% for $R = CH_3$). $Me_3Sn-(CH_2)_3COPh$ also gave
about 20% of trimethylvinyltin (the same product was also obtained for the
analogous $Me_3Sn-(CH_2)_3COCH_3$), important quantities of $PhCOCH_3$
(40%) and about 10% of $(PhCOCH_2)_2$ and of $(PhC(CH_3)OH)_2$.

2. *Unsymmetrical (Mixed) Vinylic and Acetylenic Derivatives*

   a. *Electrophilic Substitution at an Olefinic Carbon Atom*

   (1) *Stereochemistry of bimolecular electrophilic substitution reactions at an
       olefinic carbon atom: retention of configuration*

The stereochemistry of the vinyl carbon-metal cleavage has been studied
by several authors [see Ref. (*17*)] and the reaction, which is of the type:

$$\underset{}{>}C=\overset{|}{C}-MR_n + E-N = \underset{}{>}C=\overset{|}{C}-E + N-MR_n$$

occurs generally with retention of configuration, in agreement with the rule
stated in 1948 by Nesmeyanov and Borisov (*275*).
   Cis- or *trans-*dipropenyltin dichloride react with HgX_2 to give pure *cis-* or
*trans-*propenylmercury chloride, respectively (*275*).
   Tetrapropenyltin also reacts with retention of configuration with butyl
lithium (*352*) or with phenyllithium (*354*).
   Cis- and *trans-*2-butenyltrimethyltin react with iodine in methanol also
with retention of configuration (*17*).

   (2) *Mechanism of bimolecular electrophilic substitutions at an olefinic
       carbon atom*

The rates of the reactions of a series of vinylic organotin compounds with
iodine suggest that the transition state must bear a rather localized positive
charge centered around the β-carbon atom and the stereochemical results
show quite clearly that a fully dipolar structure involving a complete breakdown of the π-bond (with localized unit charges) should be disregarded, such
an extreme structure implying free rotation around the central bond.
   A highly polar transition state:

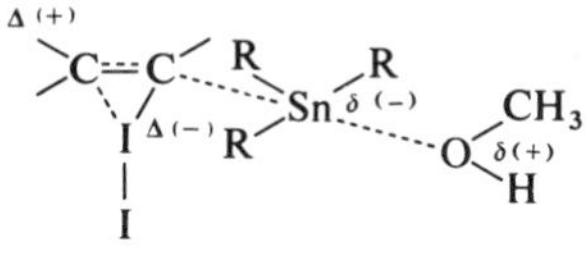

is suggested (*17*) in order to interpret the reactivity sequences (a) and (b):

(a) $(CH_3)_2C=CH-$ ≫ $\underset{H}{\overset{H_3C}{>}}C=C\underset{\diagdown}{\overset{CH_3}{\diagup}}$ ~ $\underset{H_3C}{\overset{H}{>}}C=C\underset{\diagdown}{\overset{CH_3}{\diagup}}$ ≫

$CH_2=CH-$ ~ $CH_2=C\underset{\diagdown}{\overset{C_2H_5}{\diagup}}$

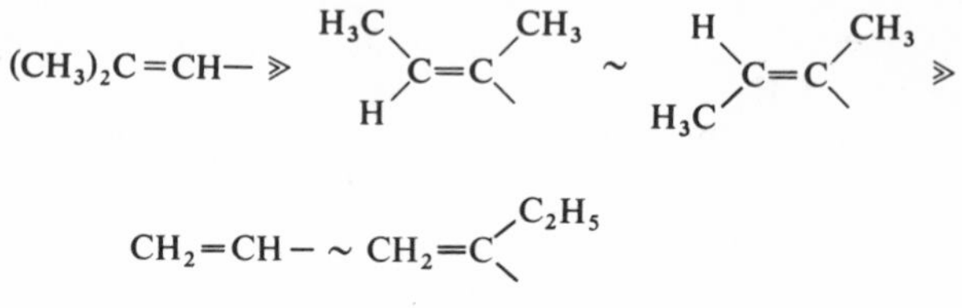

(b) $R = CH_3$ ~ $C_2H_5 > nC_4H_9 > isoC_3H_7 > C_2H_3$

and the observed salt effect and the retention of configuration of the vinyl group.

b. Electrophilic Substitution at an Acetylenic Carbon Atom. The high electronegativity of the alkynyl group differentiates the alkynyl-metal bond from the other alkyl-metal bonds; there has been little investigation of the chemical properties of the acetylenic organotin compounds but it is nevertheless clear that this facilitates both electrophilic attack at the carbon atom and also nucleophilic attack on the tin (*246, 435, 455*).

Cu^+ and Ag^+ break $Sn-C\equiv C$ bonds (*246*).

$R_3Sn-C\equiv C-CH_2-CH_2-O-CH=CH_2$ reacts easily with butanol and the cleavage of the extremely labile $Sn-C\equiv C$ bond occurs (*455*).

$Cl-C\equiv C-SnMe_3$ reacts instantaneously with water (*411*) and tricyclohexyltin halides are electrophilic enough to cleave the acetylenic carbon-tin bonds of bis-(trimethylstannyl)butadiyne (*160–162*).

Bromine cleaves diethyl(triethylstannylethynyl)phosphonate $Et_3Sn-C\equiv C-P(O)(OEt)_2$ readily although this compound is more stable to hydrolysis than other ethynyltins (*455*).

Aldehydes and ketones are also able to react with $C_6H_5-C\equiv C-SnEt_3$: Mirskov (*264*) has studied the reaction of chloral with triethylstannylphenylacetylene and Neumann (*201*) has tried successfully the analogous reaction with cyclohexanone.

In the presence of bases, $R_3Sn-C\equiv C-CH_3$ is isomerized into the allenic and propargylic compounds (*321*):

$$R_3Sn-C\equiv C-CH_3 \overset{B}{\underset{}{\rightleftharpoons}} R_3Sn-CH=C=CH_2 \overset{B}{\underset{}{\rightleftharpoons}} R_3Sn-CH_2-C\equiv CH$$

3. Unsymmetrical (Mixed) Aromatic Derivatives

The main reaction of aryltins is the electrophilic substitution at the aromatic carbon atom, and the corresponding $C_{Ar}-Sn$ bond is usually the first one to be broken when a competition is possible between alkyl and aryl cleavage (*181*). This feature has been used to synthesize tetraorganotins with four different groups attached to the metal, starting with tetraphenyltin or an alkyltriphenyltin (*144a*, *225a*). Interestingly, it has been found that dry HCl in methanol or even in benzene cleaves only one aryl group (*144a*), whereas halogenation has to be carefully controlled to achieve the same result (*225a*). The most general sequence for electrophilic carbon-tin cleavages is then, according to the preceding paragraphs:

allyl $\gg$ aryl, vinyl $\rangle$ alkyl

the difference between aryl and vinyl groups depending on the substituents they bear. Free radical, and alkyl- or aryllithium induced cleavages (*457*) may follow other sequences.

It should be stressed that it is not always clear whether a given reaction is to be classified as an electrophilic substitution on carbon or a nucleophilic displacement on tin. The subdivision which is proposed here is arbitrary and stems from feelings one might have about the rate-determining step (in two-step processes) or rate-determining factor (in one-step processes). Where kinetic or mechanistic studies are not available, the situation is obscure and no decision can be reached, as in the insertion of sulfur or selenium in a carbon-tin bond of tetraphenyltin (*342–344*) or in the pyrolytic bimolecular elimination of trimethyl iodide from iodobenzene and hindered phenyltrimethyltins (*364*).

a. Electrophilic Substitution at an Aromatic Carbon Atom. Aryltrialkyltins have been cleaved under a variety of conditions, and kinetic results are available for I_2 in CCl_4 (*36a*), in methanol (*53, 54, 56, 270, 271*), in chlorobenzene, and cyclohexane (*260*), for HCl (*55*) and Br_2 (*2a*) in methanol, for $HClO_4$ in methanol-water (*38, 103a*), for $(CH_3COO)_2Hg$ in tetrahydrofuran (*163*), and for the solvolyses in acetic acid (*271a*). Electron-releasing substituents always accelerate the reactions.

Iododestannylations in nonpolar solvents (carbon tetrachloride, cyclohexane) are second order with respect to the electrophile, meaning that the transition state contains two iodine molecules (or four iodine atoms); substituent effects on rates are then difficult to interpret, because there are many possibilities for accommodating the extra halogen molecule. Eaborn (*36a*) has discussed two important sites for the second iodine molecule; the highly polarizable electrons of the aromatic ring, and a simultaneous coordination with the tin atom and the first iodine molecule; his conclusion is that the second possibility is in better agreement with some peculiar substituent effects than the first one. There is some evidence that the second iodine molecule acts as a nucleophile on the tin atom, since very small amounts of methanol added to cyclohexane strongly increase the rate and progressively restore a first-order reaction with respect to the halogen (*260*).

Despite these difficulties, it has been possible to find a reasonably good correlation between the rates and substituent constants (*36a*). With $(CH_3COO)_2Hg$ in THF (*163*) there is a linear correlation of log (k/k_0) vs σ, rather than σ^+ as in classical aromatic substitutions, suggesting that a localized σ-complex is a poor approximation to the true transition state.

The situation is better in the more polar solvents methanol and acetic acid. The reactions are strictly first order in electrophile, allowing much simpler hypotheses for the transition state. Moreover, these media favor highly polarized species and intermediates, resulting in a much closer adherence to σ^+ substituent constants. The sensitivity is, however, very low ($\rho = -2.5$, as compared with -8 to -12 for most aromatic electrophilic substitutions), showing that the electron demand from the substituents is not large, probably because of the high polarizability of the tin atom.

In these solvents, the reaction is most probably a two-step process, the first stage being rate determining (*270*), and it is interesting to note, in this connection, that the acetolysis in CH_3COOD shows a large solvent isotope effect. This is good evidence that here again the localized σ-complex is far from representing the true transition state.

The reactivity of aryltrialkyltins decreases as the size of the alkyl groups increases (*54*), and it has been shown (*270*) that this is due to a steric inhibition opposing the attack of the entering electrophile. *Ortho* effects show up as a delicate balance between retardation of electrophilic attack and acceleration by steric decompression: when the leaving group is $-Sn(CH_3)_3$, two *ortho* methyl groups have no special influence at all, but when the bulkier $-Sn(nC_3H_7)_3$ is to be expelled, the two *ortho* methyls induce a slight but clear-cut rate enhancement because of the relief of the overcrowding in the starting material (*271*). This decompression is, however, much less dramatic here than in the case of analogous silicon compounds, where $-Si(CH_3)_3$ is displaced at an immeasurably high rate when two *ortho* methyls are present (*28a, 98a*). The difference between silicon and tin derivatives is clearly due to the longer carbon-tin bond which holds the interacting groups further apart.

The fact that 1-naphthyl- and 2-naphthyltrimethyltins react with I_2 (or HCl) at the same rate (*53-55*), contrary to all traditions in naphthalene chemistry, must be due to some influence of the *peri* hydrogen. The corresponding naphthyltri*iso*propyltins do, however, react in the expected sequence, 1-naphthyl- faster than 2-naphthyl-, because of the aforementioned steric decompression.

The rules derived from kinetic studies can be extrapolated to predict or interpret, qualitative results. Thus, the cleavage of *ortho*biphenyle-bis-(2-biphenylyl)tin with hydrogen chloride

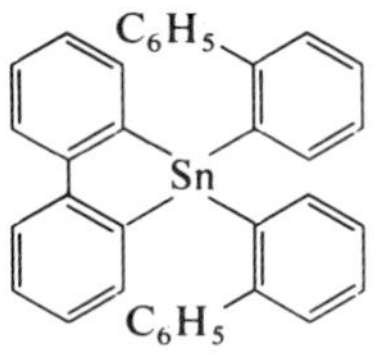

$$+ \ HCl \ = \ (C_{12}H_9)_3SnCl$$

gives tris-(2-biphenylyl)tin chloride as the primary product (*125*), because electrophilic substitution is faster at the 2-position of a *planar* biphenyl than at the 2-position of a *twisted* biphenyl.

The use of a trialkyltin group as a probe for electrophilic substitutions is justified by the finding that this substituent has an almost negligible perturbating effect on the electronic properties of aromatic systems (*12, 56, 63*).

Other electrophilic substitutions, such as the redistribution with tin tetrahalides (*65, 214*), reaction with $C_6H_5PCl_2$ (*213*), BCl_3 (*65*), or BBr_3 (*310*) have found interesting synthetic use, but no mechanistic nor kinetic studies seem to exist.

b. Nucleophilic Displacement at the Tin Atom. Substituted phenyltrimethyltins react with sodium methoxide in methanol to yield trimethyltin methoxide, or compounds derived from it, and the corresponding substituted benzene. The kinetics of this surprisingly smooth reaction have been examined by Eaborn (*100*): the substituent effects roughly parallel the results for the base-catalyzed hydrogen exchange reaction in aromatic hydrocarbons, and it is fair to assume that the transition states bear some resemblance to analogous phenyl carbanions.

Perhaloaryltins undergo facile base-catalyzed cleavages: $(C_6F_5)_4Sn$ is cleaved by KOH as easily as by HCl (*419*); $C_6F_5Sn(CH_3)_3$ solvolyzes in aqueous methanol, but a trace of acid completely inhibits this reaction (*103*); recrystallization of $C_6F_5Sn(CH_3)_3$ in ethanol containing some KF gives pentafluorobenzene and trimethyltin fluoride (*66*). Other examples include the formation of benzene from phenyltin chlorides in DMSO in the presence of chelating agents at elevated temperatures (*254, 255, 272, 273*), the cleavage of the carboranyl-tin bond by potassium hydroxide (*49*), or the very fast solvolysis of 2-pyridyltrimethyltin in hydroxylic solvents (*10*).

Mixed aryltins are thus more sensitive to nucleophilic attack than fully saturated tetraalkyltins, and the sequence of reactivity is:

ethynyl, fluorenyl (*459*) > aryl > saturated alkyl

c. Photochemistry. When 1-naphthyltrimethyltin, dissolved in methanol, is irradiated through Pyrex, the products are trimethyltin methoxide, or compounds derived from it, and naphthalene. Labeling experiments have shown that this light-induced cleavage is very similar to electrophilic substitutions at aromatic carbons. This aryltin is photostable in cyclohexane solutions, but is smoothly cleaved when small amounts of acetic acid are added before the photolysis.

The enhanced reactivity of the excited state of the compound is probably due to changes in the electronic properties of the naphthalene system, as suggested by quantum-mechanical calculations.

Acknowledgment—The authors wish to express their thanks to Dr. Raymonde Nasielski for her help in preparing the manuscript.

APPENDICES

The appendices are arranged in somewhat arbitrary orders of hierarchy. A first classification is based on symmetry: the first four appendices include symmetrical tetraorganotins; the next twenty-two collect compounds where three substituents are identical; then come the derivatives having two groups of two identical substituents; later appendices list tetraorganotins with three types of ligands; the last ones give the newly made compounds having four different radicals attached to the metal.

In every class, the hierarchy is, in decreasing order: alkyl over alkenyl over alkynyl over aryl; in a given group, the substituents are arranged according to the number of carbon atoms, with the rule that the first heteroatom in the chain stops the counting: $nBu-O-CH_2-CH_2-CH_2-$, $H_2N-CO-CH_2$ $-CH_2-$, $CH_3O-CO-CH(SnR_3)-CH_2-$ are three-carbon radicals.

For consistency, $C=O$ and $C\equiv N$ groups attached to tin are listed under alkenyl- and alkynyltins respectively. $CH_3O-CO-SnR_3$ would be a " one-carbon alkenyltin," and $N\equiv C-SnR_3$ a " one-carbon alkynyltin."

Compounds having two tin atoms are considered as having a fortuitous tin-bearing group on one of the substituents.

The appendices contain the compounds already listed by Ingham et al. (*181*) and by Weiss (*443*), and the reader is referred to these reviews for most data. Other references are newer ones, or serve to complete the other compilations.

APPENDICES

Appendix 1. Symmetrical tetraalkyltins 664
Appendix 2. Symmetrical tetraalkenyltins 669
Appendix 3. Symmetrical tetraalkynyltins 670
Appendix 4. Symmetrical tetraaryltins 671
Appendix 5. Alkyltrimethyltins.................................... 675
Appendix 6. Alkenyltrimethyltins.................................. 689
Appendix 7. Alkynyltrimethyltins.................................. 695
Appendix 8. Aryltrimethyltins..................................... 697
Appendix 9. Alkyltriethyltins 701
Appendix 10. Alkenyltriethyltins 713
Appendix 11. Alkynyltriethyltins 720
Appendix 12. Aryltriethyltins 726
Appendix 13. Alkyltripropyltins.................................... 727
Appendix 14. Alkenyltripropyltins.................................. 730
Appendix 15. Alkynyltripropyltins.................................. 732
Appendix 16. Aryltripropyltins..................................... 733
Appendix 17. Triisopropyl-, tricyclopropyl-, triallyltins.................. 334
Appendix 18. Alkyltributyltins 735
Appendix 19. Alkenyltributyltins 744
Appendix 20. Alkynyltributyltins 746
Appendix 21. Aryltributyltins 747
Appendix 22. Other alkyl-, alkenyl-, alkynyl-, and aryltrialkyltins 748
Appendix 23. Alkyltriphenyltins.................................... 758
Appendix 24. Other alkyltriaryltins 766
Appendix 25. Aryltriphenyltins..................................... 767
Appendix 26. Other ArSnAr′$_3$ 769
Appendix 27. Dialkyldimethyltins 770
Appendix 28. Dialkenyl- and dialkynyldimethyltins 773
Appendix 29. Dialkyl-, dialkenyl-, and dialkynyldiethyltins 775
Appendix 30. Dialkyl-, dialkenyl-, and dialkynyldi-n-propyltins 778
Appendix 31. Dialkyldiisopropyltins 780
Appendix 32. Dialkyl-, dialkenyl-, and dialkynyldi-n-butyltins 781
Appendix 33. Dialkyldi-isobutyltins................................. 788
Appendix 34. Other R$_2$SnR′$_2$ 789
Appendix 35. Dialkyl-, dialkenyl-, and dialkynyldiaryltins 793
Appendix 36. Diaryldiphenyltins 799
Appendix 37. Other Ar$_2$SnAr′$_2$ 803
Appendix 38. Tetraorganotins with three types of alkyl groups R$_2$SnR′R″... 804
Appendix 39. Tetraorganotins with three types of ligands and at least one
             aryl group 806
Appendix 40. Compounds with four different alkyl groups bound to tin..... 807
Appendix 41. Compounds with four different substituents attached to tin
             and at least one aryl group............................ 808

APPENDIX 1

SYMMETRICAL TETRAALKYLTINS

R or R_4Sn	Important physical constants including boiling point, melting point, refractive index, density, chromatographic data	Spectroscopic properties including infra-red, Raman, ultra-violet, nuclear magnetic resonance, Mössbauer and mass spectra and other properties
CH_3	b_{748}: 76.6°C; m: 218.18°K n_D^{20}: 1.4415; d_{25}: 1.2905 (*147, 173, 181, 265, 403, 415, 422, 443*); GLC (*172, 312*)	ir (*106, 176, 181, 185, 443*); Raman (*176, 443*); uv (*375*); NMR (*43, 51, 95–98, 155, 185, 242, 245, 256a, 395, 405, 406, 434, 443*); MB (*74, 149, 169, 189, 190, 412, 414*); MS (*44, 93, 165, 443, 449*) (—) ion MS (*205*); kinetics (*40, 41, 129, 130*); dipole moments (*290*)
$(CH_3)_3SiCH_2$	$b_{0.2}$: 94°C; n_D^{25}: 1.4839; d_{25}: 1.018 (*181, 443*)	
$CH_3O—CH_2$	$b_{0.05}$: 64°C; (*346*)	NMR (*346*)
$ClCH_2$	b_5: 148.5°C (*181, 443*); m: 49°C	MB (*149*)
$BrCH_2$	m: 57°C (*181, 443*)	
ICH_2	m: 76°C (*181, 443*)	
CH_3CH_2	b: 181°C; b_{12}: 63–66°C; m: 142.15°K n_D^{D}: 1.4691–1.4738 (*6, 7, 181, 269, 290, 312, 327, 384, 390, 401, 422, 437, 438, 443, 458*); d_{20}: 1.1990; GLC (*172, 239, 443*); TLC (*443*)	ir (*242, 430, 432, 443*); Raman (*176, 443*); uv (*443*); NMR (*242, 430, 432, 443*); MB (*149, 443*); MS (*44, 59, 93, 165, 193*); dipole moment (*290, 443*); kinetics (*2, 40, 41, 129–133, 135, 136*)
$\left(\begin{array}{c}CH_2CH_2\\CH_2CH_2\end{array}\right)_2 Sn$	b_{30}: 108–110°C (*60*)	MS (*60*)
CH_3CHCl	b_2: 142°C (*181*); n_D^{20}: 1.5363 (*443*); d_{20}: 1.5363	ir, Raman (*78*); NMR (*194, 433*); MB (*149*); kinetics (*136*)
$CH_2=CH—CH_2$	b_4: 87–8°C; n_D^{32}: 1.5324; $d_{30.5}$: 1.243 (*181, 443*) m: 23–23.5°C; n_D^{20}: 1.5339; d_{20}: 1.4358 (*34, 46, 187, 332, 443*)	NMR (*35, 443*); kinetics (*129*)
$N\equiv C—CH_2CH_2$		MB (*149*)

Compound	Properties	References/Methods
$NaOOC$—CH_2CH_2 $HOOC$—CH_2CH_2 $(CH_3)_2CH$ 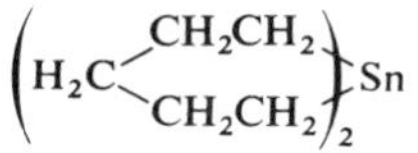	$(187, 331a)$ m: 104–5°C $(331a)$ b_{10}: 103–4°C; b_4: 89°C; $n_D^{20.2}$: 1.4851; d_{20}: 1.1237; GLC $(73, 181, 298, 418, 438, 443)$	NMR $(14a, 433)$, MS (44); kinetics (136)
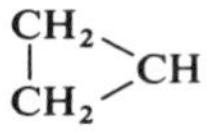 $\left(\begin{array}{c} H_2C \diagdown^{CH_2CH_2} \\ {}_{CH_2CH_2} \end{array} \right)_2 Sn$	$b_{0.3}$: 67–8°C; n_D^{25}: 1.5202 $(367a, 443)$	ir (443)
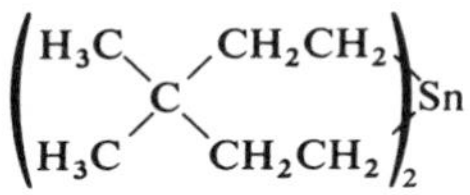 $\begin{array}{c} H_3C \diagdown^{CH_2CH_2} \\ {}_{H_3C} C \diagup_{CH_2CH_2} \end{array} Sn$	$b_{0.0001}$: 75–82°C; n_D^{20}: 1.518 $(315–318)$	
$CH_3(CH_2)_3$	b_8: 152–3°C; m: 176.1°K; n_B^{25}: 1.4733; d_{20}: 1.0541 $(25, 47a, 84, 104, 181, 215, 269, 290, 350, 402, 443, 448)$; GLC, TLC $(119, 122, 312, 443)$	ir $(121, 123, 258, 443)$; Raman (123); uv (79); MB $(149, 443, 463)$; NMR (433); dipole moment (290); kinetics $(2, 136, 186)$
$(CH_3CH_2CH_2CH_2)_4{}^{113}Sn$	(426)	
$(CH_3)_2CH$—CH—CH_2 $\quad\quad\quad\quad CH_3$	b_8: 128–9°C; n_D^{20}: 1.4742–50 d_{20}: 1.0517 $(181, 443)$ n_D^{20}: 1.5110; d_{20}: 1.2860 $(187, 443)$	dipole moment (290)
$N{\equiv}C$—CH—CH_2 $\quad\quad\quad CH_3$ CH_3CH_2CH $\quad\quad CH_3$	b_{10}: 148–50°C; n_D^{20}: 1.4977 $(285, 443)$	
$CH_3(CH_2)_4$	b_{10}: 182°C; n_D^{17}: 1.4738; d_{20}: 1.0159; GLC; paper chrom. $(181, 443)$	Raman (443); velocity sound (298)

Continued

APPENDIX 1—*continued*

R or R$_4$Sn	Important physical constants including boiling point, melting point, refractive index, density, chromotographic data	Spectroscopic properties including infra-red, Raman, ultra-violet, nuclear magnetic resonance Mössbauer and mass spectra and other properties
(CH$_3$)$_2$CHCH$_2$CH$_2$	b$_{2.4}$: 145–50°C; b$_3$: 148–52°C n_D^{20}: 1.4710; GLC, paper chrom (*181, 443*)	
(CH$_3$CH$_2$)$_2$CH	(*443*)	
(CH$_3$)$_2$C—CH$_2$CH$_3$ (with CH$_3$CH$_2$ and CH$_3$ branches)	b$_{19}$: 157°C (*443*)	
(CH$_3$)$_3$C—CH$_2$ CH$_3$CH$_2$CH$_2$CH—CH$_3$	m: 134–5.5°C (*83, 443, 461*) (*181, 443*)	NMR (*462*)
CH$_2$CH$_2$—CH CH$_2$CH$_2$ (ring)	b$_{0.4}$: 155–60°C; m: 76°C (*83, 443*); m: 68–8.5°C (*44*)	MS (*44*)
CH=CH—CH CH=CH (ring)	m: 71–73°C or 76–77.2°C (*181, 443*)	NMR (*117*)
CH$_3$(CH$_2$)$_5$	b$_{1.5}$: 187–90°C; b$_3$: 193°C n_D^{16}: 1.4756; d$_{20}$: 0.9936 (*181, 443*) (*443*)	
(CH$_3$)$_2$CHCH$_2$CH$_2$CH$_2$	m: 263°C (*181, 217, 443*)	MB (*199, 167, 168*)
H C=C CH H$_3$C CH=CH	(*118*)	NMR (*118*)

Compound	Properties	References
$CH_3(CH_2)_6$ $C_6H_5-CH_2$ $o\text{-}Cl-C_6H_4-CH_2$	b_3: 218°C; n_D^{20}: 1.4702; d_{20}: 0.9746 (181, 443) m: 41.5–3°C (181) m: 96°C (181)	uv, ir (443); NMR (431)
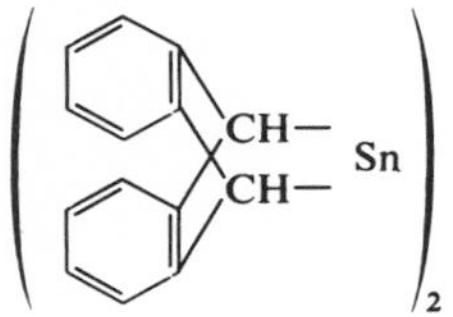	m: 227–8 (107, 325)	
$CH_3(CH_2)_7$	b_{10}: 268°C; b_1: 224°C; n_D^{20}: 1.4677–1.4709; d_{20}: 0.9609; GLC; paper chrom. (33, 181, 290, 443) (181, 443)	ir, Raman (443); dipole moment (290)

$CH_3CH_2CH_2CH_2-CH-CH_2$
         $\overset{\displaystyle |}{CH_3CH_2}$
         CH_3		

$(CH_3)_2CHCHCH_2-C-CH_2$ $\overset{\displaystyle |}{CH_3}$	b_1: 183°C; n_D^{25}: 1.4798; d_{27}: 0.9792 (462)	
$C_6H_5-CH_2CH_2$ $(CH_3)_3C-CH_2-CH-CH_2CH_2$ CH_3	b_{12}: 288°C (181) (181, 443)	
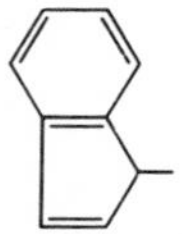	m: 215°C (181, 443)	

Continued

APPENDIX 1—continued

R or R$_4$Sn	Important physical constants including boiling point, melting point, refractive index, density, chromatographic data	Spectroscopic properties including infra-red, Raman, ultra-violet, nuclear magnetic resonances Mössbauer and mass spectra and other properties
C$_6$H$_5$—CH$_2$CH$_2$CH$_2$ C$_6$H$_5$—CH—CH$_2$ CH$_3$	(462) b$_3$: 290°C (462)	
(CH$_3$)$_2$CH(CH$_2$)$_7$	(443)	
C$_6$H$_5$—C—CH$_2$ H$_3$C CH$_3$	m: 96–7°C (330, 462)	NMR (462); MB (149, 167, 330)
CH$_3$(CH$_2$)$_{11}$	m: 15–6°C; n$_D^{20}$: 1.4736 (181, 443)	
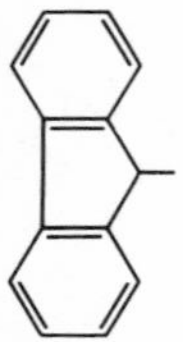	m: 285–90°C (dec) (181, 443)	
CH$_3$(CH$_2$)$_{13}$ CH$_3$(CH$_2$)$_{15}$ CH$_3$(CH$_2$)$_{17}$ CH$_3$(CH$_2$)$_7$—CH=CH—(CH$_2$)$_8$	m: 33–4°C (181, 443) m: 36–41°C (181, 443) m: 47°C (181, 443) (443)	

APPENDIX 2

SYMMETRICAL TETRAALKENYLTINS

R or R_4Sn	Important physical constants	Other properties
$CH_2=CH$	b_{766}: 160–3°C; b_{17}: 55–7°C; n_D^{25}: 1.4914–1.4993; d_{25}: 1.246–1.267 (166, 181, 269, 395, 443)	ir (176, 443); NMR (35, 233, 250, 443); kinetics (17)
$CF_2=CF$ $CH_3—CH=CH$ *cis*	b_{19}: 52–4°C; n_D^{23}: 1.3780; d_{23}: 1.9480 (443) $b_{0.2}$: 57–9°C; n_D^{25}: 1.5178 (181) b_4: 91°C; n_D^{20}: 1.5205 (443)	ir (67, 355); NMR (429)
trans	$b_{0.2}$: 53–6°C; n_D^{25}: 1.5064 (358) b_1: 84°C; n_D^{20}: 1.5110 (67, 355) b_8: 66–7°C; n_d^{20}: 1.5110 d_{20}: 1.3153 (181, 355, 358, 443)	ir (67, 355); NMR (429)
$CH_2=C$ — CH_3 $(CH_3)_2CH—CH_2—C$ $=CH_2$	(443)	
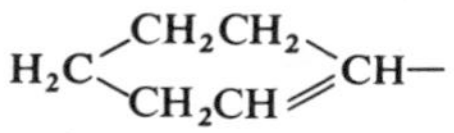 H_2C CH_2CH_2 CH — CH_2CH =	(443)	
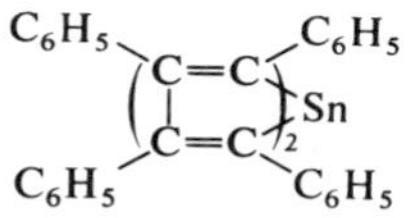	m: 281–2°C (219, 221)	MB (149)

APPENDIX 3

Symmetrical Tetraalkynyltins

R in R_4Sn	Important physical constants	Other properties
$HC\equiv C$	(*85*, *443*)	ir (*339*)
$(CH_3)_3Si—C\equiv C$	dec 140°C (*199*)	
$CH_3—C\equiv C$	m: 139–150°C (*85*, *443*)	uv, NMR (*224*)
$H_2C\begin{smallmatrix}\diagup CH_2CH_2 \diagdown \\ \diagdown CH_2CH_2 \diagup\end{smallmatrix}CH-C\equiv C$	m: 130°C (*161*)	
$C_6H_5—C\equiv C$	m: 174°C (dec) (*85*, *181*, *443*)	
p-Cl—$C_6H_4—C\equiv C$	m: 161°C (*85*, *162*)	
p-Br—$C_6H_4—C\equiv C$	m: 170°C (*85*, *162*)	

APPENDIX 4

SYMMETRICAL TETRAARYLTINS

Ar or Ar₄Sn	Important physical constants	Other properties
C_6H_5	m: 228–230°C (443)	ir (86, 443); Raman (443); uv (443); NMR (443); MB (443); dipole moment (443); thermochemical data (422, 443); kinetics (36a)
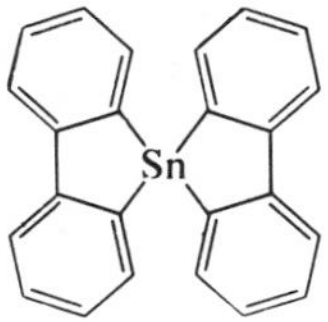	(443)	ir (125)
o-CH_3O—C_6H_4	m: 234–235°C (443)	
o-C_6H_5O—C_6H_4	m: 180–184°C (443)	
m-HO—C_6H_4	m: 134.8°C (443)	
p-CH_3O—C_6H_4	m: 104°C (443)	
p-C_2H_5O—C_6H_4	(443)	
p-C_6H_5O—C_6H_4	(443)	
p-$(CH_3)_2N$—C_6H_4	m: 190°C (dec) (443)	
p-$CH_3I \cdot (CH_3)_2N$—C_6H_4	m: >180°C (dec) (443)	
p-$(CH_3)_2SO_4 \cdot (CH_3)_2N$—$C_6H_4$	m: 144–145°C (443)	¹H and ¹⁹F NMR (252)
p-FC_6H_4	m: 197–199°C (443)	uv (443); ir (443)
p-ClC_6H_4	m: 220–222°C (72, 419, 443, 310)	ir (419)
C_6F_5	m: 446–449°C (dec) (145)	uv (145)
C_6Cl_5	m: 343–345°C (443)	
p-$(CH_3)_3Si$—C_6H_4		

Continued

APPENDIX 4—*continued*

R or R₄Sn	Important physical constants	Other properties
$o\text{-}C_6F_4$, $o\text{-}C_6F_4$, $o\text{-}C_6F_4$, $o\text{-}C_6F_4$ Sn	m: 227–229°C (71, 72)	ir (71, 72)
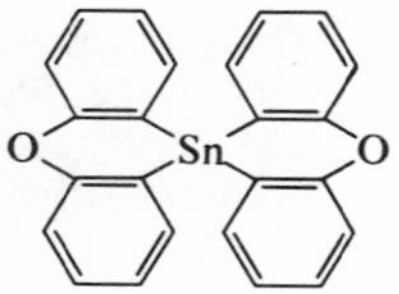 (structure)	m: 220–221°C (214)	
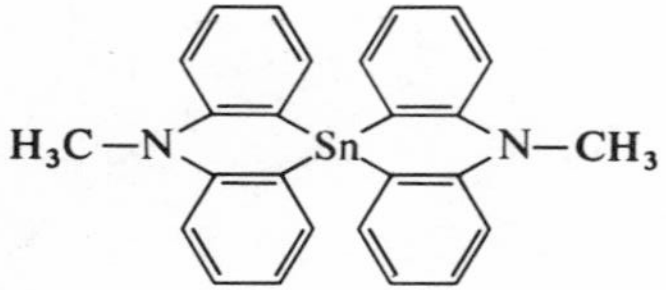 (structure)	m: 164–166°C (213)	ir (213); uv (213); NMR (213)
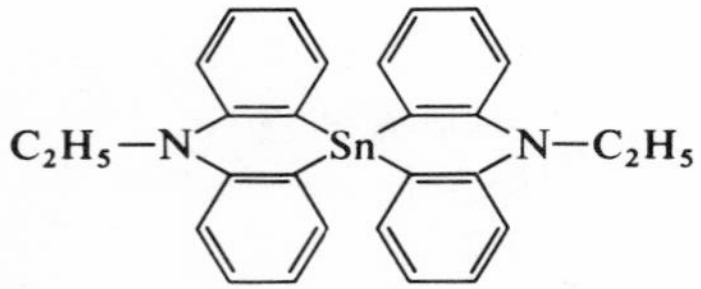 (structure)	m: 210–211°C (145a)	

	m: 259–360°C (213)	ir (213); uv (213); NMR (213)
o-CH₃—C₆H₄	m: 217.5–219.5°C (443)	ir (443); uv (443)
m-CH₃—C₆H₄	m: 128.4–129.6°C (443)	
p-CH₃—C₆H₄	m: 238°C (443)	

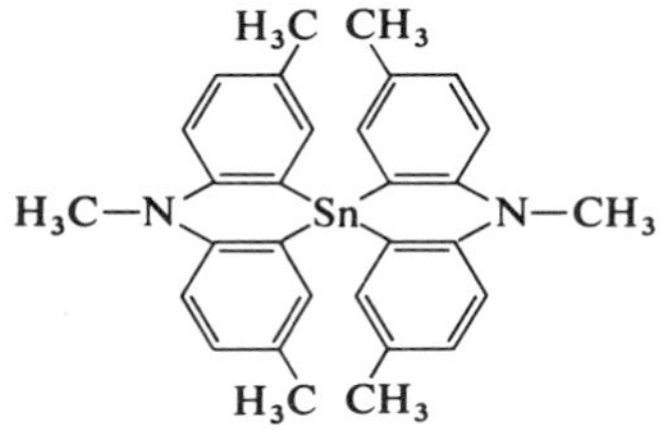	m: 209–211°C (213)	ir (213); uv (213); NMR (213)

m-CF₃—C₆H₄	m: 143–147°C (443)	
p-CF₃—C₆H₄	m: 150–150.7°C (443)	
p-CHO—C₆H₄	m: 180–182°C (443)	
p-(CH₂O)₂CH—C₆H₄	m: 268–270°C (443)	ir (443)
p-CH₂=CH—C₆H₄	m: 85°C (443)	ir (443)
p-CH₂=CH—CH₂—C₆H₄	m: 78°C (443)	
2,4,6-(CH₃)₃C₆H₂	m: >320°C (dec) (19, 443)	
p-(CH₃)₃C—C₆H₄	m: 295°C (443)	
1-Naphthyl	m: 310–320°C (19, 443)	
p-cycloC₆H₁₁—C₆H₄	m: 220°C (443)	
o-C₆H₅—C₆H₄	m: 300–301°C (18, 443)	

Continued

APPENDIX 4—*continued*

R or R$_4$Sn	Important physical constants	Other properties
m-C$_6$H$_5$—C$_6$H$_4$	m: 145.5–145.8°C (*18, 443*)	
p-C$_6$H$_5$—C$_6$H$_4$	m: 268.5°C (*18, 443*)	
C$_{12}$H$_6$Cl$_3$(trichlorobiphenyl)	(*443*)	
9-Phenanthryl	m: 360–370°C (dec) (*19, 443*)	
2-Thienyl	(*443*)	
2-(5-chlorothienyl)	(*443*)	
2-Quinolyl	(*443*)	
6-Quinolyl	(*443*)	

APPENDIX 5

ALKYLTRIMETHYLTINS

R in $RSn(CH_3)_3$	Important physical constants	Other properties
$[(CH_3)_3SnCH_2]_2B$—CH_2 $BrCH_2$	$b_{0.15}$: 90–1°C (181, 443); b_{11}: 46–50°C; n_D^{25}: 1.5070; d_{25}: 1.722 (181, 443)	
$BrCl_2C$	(360)	NMR (360)
$(CH_3)_3Sn$—$CBrCl$	$b_{0.0002}$: 61°C; n_D^{25}: 1.5502 (365)	MB (149, 193); ir (193); NMR (193, 203)
$ClCH_2$	b_{18}: 46.5°C; n_D^{20}: 1.4893; d_{20}: 1.5071 (39, 181, 203, 443)	
$HCCl_2$	b_{38}: 86–7°C; (362)	NMR (362)
CCl_3	(65, 66, 87, 88, 367)	NMR (360)
$(CH_3)_3Sn$—$ClCl$	(365)	
$LiCl_2C$	(362)	
$(CH_3)_3Si$—CCl_2	b_{10}: 84°C; n_D^{25}: 1.4992 (362)	
$(CH_3)_3Sn$—CCl_2	$b_{0.0002}$: 48–50°C; n_D^{25}: 1.5326 (362, 365, 368)	
$(CH_3)_3Sn$—$CClF$	n_D^{25}: 1.5253 (368)	
FCH_2	b_{745}: 97–101°C; n_D^{20}: 1.4443; d_{20}: 1.4328 (203)	ir (193); NMR (193, 203); MB (149, 193)
CF_3	b: 100–1°C (61, 181, 356, 366, 443); GLC (443)	ir (177, 443); NMR (443)
ICH_2	$b_{6.5}$: 53–4.5°C; n_D^{25}: 1.5510 (181, 443) (443)	
$ClMgCH_2$	(218)	
$\overset{(+)}{N}{\equiv}N$—$\overset{(-)}{C}H$		
$(CH_3)_2N$—$N{=}N$—CH_2	not isolated (218)	
$\begin{matrix} CH_2 \\ | \\ CH_2 \end{matrix}{>}N$—$CH_2$	b_{20}: 54–5.5°C; n_D^{20}: 1.4820; d_{20} 1.3104 (203)	ir (193), NMR (193, 204); MB (193)

Continued

APPENDIX 5—continued

R in $RSn(CH_3)_3$	Important physical constants	Other properties
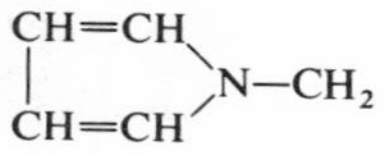 $CH=CH$ $\quad\quad\diagdown$ $\quad\quad\quad N-CH_2$ $\quad\quad\diagup$ $CH=CH$	$b_{0.8}$: 55.7–6°C; n_D^{20}: 1.5279; d_{20}: 1.3511 (203) b_{65}: 59.2–59.5°C; n_D^{20}: 1.4570; d_{20}: 1.3190 (193)	ir (193), NMR (193, 204); MB (193)
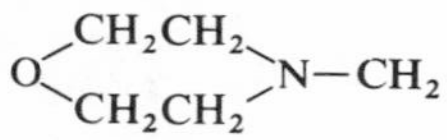 $\quad CH_2CH_2$ $O\diagdown\quad\quad\diagup N-CH_2$ $\quad CH_2CH_2$	$b_{1.2}$: 66°2–67°C; n_D^{20}: 1.4998; d_{20}: 1.3207 (203)	ir, NMR, MB (193)
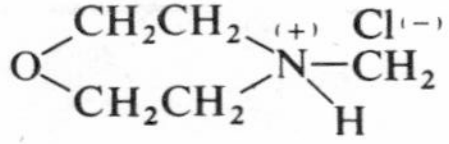 $\quad CH_2CH_2\overset{(+)}{\diagdown}\;Cl^{(-)}$ $O\quad\quad\quad N-CH_2$ $\quad CH_2CH_2\diagup\quad H$	m: 106.6–7.8°C (203)	
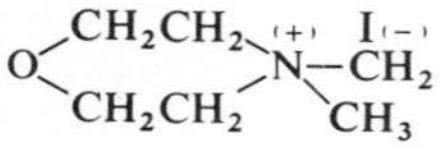 $\quad CH_2CH_2\overset{(+)}{\diagdown}\;I^{(-)}$ $O\quad\quad\quad N-CH_2$ $\quad CH_2CH_2\diagup\quad CH_3$	m: 192.83°C (203)	ir, NMR, NB (193)
$HO-CH_2$ CH_3O-CH_2 $C_2H_5O-CH_2$ $CH_3-\underset{\underset{O}{\parallel}}{C}-O-CH_2$	$b_{6.5}$: 58–9°C (181, 443) b_{65}: 59.2–9.5°C; n_D^{20}: 1.4570; d_{20}: 1.3190 (203) b_{45}: 64°C; n_D^{20}: 1.4553 (39) b_{16}: 48.5–50°C; n_D^{20}: 1.4874 d_{20}: 1.3299 (203)	ir (193); NMR (193, 203); MB (149, 193) NMR (203); MB (149)
C_6H_5-O-CH $\quad\quad\quad\quad\mid$ $\quad\quad\quad\quad OCH_3$ $(C_6H_5)_3P-CH_2$	b_1: 88–9°C; n_D^{20}: 1.4931; d_{20}: 0.9817 (191) (181, 443)	

Compound	Properties	Methods / References
$(CH_3)_2SiH$—CH_2	b: 153–4°C (341)	ir, NMR (341)
$(CH_3)_3Si$—CH_2	b: 165–6°C; b_{24}: 64–5°C; n_D^{25}: 1.4569–94; d_{25}: 1.1244–1.136 (181, 443)	
Cl_2CH_3Si—CH_2	b_4: 58–9°C; n_D^{25}: 1.4824; d_{25}: 1.415 (181, 443)	
$[$—O—$Si(CH_3)$—$CH_2Sn(CH_3)_3]_n$	n_D^{25}: 1.4993; d_{25}: 1.448 (443)	
$CH_3(CH_3O)_2Si$—CH_2	b_{18}: 77.5–81°C; n_D^{25}: 1.4523; d_{25}: 1.248 (181, 443)	
$N{\equiv}C$—S—CH_2	b_4: 104–5°C; n_D^{25}: 1.5247; d_{25}: 1.491 (181, 443) (173, 181, 443)	ir, Raman, NMR (181, 443)
$(CH_3)_3SnCH_2$	b: 105°C; n_D^{20}: 1.4527 (181); GLC (312, 443)	ir (176, 443), Raman, NMR (43, 400); MS (44, 165, 449); kinetics (40, 41)
CH_3CH_2	m: 58–9°C (362)	NMR (362)
CH_3CCl_2	(68)	ir, NMR (68)
$HCFCl$—CF_2	(68)	ir (443)
HCF_2—CH_2	(68)	ir, NMR (31)
HCF_2—CHF	GLC (68)	(69)
HCF_2—CF_2	GLC (443)	ir (443)
CF_3—CF_2	(30, 31)	
$(CO)_4Co$—CF_2CF_2	(69)	
$(CO)_5Mn$—CF_2CF_2	(68, 443)	
$(CH_3)_3Sn$—CF_2CF_2	b_1: 68–9°C; n_D^{20}: 1.5075; d_{20}: 1.4134 (320)	ir (126), NMR (320)
$(CH_3)_2N$—C(=O)—CH_2	b_2: 82–4°C; n_D^{20}: 1.4961; d_{20}: 1.2878	ir, NMR
$(C_2H_5)_2N$—C(=O)—CH_2	(218)	
C_6H_5—N—C(=O)—CH_2 (with N=N—CH ring)		

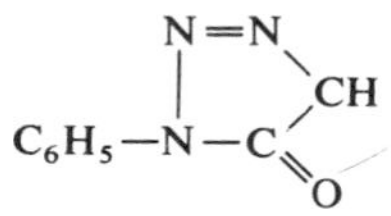

Continued

APPENDIX 5—*continued*

R in $RSn(CH_3)_3$	Important physical constants	Other properties
$CH_3CH_2CH_2$	b: 130.8°C; n_D^{20}: 1.4741 (312, 313); GLC (312)	kinetics (41)
$CH_2{=}CH{-}CH_2$	b: 128–30°C (181, 443); n_D^{20}: 1.4725–42 (35, 335); d_{20}: 1.2548 (35, 208)	uv (308); ir (105, 443), Raman (443) NMR (35, 94); kinetics (253)
$HC{\equiv}C{-}CH_2$	b_{755}: 135°C; b_{400}: 111–2°C b_{100}: 76–8°C (225) (68)	ir, NMR (223)
CF_3CFHCF_2		F—NMR (68), NMR (68)
$CF_3{-}CH_2{-}CH$ (with $Sn(CH_3)_3$)	b_{29}: 108°C (76)	ir, NMR (76)
$N{\equiv}C{-}CH_2CH_2$	(229)	
$CH_3{-}\underset{\underset{O}{\parallel}}{C}{-}CH_2$	(141, 149)	MB (149); kinetics (141)
$CH_3O{-}\underset{\underset{O}{\parallel}}{C}{-}CH_2CH_2$	(227)	NMR (231)
$C_2H_5O{-}\underset{\underset{O}{\parallel}}{C}{-}CH_2CH_2$	(227)	NMR (231)
$(CH_3)_2CH$	b_{120} (40); 123°C (322); 106–7°C (115) n_D^{25}: 1.4507; d_{25}: 1.198 (323) GLC (322, 323)	NMR (43); MS (44, 409a) parachors (324) heats of comb. (73) kinetics (40–43)
$\underset{CH_2}{\overset{CH_2}{|}}{>}CH$	b: 129–30°C; n_D^{25}: 1.4720; (17a, 41, 443)	kinetics (17a, 41)
$\underset{CCl_2}{\overset{CH_2}{|}}{>}CH$	n_D^{25}: 1.5059 (369)	ir, NMR (369)

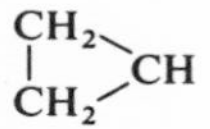

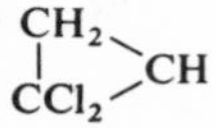

$(CH_3)_3Sn—CF_2—CF$ with CF_3	(68)	NMR (68)
$N≡C—CH$ with CH_3	(229)	
$CH_3(CH_2)_3$	b: 150°C; b_{14}: 46–6.5°C; n_D^{20}: 1.4560–7; d_{20}: 1.183 (181, 443); GLC (312, 412)	NMR (43, 400); MS (44); kinetics (40–42)
$CH_3—CH=CH—CH_2—CH_2$ *trans*	b_{761}: 147–8°C; n_D^{25}: 1.4762 (369)	NMR, ir (369); kinetics (207, 208)
$CH_3—CH=CH—CH_2—CH_2$ *cis*	b_{761}: 150–1°C; n_D^{25}: 1.4824 (369)	NMR, ir (369); kinetics (207, 208)
cis-trans mixture	GLC (114, 361)	uv (443)
$CH_2=CH—CH_2CH_2CH_2$	b: 146–8°C; n_D^{25}: 1.4688 (94, 119, 369)	ir, NMR (369)
$HCF_2—CH_2—CF_2—CH_2$	(68)	
$HCF_2—CFH—CF_2—CFH$	(68)	
$(CH_3)_3Sn—CF_2CFHCF_2CFH$	(68)	
$HCF_2(CF_2)_3$	GLC (68)	ir, NMR (68)
$(CH_3)_3Sn—CF_2CFHCF_2CFH$	(68)	NMR, F-NMR (68)
$(CH_3)_3Sn—(CF_2)_4$	(68)	
$CH_3—C—CH_2CH_2$ with $=O$	(256)	
$(CH_3)_3Sn—(CH_2)_4$	(443)	
$(CH_3)_2CH—CH_2$	b_{37}: 58°C; n_D^{20}: 1.4552; (181, 341, 443)	ir, NMR (341, 409); kinetics
$CH_2=C—CH_2$ with CH_3	(443)	
$HCCl_2—CH—CH_2$ with CH_3	n_D^{25}: 1.5005 (359)	NMR (359)
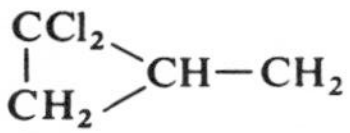 CCl_2 / CH_2 \ $CH—CH_2$	$b_{1.4}$: 57.5–8°C; n_D^{25}: 1.5041 (369)	

Continued

APPENDIX 5—*continued*

R in RSn(CH₃)₃	Important physical constants	Other properties
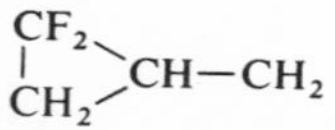 $CF_2{-}CH{-}CH_2$ (cyclopropane)	n_D^{25}: 1.4450 (366)	
$CH_3CH_2{-}CH{-}CH_3$	b: 145.5–6°C; n_D^{20}: 1.4614 (210); b: 146–8°C; n_D^{20}: 1.4630 (409)	
$CH_2{=}CH{-}CH{-}CH_3$	(208)	
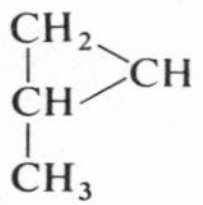 $CH_2{-}CH{-}CH_3$ (cyclopropane)	GLC (17a)	ir, NMR (17a); kinetics (16)
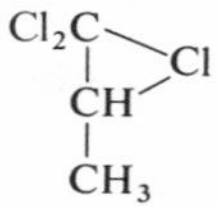 $Cl_2C{-}CH{-}CH_3$ (cyclopropane)	(371)	
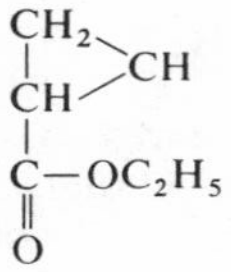 $CH_2{-}CH{-}C({-}OC_2H_5){=}O$ (cyclopropane)	b₁: 72–6°C (17a)	NMR (17a)
$(CH_3)_3C$	b: 134°C (322); m: 42–3°C (43); GLC (40); (41, 42, 322, 323) b₀.₀₂: 78–80°C (62)	NMR (43); MS (44, 170, 216); heats of comb. (73)
$(CH_3)_2N{-}CH_2{-}C(CH_3){-}C{\equiv}N$		

$CH_3(CH_2)_4$	b: 172°C; n_D^{20}: 1.4559; d_{15}: 1.1586 (181, 443)	
$CH_3CH_2-CH=CH-CH_2$	(289); GLC (311)	
$CH_3-CH=CH-CH_2CH_2$	GLC (289, 311, 443)	
$CH_2=CH-CH_2CH_2CH_2$	(443)	
$Br-(CH_2)_5$	b_{18}: 124°C (181)	
$HCCl_2-CH_2-CH_2-CH=CH-CH-CH_2$	$b_{0.7}$: 64–6°C; n_D^{25}: 1.5131 (369)	ir, NMR (369)
$(CH_3)_3Pb-(CH_2)_5$	$b_{17.5}$: 162°C (181)	
$CH_3-C-CH_2CH_2CH_2$ $\parallel$ O	(256)	
$(CH_3)_2CH-CH_2CH_2$	b: 164°C; n_D^{20}: 1.4470; d_{21}: 1.1306 (181, 443)	
$(CH_3)_2C=CH-CH_2$	(114)	
$CH_2=C-CH_2CH_2$ $\vert$ CH_3	(114)	
$CCl_2-CH-CH_2CH_2$ $\diagdown CH_2 \diagup$	$b_{3.1}$: 81–3°C; n_D^{25}: 1.5054 (369)	
$CH_3-CH=C$ $\vert$ CH_3	(114)	
$CH_2=CH-CH-CH_2$ $\vert$ CH_3	(114)	
CCl_2 $\vert$ $CH-CH-CH_2$ cis/trans $\vert$ CH_3	$b_{4.3}$: 83–5°C; n_D^{25}: 1.5004 (369)	
$CH_3CH_2CH_2-CH$ $\vert$ CH_3	$b_{2.2}$: 73.5–74°C; n_D^{25}: 1.5018 (369)	ir, NMR (369)
trans	b_{25}: 69°C (409)	

Continued

M. *Gielen and J. Nasielski*

APPENDIX 5—*continued*

R in RSn(CH$_3$)$_3$	Important physical constants	Other properties
CH$_3$—CH=CH—CH— $\quad\quad\quad\quad$ CH$_3$	GLC (443)	
(CH$_3$CH$_2$)$_2$CH	b$_{25}$: 69°C (409)	
CH$_2$CH$_2$ CH$_2$CH$_2$ CH	b$_{25}$: 77°C; n_D^{20}: 1.4884 (409)	
CH—CH$_2$ $\Vert$ $\quad\quad$ CH CH—CH$_2$	(114)	
CH=CH CH$_2$CH$_2$ CH	(114)	
CH=CH $\vert\quad\quad$ CH CH=CH	b$_{10}$: 85°C; b$_1$: 56–60°C; (184)	NMR (443)
HCCl$_2$C(CH$_3$)$_2$—CH$_2$ (CH$_3$)$_2$CH—CH $\quad\quad\quad\quad\quad$ CH$_3$	(366) b$_{30}$: 71-2°C; n_D^{20}: 1.4669 (409)	
CH$_3$CH$_2$—C(CH$_3$)$_2$ HCF$_2$(CF$_2$)$_5$	b: 156–8°C (409) (68)	

Structure	Data
CH₃CH₂CH₂CH₂—CH (CH₃)₃Sn—CH₂ (CH₃CH₂)₂CH—CH₂	(311)
$H_2C\Big\langle \begin{smallmatrix}CH_2CH_2\\CH_2CH_2\end{smallmatrix}\Big\rangle CH$	b: 182-4°C; n_D^{20}: 1.4654 (409) NMR (89a); MS (44); parachors (324)
$H_2C\Big\langle \begin{smallmatrix}CH=CH\\CH_2CH_2\end{smallmatrix}\Big\rangle CH$	(114) b: 203-4°C; (45); b₁₄: 74-6°C; n_D^{20}: 1.4937 (409); n_D^{25}: 1.4914; d_{25}: 1.216 (322); GLC (323)
$HC\Big\langle \begin{smallmatrix}CH—CH_2\\CH_2CH_2\end{smallmatrix}\Big\rangle CH$	b₁₂: 80-2°C; n_D^{20}: 1.5067 (114, 409)
(CH₃)₂—CH—CH₂ CH₃	b₂₂: 80°C; n_D^{20}: 1.4649 (409)
(CH₃)₂C=C—CH₂ CH₃	(114)
CH₂=CH—CH—CH₂ CH₃ CH₃	(114)
(CO)Ni—C₅H₄(CH₃) (CO)₄Ti—C₅H₄(C₂H₅)	(443) (443)
$H_2C\Big\langle \begin{smallmatrix}CH_2CH_2\\CH_2—CH—\end{smallmatrix}\Big\rangle CH$ CH₃	b₁₀: 88-9°C; n_D^{20}: 1.5003 (409) NMR (409)

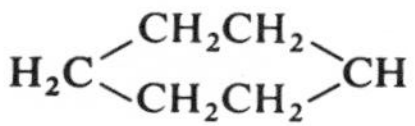

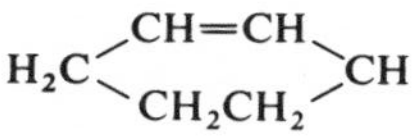

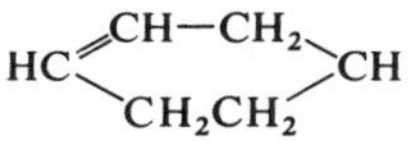

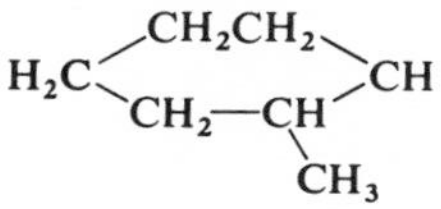

Continued

APPENDIX 5—*continued*

R in RSn(CH$_3$)$_3$	Important physical constants	Other properties
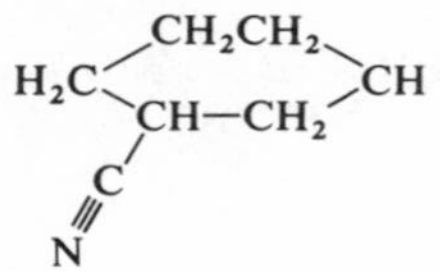 CH_2CH_2 H_2C—CH—CH$_2$ $C\equiv N$ (bicyclic nitrile)	b$_{13}$: 138–40°C (409)	
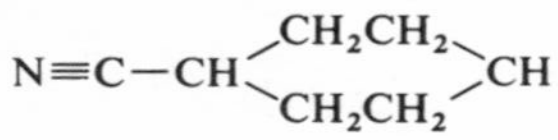 $N\equiv C$—CH$<$ $\frac{CH_2CH_2}{CH_2CH_2}>$CH	b$_{13}$: 138–40°C (409)	
C_6H_5—CH$_2$	b$_9$: 90°C (181, 268, 443)	uv (268), NMR (43, 400), MS (44, 427, 449); EPR (407); kinetics (37)
p-Br—C$_6$H$_4$—CH$_2$	b$_6$: 126°C; b$_{1.5}$: 99°C; n_D^{25}: 1.5570 (37, 443)	NMR (43)
m-Cl—C$_6$H$_4$—CH$_2$	b$_{1.2}$: 89.5°C; n_D^{23}: 1.5569 (37)	
p-Cl—C$_6$H$_4$—CH$_2$	b$_9$: 124°C; b$_2$: 96°C (37, 443); n_D^{25}: 1.557 (37)	
p-F—C$_6$H$_4$—CH$_2$	b$_{1.8}$: 69°C; n_D^{25}: 1.5261 (37) (38)	
p-Li—C$_6$H$_4$—CH$_2$		
p-(CH$_3$)$_3$Si—C$_6$H$_4$—CH$_2$	b$_{7-8}$: 133–5°C; n_D^{20}: 1.5251 (443)	
p-(CH$_3$)$_3$Sn—C$_6$H$_4$—CH$_2$	b$_{0.04}$: 98–100°C; n_D^{20}: 1.5550 (38)	
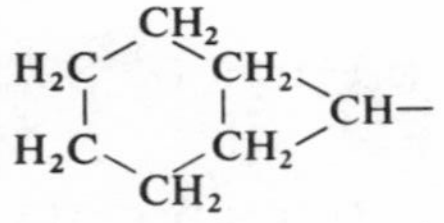 CH_2—CH— H_2C CH$_2$ H_2C CH$_2$ (cyclohexyl)	b$_{10}$: 95–6°C; n_{Do}^{20}: 1.5018 (409)	

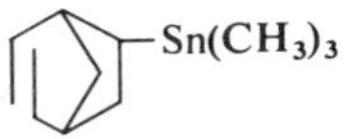

Structure	Ref.	Properties	Methods
Sn(CH₃)₃ (bicyclic)	(209)		
cage, Sn(CH₃)₃	(209)		
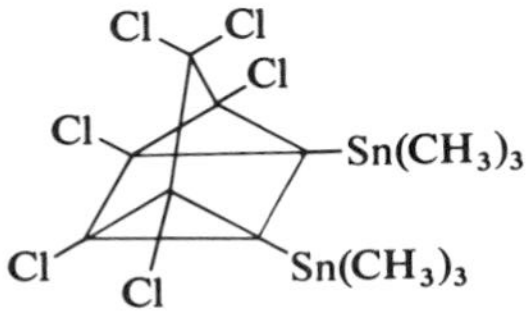 cage, Cl, Sn(CH₃)₃	(364); m: 139–41°C (dec.)		ir, NMR (364)
$CH_3(CH_2)_7$	$b_{0.03}$: 56–8°C; n_D^{25}: 1.4587; d_{25}: 1.0802 (181, 443)		
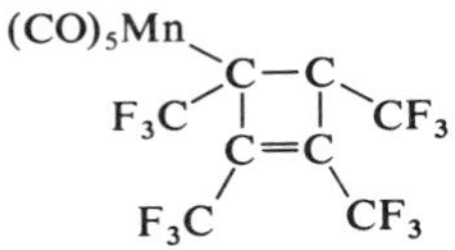 $(CO)_5Mn$ — ... CF_3 / F_3C — ... CF_3 / F_3C	(32)		ir, ^{19}F NMR (32)
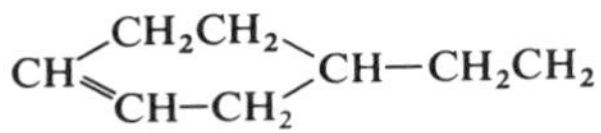 $CH \overset{CH_2CH_2}{\underset{CH-CH_2}{<}} CH-CH_2CH_2$	(114)		
$o\text{-}CH_3\text{—}C_6H_4\text{—}CH_2$	(139) $b_{0.7}$: 62°C; n_D^{25}: 1.5384 (39)		NMR (43); MS (44)
$m\text{-}CH_3\text{—}C_6H_4\text{—}CH_2$			NMR (43); MS (44)

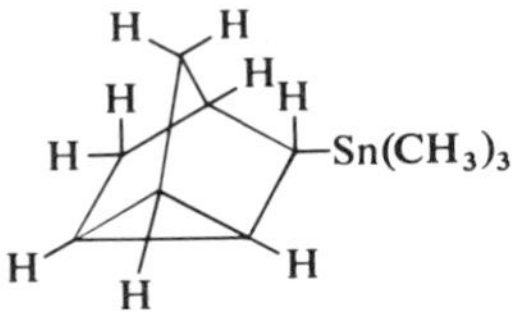

Continued

APPENDIX 5—*continued*

R in $RSn(CH_3)_3$	Important physical constants	Other properties
p-CH_3—C_6H_4—CH_2 C_6H_5—CH(—C≡N)	b_1: 69°C; n_D^{25}: 1.5383 (*39*) (*184*)	NMR (*43*); MS (*44*)
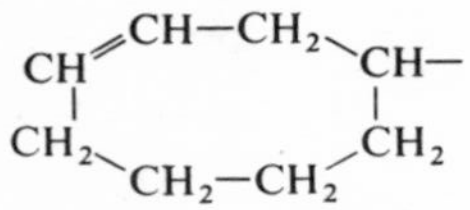	(*114*)	
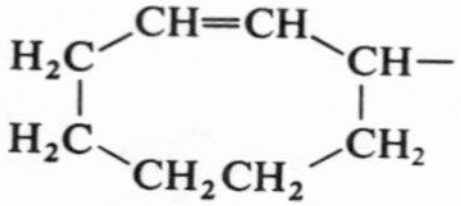	(*114*)	
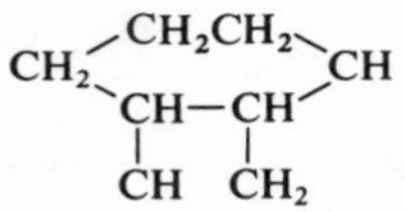	(*114*)	
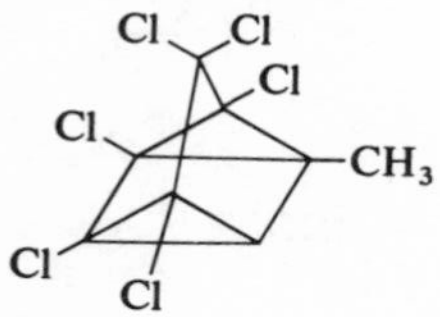	m: 64–7°C (*364*)	uv, ir, NMR (*364*)

$C_6H_5-\overset{\overset{\displaystyle O}{\|}}{C}-CH_2CH_2$　　(256)

[indane structure]　　b_{10}: 128°C; n_D^{25}: 1.5508 (409)　　NMR (409)

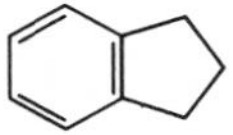

[indene structure]　　(184)

$CH_3-(CH_2)_9$
$C_6H_5-\overset{\overset{\displaystyle O}{\|}}{C}-CH_2CH_2CH_2$　　$b_{0.05}$: 67°C; n_D^{25}: 1.4602; d_{25}: 1.0487 (181, 443)
(256)

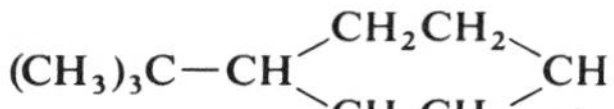

$(CH_3)_3C-CH\!\!\begin{array}{c}CH_2CH_2\\ \diagup \quad \diagdown CH\\ CH_2CH_2\end{array}$ $\begin{array}{l}cis\\ trans\end{array}$　　(89a); GLC (89a)　　NMR (89a), MS (89a)

$H_3C-C\!=\!\!\begin{array}{c}CH_2CH_2\\ \diagup \quad \diagdown CH\\ \\ C\\ \diagdown \quad \diagup CH_2\\ CH_2CH_2\end{array}$
H_3C-　　GLC (89a)　　NMR, MS (89a)

[substituted structure with CH_3, CH_2 groups]　　(114)

[branched structure with CH_3, CH_2CH_2 groups]　　(114)

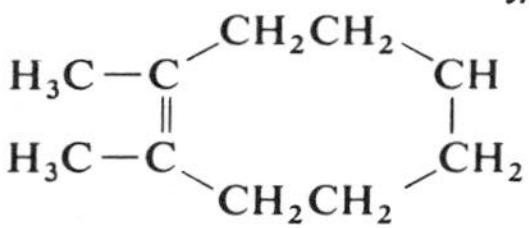

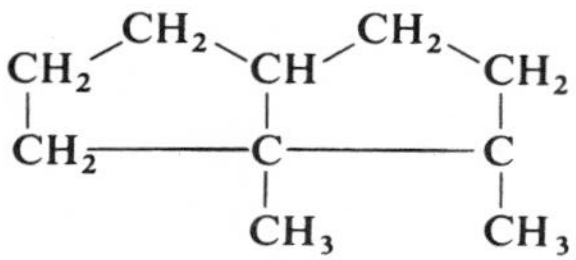

Continued

APPENDIX 5—*continued*

R in $RSn(CH_3)_3$	Important physical constants	Other properties
$CH_3{-}(CH_2)_{11}$	b_{14}: 158–60°C; n_D^{25}: 1.4610; d_{25}: 1.0285 (*181, 443*)	
$(C_6H_5)_2C{-}C{\equiv}N$	(*184*)	
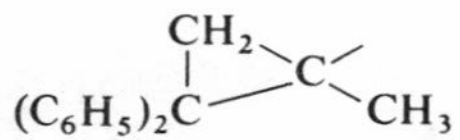 $(C_6H_5)_2C{\overset{CH_2}{\underset{}{}}}C{\overset{}{\underset{CH_3}{}}}$	n_D^{21}: 1.5742 (*398*); $[\alpha]_D^{21} = +11°6 \text{ or } -16°1$ ($c = 1.45$ in $CHCl_3$) (*398*)	

APPENDIX 6

ALKENYLTRIMETHYLTINS

R in RSn(CH$_3$)$_3$	Important physical constants	Other properties
CH$_2$=CH	b: 99–100°C; n_D^{25}: 1.4536–44 d_{25}: 1.1237 or 1.265 (181, 443)	ir (94, 105), uv (308), MB (4, 149, 443); kinetics (17a)
(C$_4$H$_9$)$_2$Sb—CH=CH	$b_{0.5}$: 102–4°C; n_D^{20}: 1.5400 (280)	
Cl$_2$C=CCl	b_{20}: 111°C (66)	ir (65)
C$_2$H$_2$F	(29)	
CHF=CH	(29)	
CF$_2$=CH	(29)	
CF$_2$=CF	b: 110.5°C (29); GLC (68)	ir (68)
(CH$_3$)$_3$Sn—CH=CH	b: 194.5°C (181)	
CH$_3$—CH=CH cis	b: 127–30°C; n_D^{25}: 1.4690 (351)	ir (443)
trans	b: 125–8°C; n_D^{25}: 1.4638 (351, 355, 358, 363a)	
CH$_2$=C=CH	b_{100}: 76°C (223, 224)	ir (223)
CH$_2$=C=CD	(225b)	-MS (225c)
CF$_3$—CH=CH	b: 129 (76)	ir, NMR (76)
N≡C—CH=CH	(231)	NMR (231)
CH$_3$O—C(=O)—CH=CH	(227, 231)	NMR (231)
C$_2$H$_5$O—C(=O)—CH=CH	(227, 228, 231)	NMR (231)
CH$_2$=C(—CH$_3$)	(208, 351, 355)	

Continued

APPENDIX 6—*continued*

R in RSn(CH₃)₃	Important physical constants	Other properties
$CH_2{=}C{\diagdown}CF_3$	b: 129°C (76)	ir, NMR (76)
$CF_3{-}C{=}C{\diagup}{\diagdown}CF_2$	(77)	F-NMR, ir (77)
$CH_2{=}C{-}C{\equiv}N$	b_{18}: 78–80°C; n_D^{20}: 1.4982 (228)	NMR (231)
$CHD{=}C{-}C{\equiv}N$	(232)	
$CH_2{=}C{-}C{\diagdown}^{-OCH_3}_{=O}$	(227)	NMR (231)
$CHD{=}C{-}C{\diagdown}^{-OCH_3}_{=O}$	(232)	

Structure	Preparation	Characterization
$CH_2{=}C\!\!\begin{array}{c}\\ \mid\\ C{-}OC_2H_5\\ \parallel\\ O\end{array}$	(227, 228)	NMR (231)
$(CH_3)_2C{=}CH$ $CH_3{-}CH{=}C$	GLC (17)	NMR (17)
$CH_3{-}C\!\!\begin{array}{c}\\ \mid\\ CH_3\end{array}$	GLC (17, 208)	NMR (17, 208)
$CH_3{-}C\!\!\begin{array}{c}\\ \mid\\ CH_2CH_3\end{array}$ $CF_3{-}CH{=}C$	GLC (17, 208)	NMR (17, 208)
$CF_3{-}CH{=}C\!\!\begin{array}{c}\\ \mid\\ CF_3\end{array}$ $(CO)_2(C_5H_5)Fe{-}C{=}C\!\!\begin{array}{c}F_3C\ \ CF_3\\ \diagdown\ \diagup\\ C{=}C\\ \mid\ \ \mid\end{array}$	b_{751}: 124 (76)	ir (76); NMR (76)
$N{\equiv}C{-}CH{=}C\!\!\begin{array}{c}\\ \mid\\ C{\equiv}N\end{array}$	(32)	ir, MS (32)
$CH_3{-}CH{=}C\!\!\begin{array}{c}\\ \mid\\ C{-}OC_2H_5\\ \parallel\\ O\end{array}$	(231)	NMR (231)
$C_2H_5O{-}C{-}CH{=}C\!\!\begin{array}{c}\\ \parallel\ \ \ \ \ \mid\\ O\ \ \ \ \ CH_3\end{array}$	(234, 235)	NMR (231)
$C_2H_5O{-}C{-}CH{=}C\!\!\begin{array}{c}\\ \parallel\ \ \ \ \ \mid\\ O\ \ \ \ \ C{-}OC_2H_5\\ \ \ \ \ \ \ \ \ \parallel\\ \ \ \ \ \ \ \ \ O\end{array}$	(234–235)	NMR (231)
	$b_{0.07}$: 71-2°C; (228)	NMR (231)

Continued

APPENDIX 6 —*continued*

R in RSn(CH₃)₃	Important physical constants	Other properties
$(CH_3)_3Sn-C=C$ with F_3C, CF_3	$b_{0\cdot001}$: 53°C; (75)	NMR (75)
$C_2H_5O-C-C\equiv C$; $(CH_3)_2N-C-OC_2H_5$, O, O	$b_{0\cdot02}$: 100°C (62)	
$CH_3CH_2CH_2-CH=CH$; $CH_3-C=C-CH_3$	GLC (31l)	
$CH_3-CH=C-CH_3$	(21l)	
$CH_3-CH=C-CH_2CH_3$	(208)	
$(CH_3)_2C=C-CH_3$	(208)	
$CH_2=C-CH(CH_3)_2$	(208)	
$C_4H_9-CH=CH$; $CH_3-CH=C$	(23l)	NMR (23l)
$(CH_3)_2C-CH(CH_3)_2$; CH_2CH_3	(208)	

$CH_3(CH_2)_4$—CH=CH   GLC (311)

$(CH_3)_3$Sn—CH=CH—CH=CH—$CH_2CH_2CH_2$—CH=CH   GLC (311)

$CH_3(CH_2)_3$—CH=C— with —CH_3 (311)

$CH_3CH_2CH_2$—CH=C— with —CH_2CH_3 GLC (311)

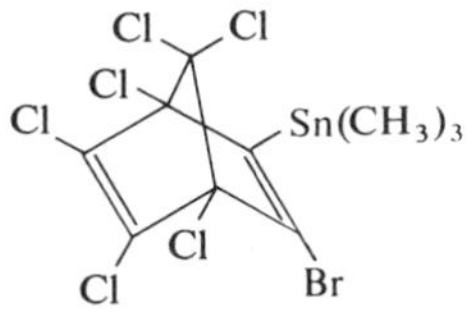

m: 85–6.5°C (363)   ir (370)

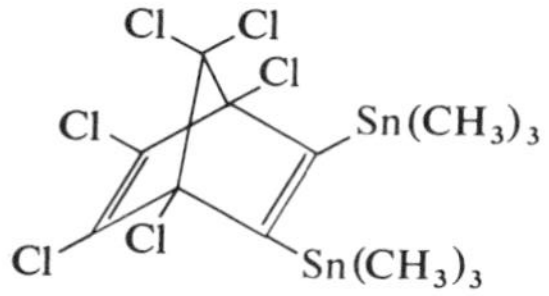

m: 89–90°C (108, 364)   uv, ir, NMR (364)

$CH_3(CH_2)_5$—CH=CH   (311)

$CH_3CH_2CH_2$—CH=C— with —$CH_2CH_2CH_3$ (311)

C_6H_5—CH=CH—CH=CH   cis trans b_{35}: 110–4°C; n_D^{25}: 1.5530 (231); n_D^{25}: 1.5666 (429)   ir, uv, NMR (231); ir, uv, NMR (443)

CH_2=C with C_6H_5 b_2: 110°C; n_D^{20}: 1.5570; d_{20}: 1.3050 (22)

Continued

APPENDIX 6—*continued*

R in RSn(CH$_3$)$_3$	Important physical constants	Other properties
C$_6$H$_5$—C=CCl (CH$_3$)$_2$N	b$_{0.04}$: 60–89°C (dec.) (62)	
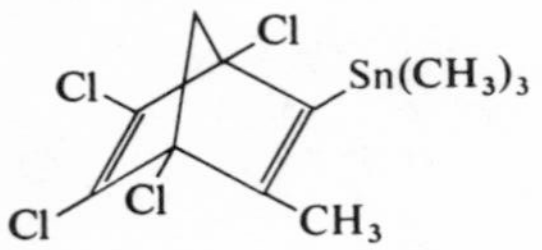	m: 83–5°C; (364)	uv, ir, NMR (364)
CH$_3$(CH$_2$)$_6$—CH=CH	GLC (311)	
(CH$_3$)$_3$Sn—CH=CH(CH$_2$)$_6$—CH=CH	GLC (311)	
CH$_3$(CH$_2$)$_3$—CH=C	GLC (311)	
CH$_3$—CH$_2$—CH$_2$ C$_6$H$_5$—CH=C—CH$_3$	(211)	
CH$_3$—CH=C—C$_6$H$_5$	(211)	
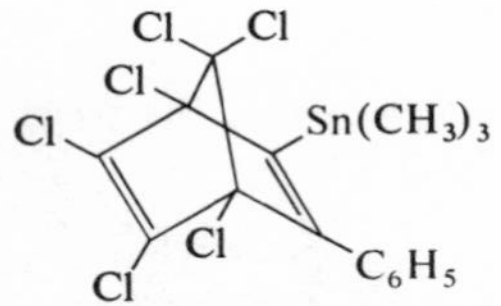	m: 101.5–2.5°C; (364)	uv, ir, NMR (364)

APPENDIX 7

ALKYNYLTRIMETHYLTINS

R in $RSn(CH_3)_3$	Important physical constants	Other properties
$N{\equiv}C$	m: 182°C (241)	MB, (149, 413), XR (340)
$HC{\equiv}C$	b: 95–6°C (443); 98°C (385)	ir (385, 443); NMR (307)
	b_{150}: 58°C; (385); n_D^{20}: 1.4626; d_{20}:	
	1.3602 (385), b_{80}: 40°C; n_D^{20}: 1.4537;	
	d_{20}: 1.2618 (456)	
$Br{-}C{\equiv}C$	b_{14}: 67–8°C; n_D^{20}: 1.5175; d_{20}: 1.7396	
	(452, 454)	
$Cl{-}C{\equiv}C$	b_{44}: 67°C; n_D^{20}: 1.4915 (411)	ir, Raman (411)
$(CH_3)_3Ge{-}C{\equiv}C$	b_{47}: 41–4°C (113)	ir, NMR (113)
$(CH_3)_3Si{-}C{\equiv}C$	b_{25}: 24–5°C (113)	ir, NMR (113)
$(CH_3)_3Sn{-}C{\equiv}C$	b_1: 63°C (452); b_{23}: 102°C (453); b_{16}:	(85, 443)
	97–8°C; $b_{0.2}$: 90–100°C (243, 443);	
	m: 57.5–9°C (443); 59–60°C (443) 58°C	
	(197, 453); 55–7°C (456)	
$(C_2H_5)_3Sn{-}C{\equiv}C$	$b_{1.5}$: 59°C; n_D^{20}: 1.4710; d_{20}: 1.1162 (85, 385)	
$CH_3{-}C{\equiv}C$	$b_{0.2}$: 25–6°C; b_{100}: 76–8°C (57);	ir (443), NMR (396, 397)
	GLC (223)	
$CF_3{-}C{\equiv}C$	b: 125°C (77)	ir, F-NMR (77)
$CH_2{=}CH{-}C{\equiv}C$	b_{10}: 46.5–49°C; n_D^{20}: 1.5058–67;	ir, NMR (443)
	d_{20}: 1.3066–1.3103 (85, 443)	
$(CH_3)_3Sn{-}C{\equiv}C{-}C{\equiv}C$	m: 140°C (85, 160, 443)	
$CH_3CH_2CH_2{-}C{\equiv}C$	b: 172°C (184, 443)	
$CH_3{-}CH{=}CH{-}C{\equiv}C$	b_{10}: 65–7°C; n_D^{20} 1.5088;	
	d_{20}: 1.2771 (85, 443)	
$(CH_3)_2CH{-}C{\equiv}C$	b_{10}: 50°C; n_D^{20}: 1.4676;	dipole moment (85)
	d_{20}: 1.2076 (85, 443)	

Continued

APPENDIX 7

R in RSn(CH₃)₃	Important physical constants	Other properties
$CH_2\!=\!C\!-\!C\!\equiv\!C$, with CH_3	b_5: 40–2°C; b_{10}: 57–8°C (85, 223, 443); n_D^{20}: 1.5013 (85); n_D^{28}: 1.4958 (223); d_{20}: 1.2499 (85)	ir (223); uv (223)
$CH_3(CH_2)_3\!-\!C\!\equiv\!C$	b_{12}: 82°C (184, 443)	
$\overset{CH_2CH_2}{\underset{CH_2CH}{\big>}}C\!-\!C\!\equiv\!C$	b_3: 68–70°C (223, 443)	ir (223)
$H_2C\overset{CH_2CH_2}{\underset{CH_2CH}{\big<}}C\!=\!C\!-\!C\!\equiv\!C$	b_3: 68–70°C (224)	uv, NMR (224)
$C_6H_5\!-\!C\!\equiv\!C$	$b_{1.5}$: 107°C (443); b_2: 87–88°C (85); $b_{0.3}$: 68°C (184); n_D^{20}: 1.5720; d_{20}: 1.3324 (85)	

APPENDIX 8

ARYLTRIMETHYLTINS

Ar in ArSn(CH₃)₃	Important physical constants	Other properties
C_6H_5	b_{760}: 205°C (443); $b_{0.5}$: 76.5°C; n_D^{25}: 1.5330 (443); d_{25}: 1.326 (443) mol. refr.: 56.45 (324); surf. tens.: 28.9 (324); parachor: 422 (324)	uv (267, 443); NMR (43, 212, 400); MS (137); MB (443); dipole moment (174, 443); kinetics (2a, 36a, 53, 55, 91, 103b, 103a, 270, 400); thermochemical data (443)
o-CH_3O—C_6H_4	$b_{1.2}$: 70°C; n_D^{20}: 1.5369 (99)	kinetics (100)
m-CH_3O—C_6H_4	$b_{0.4}$: 61°C (99); n_D^{25}: 1.5389 (99)	MS (137); kinetics (100; NMR (43)
p-CH_3O—C_6H_4	b_{15}: 125–127°C (443); b_4: 102°C (100); n_D^{25}: 1.5392; n_D^{20}: 1.5430 (52, 100)	NMR (43); MS (137); dipole moment (174, 443); kinetics (2a, 36a, 53, 55, 100, 103a)
m-NH_2—C_6H_4		kinetics (100)
p-$(CH_3)_2N$—C_6H_4	$b_{0.85}$: 97°C (99); m: 40–41°C (174)	dipole moment (174, 443); kinetics (100)
p-$(CH_3)_3N$—C_6H_4 (iodide) +		
o-FC_6H_4	m: 186–187°C (dec) (99)	kinetics (100)
	$b_{0.5}$: 32°C (100); b_7: 63–64° C (103) n_D^{25}: 1.5221 (103); 1.5227 (100)	kinetics (100)
m-FC_6H_4	$b_{1.8-2.4}$: 55–57°C (103); n_D^{25}: 1.5172 (103)	kinetics (100)
p-FC_6H_4	$b_{0.7-0.8}$: 50–51°C (103); n_D^{25}: 1.5160 (103), 1.5149 (100)	dipole moment (174); kinetics (100)
C_6F_5	b_{20}: 97.5°C (103), b_{50}: 118–119°C (310); n_D^{20}: 1.4726 (103), 1.4744 (310)	
o-ClC_6H_4	$b_{0.5}$: 47°C (100); n_D^{25}: 1.5977 (100)	kinetics (100)
m-ClC_6H_4	$b_{3.5}$: 96°C (443), $b_{3.5}$: 84°C (100); n_D^{25}: 1.5491 (100)	kinetics (36a, 100, 103a)
p-ClC_6H_4	b_2: 80°C (443), b_{22}: 122–126°C (443); n_D^{20}: 1.5516 (443)	ir (443); dipole moment (174, 443); kinetics (36a, 100, 103a, 443)
$2,3,4,5$-Cl_4C_6H		kinetics (364)

Continued

APPENDIX 8—*continued*

Ar in $ArSn(CH_3)_3$	Important physical constants	Other properties
C_6Cl_5	m: 119–120°C (65, 374) (108)	ir (66); uv (66); NMR (66)
o-BrC_6H_4	$b_{0.3}$: 62°C (99); n_D^{25}: 1.5672 (99)	kinetics (100)
m-BrC_6H_4	$b_{0.2}$: 64°C (100), b_{15}: 124°C (443); n_D^{20}: 1.5709 (52), n_D^{25}: 1.5669 (100); d_{15}: 1.6489 (443)	NMR (43); MS (137); kinetics (2a, 53, 55, 100); dipole moment (174)
p-BrC_6H_4	$b_{1.5}$: 109°C (99); n_D^{25}: 1.6000 (99)	
3,5-$Br_2C_6H_3$	m: 218°C (443)	kinetics (100)
o-IC_6H_4	$b_{1.5}$: 87°C (99); n_D^{25}: 1.5171 (99)	NMR (43); MS (137); kinetics (56, 100)
m-$(CH_3)_3Si$—C_6H_4	m: 103–104°C (52, 100)	kinetics (100)
p-$(CH_3)_3Si$—C_6H_4	$b_{0.4}$: 85°C (99); n_D^{25}: 1.5832 (99)	
p-CH_3S—C_6H_4	m: 232–233°C (108, 443)	ir (443); NMR (43); kinetics (56)
o-$(CH_3)_3Sn$—C_6H_4	m: 124–125°C (52)	
p-$(CH_3)_3Sn$—C_6H_4	m: 148–149.5°C (374)	
2,3,5,6-Cl_4-4-$(CH_3)_3SnC_6$	b_7: 90°C (99); n_D^{25}: 1.5379 (99)	NMR (43); MS (137); kinetics (100, 271)
o-$CH_3C_6H_4$	$b_{0.6}$: 64–67°C (443), $b_{0.9}$: 55°C (100); n_D^{20}: 1.5330 (52), n_D^{25}: 1.5309 (100)	NMR (43); MS (137); kinetics (2a, 53, 55, 100)
m-$CH_3C_6H_4$	b_{760}: 224.4°C (52), $b_{1.2}$: 69°C (100); n_D^{20}: 1.5330 (52), n_D^{25}: 1.5294 (100)	NMR (43, 212); MS (137); kinetics (2a, 36a, 53, 55, 100, 103a); dipole moment (174)
p-$CH_3C_6H_4$		
p-$HOOC$—C_6H_4	m: 131–132°C (443) (108)	pK (63)
2-$(CH_3)_3Sn$—C_6H_3-4-$COOCH_3$		kinetics (100)
o-$CF_3C_6H_4$	$b_{3.6}$: 67°C (99); n_D^{25}: 1.4920 (99)	kinetics (100)
m-$CF_3C_6H_4$		kinetics (100)
p-$CF_3C_6H_4$		kinetics (38)
p-$(CH_3)_3SiCH_2$—C_6H_4	$b_{2.4}$: 114–115°C (38); n_D^{25}: 1.5278 (38)	kinetics (38)
p-$(CH_3)_3GeCH_2$—C_6H_4		

Compound	Properties	Methods
$p\text{-}(CH_3)_3SnCH_2\text{—}C_6H_4$	$b_{0.04}$: 98–100°C (443); n_D^{25}: 1.5550 (443)	kinetics (38)
$2,3\text{-}(CH_3)_2C_6H_3$	$b_{0.8}$: 78°C (99); n_D^{25}: 1.5419 (99)	NMR (43); kinetics (271)
$2,4\text{-}(CH_3)_2C_6H_3$	$b_{2.5}$: 84°C (99); n_D^{25}: 1.5363 (99)	NMR (43); MS (137); kinetics (271)
$2,6\text{-}(CH_3)_2C_6H_3$		
$3,5\text{-}(CF_3)_2C_6H_3$	$b_{8.5}$: 81–82°C (99); n_D^{25}: 1.4445 (99)	
$\text{-}(CH_3)_3Sn\text{—}C_6H_4\text{—}CH_2\text{—}CH_2\text{—}Sn(CH_3)_2$	m: 64–68°C (443)	ir (443); MB (443)
$\text{-}p\text{-}C_6H_4\text{—}Sn(CH_3)_2\text{—}CH_2\text{—}CH_2\text{-}p\text{-}C_6H_4$	$b_{0.5}$: 68°C (443); n_D^{20}: 1.5643, 1.5648 (443); d_{20}: 1.3020, 1.2990 (443)	
$p\text{-}CH_2=CH\text{—}C_6H_4$	b_1: 72–73°C (102); n_D^{25}: 1.5595 (102)	kinetics (100)
$o\text{-}CH\equiv C\text{—}C_6H_4$	$b_{0.35}$: 56.5°C (102); m: 32–33°C (102)	kinetics (100)
$p\text{-}HC\equiv C\text{—}C_6H_4$	$b_{0.18}$: 87.5–88.5°C (102); n_D^{25}: 1.5428 (102)	
$m\text{-}(CH_3)_3Si\text{—}C\equiv C\text{—}C_6H_4$	$b_{0.7}$: 111–112°C (102); n_D^{25}: 1.5466 (102);	
$p\text{-}(CH_3)_3Si\text{—}C\equiv C\text{—}C_6H_4$	m: 31–32.5°C (102)	
$2,4,6\text{-}(CH_3)_3C_6H_2$	$b_{0.1}$: 65–66°C (212); m: 35–36°C (212)	NMR (212)
$3,4,5\text{-}(CH_3)_3C_6H_2$	$b_{0.1}$: 80–81°C (212); m: 25°C (212)	NMR (212)
$p\text{-}CH_2=C(CH_3)\text{—}C_6H_4$	$b_{0.0003}$: 49–51°C (443); n_D^{20}: 1.5574; d_{20}: 1.2743 (443)	ir (443)
$p\text{-}(CH_3)_3C\text{—}C_6H_4$	m: 72–75°C (260), 74°C (99)	NMR (43); kinetics (100, 260)
1-Naphthyl	b_1: 120–121°C (52); n_D^{20}: 1.6119 (52)	NMR (43); MS (137); kinetics (53, 55, 100)
2-Naphthyl	b_1: 115°C (52); m: 29–29.5°C (52) (108)	NMR (43); MS (137); kinetics (53, 55)
$2\text{-}C_6H_5\text{—}C_6H_4$	$b_{0.2}$: 107°C (99); n_D^{25}: 1.5960 (99)	kinetics (100)
$3C_6H_5\text{—}C_6H_4$	$b_{0.3}$: 118–119°C (443); m: 53°C (81), 52°C (100)	uv (82); NMR (81); kinetics (100)
$4\text{-}C_6H_5\text{—}C_6H_4$	m: 273°C (108, 443)	
$2\text{-}(2\text{-}IC_6H_4)\text{—}C_6H_4$	m: 70°C (81)	uv (82); NMR (81)
$4\text{-}(4\text{-}Me_3SnC_6H_4)\text{—}C_6H_4$	b_2: 180°C (52); m: 56–57°C (52)	NMR (43); MS (137); kinetics (53, 55)
9-Phenanthryl	m: 193–196°C (443)	NMR (443)
$2\text{-}CH_3\text{-}3,4,5,6\text{-}(C_6H_5)_4C_6$	m: 325–326°C (443)	
$C_6(C_6H_5)_5$	m: 284–286°C (443)	
$2\text{-}(m\text{-}CH_3C_6H_4)\text{-}3,4,5,6\text{-}(C_6H_5)_4C_6$	m: 289°C (443)	
$2\text{-}(p\text{-}CH_3C_6H_4)\text{-}3,4,5,6\text{-}(C_6H_5)_4C_6$		

Continued

APPENDIX 8—*continued*

Ar in $ArSn(CH_3)_3$	Important physical constants	Other properties
2-Pyridyl		pK (*12*); kinetics (*10*)
	$ArSn(CH_2X)_3$	
$C_6H_5—Sn(CH_2Cl)_3$	$b_{0.1}$: 140–142°C (*443*); n_D^{20}: 1.6031 (*443*)	
$C_6H_5—Sn(CH_2I)_3$	$b_{0.05}$: 180°C (*443*)	

APPENDIX 9

ALKYLTRIETHYLTINS

R in $RSn(C_2H_5)_3$	Important physical constants	Other properties
CH_3	b_{745}: 159°C n_D^{20}: 1.4656; d_{20}: 1.2160; GLC (*181, 312, 443*)	ir (*178*); NMR (*43, 400*); MS (*44, 165*); MB (*149, 165, 193*); kinetics (*40–42, 109*)
$ClCH_2$	b_{10}: 84.5–5.5°C; n_D^{20}: 1.4947; d_{20}: 1.3383 (*202, 443*)	MS (*193*); MB (*149, 193*)
Cl_2CH	b_{92}: 133.5°C; n_D^{20}: 1.5078; d_{20}: 1.4420 (*425*)	
CF_3	GLC (*443*)	ir (*443*)
$(CH_3)_2N—CH_2$	b_1: 56.5–7.5°C; n_D^{20}: 1.4843; d_{20}: 1.1829 (*202*)	MB (*149, 193, 203*); MS (*193*)
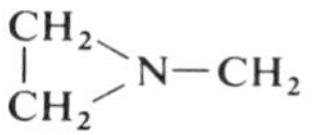 $\begin{array}{c}CH_2\\ \mid \\ CH_2\end{array}\!\!>\!\!N—CH_2$	$b_{0.2}$: 43.5–4.5°C; n_D^{20}: 1.4912; d_{20}: 1.2325 (*202*)	MB, MS (*193*)
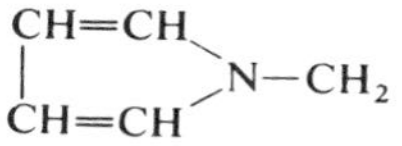 $\begin{array}{c}CH=CH\\ \mid \\ CH=CH\end{array}\!\!>\!\!N—CH_2$	$b_{0.2}$: 86.2°C; n_D^{20}: 1.5259; d_{20}: 1.2584 (*202*)	MB, MS (*193*)
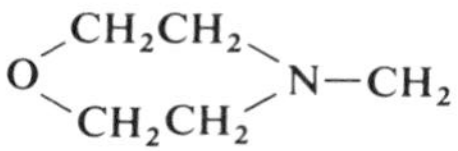 $O\!<\!\!\begin{array}{c}CH_2CH_2\\ CH_2CH_2\end{array}\!\!>\!\!N—CH_2$	$b_{0.1}$: 83.5–4.5°C; n_D^{20}: 1.5039; d_{20}: 1.2427 (*202*)	MB, MS (*193*)
$CH_3O—CH_2$	b_{15}: 68–9°C; n_D^{20}: 1.4754; d_{20}: 1.2462 (*203*)	ir (*193*), MS (*193*); MB (*149, 193*)
$CH_3CH_2O—CH_2$	$b_{14.5}$: 87.4–8.5°C; n_D^{20}: 1.4720; d_{20}: 1.2194 (*222*)	

Continued

APPENDIX 9—continued

R in $RSn(C_2H_5)_3$	Important physical constants	Other properties
$CH_3-C(=O)-O-CH_2$ $C_6H_5O-CH(CH_3-O)$	b_{16}: 48.5–50°C (61.2–2.6°C) n_D^{20}: 1.4874 (1.4462) d_{20}: 1.3249 (1.3991) (203) $b_{1.5}$: 122–3°C; n_D^{20}: 1.5024; d_{20}: 0.9793 (191)	MB (149)
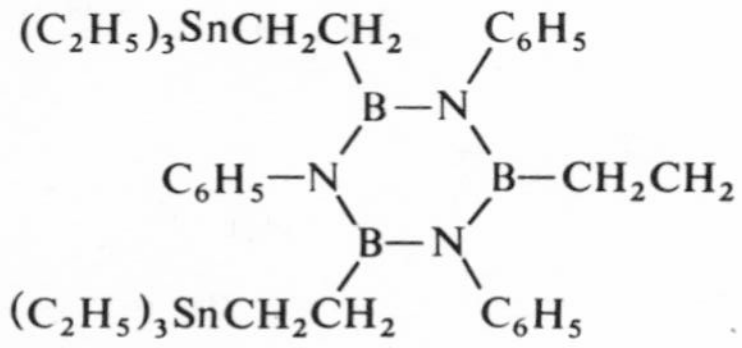 $(C_2H_5)_3SnCH_2CH_2$ borazine ring $(C_2H_5)_3SnCH_2CH_2$	m: 87–8°C (443)	ir (443)
CH_3CHCl CF_3CF_2 $N\equiv C-CH_2$	dec −20°C (443) GLC (443) b_1: 49.8–50°C; n_D^{20}: 1.4760; d_{20}: 1.2730 (184, 193, 203)	ir, F-NMR (443) MB, MS (193)
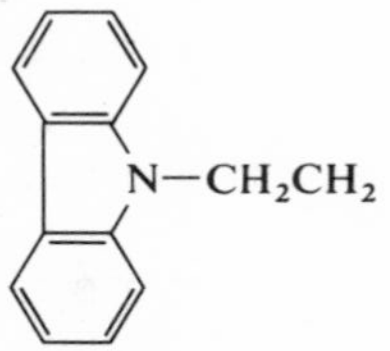 carbazolyl—CH_2CH_2	(443)	
$Cl_3Si-CH_2CH_2$	$b_{0.6}$: 85°C (181, 443)	

Compound	Properties	Methods
$(CH_3O)_3Si{-}CH_2CH_2$	$b_{0.4}$: 78°C; n_D^{25}: 1.4638; d_{25}: 1.209 (181, 443)	
$CH_3CH_2OCH_2CH_2$ $CH_3(CH_2)_3OCH_2CH_2$ $(CH_3)_2CHCHCH_2OCH_2CH_2$ $CH_3{-}C{-}OCH_2CH_2$, =O	b_{11}: 96–8°C; n_D^{20}: 1.4730 (443) b_{12}: 114–20°C; n_D^{20}: 1.4807 (443) b_{14}: 122°C; n_D^{20}: 1.4719 (443)	
$(CH_3)_2N{-}C{-}CH_2$, =O	$b_{1.5}$: 98–100°C; n_D^{20}: 1.5050; d_{20}: 1.2801 (320)	ir, NMR (320)
$(C_2H_5)_2N{-}C{-}CH_2$, =O	b_1: 101–3°C; n_D^{20}: 1.4995; d_{20}: 1.2250 (292, 320)	ir, NMR (320)
$CH_3O{-}C{-}CH_2$, =O	b_2: 72°C; n_D^{20}: 1.483; d_{20}: 1.296 (249)	ir (443)
$C_2H_5O{-}C{-}CH_2$, =O	b_1: 88–90°C; (333); b_2: 78–9°C (292) n_D^{20}: 1.4794–6 (292, 333, 443)	
$C_3H_7O{-}C{-}CH_2$, =O	b_2: 91–2°C; n_D^{20}: 1.4778; d_{20}: 1.2126–94 (249, 443)	ir (443)
$CH_3CH_2CH_2$	b_{748}: 193°C; n_D^{20}: 1.4726 (181); GLC (312, 443)	MB (149, 193)
$CH_2{=}CH{-}CH_2$	b_{10}: 76–7°C; n_D^{20}: 1.4900; d_{20}: 1.2231 (181, 201) (307)	ir, Raman (181, 443)
$HC{\equiv}C{-}CH_2$ $Cl_3C{-}CH_2CH_2$ $Cl_3C{-}CH_2{-}CHCl$ $Cl_3C{-}CH_2{-}CHBr$ $N{\equiv}C{-}CH_2CH_2$ $HO{-}CH_2CH_2CH_2$	$b_{0.25}$: 74°C; n_D^{25}: 1.5806 (181, 443) $b_{0.3}$: 100°C; n_D^{25}: 1.5230 (181, 443) $b_{0.9}$: 115–9°C; n_D^{25}: 1.5425 (181, 443) b_{12}: 128–30°C; n_D^{20}: 1.4912 (229, 443) b_{12}: 128–30°C; n_D^{20}: 1.4960 (443)	NMR (307) ir (443)

Continued

APPENDIX 9—*continued*

R in RSn(C$_2$H$_5$)$_3$	Important physical constants	Other properties
CH$_3$—C(=O)—OCH$_2$CH$_2$CH$_2$	(333, 443)	
HO—CH$_2$CH$_2$—O—CH$_2$CH$_2$CH$_2$	b$_{12}$: 128–30°C; n_D^{20}: 1.4960 (443)	ir (443)
(O)CH—CH$_2$—O—CH$_2$CH$_2$CH$_2$ (epoxide, CH$_2$)	b$_{0.2}$: 96–100°C (443)	
H$_2$NCH$_2$—CH—CH$_2$—O—CH$_2$CH$_2$CH$_2$ | OH	b$_{0.001}$: 80–100°C; n_D^{20}: 1.5043 (443)	
CH$_3$—C(=O)—CH$_2$	b$_6$: 100.5–1°C; n_D^{20}: 1.4991; d_{20}: 1.2875 (292, 294, 319, 443)	ir, Raman (443), MB (146, 149, 443)
CH$_3$O—C(=O)—CH$_2$CH$_2$	b$_{11}$: 117–9°C; n_D^{20}: 1.4793 (227, 443)	NMR (231)
C$_2$H$_5$O—C(=O)—CH$_2$CH$_2$	b$_{0.17}$: 58–9.5°C; n_D^{20}: 1.4762; d_{20}: 1.231 (227, 333, 443)	NMR 231)
H$_2$N—C(=O)—CH$_2$CH$_2$	m: 52–3°C; b$_{0.15}$: 132–4°C (443)	
(C$_2$H$_5$)$_3$SnCH$_2$CH$_2$CH$_2$ (CH$_3$)$_2$CH	b$_{0.17}$: 108°C; n_D^{20}: 1.5088 (287, 443); b$_{719}$: 192–4°C; n_D^{19}: 1.4772; d_{12}: 1.1733 (181, 201, 443)	

Compound		
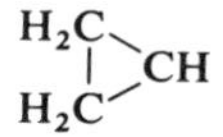 H₂C\ /CH (triangle)	(17a)	
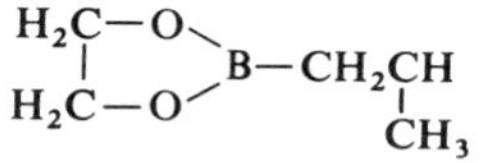 H₂C—O\ /B—CH₂CH(CH₃), H₂C—O	b₂: 125°C (47)	NMR (47)
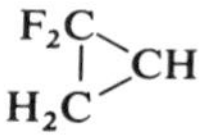 F₂C\ /CH (triangle)	n_D^{25}: 1.4576 (366)	ir, NMR (366)
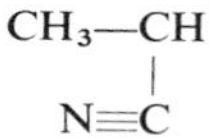 CH₃—CH, N≡C	(229)	
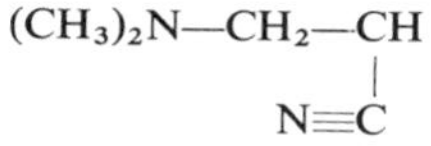 (CH₃)₂N—CH₂—CH, N≡C	b₀.₀₂: 97°C (62)	
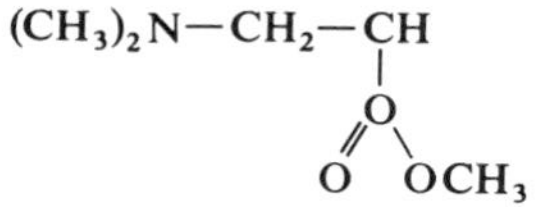 (CH₃)₂N—CH₂—CH, O O OCH₃	b₀.₀₂: 88°C (62)	
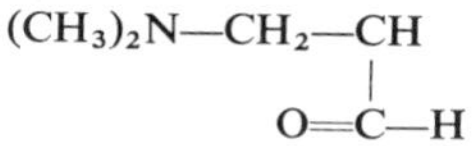 (CH₃)₂N—CH₂—CH, O=C—H	b₀.₀₃: 86°C (62)	
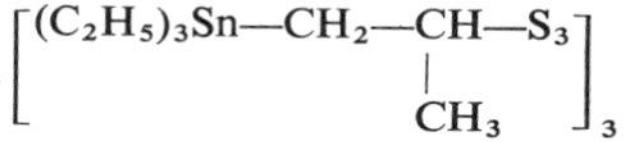 [(C₂H₅)₃Sn—CH₂—CH₂—CH—S₃]₃, CH₃	(443)	ir (349)
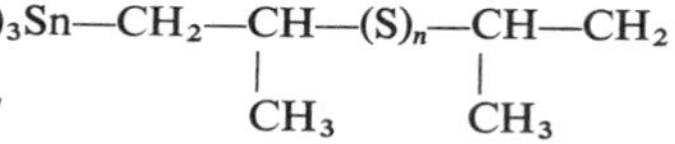 (C₂H₅)₃Sn—CH₂—CH₂—CH—(S)ₙ—CH—CH₂, CH₃ ⋯ CH₃ ⋯ CH₃ CH₂; $n = 6,7$		

Continued

APPENDIX 9—continued

R in RSn(C$_2$H$_5$)$_3$	Important physical constants	Other properties
CH$_3$CH$_2$CH$_2$CH$_2$	b$_{15}$: 99–101°C; b$_4$: 73–5°C n_D^{20}: 1.4736; d$_{20}$: 1.1457 (181, 345, 390, 399, 401, 443)	MS (44); kinetics (40–42)
CH$_3$—CH=CH—CH$_2$	b$_{12}$: 95–8°C; n_D^{20}: 1.493 (286) b$_{10}$: 87–90°C; n_D^{20}: 1.483 (287)	
CH$_2$=CH—CH$_2$CH$_2$	b$_{14}$: 96–8°C; n_D^{20}: 1.484 (286)	ir (286)
(C$_2$H$_5$)$_3$Sn—CH$_2$CH$_2$CH$_2$CH$_2$	b$_{0.0001}$: 93–7°C; n_D^{20}: 1.516 (286, 287)	
C$_2$H$_5$O—C(=O)—CH$_2$CH$_2$CH$_2$	b$_{14}$: 138–40°C; n_D^{20}: 1.4742 (333)	
(CH$_3$)$_2$CH—CH$_2$	b$_{10}$: 86°C (181)	
CH$_2$=CH—CH$_2$ / —CH$_3$	b$_4$: 73–4°C; n_D^{20}: 1.4882 (443)	ir (443)
H$_2$N—C(=O)—CH(—CH$_3$)—CH$_2$	m: 20–30°C; b$_{0.001}$: 136–8°C (443)	
CH$_3$O—C(=O)—CH(—CH$_3$)—CH$_2$	b$_{10}$: 100–2°C; n_D^{20}: 1.4792 (443)	
(C$_2$H$_5$)$_3$Sn—CH$_2$—C(CH$_3$)$_2$—(S)$_n$—C(CH$_3$)$_2$—CH$_2$ CH$_3$CH$_2$—CH(—CH$_3$)	b$_{10}$: 115°C (144)	ir (349) ir, NMR, MS (144)
(CH$_3$)$_2$N—CH(CH$_3$)—CH CH$_3$ HC=O	b$_{0.01}$: 80°C (62)	

$C_2H_5O-C(-O)-CH_2-CH(-CH_3)$: b_{13}: 135–6°C; n_D^{20}: 1.4782 (443)   MS (143)

(143)

$(CH_3)_3C-$ / $(CH_3)_2C-C\equiv N$: b_{13}: 125°C; n_D^{20}: 1.4983 (284)   ir (286)

$CH_3(CH_2)_4$: b_{10}: 102°C (181)

$CH_3CH_2-CH=CH-CH_2$: b_{12}: 100–4°C (286)

$CH_3-CH=CH-CH_2CH_2$: b_{12}: 100–4°C (286)

$CH_2=CH-CH_2CH_2CH_2$: b_{10}: 95°C; n_D^{20}: 1.4755 (287)

$Br(CH_2)_5$: b_{15}: 155.5°C (181)

$(C_2H_5)_3Sn-(CH_2)_5$: $b_{0.001}$: 108°C; n_D^{20}: 1.5048 (181, 287, 288, 443)

$(CH_3)_2CH-CH_2CH_2$: $b_{18.5}$: 111°C (181)

$CH_3-C(-CH_3)=CH-CH_2$: b_{12}: 103–8°C; n_D^{20}: 1.5030 (286)

$CH_2=C(-CH_3)-CH_2CH_2$: b_{12}: 100–4°C; n_D^{20}: 1.4857 (286)

$CH_3-CH=C(-CH_3)-CH_2$: b_{12}: 103–6°C (286)

$CH_2=CH-CH(-CH_3)-CH_2$: b_{12}: 103–6°C (286)

$CH=CH-CH(-CH_2CH_2)$ / $CH=CH-CH(-CH=CH)$: b_{12}: 110–3°C; n_D^{20}: 1.5111 (286)

Continued

APPENDIX 9—continued

R in RSn(C₂H₅)₃	Important physical constants	Other properties
$(CH_3)_3C$—CH_2	b_4: 92–3.5°C; n_D^{30}: 1.5192 $b_{0.001}$: 65°C (443)	NMR (443)
$CH_3(CH_2)_5$	b_{17}: 106–8°C; n_D^{25}: 1.4690 (443) d_{20}: 1.1106 (461)	
CH_2=CH—$(CH_2)_4$	$b_{0.75}$: 102–4°C (181, 443)	
$(C_2H_5)_3Sn$—$(CH_2)_6$	b_{13}: 115–9°C; n_D^{20}: 1.4820 (443) (443)	
$H_2C\!\!\begin{array}{c} CH_2CH_2 \\ \diagdown \\ CH_2CH_2 \end{array}\!\!CH$	b_1: 83.5°C (142)	ir, NMR, MS (142)
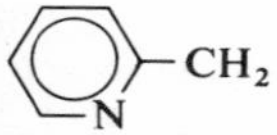 pyridine—CH_2	b_{3-4}: 120–1°C; n_D^{20}: 1.531 (181)	
$H_2C\!\!\begin{array}{c} CH_2CH_2 \\ \diagdown \\ CH_2\!-\!C{=}O \end{array}\!\!CH$	(181, 443)	(443)
$CH_3\!-\!C{=}C\!-\!CH_2$ with H_3C, CH_3	b_{11}: 109–11°C; n_D^{20}: 1.4950 (286)	
$CH_2{=}C\!-\!CH\!-\!CH_2$ with H_3C, CH_3	b_{11}: 109–11°C (286)	

Structure	Properties
Br—C$_6$H$_4$—CH$_2$	(443)
C$_6$H$_4$(Cl)—CH$_2$	b_1: 89.5°C; $\frac{23}{D}$: 1.5569 (443)
Cl—C$_6$H$_4$—CH$_2$	b_2: 96°C; n_D^{25}: 1.557 (443)
F—C$_6$H$_4$—CH$_2$	b_2: 69°C; n_D^{25}: 1.5261 (443)
H$_2$C$\langle$CH$_2$CH$_2\rangle$CH—C≡N	$b_{0.001}$: 98°C (284)
CH$_3$(CH$_2$)$_7$	b_4: 135–8°C (181), b_{10}: 142°C (443) $b_{0.7}$: 92°C; n_D^{20}: 1.4717 (287)
CH$_2$=CH—(CH$_2$)$_6$	b_{12}: 143–6°C; n_D^{20}: 1.4845 (443)
(C$_2$H$_5$)$_3$Sn—(CH$_2$)$_8$	$b_{0.001}$: 140–50°C; n_D^{20}: 1.5032 (443)

(CH$_3$)$_3$C—CH$_2$—CH$_2$—CH—CH$_2$
       $\mid$
      CH$_3$
	b_{10}: 123°C; n_D^{20}: 1.4747 (287)

Continued

APPENDIX 9—*continued*

R in RSn(C$_2$H$_5$)$_3$	Important physical constants	Other properties
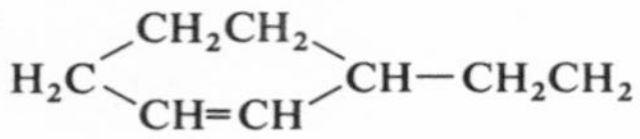 H$_2$C—CH$_2$—CH—CH$_2$CH$_2$ (ring, CH=CH)	$b_{0.2}$: 81.5°C; n_D^{20}: 1.5120 (443)	
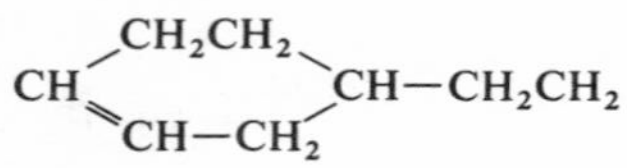 (ring: CH$_2$CH$_2$, CH—CH$_2$CH$_2$, CH—CH$_2$, CH=)	$b_{0.15}$: 82°C; n_D^{20}: 1.5045 (287)	
	b_{10}: 110–120°C; n_D^{20}: 1.5260 (443)	
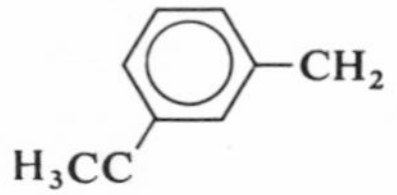 H$_3$CC$_6$H$_4$CH$_2$ (meta)	(443)	
 H$_3$CC$_6$H$_4$CH$_2$ (para)	(443)	
CH$_3$—(CH$_2$)$_8$	b_5: 144–6°C; n_D^{20}: 1.4699; d_{20}: 1.0553 (443)	
C$_6$H$_5$—CH—CH$_2$ (—CH$_3$)	b_{13}: 152–7°C; n_D^{20}: 1.5279 (443)	
C$_6$H$_5$—CH=CH—CH—CH$_2$	$b_{0.5}$: 108°C; n_D^{20}: 1.5645 (334)	ir; uv (334)

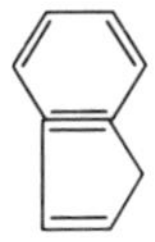

	$b_{0.15}$: 100–2°C; n_D^{30}: 1.5752 (*443*)
$(CH_3)_2N$—CH—CH $\quad\quad\quad$ | $\quad$ | $\quad\quad\quad C_6H_5C{=}O$ $\quad\quad\quad\quad\quad$ | $\quad\quad\quad\quad\quad$ H	$b_{0.02}$: 69–71°C (*62*)
CH_3—$(CH_2)_9$	b_{13}: 166–9°C; n_D^{20}: 1.4777 (*443*)
$(C_2H_5)_3Sn$—$(CH_2)_{10}$	b_{15}: 248°C (*181*)
	$b_{0.001}$: 107–9°C; n_D^{20}: 1.5481 (*443*)
	b_{3-4}: 144–5°C; n_D^{20}: 1.5364 (*181*)
	b_{12}: 167–170°C; n_D^{20}: 1.5321 (*286*)
CH_3O—C(=O)—$(CH_2)_{10}$	$b_{0.001}$: 115–7°C; n_D^{20}: 1.4802 (*443*)
C_2H_5O—C(=O)—$(CH_2)_{10}$	$b_{0.0001}$: 110°C; n_D^{20}: 1.4738 (*443*)

Continued

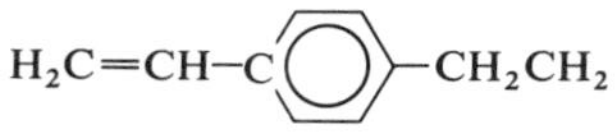

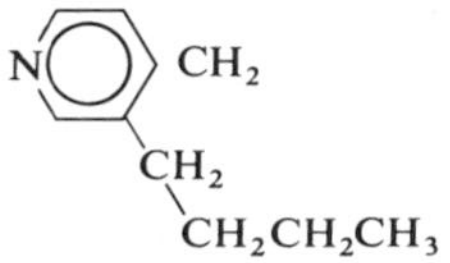

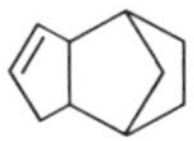

APPENDIX 9—*continued*

R in $RSn(C_2H_5)_3$	Important physical constants	Other properties
$CH_3(CH_2)_{11}$	b_1: 158–64°C (181, 443)	
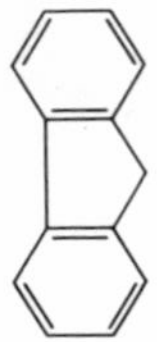	$b_{0.15}$: 151°C; n_D^{20}: 1.6229 (37, 443)	
$N{\equiv}C{-}C(C_6H_5)_2$	(184)	

APPENDIX 10

ALKENYLTRIETHYLTINS

R in RSn(C$_2$H$_5$)$_3$	Important physical constants	Other properties
C$_6$H$_{11}$—NH—C$\!=\!$O	b$_{0.1}$: 105–6°C; m: 28°C; n_D^{20}: 1.4910 (443)	ir, uv (443)
CH$_2$=CH	b: 174–5°C; b$_7$; 53–4°C; n_D^{20}: 1.4780–809; d$_{20}$: 1.2133 (17, 181, 443) (231)	NMR (231)
H$_2$C=C—OC$_2$H$_5$	(231)	NMR (231)
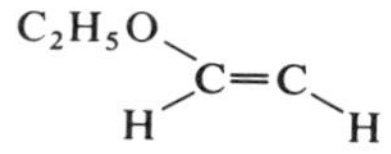 C$_2$H$_5$O—C=C—H, H	(231)	NMR (231)
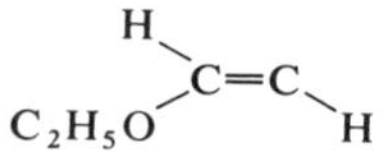 H—C=C—H, C$_2$H$_5$O	(231)	NMR (231)
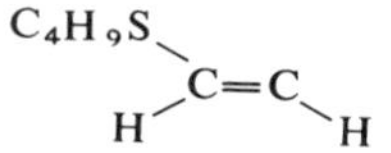 C$_4$H$_9$S—C=C—H, H	(231)	NMR (231)
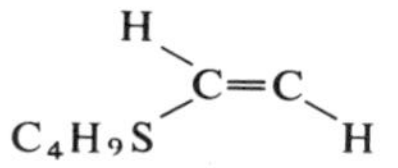 H—C=C—H, C$_4$H$_9$S	(231)	NMR (231)

Continued

APPENDIX 10—continued

R in $RSn(C_2H_5)_3$	Important physical constants	Other properties
CF_2=CF	b_{12}: 66–7°C; or 55–7°C; n_D^{20}: 1.4168 or 1.4392; d_{20}: 1.401 or d_{25}: 1.595 (443)	ir, F-NMR (443)
CH_3—CH=C—O—CH—CH_3	(380a)	
(with C_4H_9O)		
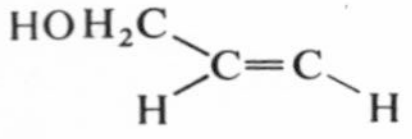 HOH_2C—C=C—H (with H and $HOCH_2$)	$b_{0.07}$: 65–80°C (228)	NMR (231)
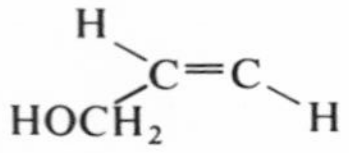 H—C=C—H (with $HOCH_2$)	$b_{0.07}$: 65–80°C (228)	NMR (231)
C_4H_9O—CH—O—CH_2—CH=CH (CH_3)	$b_{0.5}$: 106–7°C; n_D^{20}: 1.4748; d_{20}: 1.1318 (435)	
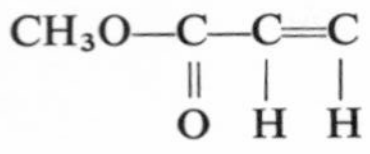 CH_3O—C—C—C (=O, H, H)	(227)	NMR (231)
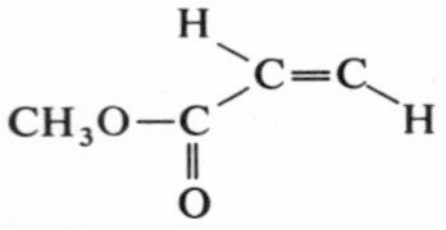 H—C=C—H / CH_3O—C=O	(227)	NMR (231)

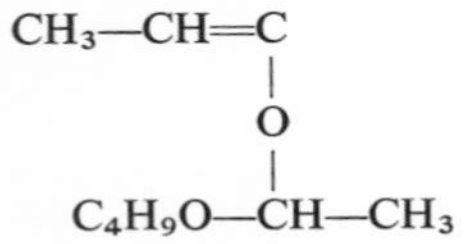

Structure		
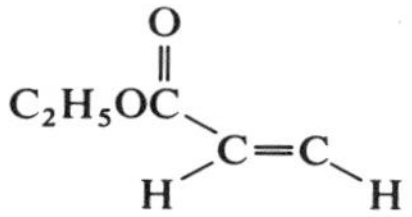 $C_2H_5OC(=O)-C=CH$ (with H)	(227, 228)	NMR (231)
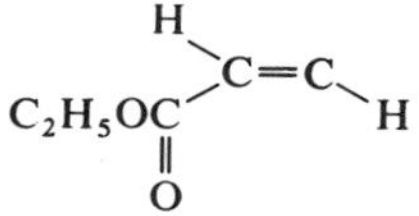 C_2H_5OC (with H, C=C-H, O)	(227, 228)	NMR (231)
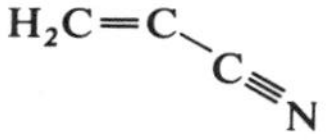 $H_2C=C-C\equiv N$	$b_{0.01}$: 53–4°C (228)	NMR (231)
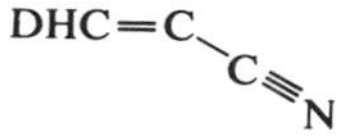 $DHC=C-C\equiv N$	(232)	
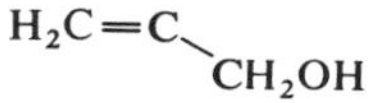 $H_2C=C-CH_2OH$	$b_{0.07}$: 65–80°C; (228)	NMR (231)
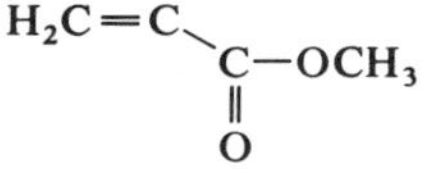 $H_2C=C-C(=O)-OCH_3$	(227)	NMR (231)
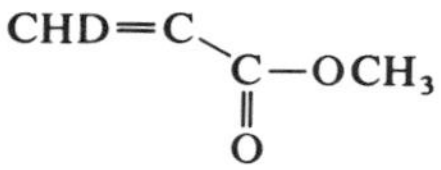 $CHD=C-C(=O)-OCH_3$	(232)	NMR (237)

Continued

APPENDIX 10—continued

R in RSn(C_2H_5)$_3$	Important physical constants	Other properties
$H_2C=C-\overset{\displaystyle \underset{\|}{O}}{C}-OC_2H_5$	(227, 228)	NMR (231)
$CH_2=CH-CH=CH$	(443) b_2: 50-1°C; n_D^{20}: 1.5062; d_{20}: 1.2306 (307)	ir (453), NMR (307, 453)
$HC\equiv C-CH=CH$	b_2: 106-7°C; n_D^{20}: 1.5031; d_{20}: 1.2511 (435)	
$HO-CH_2CH_2-CH=CH$	$b_{0.05}$: 116°C; n_D^{20}: 1.4732; d_{20}: 1.1129 (435)	
$C_4H_9O-\underset{\underset{\displaystyle CH_3}{\|}}{CH}-O-CH_2CH_2-CH=CH$	$b_{1.5}$: 86-7°C; n_D^{20}: 1.4930; d_{20}: 1.1827 (435)	
$CH_2=CH-O-CH_2CH_2-CH=CH$	b_2: 126°C; n_D^{20}: 1.4702; d_{20}: 1.1067 (435)	
$C_4H_9O-\underset{\underset{\displaystyle CH_3}{\|}}{CH}-O-\underset{\underset{\displaystyle CH_3}{\|}}{CH}-CH=CH$		
$CH_3CH_2-CH=\underset{\underset{\displaystyle CH_3}{\|}}{C}$	(380a)	
$C_4H_9O-\underset{\underset{\displaystyle CH_3}{\|}}{CH}-O$	b_2: 80-2°C; n_D^{20}: 1.4979 (228); d_{20}: 1.2594 (443)	ir (443)
$CH_3-CH=\underset{\underset{\displaystyle COOCH_3}{\|}}{C}$		
$CH_3-CH=\underset{\underset{\displaystyle COOC_2H_5}{\|}}{C}$	$b_{0.15}$: 49-57°C (228)	

Structure	Properties	Method (Ref.)
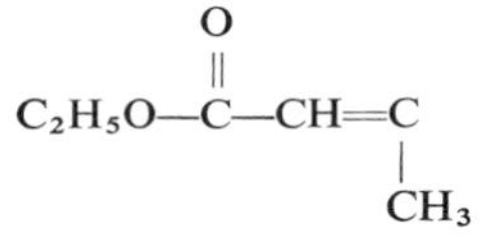 C_2H_5O—$C(=O)$—CH=C(CH_3)	$b_{0.15}$: 49–57°C (228)	NMR (231)
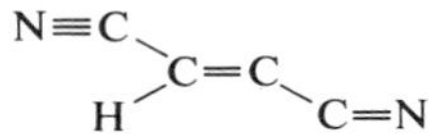 $N{\equiv}C$—$C(H)$=C—$C{\equiv}N$	(231)	NMR (231)
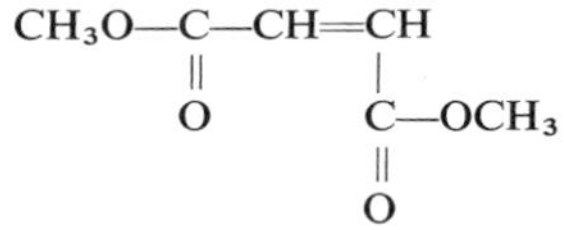 CH_3O—$C(=O)$—CH=CH—$C(=O)$—OCH_3	b_3: 115–6°C; n_D^{20}: 1.4997; d_{20}: 1.3252 (443)	ir (443)
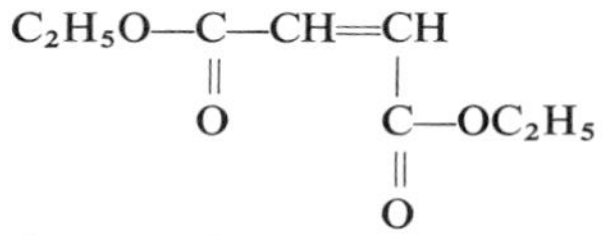 C_2H_5O—$C(=O)$—CH=CH—$C(=O)$—OC_2H_5	b_2: 125–6°C; n_D^{20}: 1.4921; d_{20}: 1.266 (443); $b_{0.04}$: 90–3°C (228)	ir (443) NMR (231)
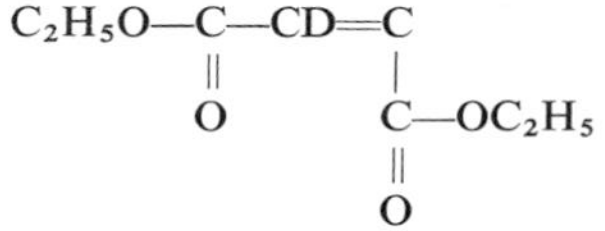 C_2H_5O—$C(=O)$—CD—$C(=O)$—OC_2H_5	(232)	
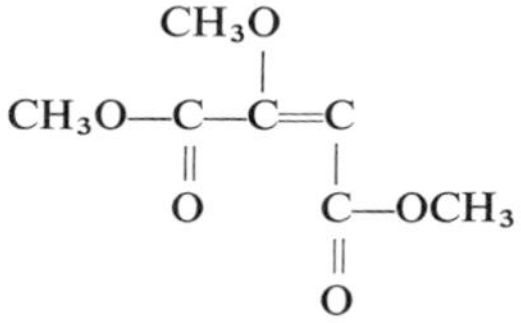 CH_3O—$C(=O)$—C(OCH_3)=C—$C(=O)$—OCH_3	b_2: 136.5°C; n_D^{20}: 1.4988; d_{20}: 1.3265 (248)	ir (443)

Continued

APPENDIX 10—*continued*

R in $RSn(C_2H_5)_3$	Important physical constants	Other properties
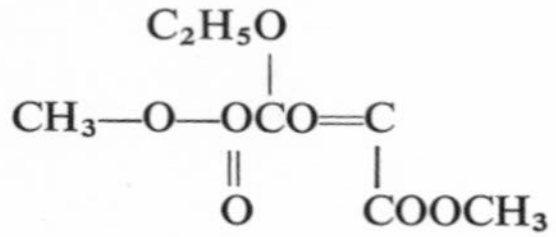 $CH_3-O-OCO=C$ with C_2H_5O and $COOCH_3$	b_2: 145–6°C; n_D^{20}: 1.4935; d_{20}: 1.2929 (443)	ir (443)
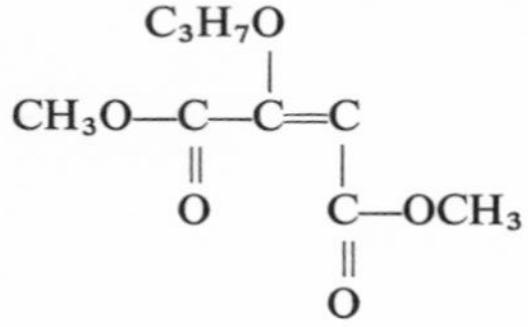 $CH_3O-C-C=C-C-OCH_3$ with C_3H_7O and $=O$, $=O$	b_1: 149–50°C; n_D^{20}: 1.4911; d_{20}: 1.2668 (443)	ir (443)
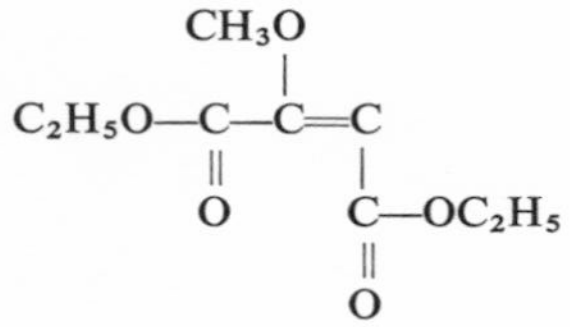 $C_2H_5O-C-C=C-C-OC_2H_5$ with CH_3O and $=O$, $=O$	b_3: 154–5°C; n_D^{20}: 1.4919; d_{20}: 1.269 (443)	ir (443)
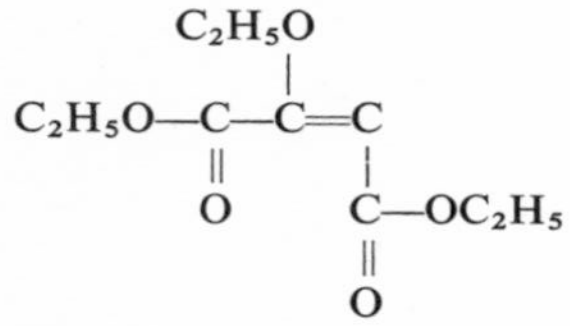 $C_2H_5O-C-C=C-C-OC_2H_5$ with C_2H_5O and $=O$, $=O$	b_3: 156–8°C; n_D^{20}: 1.4901; d_{20}: 1.2424 (443)	ir (443)
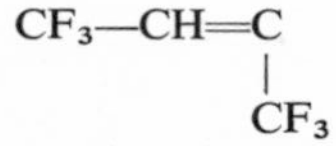 $CF_3-CH=C$ with CF_3	b_{24}: 86°C (76)	

$CH_3-CH=C=C$
$\quad\quad\quad\quad |$
$\quad\quad\quad\quad CH_3$ (70)

$C_4H_9O-CH-O-C(CH_3)_2-CH=CH$ b$_2$: 125–6°C: n_D^{20}: 1.4731; d_{20}: 1.1034 (435)
$\quad\quad\quad\quad\quad |$
$\quad\quad\quad\quad\quad CH_3$

$C_4H_9-CH=CH$ GLC (235, 236)   NMR (231)
$CH_3CH_2-C\equiv C-CH=CH$ b$_2$: 88–9°C; n_D^{20}: 1.5093; d_{20}: 1.1757 (453)   ir, NMR (453)
$CH_2=C$ (234)
$\quad\quad |$
$\quad\quad C_4H_9$

$C_6H_5-CH=CH$ b$_{0.15}$: 86–7°C; n_D^{20}: 1.5579 (443)   NMR (231)
$CH_3CH=C\equiv C-C$ GLC (211)
$\quad\quad\quad\quad\quad\quad |$
$\quad\quad\quad\quad\quad\quad CH_3$

$(C_6H_5)_3C-CH_2-C\equiv C-C$ m: 150–0.5°C (246, 443)   ir (443)
$\quad\quad\quad\quad\quad\quad\quad\quad\quad\quad |$
$\quad\quad\quad\quad\quad\quad\quad\quad\quad\quad CH_3\quad C(C_6H_5)_3$

APPENDIX 11

ALKYNYLTRIETHYLTINS

R in $RSn(C_2H_5)_3$	Important physical constants	Other properties
$N{\equiv}C$ $HC{\equiv}C$	m: 165°C (241, 284, 285) b_{15}: 49–50°C; n_D^{20}: 1.4770; (85) d_{20}: 1.2458 (195, 385, 443) b_{15}: 60°C (376); b_{14}: 68°C (197) b_5: 45°C; n_D^{20}: 1.4783; d_{20}: 1.2486 (456)	MB (149) ir (241) ir (387, 446) NMR (307)
$(C_2H_5O)_2\overset{\underset{\|}{O}}{P}{-}C{\equiv}C$	b_1: 150–1°C; n_D^{20}: 1.4899–908; b_2: 157–8°3; d_{20}: 1.2697–809 (455)	
$(CH_3)_3Si{-}C{\equiv}C$	b_9: 107°C; n_D^{20}: 1.4805; d_{20}: 1.1450 (196, 385, 387)	
$(CH_3)_3Sn{-}C{\equiv}C$ $(C_2H_5)_3Sn{-}C{\equiv}C$	See Appendix 7 $b_{0.05}$: 123°C; m: −52°C; b: 294°C; n_D^{20}: 1.5089; d_{20}: 1.3411 (443) b_{13}: 155–6°C; n_D^{20}: 1.5080 (385) b_5: 136–7°C (376); b_5: 139°C (197) $b_{1.5}$: 116–8°C; n_D^{20}: 1.5085–9 (197, 454) d_{20}: 1.3430–25 (180, 443)	MB (149)
$C_2H_5O{-}C{\equiv}C$	$b_{0.18-0.1}$: 114–5°C (243) b_2: 80–1°C; b_1: 69–70°C n_D^{20}: 1.4825, 1.4830 d_{20}: 1.2349; 1.2310 (320)	ir (320)
$C_2H_5S{-}C{\equiv}C$	b_1: 96–8°C; n_D^{20}: 1.5212; d_{20}: 1.2700 (454)	
$Cl{-}C{\equiv}C$	b_1: 50–1°C; n_D^{20}: 1.5010; d_{20}: 1.5543 (454)	

$Br-C\equiv C$	b_1: 62-3°C; n_D^{20}: 1.5096; d_{20}: 1.5556 (454)	ir (387, 443)
$CH_3-C\equiv C$	b_1: 40°C; n_D^{20}: 1.4866; d_{20}: 1.2273 (85, 372, 443)	ir (387a)
$N\equiv C-C\equiv C$	b_{15}: 126°C; m: 47°C (283) (387a)	
$O=CH-C\equiv C$		
$CH_3O-CH_2-C\equiv C$	$b_{0.55}$: 62-3°C; n_D^{20}: 1.4878; d_{20}: 1.2404 (377, 381, 389)	
$(CH_3)_3SiO-CH_2-C\equiv C$	$b_{2.5}$: 100-2°C; n_D^{20}: 1.4740; d_{20}: 1.1452 (263, 382)	
$(C_2H_5)_3Sn-O-CH_2-C\equiv C$	b_5: 160°C; b_1: 124-5°C; (383) n_D^{20}: 1.5145 (385), 1.5128 (383) d_{20}: 1.3541 (385), 1.3751 (383)	(380, 443)
$CH_3OCH_2OCH_2-C\equiv C$	b_2: 114-5°C; n_D^{20}: 1.4834; d_{20}: 1.2457 (389)	ir (373)
$C_4H_9O-\underset{\underset{CH_3}{\vert}}{CH}-O-CH_2-C\equiv C$	$b_{0.35}$: 105-6°C; n_D^{20}: 1.4742; d_{20}: 1.1460 (379, 381, 443)	ir
$CH_2=CHO-CH_2CH_2-O-CH_2-C\equiv C$	b_1: 105°C; n_D^{20}: 1.4922 (391)	
$CH_2=CH-O-CH_2CH_2-O-CH_2CH_2O-CH_2-C\equiv C$	b_1: 143-5°C; n_D^{20}: 1.4900; d_{20}: 1.2072 (391)	
$CH_3-\underset{\overset{\Vert}{O}}{C}-OCH_2-C\equiv C$	$b_{0.5}$: 84°C; n_D^{20}: 1.4887; d_{20}: 1.235 (389)	
$CH_3O-\underset{\overset{\Vert}{O}}{C}-C\equiv C$	$b_{0.4}$: 82-4°C; n_D^{20}: 1.4985 (227)	NMR (231)
$C_2H_5O-\underset{\overset{\Vert}{O}}{C}-C\equiv C$	(231)	NMR (231)
$CH_3CH_2-C\equiv C$	b_1: 52°C; n_D^{20}: 1.4903; d_{20}: 1.1953 (454, 456)	

Continued

APPENDIX 11—*continued*

R in $RSn(C_2H_5)_3$	Important physical constants	Other properties
$CH_2=CH-C\equiv C$	b_{10}: 90°C (182, 392, 393, 394, 443); (306, 378); b_3: 78–9°C (376); b_2: 62–3°C (200) 72–5°C (197); n_D^{20}: 1.5073–100 (182, 394, 443); n_D^{20}: 1.4910–95 (392, 393); d_{20}: 1.2165–2230 (182), (200, 376, 394, 443)	ir (372, 387, 443) dipole morn. (443) NMR (307, 443)
$HC\equiv C-C\equiv C$	b_2: 67–8°C; (451); b_1: 60°C (453); n_D^{20}: 1.5273 (451), 1.5262 (453); d_{20}: 1.2626 (453); 1.2891 (451)	NMR (307)
$(C_2H_5)_3Sn-C\equiv C-C\equiv C$	$b_{0.5}$: 156°C; n_D^{20}: 1.5483 d_{20}: 1.3640 (453)	
$(C_2H_5)_2N-CH=CH-C\equiv C$	$b_{1.5}$: 125–6°C; n_D^{20}: 1.5470; d_{20}: 1.1648 (453) (387a)	
$CH_3O-CH_2CH_2-C\equiv C$		
$CH_3OCH_2O-CH_2CH_2-C\equiv C$	b_1: 101–2°C; n_D^{20}: 1.4923; d_{20}: 1.2166 (263)	ir (373)
$CH_2=CH-OCH_2CH_2-C\equiv C$	b_2: 107.5°–8°C (85); b_1: 114–6°C (735); $b_{0.3}$: 111–2°C; (377); n_D^{20}: 1.4749 (377) 1.4925 (85); 1.4875 (435); d_{20}: 1.1290 (377); 1.1993 (85); 1.1186 (435)	

$C_4H_9O-CH-O-CH_2CH_2-C\equiv C$
         |
         CH_3
	b_2: 132–4°C (443); $b_{0.3}$: 111–2°C n_D^{20}: 1.4742 (443); 1.4749 (379) d_{20}: 1.1330 (443); 1.1290 (379)	

$(CH_3)_3SiO-CH_2CH_2-C\equiv C$	$b_{2.5}$: 108–10°C; n_D^{20}: 1.4725; d_{20}: 1.1173 (389)	ir (373)
$(C_2H_5)_3SnO-CH_2CH_2-C\equiv C$	b_1: 134–5°C; n_D^{20}: 1.5086; d_{20}: 1.3412 (383, 443)	

$CH_3-C-O-CH_2CH_2-C\equiv C$
       $\\|$
       O
	$b_{0.5}$: 92°C; n_D^{20}: 1.4858; d_{20}: 1.2412 (389)	

$CHCH_3O=CH-C\equiv C$	b_{13}: 138°C (283)	

$C_4H_9O-CH=CH-CH-C\equiv C$ $b_{0.5}$: 107-8°C; n_D^{20}: 1.5098; d_{20}: 1.1760 (385)

$CH_3O-CH-C\equiv C$ (CH_3) $b_{0.8}$: 57-7.5°C; n_D^{20}: 1.4790; d_{20}: 1.1969 (389)

$(CH_3)_3SiO-CH-C\equiv C$ (CH_3) $b_{1.5}$: 86°C; n_D^{20}: 1.4672; d_{20}: 1.1089 (389)

$(C_2H_5)_3SnO-CH-C\equiv C$ (CH_3) $b_{0.5}$: 111-2°C; (383, 443); b_2: 138°C (385); n_D^{20}: 1.5005 (385); 1.5039 (383, 443); d_{20}: 1.3313 (383) 1.2969 (385)

$(C_2H_5)_3Sn-C\equiv C-CH-O-CH-O-CH-C\equiv C$ (CH_3, CH_3, CH_3) b_1: 156°C; n_D^{20}: 1.4962; d_{20}: 1.2449 (435) ir (373)

$CH_3OCH_2O-CH-C\equiv C$ (CH_3) b_1: 95°C; n_D^{20}: 1.4756; d_{20}: 1.1967 (389)

$C_4H_9O-CH-O-CH-C\equiv C$ (CH_3, CH_3) b_2: 120°C (385); $b_{0.45}$: 104°C (379, 443); n_D^{20}: 1.4722 (385); 1.4697 (379, 443); d_{20}: 1.1075 (379); 1.1176 (385, 443)

$CH_3-C-O-CH-C\equiv C$ ($=O$, CH_3) $b_{0.7}$: 78°C; n_D^{20}: 1.4818; d_{20}: 1.2226 (389)

$CH_3CH_2CH_2-C\equiv C$
$CH_3-CH=CH-C\equiv C$ b_1: 64°C; n_D^{20}: 1.4812; d_{20}: 1.1625 (456)
b_{10}: 104-5°C (85); 107-8°C (443)
n_D^{20}: 1.5102; 1.5112 (85); d_{20}: 1.1924; 1.2183 (85)

$(CH_3)_2CH-C\equiv C$ b_{10}: 9.15°C; n_D^{20}: 1.4778; d_{20}: 1.1478 (85, 443)

$CH_2=C-C\equiv C$ (CH_3) b_{10}: 97.0-.5°C; n_D^{20}: 1.5040; d_{20}: 1.2043 (85, 443)

Continued

APPENDIX 11—*continued*

R in $RSn(C_2H_5)_3$	Important physical constants	Other properties
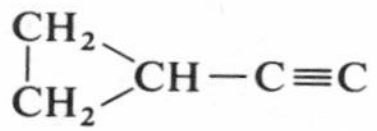 cyclopropyl–$C \equiv C$ (CH_2–CH_2 ring, CH–$C \equiv C$)	b_1: 76–7°C; n_D^{20}: 1.5041; d_{20}: 1.2155 (85, 443)	
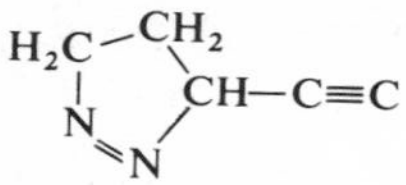 pyrazoline: H_2C–CH_2, CH–$C \equiv C$, $N = N$	(85, 290, 443)	
CH_3O–$C(CH_3)_2$–$C \equiv C$	$b_{0.4}$: 58–9°C; n_D^{20}: 1.4759; d_{20}: 1.1669 (85)	
C_4H_9O–$CH(CH_3)$–O–$C(CH_3)_2$–$C \equiv C$	$b_{0.37}$: 102°C; n_D^{20}: 1.4680; d_{20}: 1.1010 (379); 1.0727 (385): 1.3015 (443); $b_{1.5}$: 112°C; n_D^{20}: 1.4670 (385)	
$(CH_3)_3SiO$–$C(CH_3)_2$–$C \equiv C$	$b_{0.8}$: 70°C; n_D^{20}: 1.4646; d_{20}: 1.0898 (389)	
$(C_2H_5)_3SnO$–$C(CH_3)_2$–$C \equiv C$	$b_{0.5}$: 113–4°C; n_D^{20}: 1.4987; d_{20}: 1.3006 (383)	
CH_3O–CH_2O–$C(CH_3)_2$–$C \equiv C$	$b_{0.5}$: 73–4°C; n_D^{20}: 1.4746; d_{20}: 1.1814 (383)	ir (373)
CH_3–$C(=O)$–O–$C(CH_3)_2$–$C \equiv C$	$b_{0.6}$: 67–8°C; n_D^{20}: 1.4793; d_{20}: 1.2044 (389)	
C_6H_5–$C(=O)$–O–$C(CH_3)_2$–$C \equiv C$	b_1: 135°C; n_D^{20}: 1.5228; d_{20}: 1.2124 (389)	ir (373)
C_4H_9–$C \equiv C$	b_3: 105°C; n_D^{20}: 1.4820 (156)	
CH_3CH_2–$C \equiv C$–$C \equiv C$	b_1: 100–1°C; d_{20}: 1.2127; n_D^{20}: 1.5293 (451)	

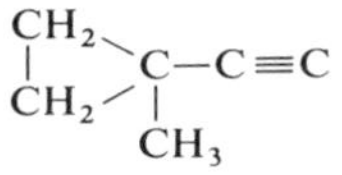

b_2: 83–5°C; n_D^{20}: 1.4948; d_{20}: 1.1737 (443)

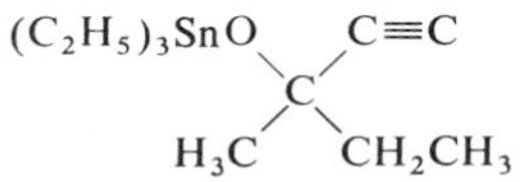

b_2: 131°C; n_D^{20}: 1.4979; d_{20}: 1.2767 (159)

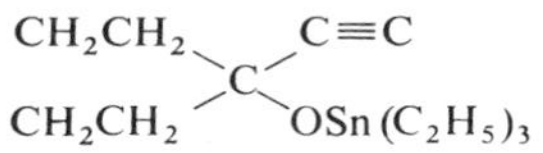

b_2: 157°C; n_D^{20}: 1.5041; d_{20}: 1.2966 (159)

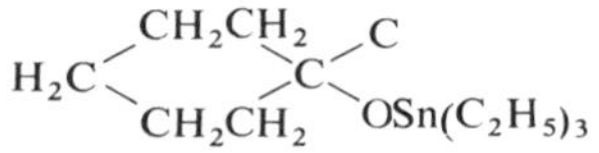

b_1: 152°C; n_D^{20}: 1.5118; d_{20}: 1.2902 (159)

$b_{0.35}$: 93°C (385); $b_{0.5}$: 109°C (283);   ir (387)
b_1: 105°C (156); 108–9°C (383);
b_2: 120°C (385); b_7: 136–40°C (390); n_D^{20}:
1.5541 (156): 1.5562 (383);
d_{20}: 1.2470 (85, 181, 184, 201, 248, 264, 290, 386)

$b_{0.18}$: 119°C (85, 283)

b_2: 190°C; n_D^{20}: 1.5503; d_{20}: 1.3408 (198, 388, 389a) (443)

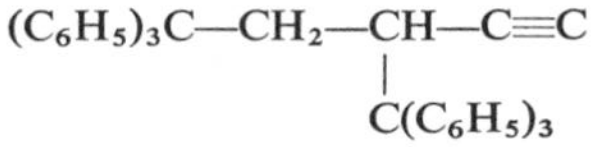

APPENDIX 12
ARYLTRIETHYLTINS

Ar in $ArSn(C_2H_5)_3$	Important physical constants	Other properties
C_6H_5	b_6: 113–114°C (443), b_{14}: 129.5–130.5°C (163); n_D^{20}: 1.5349 (443)	ir (443); NMR (400); MS (137); kinetics (36a, 163)
o-HO—C_6H_4	b_{15}: 155–156°C (443); n_D^{25}: 1.5379 (443) d_{25}: 1.3150, 1.3229 (443)	
m-CH_3O—C_6H_4	b_7: 144–145°C (163)	kinetics (163)
p-CH_3O—C_6H_4	b_5: 138–138.5°C (163); b_{12}: 157–158°C (443); n_D^{20}: 1.5410 (443)	kinetics (163)
p-$(CH_3)_2N$—C_6H_4	b_3: 172–173°C (443); n_D^{20}: 1.5610 (443); d_{20}: 1.2425 (443)	
m-ClC_6H_4	b_6: 142°C (163)	kinetics (163)
p-ClC_6H_4	$b_{6.5}$: 141–141.5°C (163)	kinetics (163)
p-BrC_6H_4	b_6: 150–151°C, b_{14}: 165°C (443); d_{15}: 1.4964	
p-IC_6H_4	b_{10}: 174–175; d_{15}: 1.5475	
m-$CH_3C_6H_4$	b_9: 133.5–134°C (163)	kinetics (163)
p-$CH_3C_6H_4$	b_1: 91–93°C (443), b_9: 127.5–128°C (163); n_D^{25}: 1.5330	kinetics (163)
m-$CF_3C_6H_4$	$b_{0.3}$: 63°C (99); n_D^{20}: 1.4869 (99)	
p-HOOC—C_6H_4	m: 44.5–46.5°C (443)	pK (63)
p-CH_3—CH(OH)—C_6H_4	b_4: 112–114°C (443); n_D^{20}: 1.5422	
p-CH_2=CH—C_6H_4	b_4: 100–102°C (443), $b_{0.5}$: 101°C (443); n_D^{20}: 1.5388, 1.5530 (443); d_{20}: 1.2556 (443)	
CFCl=CF—C_6H_4	b_4: 170°C (443)	
p-CH_2=C(CH_3)—C_6H_4	b_2: 129–130°C (443); n_D^{25}: 1.544 (443); d_{25}: 1.2311 (443)	
CH_2=CH—CH_2—C_6H_4	b_2: 150–152°C (443); n_D^{20}: 1.5360 (443); d_{20}: 1.2958 (443); surf. tens. (443)	
4-(3-isopropenyl)pyrazolyl	b_1: 177–178°C (443); n_D^{20}: 1.5342 (443); d_{20}: 1.3424	

APPENDIX 13

ALKYLTRIPROPYLTINS

R in $RSn(CH_2CH_2CH_3)_3$	Important physical constants	Other properties
CH_3	b_{11}: 94-6°C; d_{23}: 1.125 (*181, 313*); GLC (*312, 443*)	
CH_3CH_2	b_{10}: 101°C (*181, 312, 443*) GLC	
$(CH_3)_2N-\overset{\underset{\displaystyle \parallel}{O}}{C}-CH_2$	$b_{2.5}$: 114-6°C; n_D^{20}: 1.5014; d_{20}: 1.1960 (*320*)	ir, NMR (*320*)
$CH_3O-\overset{\underset{\displaystyle \parallel}{O}}{C}-CH_2$	b_1: 92-3°C; n_D^{20}: 1.4818; d_{20}: 1.2064 (*443*)	
$C_2H_5O-\overset{\underset{\displaystyle \parallel}{O}}{C}-CH_2$	b: 217-9°C; b_1: 105-7°C; n_D^{20}: 1.4784; d_{20}: 1.1789 (*181, 443*)	
$C_3H_7O-\overset{\underset{\displaystyle \parallel}{O}}{C}-CH_2$	b_1: 110-1°C; n_D^{20}: 1.4772; d_{20}: 1.1538 (*443*)	
$CH_2{=}CH-CH_2$	b_{4-5}: 101-3°C; n_D^{20}: 1.4972; d_{20}: 1.897 (*443*)	NMR (*433*)
$N{\equiv}C-CH_2CH_2$	b_{12}: 157-60°C (*181, 443*)	
$NH_2CH_2CH_2CH_2$	$b_{0.001}$: 78-9°C (*181, 443*)	
$CH_3-\overset{\underset{\displaystyle \parallel}{O}}{C}-CH_2$	b_1: 98-100°C; n_D^{20}: 1.4865; d_{20}: 1.1983 (*181, 443*)	ir; Raman (*181, 443*)
$NH_2-\overset{\underset{\displaystyle \parallel}{O}}{C}-CH_2CH_2$	m: 44-7°C; $b_{0.4}$: 155-161°C (*181, 443*)	
$NaO-\overset{\underset{\displaystyle \parallel}{O}}{C}-CH_2CH_2$	(*443*)	

Continued

APPENDIX 13—*continued*

R in RSn(C$_2$H$_5$)$_3$	Important physical constants	Other properties
CH$_3$O—C(=O)—CH$_2$CH$_2$	b$_{12}$: 145–50°C (*181, 443*); b$_{0.4}$: 108–10°C (*227*)	NMR (*231, 433*)
(C$_3$H$_7$)$_3$Sn—CH—CH$_2$ C(=O)—OCH$_3$	b$_{0.0002}$: 120–3°C (*443*)	
(C$_3$H$_7$)$_3$Sn—CH$_2$—CH CH$_3$O—C=O	see preceding compound	
CH$_3$(CH$_2$)$_3$	b$_{37}$: 137–8°C; n_D^{20}: 1.4741; d_{20}: 1.0917 (*181, 345, 399*) GLC (*312, 443*) b$_{0.001}$: 78–9°C (*443*) b$_{0.5}$: 110°C (*443*)	
N≡C—CH$_2$CH$_2$CH$_2$ CH$_3$—C—CH$_2$CH$_2$ ‖ N—OH		
CH$_3$—C—CH$_2$CH$_2$ ‖ N—NH—C(=O)—NH$_2$	m: 78–80°C (*443*)	
CH$_3$—C—CH$_2$CH$_2$ ‖ N—NH—C$_6$H$_3$(NO$_2$)$_2$	m: 48–50°C (*443*)	

$CH_3-\underset{\underset{O}{\parallel}}{C}-CH_2CH_2$	$b_{0.2}$: 84–9°C (*181, 443*)	
$C_2H_5O-\underset{\underset{O}{\parallel}}{C}-CH_2CH_2CH_2$	$b_{0.7}$: 117–9°C (*181, 443*)	
$(CH_3)_2CH-CH_2$ $C_2H_5O-\underset{\underset{O}{\parallel}}{C}-CH_2-\underset{\underset{CH_3}{\vert}}{CH}$	b_{18}: 128°C (*181*) $b_{0.6}$: 111–2°C (*181, 443*)	
$(C_3H_7)_3Sn(CH_2)_6$	(*443*)	magn. succept., parachor (*443*)
 $\underset{N}{\bigcirc}CH_2CH_2$	(*181, 291, 428*)	
$C_6H_5-CH_2CH_2$ $C_6H_5-\underset{\underset{O}{\parallel}}{C}-CH_2$	$b_{0.007}$: 118–21°C (*181, 443*) b: 155–60°C (*181, 443*)	NMR (*433*)
$C_6H_5-\underset{\underset{N}{\parallel}}{C}=CH_2CH_2$ $\quad \searrow NH-C_6H_3(NO_2)_2$	m: 106°C (*443*)	
$C_6H_5-\underset{\underset{O}{\parallel}}{C}-CH_2CH_2$	$b_{0.05-0.3}$: 158–65°C (*181, 443*)	
$C_6H_5-CH_2-\underset{\underset{N\equiv C}{\vert}}{CH}$	$b_{0.0003}$: 130–41°C (*443*)	
$CH_3(CH_2)_9$	b_5: 182–3°C; n_D^{20}: 1.4640; d_{20}: 1.0241 (*443*)	

APPENDIX 14

ALKENYLTRIPROPYLTINS

R in $RSn(CH_2CH_2CH_3)_3$	Important physical constants	Other properties
$CH_2{=}CH$	b_8: 90°C; n_D^{23}: 1.4776; d_{25}: 1.131 (17a, 181, 443)	
$(C_2H_5)_3Si{-}CH{=}CH$	b_2: 126°C; n_D^{20}: 1.4860; d_{20}: 1.0585 (281)	ir, NMR (281)
$(C_3H_7)_3Sn{-}CH{=}CH$	$b_{1.5}$: 164; n_D^{20}: 1.5090; d_{20}: 1.2190 (281)	ir, NMR (281)
$HO{-}CH_2{-}CH{=}CH$	$b_{0.006}$: 1206-2°C (181, 443)	
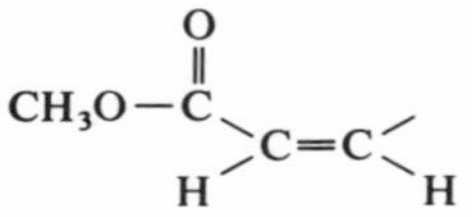	(227) GLC	NMR (231)
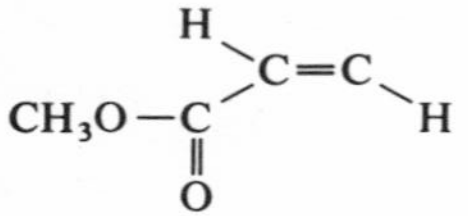	(227) GLC	NMR (231)
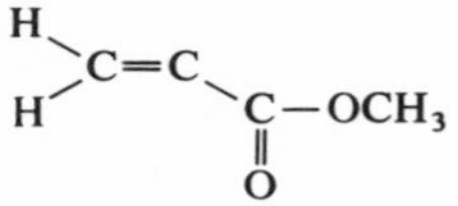	(227) GLC	NMR (231)
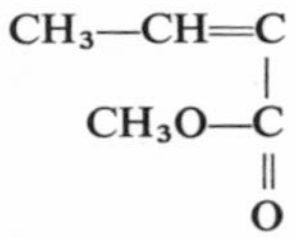	b_2: 116.5°C; n_D^{20}: 1.4932; d_{20}: 1.888 (443)	ir (443)

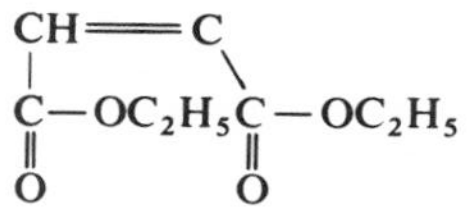

$$CH{\equiv}C$$
$$\underset{O}{\overset{\,}{\underset{\|}{C}}}{-}OC_2H_5\quad \overset{\,}{\underset{\|}{C}}{-}OC_2H_5$$

b$_1$: 140°C; n_D^{20}: 1.4882; d_{20}: 1.1451 (*443*)   ir (*443*)

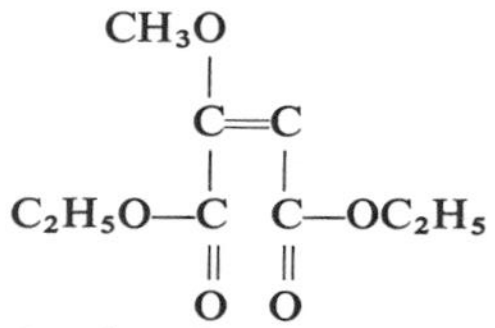

$$CH_3O$$
$$\underset{C_2H_5O{-}C}{\overset{\,}{C{=}C}}\quad \underset{O\ \ O}{\overset{\|\ \ \|}{\,}} C{-}OC_2H_5$$

b$_1$: 159–60°C; n_D^{20}: 1.4889; d_{20}: 1.2045 (*443*)   ir (*443*)

$$CH_3(CH_2)_3{-}CH{=}CH$$
$$C_6H_5{-}CH{=}CH$$

b$_{0.1}$: 75–80°C (*181, 443*)
b$_{0.0001}$: (119–120°C (*181, 443*)

APPENDIX 15

ALKENYLTRIPROPYLTINS

R in $RSn(n\text{-}C_3H_7)_3$	Important physical constants	Other properties
$HC{\equiv}C$	b_2: 67°C; n_D^{20}: 1.4780; d_{20}: 1.1545 (385); b_{10}: 91°C; n_D^{20}: 1.4780; d_{20}: 1.1555 (376); $b_{0.3}$: 46°C; n_D^{20}: 1.4772; d_{20}: 1.1595 (456)	
$(C_3H_7)_3Sn{-}C{\equiv}C$	b_6: 188–9°C; n_D^{20}: 1.5040; d_{20}: 1.2461 (385, 443); b_3: 178–9°C; (376) $b_{0.1-0.12}$: 136–7°C; n_D^{20}: 1.5005 (85, 243)	
$CH_2{=}CH{-}C{\equiv}C$	b_3: 97–100°C; n_D^{20}: 1.4910; d_{20}: 1.1391–1.1293; 1.4910 (182, 200, 376, 393)	
$HC{\equiv}C{-}C{\equiv}C$	b_1: 103°C; n_D^{20}: 1.5110; d_{20}: 1.1343 (453)	
$(C_3H_7)_3Sn{-}O{-}\overset{\underset{\mid}{CH_3}}{CH}{-}C{\equiv}C$	b_1: 165°C; n_D^{20}: 1.4970; d_{20}: 1.2139 (385)	
$(C_3H_7)_3Sn{-}O{-}C(CH_3)_2{-}C{\equiv}C$	b_4: 172°C; n_D^{20}: 1.4925; d_{20}: 1.2073 (385)	
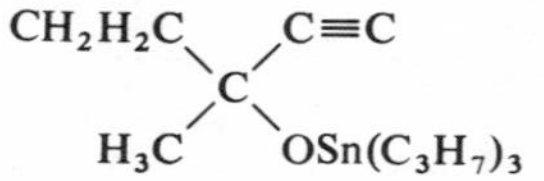 $\underset{H_3C}{\overset{CH_2H_2C}{{>}}}\underset{OSn(C_3H_7)_3}{\overset{C{\equiv}C}{C{<}}}$	b_2: 168–70°C; n_D^{20}: 1.4930; d_{20}: 1.1826 (159)	
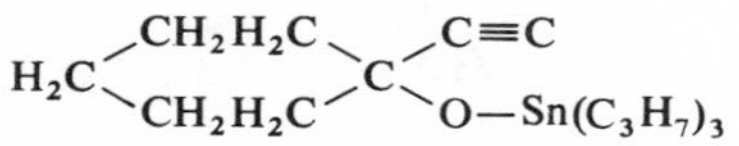 $\underset{H_2C{-}CH_2H_2C}{\overset{CH_2H_2C}{{>}}}\underset{O{-}Sn(C_3H_7)_3}{\overset{C{\equiv}C}{C{<}}}$	b_2: 200°C; n_D^{20}: 1.5051; d_{20}: 1.2112 (159)	
$C_6H_5{-}C{\equiv}C$	b_1: 151°C; n_D^{20}: 1.5388; d_{20}: 1.1811 (385)	
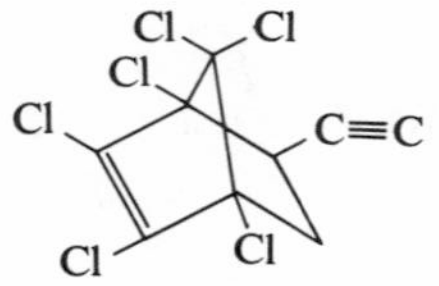	$b_{2.5}$: 209°C; n_D^{20}: 1.5410; d_{20}: 1.4195 (198, 388, 389a)	

APPENDIX 16

ARYLTRIPROPYLTINS

Ar in $ArSn(n\text{-}C_3H_7)_3$	Important physical constants	Other properties
C_6H_5	b_{15}: 150°C (443)	MS (137)
$o\text{-}FC_6H_4$	b_5: 120–125°C (183); n_D^{30}: 1.707 (183)	
$o\text{-}ClC_6H_4$	b_8: 155–156°C (183); n_D^{30}: 1.707 (183)	
$o\text{-}BrC_6H_4$	b_5: 165°C (183); n_D^{30}: 1.548 (183)	
$p\text{-}BrC_6H_4$	b_4: 168°C (443); d_{15}: 1.3722 (443)	
$o\text{-}IC_6H_4$	b_8: 189–192°C (183); n_D^{30}: 1.665 (183)	
$o\text{-}(n\text{-}C_3H_7)_3Sn\text{—}C_6H_4$	b_4: 145°C (183); n_D^{25}: 1.713 (183)	
$2,4\text{-}(CH_3)_2C_6H_3$		kinetics (271)
$2,6\text{-}(CH_3)_2C_6H_3$		kinetics (271)
$p\text{-}CH_2{=}CH\text{—}CH_2\text{—}C_6H_4$	$b_{4.5}$: 172–175°C (443); n_D^{20}: 1.5332 (443); d_{20}: 1.1847 (443)	

APPENDIX 17

TRIISOPROPYL-, TRICYCLOPROPYL-, TRIALLYLTINS

R in $RSn[CH(CH_3)_2]_3$	Important physical constants	Other properties
CH_3	b_9: 87°C; (109); $b_{1.6}$: 46–8°C (14a)	NMR, MS (14a)
$CH_2{=}CH{-}CH_2$	b_5: 98–101°C; n_D^{20}: 1.4763; d_{20}: 1.0727 (443)	
$N{\equiv}C{-}CH_2CH_2$	(229)	
$CH_3{-}CH$ | $N{\equiv}C$	(229)	
C_6H_5	$b_{0.3}$: 82°C (99), b_1: 113–114°C (54); n_D^{20}: 1.5377 (54), n_D^{25}: 1.5303 (99)	MS (137); kinetics (54, 270)
$o\text{-}CH_3C_6H_5$	m: 25°C (54)	kinetics (271)
1-Naphthyl		kinetics (271)
2-Naphthyl	b_2: 158–159°C (54); n_D^{20}: 1.5827 (54)	kinetics (54)

R in $RSn(\text{cyclo } C_3H_5)_3$		
CH_3	(443)	ir (443)
$CH_3{-}(CH_2)_3$	b_1: 84–86°C (443); n_D^{25}: 1.5040 (443), n_D^{25}: 1.4912 (367a)	ir (443)
C_6H_5	$b_{0.2}$: 93°C (443); n_D^{25}: 1.5604 (443)	ir (443)

$RSnR_3'$		
$CH_3(CH_2)_3{-}Sn(CH_2{-}CH{=}CH_2)_3$	b_{10}: 116–119°C; n_D^{25}: 1.5162; d_{25}: 1.1335 (181, 443)	

APPENDIX 18

ALKYLTRIBUTYLTINS

R in $RSn(n\text{-}C_4H_9)_3$	Important physical constants	Other properties
CH_3	b_{11}: 122–4°C; d_{20}: 1.0901 (*181, 443*)	NMR (*400*)
	GLC (*312*)	
	(*87*)	
Br_3C		
$ClCH_2$	$b_{0.5}$: 108–12°C; n_D^{25}: 1.4801; d_{25}: 1.135 (*443*)	
Cl_2CH	$b_{1.3}$: 114–6°C; n_D^{20}: 1.4965; d_{20}: 1.2590 (*425*)	
Cl_3C	(*87*)	
ICH_2	$b_{0.5}$: 108–12°C; n_D^{20}: 1.4801 (*181*)	
$CH_3CH_2O\text{—}CH_2$	$b_{1.4}$: 116–8°C; n_D^{20}: 1.4775; d_{20}: 1.1503 (*222*)	
$C_6H_5\text{—}O\text{—}CH$	$b_{1.5}$: 186–8°C; n_D^{20}: 1.5140;	
$\quad\quad\quad\; \underset{\displaystyle CH_3\text{—}O}{\big|}$	d_{20}: 1.1642 (*191*)	
$(CH_3)_2HSi\text{—}CH_2$	b_5: 133°C; n_D^{25}: 1.4764; d_{25}: 1.047 (*181, 443*)	
$C_2H_5O(CH_3)_2Si\text{—}CH_2$	b_5: 147°C; n_D^{25}: 1.4682; d_{25}: 1.053 (*181, 443*)	
$(C_4H_9)_3Sn\text{—}CH_2\text{—}Si(CH_3)_2\text{—}O\text{—}Si(CH_3)_2\text{—}CH_2$	n_D^{20}: 1.4850 (*181, 443*)	
$(CH_3)_2ClSi\text{—}CH_2CH_2\text{—}Si(CH_3)_2\text{—}CH_2$	b_{30}: 180°C; n_D^{20}: 1.4836; d_{25}: 1.066 (*181, 443*)	
$(C_4H_9)_3SnCH_2Si(CH_3)_2\text{—}CH_2CH_2Si(CH_3)_2\text{—}$ $\quad O\text{—}Si(CH_3)_2\text{—}CH_2CH_2Si(CH_3)_2\text{—}CH_2$	n_D^{25}: 1.4850; d_{25}: 1.045 (*181, 443*)	
CH_3CH_2	$b_{0.15}$: 71–3°C; n_D^{25}: 1.471 (*14a, 181, 345, 401, 443*)	MS (*14a*)
CF_3CF_2	$b_{0.04}$: 48°C; (*443*)	F-NMR, ir (*443*)
$N\!\equiv\!C\text{—}CH_2$	$b_{1.3}$: 144°C; n_D^{18}: 1.4814 (*181, 184, 292, 303, 443*)	
$(CH_3)_2CH\text{—}CH_2\text{—}O\text{—}CH_2CH_2$	$b_{0.25}$: 105–7°C; n_D^{20}: 1.4707 (*443*)	
$O\!=\!CH\text{—}CH_2$	dec. dist. (*276*)	
$(CH_3)_2N\text{—}\underset{\displaystyle \underset{O}{\|\!|}}{C}\text{—}CH_2$	$b_{0.03}$: 130–2°C; n_D^{20}: 1.4925; d_{20}: 1.1316 (*320*)	ir, NMR (*320*)

Continued

APPENDIX 18—continued

R in $RSn(C_2H_5)_3$	Important physical constants	Other properties
$CH_3O-C(=O)-CH_2$	(86, 247)	
$C_2H_5O-C(=O)-CH_2$	b_{10}: 159–63°C (181, 303, 443)	
$HS-CH_2CH_2$	$b_{0.2}$: 70–80°C (dec.); n_D^{25}: 1.5068 (443)	ir (443)
$CH_3-C(=O)-S-CH_2CH_2$	$b_{0.3}$: 115°C; n_D^{25}: 1.5006 (443)	ir (443)
$CH_3CH_2CH_2$	b_5: 125–6°C (109); GLC (312)	MS (14a)
$CH_2=CH-CH_2$	$b_{0.6}$: 94–5°C; b_{17}: 155°C; n_D^{25}: 1.4833; d_{25}: 1.073 (181, 443)	ir (443)
$CF_3CF_2CF_2$	$b_{0.2}$: 132–4°C; (181, 229, 331a, 443)	F-NMR (443)
$N\equiv C-CH_2CH_2$	b_{12}: 117–9°C or 173–6°C (181, 443); n_D^{20}: 1.4887 (443)	NMR (433)
$HO-CH_2CH_2CH_2$	$b_{1.9}$: 139°C; n_D^{20}: 1.4863; d_{20}: 1.1316 (181, 276, 277, 294, 302, 305, 443)	ir, NMR (305); Raman, uv (443)
$CH_3-C(=O)-CH_2$	(181, 331a, 443)	
$HO-C(=O)-CH_2CH_2$	(181, 331a, 443)	
$NaO-C(=O)-CH_2CH_2$		
$CH_3O-C(=O)-CH_2CH_2$	$b_{0.4}$: 140–2°C (181, 443)	NMR (433)

HS—CH₂CH₂CH₂ → $b_{0.1}$: 91°C; n_D^{25}: 1.5025 (443); ir (443)

CH₃—C(=O)—S—CH₂CH₂CH₂ → $b_{0.3}$: 120°C; n_D^{25}: 1.4982 (443); ir (443)

(CH₃)₂CH— → (349a); $b_{0.02}$; 80°C; n_D^{20}: 1.475; MS (349a)

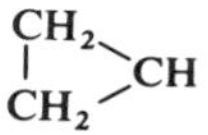

cyclopropyl-CH₂/CH₂ CH → $b_{0.7}$: 94–5°C; n_D^{25}: 1.4803 (17a, 367a, 443); ir (443); kinetics (17a)

N≡C—CH—CH₃ → (229)

(CH₃O—C(=O))₂CH → (181, 251)

(C₂H₅O—C(=O))₂CH → (181, 251)

(C₄H₉O—C(=O))₂CH → (181, 443); ir (349)

(C₄H₉)₃Sn—CH₂—CH(CH₃)—(S)ₙ—CH(CH₃)—CH₂ $n = 6;\ 7$ → (349, 443); ir (443)

CH₂=CH—CH₂CH₂ → b_{35}: 91–3°C; n_D^{25}: 1.4792; d_{25}: 1.062 (443); $b_{0.5}$: 132–4°C (303); b_3: 143–4°C; n_D^{15}: 1.4796; d_{15}: 0.9485 (181, 345, 443); $b_{0.1}$: 82–3°C; n_D^{22}: 1.4830 (443); ir (443)

N≡C—CH₂CH₂CH₂

(CH₃)₂CH—CH—CH₂

CH₂=C(CH₃)—CH₂ → $b_{0.1}$: 82–3°C; n_D^{22}: 1.4830 (443); ir (443)

H₂C—CH—CH₂ / CCl₂ → b_7: 164.5°C; n_D^{20}: 1.4900; d_{20}: 1.2040 (425)

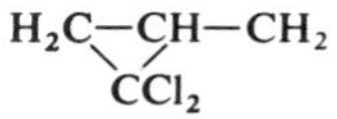

Continued

APPENDIX 18—continued

R in RSn(-C$_2$H$_5$)$_3$	Important physical constants	Other properties
(CH$_3$)$_2$HSi—CH$_2$—CH$_2$—CH—CH$_2$ CH$_3$	(443)	

CH$_3$—C—CH
  ‖   CH$_3$
  O
	b$_{0.8}$: 115°C; n_D^{20}: 1.4820; d_{20}: 1.1152 (305)	ir, NMR (305)

CH$_3$O—C—CH$_2$—CH—
       ‖   C=O
       O   CH$_3$O
	b$_{0.001}$: 122–7°C; n_D^{20}: 1.4799 (297)	ir, NMR (297)

C$_2$H$_5$O—C—CH$_2$—CH
      ‖   C=O
      O   C$_2$H$_5$O
	b$_{0.001}$: 124–8°C; n_D^{20}: 1.4777 (297)	ir, NMR (297)

C$_3$H$_7$O—C—CH$_2$—CH
      ‖   C=O
      O   C$_3$H$_7$O
	b$_{0.001}$: 125–8°C; n_D^{20}: 1.4599 (297)	ir, NMR (297)

C$_4$H$_9$O—C—CH$_2$—CH
      ‖   C=O
      O   C$_3$H$_7$O
	b$_{0.001}$: 128–35°C; n_D^{20}: 1.4582 (297)	ir, NMR (297)

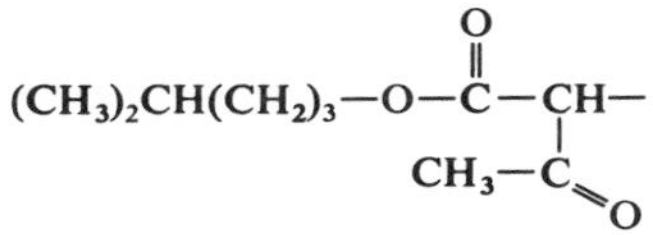

$(CH_3)_2CH(CH_2)_3-O-C-CH-$ with O= and $CH_3-C=O$ (181, 443)

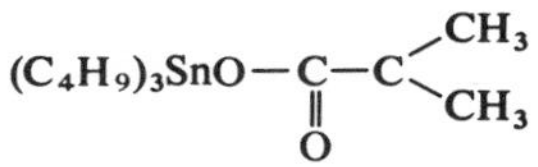

$(C_4H_9)_3SnO-C-C-C(CH_3)_2$ with CH_3, CH_3, O   (86)

ir (349)

$(C_4H_9)_3SnCH_2-C(CH_3)_2-(S)_n-C(CH_3)_2-CH_2$, $n = 6, 7$ (349)

$CH_3(CH_2)_4$ (181)

$b_{0.1}$: 108–10°C; n_D^{25}: 1.4949 (369);
b_{20}: 177–8°C; n_D^{20}: 1.4715;
d_{20}: 1.0409 (181, 443)
$b_{0.7}$: 133–8°C (181, 443)

$Cl_2CH-CH_2-CH=CH-CH_2$ ir, NMR (369)

$(CH_3)_2CH-CH_2CH_2$

$HO-C(CH_3)_2-CH_2CH_2$

$CH_3O-C-CH_2-CH-CH_2$ with O=, $C-OCH_3$ and O $b_{0.005}$: 85–95°C; n_D^{20}: 1.4788 (296)

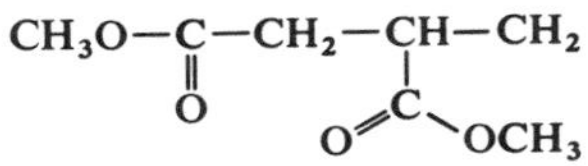

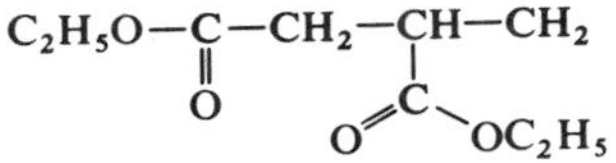

$C_2H_5O-C-CH_2-CH-CH_2$ with O=, $C-OC_2H_5$ and O $b_{0.001-0.007}$: 125–135°C; n_D^{20}: 1.4738 (296)

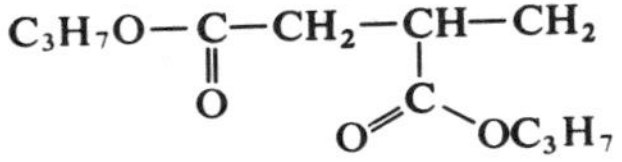

$C_3H_7O-C-CH_2-CH-CH_2$ with O=, $C-OC_3H_7$ and O $b_{0.003}$: 140–50°C; n_D^{20}: 1.4738 (296)

APPENDIX 18—*continued*

R in RSn(n-C_4H_9)$_3$	Important physical constants	Other properties
CH_3CH_2—C—CH with =O, CH_3	$b_{0.8}$: 121–3°C; n_D^{20}: 1.4808; d_{20}: 1.1084 (305)	ir; NMR
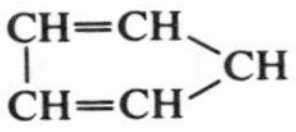 CH=CH / CH=CH —CH	$b_{0.001}$: 90°C (184)	NMR (443)
CH_3—C—CH with =O, CH_2—CH_3	$b_{0.3}$: 117–8°C; n_D^{20}: 1.481; d_{20}: 1.092 (301, 305)	ir, NMR (304, 305)
(CH_3—C)$_2$CH =O	(181, 443)	
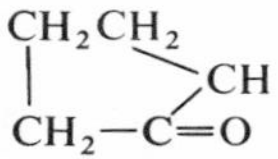 CH_2CH_2 / CH_2—C=O —CH	$b_{1.4}$: 144–6°C; n_D^{20}: 1.4930; d_{20}: 1.1397 (305)	ir, NMR (305)
(CH_3)$_2$CH—CH N≡C	(302)	
(C_2H_5O—C)$_2$CH—CH with =O, CH_3	$b_{0.001}$: 140.5°C; n_D^{20}: 1.4765 (297)	ir, NMR (297)

$(CH_3)_2CH-CH$, $C(=O)OC_2H_5$ (302)

$(C_2H_5O-C)_2(CH_3CH_2)C$, $=O$ (181, 443)

$CH_3(CH_2)_5$
$CH_2=CH-(CH_2)_4$
$CH_3-C-(CH_2)_4$, $=O$

b_7: 165°C; n_D^{17}: 1.4762; d_{17}: 1.035 (181, 443)
$b_{0.3}$: 104–6°C; n_D^{20}: 1.4795 (443)
b_1: 147–8°C; n_D^{20}: 1.4815;
d_{20}: 1.0909 (300, 443)

$(C_4H_9)_3Sn(CH_2)_6$ $b_{0.001}$: 190–200°C; n_D^{20}: 1.4936 (443)

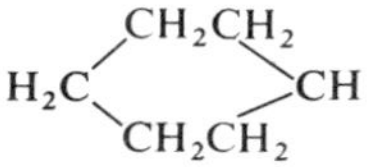

H_2C $\langle CH_2CH_2 / CH_2CH_2 \rangle$ CH MS (349a)

(349a)

H_2C $\langle CH_2 / CH_2CH_2 \rangle$ $C(=O)-CH$ (?) ir, NMR wrong structure (305)

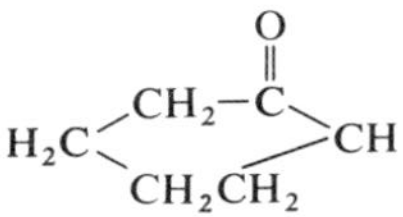

(181, 443)

$CH_3-C=C-CH_2$, CH_3 , CH_3 $b_{0.1}$: 100–2°C (286); n_D^{20}: 1.4890

$CH_2=C-CH-CH_2$, CH_3 , CH_3 $b_{0.01}$: 100–2°C (286)

$(CH_3)_3C-C-CH_2$, $=O$ $b_{0.3}$: 118°C; n_D^{20}: 1.4811; d_{20}: 1.0840 (305)   ir, NMR (305)

Continued

APPENDIX 18—continued

R in $RSn(n\text{-}C_4H_9)_3$	Important physical constants	Other properties
$CH_3(CH_2)_6$	b_3: 165–7°C; n_D^{20}: 1.4755 d_{20}: 1.025 (443)	
$CH_3(CH_2)_7$	b_4: 225°C (448); $b_{0.08}$: 126°C (287); n_D^{20}: 1.4734 (287, 345)	
$CH_2{=}CH(CH_2)_6$	$b_{0.3}$: 123–6°3; n_D^{20}: 1,4800 (443)	
$(C_4H_9)_3Sn(CH_2)_8$	$b_{0.001}$: 200–10°C; n_D^{20}: 1.4919 (443)	
$(CH_3)_3C{-}CH_2{-}CH_2{-}CH{-}CH_2$ | CH_3	$b_{0.25}$: 96°C; n_D^{20}: 1.4734 (287, 345)	
$CH_3(CH_2)_3{-}CH{-}CH_2$ | CH_2 | CH_3	$b_{0.1}$: 111–2°C; n_D^{20}: 1.476 (287, 345)	
$C_6H_5{-}CH_2CH_2$ $C_6H_5{-}C{-}CH_2$	$b_{2.4}$: 180–5°C (448)	
$NH_2{-}C{-}NH$ $={}N{-}$ $={}O$	m: 80°C (181, 443)	
$C_6H_5{-}C{-}CH_2$ $={}O$	b: 200–5°C (181, 443); $b_{0.7}$: 138°C; n_D^{20}: 1.5249; d_{20}: 1.1514 (305)	ir, NMR (305)
$C_6H_5{-}CH{=}CH{-}CH_2$	$b_{0.5}$: 138–42°C; n_D^{20}: 1.5185 (334)	ir, uv (334)

(181, 443)

C_6H_5—CH—CH$_2$
    |
    CH$_3$

$b_{0.2}$: 128–32°C; n_D^{20}: 1.511 (287)

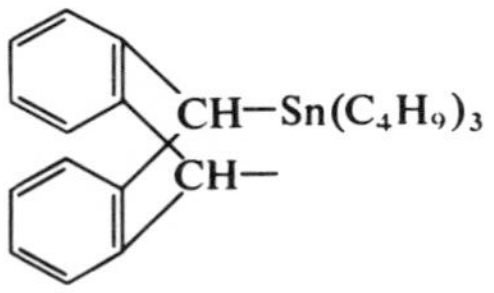

(107)

APPENDIX 19

ALKENYLTRIBUTYLTINS

R in RSn(7-C$_4$H$_9$)$_3$	Important physical constants	Other properties
CH$_2$=CH	b$_6$: 133°C; b$_{0.1}$: 73–4°C; n_D^{25}: 1.476; d$_{25}$: 1.08 (181, 261, 443, 447) (278)	ir, NMR (443)
(CH$_3$)$_3$Si—CH=CH	b$_2$: 144–6°C; n_D^{20}: 1.4851; d$_{20}$: 1.0282 (278)	ir; NMR (278)
(C$_2$H$_5$)$_3$Si—CH=CH	b$_2$: 168–70°C; n_D^{20}: 1.4897; d$_{20}$: 1.0825 (278)	ir, NMR (278)
(C$_4$H$_9$)$_3$Ge—CH=CH	b$_2$: 177–182; n_D^{20}: 1.5030–41; d$_{20}$: 1.1503–75 (278, 279)	ir, NMR (278, 279)
(C$_4$H$_9$)$_3$Sn—CH=CH		
(C$_4$H$_9$)$_3$Sn—CH=CH—Sn(C$_4$H$_9$)$_2$—CH=CH	b$_{0.02}$: 175–7°C; n_D^{20}: 1.5176 (279)	
CF$_2$=CF	b$_{0.4}$: 81–2°C; n_D^{25}: 1.4512 (443)	ir, F-NMR (443)
H$_2$C=C(N≡C)	b$_{0.1}$: 100°C; n_D^{20}: 1.4928 (228)	NMR (231)
CHD=C(N≡C)	(232)	
CHD=C—C(=O)OCH$_3$	(232)	
H$_2$C=C—CH=CH$_2$	b$_{0.4}$: 80–90°C; (13, 14)	ir, uv, NMR (13)
C$_2$H$_5$O—C(=O)—CH$_2$—CH=C(CH$_3$)	b$_{0.001}$: 105°C (228)	NMR (231)

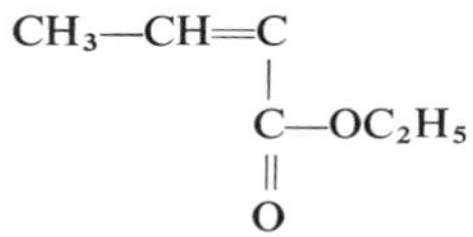

$$CH_3-CH=C\begin{array}{c} C-OC_2H_5 \\ \| \\ O \end{array}$$

$b_{0.001}$: 105°C (228, 231)   NMR (231)

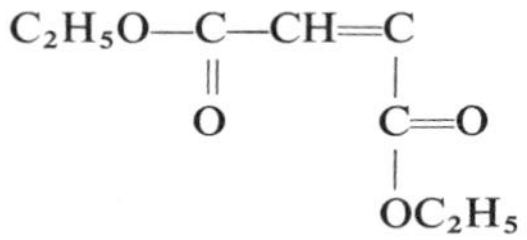

$$C_2H_5O-C-CH=C\begin{array}{c} C=O \\ | \\ OC_2H_5 \end{array}$$
$$\| \\ O$$

$b_{0.003}$: 130°C (228)   NMR (231)

$$CF_3-CH=C\begin{array}{c} CF_3 \end{array}$$

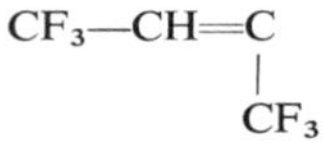

$b_{0.001}$: 72°C (76)

APPENDIX 20

ALKYNYLTRIBUTYLTINS

R in $RSn(n\text{-}C_4H_9)_3$	Important physical constants	Other properties
$N\equiv C$ $HC\equiv C$	m: 88.5°C (241) b_3: 100–1°C (376); $b_{0.2}$: 76 (456); n_D^{20}: 1.4765–70 (376, 385, 456); d_{20}: 1.1034–113 (85, 443, 456)	ir (241)
$(C_4H_9)_3Sn\!-\!C\equiv C$	b_3: 204; n_D^{20}: 1.4888; d_{20}: 1.401 (376); $b_{0.08}$ 158–9°C; n_D^{20}: 1.4935 (243, 85, 184, 443)	
$CH_2\!=\!CH\!-\!C\equiv C$	b_3: 135–6°C (182, 376, 393); $b_{1.5}$: 110°C (85); n_D^{20}: 1.4950–5 (182, 376, 393, 394); d_{20}: 1.0923–8 (182, 376, 443, 85, 200)	
$CH_3\!-\!\underset{\underset{O}{\parallel}}{C}\!-\!C\equiv C$	(373)	ir (373)
$(C_4H_9)_3Sn\!-\!C\equiv C\!-\!C\equiv C$ $(C_4H_9)_3SnO\!-\!\underset{\underset{CH_3}{\vert}}{CH}\!-\!C\equiv C$	n_D^{22}: 1.5116 (85) b_3: 200°C; n_D^{20}: 1.4875; d_{20}: 1.5558 (385)	
$(C_4H_9)_3SnO\!-\!C(CH_3)_2\!-\!C\equiv C$ $C_6H_5\!-\!C\equiv C$	b_2: 198°C; n_D^{20}: 1.4890; d_{20}: 1.1277 (385) b_1: 150°C (443); 184°C (243); n_D^{20}: 1.5270 or 1.5315 (443);	
$C_6H_5\!-\!CH_2CH_2\!-\!C\equiv C$	d_{20}: 1.1317 (85, 181, 443);	

APPENDIX 21

ARYLTRIBUTYLTINS

Ar in ArSn(n-C$_4$H$_9$)$_3$	Important physical constants	Other properties
C$_6$H$_5$	b$_{0.6}$: 139°C (443), b$_{2.5}$: 145°C (443); n_D^{20}: 1.5155 (443)	MS (137); kinetics (54)
o-FC$_6$H$_4$	b$_{12}$: 127–130°C (183); n_D^{25}: 1.491 (183)	
C$_6$F$_5$	b$_{0.5}$: 112–115°C (443), b$_{1.1}$: 132–136°C (310); n_D^{20}: 1.4801 (310)	ir (443)
o-ClC$_6$H$_4$	b$_8$: 130–135°C (183), b$_{12}$: 163–166°C (443); n_D^{20}: 1.5079 (443), n_D^{25}: 1.522 (183); d$_{20}$: 1.270 (443)	
p-ClC$_6$H$_4$	b$_8$: 115–120°C (183); n_D^{25}: 1.495 (183)	
o-BrC$_6$H$_4$	b$_8$: 127–132°C (183); n_D^{25}: 1.519 (183)	
o-IC$_6$H$_4$	b$_5$: 166–170°C (183); n_D^{25}: 1.520 (183)	
o-(n-C$_4$H$_9$)$_3$Sn—C$_6$H$_4$	b$_{0.04}$: 125°C (443); n_D^{22}: 1.5319 (443)	ir (443)
p-CH$_2$=CH—C$_6$H$_4$	b$_{3-4}$: 172–175°C (443); n_D^{20}: 1.5440 (443); d$_{20}$: 1.1502	
p-CH$_2$=CH—CH$_2$—C$_6$H$_4$		
1-Naphthyl	b$_{0.005}$: 164–164.7°C (52); n_D^{20}: 1.5660 (52)	kinetics (54)
2-Naphthyl	b$_{0.005}$: 155°C (52); n_D^{20}: 1.5649 (52)	kinetics (54)
1-Pyrenyl [incorrectly quoted as Pyrrole derivative in Ref. (443)]		kinetics 54
Ferrocenyl	b$_{0.15}$: 188–190°C (299)	
p-CH$_2$=CH—CH$_2$—C$_6$H$_4$—Sn(i-C$_5$H$_{11}$)$_3$	b$_{3.4}$: 195–198°C (443); n_D^{20}: 1.5190 (443); d$_{20}$: 1.0945	
C$_6$H$_5$—Sn(1-cyclopentadienyl)$_3$	m: 64–65°C (443)	NMR (443)

APPENDIX 22

OTHER ALKYL-, ALKENYL-, ALKYNYL-, AND ARYLTRIALKYLTINS

R in $R\,Sn\left(CH_3{-}\overset{\displaystyle CH_3}{CH}{-}CH_3\right)_3$	Important physical constants	Other properties
CH_3CH_2	b_{10}: 115°C (*181*)	
$C_4H_9O{-}CH_2CH_2$	$b_{0.6}$: 108–10°C; n_D^{20}: 1.4713 (*443*)	
$CH_2{=}CH{-}CH_2$	b: 123–5°C; n_D^{20}: 1.4972; d_{20}: 1.3631 (*423*)	
$CH_3{-}\overset{\displaystyle O}{\overset{\|}{C}}{-}OCH_2CH_2CH_2$	$b_{0.15}$: 105–7°C; n_D^{20}: 1.4767 (*443*)	
$CH_3(CH_2)_3$	(*345*)	
$(CH_3)_2CHCH_2CH_2$	$b_{16.5}$: 152.9°C (*181*)	
$CH_2{=}\underset{\displaystyle CH_3}{C}{-}\underset{\displaystyle CH_3}{CH}{-}CH_2$	$b_{0.15}$: 88–91°C (*286*) mixture: n_D (20): 1.4919	
$(CH_3)_2C{=}\underset{\displaystyle CH_3}{C}{-}CH_2$	$b_{0.15}$: 88–91°C (*286*)	
$CH_3(CH_2)_7$	$b_{0.2}$: 111–4°C; n_D^{20}: 1.4753 (*443*)	
$CH_2{=}CH{-}$	(*443*)	

$CH_3CH_2CH_2Sn(CH_2CH_2{-}\overset{\displaystyle O}{\overset{\|}{C}}{-}OCH_3)_3$ $b_{0.0004}$: 139–41°C (*181, 443*)

$CH_3(CH_2)_3Sn(CH_2CH_2{-}\overset{\|\,O}{C}{-}OCH_3)_3$	$b_{0.0004}$: 139–41°C (181, 443)
$(CH_3)_2CHCH_2Sn(CH_2CH_2{-}\overset{\|\,O}{C}{-}OCH_3)_3$	$b_{0.0001}$: 150–3°C; n_D^{20}: 1.4875 (443)
$CH_3CH_2CH_2Sn(CH_2CH_2{-}\overset{\|\,O}{C}{-}ONa)_3$	(181)
$CH_3(CH_2)_3Sn[C(CH_3)_3]_3$	(345)
$CH_3(CH_2)_3Sn(CH{-}CH_2CH_3)_3$ with CH_3	(345)
$CH_3(CH_2)_3Sn(CH_2{-}\underset{CH_3}{CH}{-}\overset{\|\,O}{C}{-}OCH_3)_3$	$b_{0.001}$: 150–5°C; n_D^{20}: 1.4836 (443)
$(CH_3)_2CH{-}CH_2Sn(CH_2{-}\underset{H_3C}{CH}{-}\overset{\|\,O}{C}{-}OCH_3)_3$	$b_{0.01}$: 165–7°C; n_D^{20}: 1.4845 (443)
$CH_3CH_2CH_2Sn(n{-}C_5H_{11})_3$ $CH_3(CH_2)_3Sn(n{-}C_5H_{11})_3$	b_{10}: 163°C (181) (181)
$CH_3{-}Sn\left(CH_2CH_2CH\overset{CH_3}{\underset{CH_3}{}}\right)_3$	b_4: 138–40°C; n_D^{15}: 1.4700; d_{15}: 1.0519 (181, 443)

Continued

APPENDIX 22—continued

	Important physical constants	Other properties
$CH_2{=}CH{-}CH_2Sn\left(CH_2CH_2CH\begin{smallmatrix}CH_3\\CH_3\end{smallmatrix}\right)_3$	b_5: 185–6°C; n_D^{20}: 1.4970; d_{20}: 1.1088 (443)	
$CH_3(CH_2)_6Sn\left(CH_2CH_2CH\begin{smallmatrix}CH_3\\CH_3\end{smallmatrix}\right)_3$	b: 218–20°C; n_D^{20}: 1.4696–1.4771; d_{20}: 0.9957–1.003 (181, 443); b_3: 158–60°C	
$CH_3CH_2Sn[CH_2{-}C(CH_3)_3]_3$	$b_{0.1}$: 76°C; n_D^{25}: 1.4754; d_{28}: 1.0428 (443, 461)	
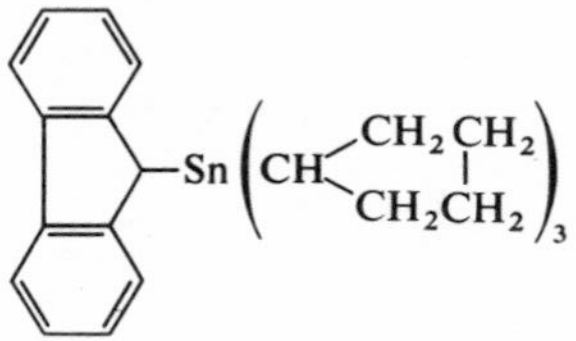 Sn$\left(CH\begin{smallmatrix}CH_2CH_2\\CH_2CH_2\end{smallmatrix}\right)_3$ fluorenyl	m: 95–7°C (443)	

Compound	Properties
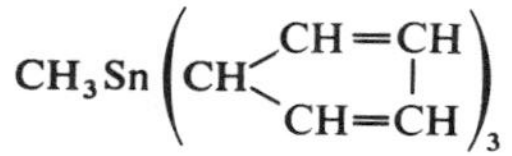 $CH_3Sn\left(CH\begin{smallmatrix}CH=CH\\ \\CH=CH\end{smallmatrix}\right)_3$	$b_{0.001}$: 115°C (443), NMR (443)
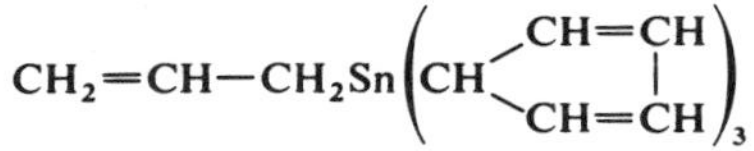 $CH_2=CH-CH_2Sn\left(CH\begin{smallmatrix}CH=CH\\ \\CH=CH\end{smallmatrix}\right)_3$	b_{12}: 193–4°C; n_D^{20}: 1.4935; d_{20}: 1.1259 (443)
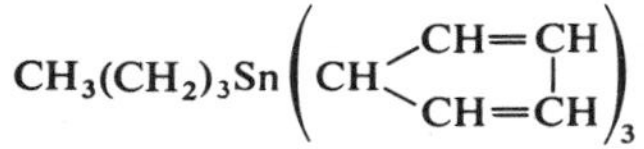 $CH_3(CH_2)_3Sn\left(CH\begin{smallmatrix}CH=CH\\ \\CH=CH\end{smallmatrix}\right)_3$	$b_{0.001}$: 150°C (443), NMR (443)
 $CH_2=CH-Sn\left(CH\begin{smallmatrix}CH=CH\\ \\CH=CH\end{smallmatrix}\right)_3$	(181, 443)
$CH_2=CH-CH_2Sn(n\text{-}C_6H_{13})_3$	b: 189–91°C; n_D^{20}: 1.5030; d_{20}: 1.0915 (423)
$CH_2-CH-CH_2-C(COO)_2Sn(n\text{-}C_6H_{13})_3$ (epoxide, O)	(443) n_D^{20}: 1.4946 (85, 160)
$CH_2=CH-Sn(n\text{-}C_6H_{13})_3$ $(n\text{-}C_6H_{13})_3Sn-C\equiv C-C\equiv C-Sn(n\text{-}C_6H_{13})_3$	
$C_8H_{17}Sn[(CH_3)C_5H_3-Zr(CO)_4]_3$	(153, 443) Continued

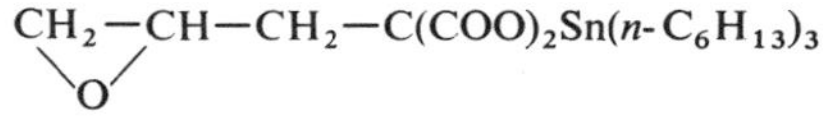

APPENDIX 22—continued

	Important physical constants	Other properties

R in R Sn $\left(\text{CH}_3-\text{CH} \underset{\text{CH}_3}{\overset{\text{CH}_3}{\big\langle}} \right)_3$

R in RSn $\left(\text{CH} \underset{\text{CH}_2\text{CH}_2}{\overset{\text{CH}_2\text{CH}_2}{\big\langle}} \text{CH}_2 \right)_3$

CH_3 — b_{15}: 221°C (181)

CH_3CH_2 — b_{15}: 227–8°C (181) (192)

$\text{CH}_2=\text{CH}-\text{CH}_2$ — b_3: 191–2°C (337);

$(\text{CH}_3)_2\text{CH}$ — m: 116–7°C (337)

$\text{CH}_3(\text{CH}_2)_3$ — m: 103–4°C (337)

$(\text{CH}_3)_2\text{CH}-\text{CH}_2$ — b_3: 201–2°C (337)

$\text{CH}_3(\text{CH}_2)_4$ — m: 57–8°C (337)

$(\text{CH}_3)_2\text{CH}(\text{CH}_2)_2$ — $b_{0.001}$: 148–51°C; (286) mixture: n_D^{20}: 1.5411

$\text{CH}_3\text{CH}_2-\text{CH}=\text{CH}-\text{CH}-\text{CH}_2$ — $b_{0.001}$: 148–51°C)286)

$\text{CH}_3-\text{CH}=\text{CH}-\text{CH}-\text{CH}_2\text{CH}_2$

$\text{CH}_3(\text{CH}_2)_5$ — b_8: 233–4°C; n_D^{18}: 1.5150; d_{18}: 1.109 (443)

$(\text{CH}_3)_2\text{C}=\overset{\underset{\text{CH}_3}{|}}{\text{C}}-\text{CH}_2$ — $b_{0.001}$: 166–9°C (286); mixture: n_D^{20}: 1.5458

$\text{CH}_2=\text{CH}-\underset{\text{CH}_3}{\overset{}{\text{CH}}}-\underset{\text{CH}_3}{\overset{}{\text{CH}}}-\text{CH}_2$ — $b_{0.001}$: 166–9°C (286)

CH$_3$(CH$_2$)$_6$	b$_7$: 143–4°C; n$_D^{18}$: 1.5190; d$_{18}$: 1.112 (443)
CH$_3$(CH$_2$)$_7$	b$_3$: 233–5°C; n$_D^{25}$: 1.5035; d$_{25}$: 1.062 (192, 443)
CH$_3$(CH$_2$)$_8$	b$_3$: 243–5°C; n$_D^{25}$: 1.5025; d$_{25}$: 1.051 (443)
CH$_3$(CH$_2$)$_9$	b$_3$: 272–4°C; n$_D^{18}$: 1.5110; d$_{10}$: 1.078 (443)
CH$_3$(CH$_2$)$_{11}$	(192)

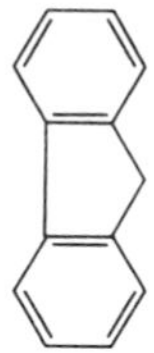

m: 133–6°C (443)

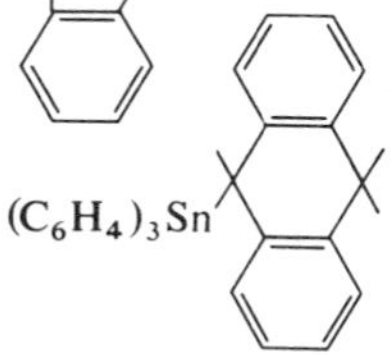

$(C_6H_4)_3Sn$

(107)

CH$_3$(CH$_2$)$_7$—CH=CH—(CH$_2$)$_8$	(192)
CH$_3$—(CH$_2$)$_{19}$	(192)
CH$_2$=CH	(192)
CH$_3$—CH=C=C—CH$_3$	(70)

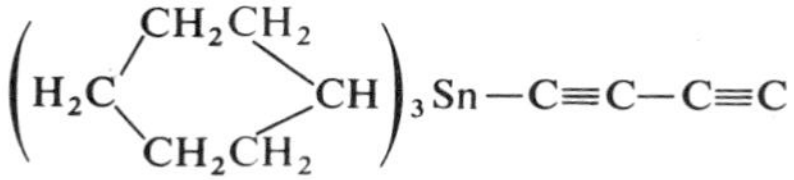

$\Big(H_2C\,\substack{CH_2CH_2\\CH_2CH_2}CH\Big)_3 Sn$—C≡C—C≡C

m: 210°C (85, 160)

RSnR'$_3$

Continued

APPENDIX 22—*continued*

	Important physical constants	Other properties
$CH_2=CH-CH_2Sn(n-C_7H_{15})_3$	b: 220–1°C; n_D^{20}: 1.5230; d_{20}: 1.1017 (*423*) (*400*)	NMR (*400*)
$CH_3Sn(CH_2-C_6H_5)_3$	m: 31–2°C (*181*)	
$CH_3CH_2Sn(CH_2-C_6H_5)_3$	(*181*)	
$CH_3(CH_2)_3Sn(CH_2-C_6H_5)_3$		
(structure: $(C_6H_5CH_2)_3Sn$ 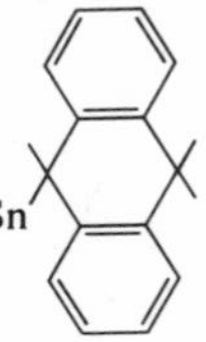 anthracene)	(*107*)	
$(C_6H_5-CH_2)_3Sn-C{\equiv}C-Sn(CH_2-C_6H_5)_3$	m: 94°C (*85, 181, 443*) (*443*)	
$HO-CH_2CH_2OCH_2CH_2CH_2Sn(n-C_8H_{17})_3$	b: 235–7°C; n_D^{20}: 1.5460; d_{20}: 1.1049 (*423*)	
$CH_2=CH-Sn(n-C_8H_{17})_3$	$b_{0.01}$: 180°C; n_D^{20}: 1.4740 (*287*)	
$(CH_3)_2CH-CH_2Sn(n-C_8H_{17})_3$	n_D^{20}: 1.4905 (*85, 160*)	
$(n-C_8H_{17})_3Sn-C{\equiv}C-C{\equiv}C-Sn(n-C_8H_{17})_3$	b: 289–90°C (*423*)	
$CH_2=CH-CH_2Sn(n-C_9H_{19})_3$		
$CH_3(CH_2)_7Sn[CH_2CH_2CH_2-CH-CH_2CH_2-CH=C(CH_3)_2]_3$ CH_3		

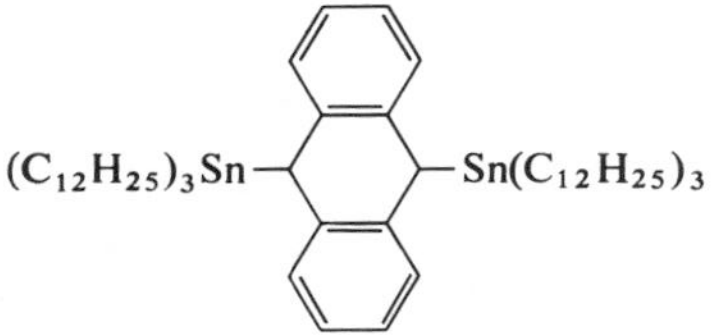

(107)

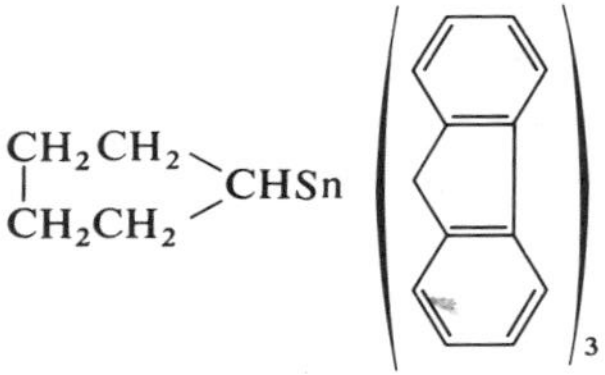

$(C_{12}H_{25})_3Sn$ ... $Sn(C_{12}H_{25})_3$

$b_{0.03}$: 57–61°C; n_D^{25}: 1.4851; d_{25}: 1.1266 (443)

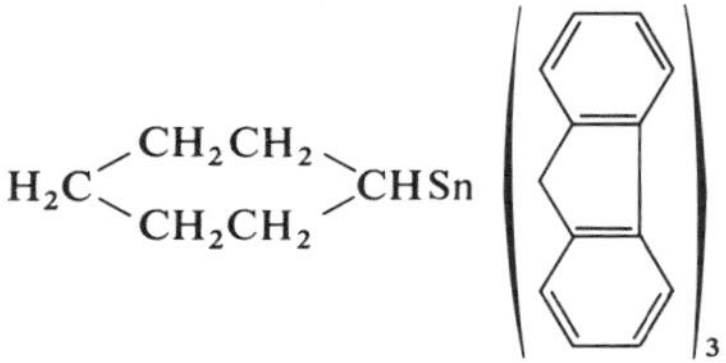

$\underset{CH_2CH_2}{\overset{CH_2CH_2}{\diagdown}}CHSn$]₃

m: 214–220°C (443)

$H_2C\underset{CH_2CH_2}{\overset{CH_2CH_2}{\diagup}}CHSn$]₃

$CH_3CO\text{-}cyclo\text{-}C_6H_{10}Sn[(C_{18}H_{37})C_5H_4\text{—}Mo(CO)_3]_3$ (153, 443)

$CH_3(CH_2)_3Sn(CH=CH_2)_3$ b_9: 77–8°C; n_D^{25}: 1.4851; d_{25}: 1.174 (181, 443)

$CH_3(CH_2)_5Sn(CH=CH_2)_3$ $b_{0.03}$: 57–61°C (181, 443)

$CH_3(CH_2)_7Sn(CH=CH_2)_3$ $b_{0.2}$: 90–3°C; n_D^{25}: 1.4819 (181, 443)

$CH_3(CH_2)_9Sn(CH=CH_2)_3$ $b_{0.05}$: 90–4°C; n_D^{25}: 1.4820; d_{25}: 1.0672 (181, 443)

Continued

APPENDIX 22—*continued*

	Important physical constants	Other properties
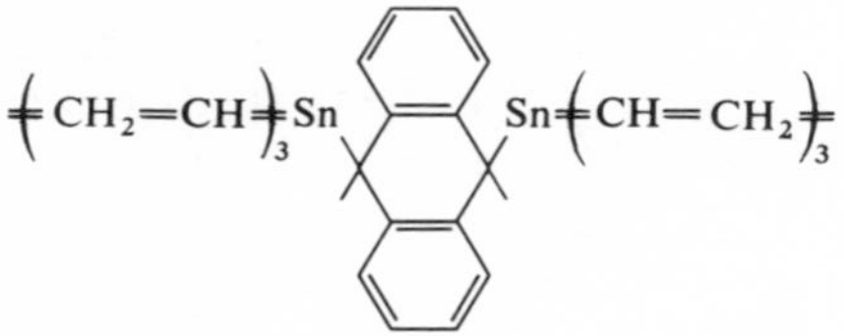 (107)		
$CH_3(CH_2)_3Sn(CF=CF_2)_3$	b_1: 44–5°C; n_D^{25}: 1.4049; d_{25}: 1.685 (443)	
$CH_3(CH_2)_3Sn(C\equiv C-C_6H_5)_3$	m: 70° (85)	
Ar in $ArSn(cycloC_6H_{11})_3$		
C_6H_5	m: 191°C (443)	kinetics (36a, 103a)
m-$CH_3O-C_6H_4$	m: 102.5°C (443)	kinetics (36a, 103a)
p-$CH_3O-C_6H_4$	m: 75°C (337), 76.5°C (443)	kinetics (36a, 103a)
p-$C_2H_5O-C_6H_4$	b_3: 225°C (337); m: 70°C (337)	
p-$(CH_3)_2N-C_6H_4$	m: 148°C (443)	kinetics (103a)
p-$(CH_3)_3\overset{+}{N}-C_6H_4$ (iodide)	m: 164°C (443)	kinetics (103a)
p-FC_6H_4	m: 155°C (443)	kinetics (36a, 103a)
m-ClC_6H_4	m: 109.5°C (443)	kinetics (36a, 103a)
p-ClC_6H_4	m: 116°C (443)	kinetics (36a, 103a)

R	m.p. / properties	ref.
$p\text{-BrC}_6\text{H}_4$	m: 124°C (443)	kinetics (36a, 103a)
$p\text{-cycloC}_6\text{H}_{11})_3\text{Sn}\!-\!\text{C}_6\text{H}_4$	m: 336–340°C (443)	kinetics (36a)
$m\text{-CH}_3\text{C}_6\text{H}_4$	m: 104°C (443)	kinetics (36a), 103a
$p\text{-CH}_3\text{C}_6\text{H}_4$	m: 111°C (443)	kinetics (36a, 103a)
$p\text{-HOOC}\!-\!\text{C}_6\text{H}_4$	m: 177°C (443)	kinetics (36a, 103a)
$p\text{C}_2\text{H}_5\text{C}_6\text{H}_4$	m: 89°C (443)	kinetics (36a, 103a)
$p\text{-CH}_2\!\!=\!\!\text{CH}\!-\!\text{CH}_2\!-\!\text{C}_6\text{H}_4$	m: 104–105°C (443)	
$p\text{-(CH}_3)_2\text{CH}\!-\!\text{C}_6\text{H}_4$	m: 74°C (443)	kinetics (36a, 103a)
$p\text{-(CH}_3)_3\text{C}\!-\!\text{C}_6\text{H}_4$	m: 139.5°C (443)	kinetics (36a, 103a)
$o\text{-C}_6\text{H}_5\!-\!\text{C}_6\text{H}_4$	m: 110–111°C (443)	kinetics (36a, 103a)
$p\text{-C}_6\text{H}_5\!-\!\text{C}_6\text{H}_4$	m: 108°C (443)	kinetics (36a, 103a)

ArSnR_3

R	Ar	m.p. / properties	ref.
$\text{C}_6\text{H}_5\!-\!\text{CH}_2$	C_6H_5	(443)	
9-Fluorenyl	C_6H_5	m: 262°C (dec) (443)	
9-Fluorenyl	1-Naphthyl	m: 291–293°C (443)	ir (443)
$\text{CH}_2\!\!=\!\!\text{CH}$	C_6H_5	$b_{0.5}$: 73–75°C (443); n_D^{25}: 1.5478 (443); d_{25}: 1.282 (443)	
$\text{CH}_2\!\!=\!\!\text{CH}$	1-(4-CH₃—Naphthyl)	(443)	
$\text{CH}_2\!\!=\!\!\text{CH}$	2-Thienyl	(443)	
$\text{CF}_2\!\!=\!\!\text{CF}$	C_6H_5	$b_{0.65}$: 60°C (443); n_D^{25}: 1.4567 (443); d_{25}: 1.614	ir (443)
$\text{C}_6\text{H}_5\!-\!\text{C}\!\equiv\!\text{C}$	C_6H_5	m: 105°C (443)	

APPENDIX 23

ALKYLTRIPHENYLTINS

R in RSn(C$_6$H$_5$)$_3$	Important physical constants	Other properties
CH$_3$	m: 61°C (212)	NMR (212, 400)
(CH$_3$)$_3$Si—CH$_2$	b$_2$: 163°C (443); n_D^{25}: 1.5943 (443); d$_{25}$: 1.2369 (443)	
(C$_6$H$_5$)$_3$P(O)—CH$_2$	m: 141–142°C (443)	NMR (443)
CH$_3$CH$_2$	m: 56–58°C, 62–63°C (443)	NMR (400, 433)
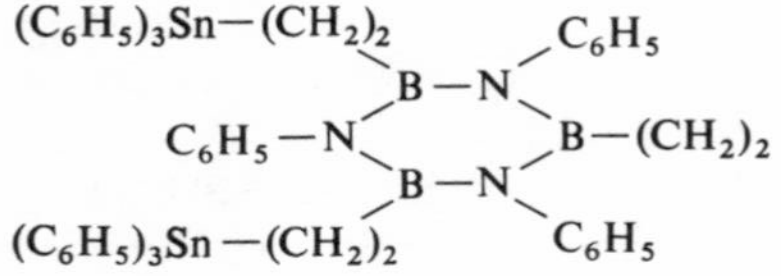 (C$_6$H$_5$)$_3$Sn—(CH$_2$)$_2$ \ B—N / C$_6$H$_5$ ... C$_6$H$_5$—N \ B—(CH$_2$)$_2$ / C$_6$H$_5$ ... (C$_6$H$_5$)$_3$Sn—(CH$_2$)$_2$	m: 219–221°C (443)	ir (443)
N≡C—CH$_2$	m: 106–109°C, 112°C (443)	
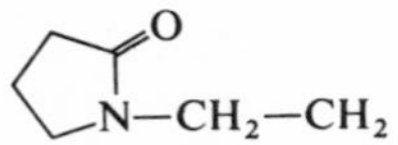 pyrrolidinone N—CH$_2$—CH$_2$	m: 74–76°C (443)	
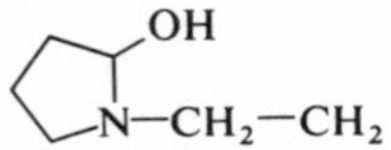 2-hydroxypyrrolidine (OH) N—CH$_2$—CH$_2$	(443)	
C$_{12}$H$_{18}$N—CH$_2$—CH$_2$	m: 207°C (443)	ir (443)
HO—CH$_2$—CH$_2$	m: 68–69°C (443)	NMR (433)
CH$_3$—COO—CH$_2$—CH$_2$	m: 65–66°C (443)	NMR (433)
C$_6$H$_5$O—CH$_2$—CH$_2$	m: 82.5–83°C (443)	

Compound	Property	Reference
$(C_6H_5)_3Si—CH_2—CH_2$	m: 207–208°C (443)	
$(C_6H_5)_3Sn—CH_2—CH_2$	m: 208–209°C (443)	ir (443)
$CH_3CH_2—CH_2$	m: 74–74.5°C (443)	
$CH_2=CH—CH_2$	m: 75.5–76°C (443)	ir (443)
$HC\equiv C—CH_2$	m: 84°C (443)	NMR (443)
$N\equiv C—CH_2—CH_2$	m: 92–93°C (331), 93–94°C (443)	NMR (433)
$(C_2H_5)_2N—(CH_2)_3$	m: −70°C (443)	
$(C_2H_5)_2CH_3\overset{+}{N}—(CH_2)_3$ (iodide)	m: 173–175°C (443)	
$CH_3SO_4^-·(C_2H_5)_2CH_3\overset{+}{N}—(CH_2)_3$	m: 118–132°C (443)	NMR (433)
$HO—(CH_2)_3$	m: 105°C (443)	
$NC—(CH_2)_2—O—(CH_2)_3$	m: 59–61°C (443)	
$(C_6H_5)_3Sn—(CH_2)_3—O—(CH_2)_3$	m: 105–108°C (443)	
$(C_2H_5O)_2CH—(CH_2)_2$	$b_{0.005}$: 168–178°C (443); m: 35.5–37.5°C (443)	
$H_2N—CO—(CH_2)_2$	m: 123–124°C	
$NaOCO—(CH_2)_2$	amorphous solid (443)	
$CH_3OCO—(CH_2)_2$	m: 46.5–47°C (443)	
$C_2H_5OCO—(CH_2)_2$	(443)	
$(C_6H_5)_3Sn—(CH_2)_2—COO(CH_2)_2—$ $OCO—(CH_2)_2$		
$CH_3CO—NH—(CH_2)_3$	m: 93–96°C (443)	
$ClCH_2—CH(OH)—CH_2$	m: 95–98°C (443)	
$Cl_3C—CH_2—CHBr$	m: 97–99°C (443)	
$(C_6H_5)_3Sn—(CH_2)_2—Si(C_6H_5)_2—(CH_2)_2$	m: 61–62°C	
$(C_6H_5)_3Sn—(CH_2)_2—CH(COOCH_3)—CH_2$	m: 143–144°C (443)	
$(C_6H_5)_3Sn—(CH_2)_2COO—CO(CH_2)_2$	m: 111–112°C (443)	
$(CH_3)_2CH$	m: 182–186°C (443) (225a)	
$cyclo C_3H_5$	m: 67–68.5°C (443)	ir (443)
$CH_3(CH_2)_3$	(443)	
$CH_3—CH=CH—CH—CH_2$	m: 80–81°C (443)	
$NC—(CH_2)_3$	m: 75–76°C (443)	kinetics (443)
$HO—(CH_2)_4$		

Continued

APPENDIX 23—continued

Ar in ArSn(CH$_3$)$_3$	Important physical constants	Other properties
HOOC—(CH$_2$)$_3$	m: 130–131°C (443)	
CH$_2$=C(CH$_3$)—CH$_2$	m: 70–73°C (443)	
HOCH$_2$—CH(CH$_3$)—CH$_2$	m: 100–102°C (443)	
CH$_3$OOC—CH(CH$_3$)—CH$_2$	b$_{0.0002}$: 173–176°C (443)	
HC≡C—CH(CH$_3$)—	m: 94°C (443)	ir (443); uv (443)
NC—CH$_2$—CH(CH$_3$)—	m: 103–104°C (443)	
(C$_6$H$_5$)$_3$Sn—(CH$_2$)$_3$	m: 182–185°C (443)	
(C$_6$H$_5$)$_3$Sn—(CH$_2$)$_4$	m: 149–150.5°C (443)	
CH$_3$—(CH$_2$)$_4$	(90)	
HO—(CH$_2$)$_5$	m: 64–66°C (443)	
HOOC—(CH$_2$)$_4$	m: 100–102°C (443)	
CH$_3$OOC—(CH$_2$)$_4$	m: 58–59°C (443)	
C$_2$H$_5$OOC—(CH$_2$)$_4$	(443)	
isoC$_5$H$_{11}$	(443)	
(CH$_3$)$_2$C=CH—CH$_2$	m: 70°C (443)	ir (443)
cycloC$_5$H$_9$	m: 111–113°C (443)	NMR (443)
1-Cyclopentadienyl	130°–121°C (443)	
CH$_3$—(CH$_2$)$_5$	m: 54°C (443); (90)	
CH$_3$—CO—(CH$_2$)$_4$	m: 70–71°C (443)	
(CH$_3$)$_2$C=C(CH$_3$)—CH$_2$	m: 64–65°C (443)	
cycloC$_6$H$_{11}$	m: 132–136°C (443)	
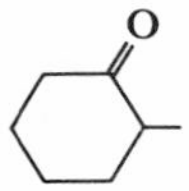	(443)	

CH₃—(CH₂)₆

$CH_3-(CH_2)_6$ b₂₋₃: 230–232°C (443); n_D^{60}: 1.0785 (443); d₆₀: 1.5286 (443)

$C_6H_5CH_2$ m: 91–92°C (443)   ir (443)

1-Pyridyl—CH₂—CH₂   m: 112–113°C (443)

4-Pyridyl—CH₂—CH₂   m: 54–55°C (90, 443)

$CH_3-CH_2)_7$ m: 93–94°C (443)

$(C_6H_5)_3Sn-(CH_2-CH-CH_2)_2$ with CH_3

$C_6H_5CH_2-CH_2$ m: 127–127.5°C (443); (90)   NMR (433)

$p-CH_3CO-NH-C_6H_4-CH_2-CH_2$ m: 154–155°C (443)

$p-(C_6H_5)_3Pb-C_6H_4-CH_2-CH_2$ m: 177–179°C (443)

$(C_6H_5)_3Sn-CH(C_6H_5)-CH_2$ m: 139–140°C (443)

$p-(C_6H_5)_3Sn-C_6H_4-CH_2-CH_2$ m: 184–186°C (443)

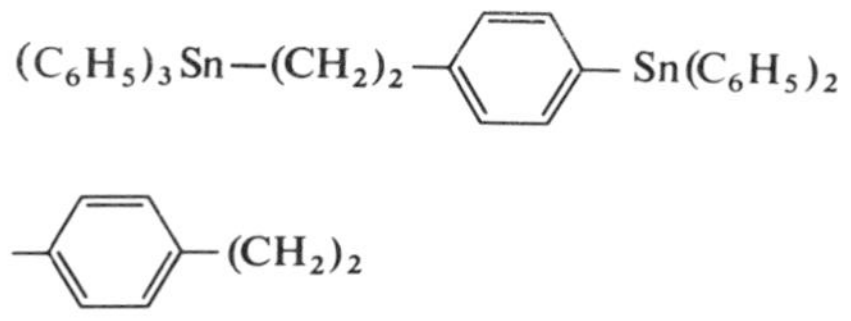

$(C_6H_5)_3Sn-(CH_2)_2-$[C₆H₄]$-Sn(C_6H_5)_2$ m: 183–185°C (443)

$(C_6H_5)_3Sn-(CH_2)_2-$[C₆H₄]$-Pb(C_6H_5)_2$ m: 180–182°C (443)

$(C_6H_5)_3Sn-$[C₆H₄]$-(CH_2)_2-Sn(C_6H_5)_2$ m: 168–169°C (443)

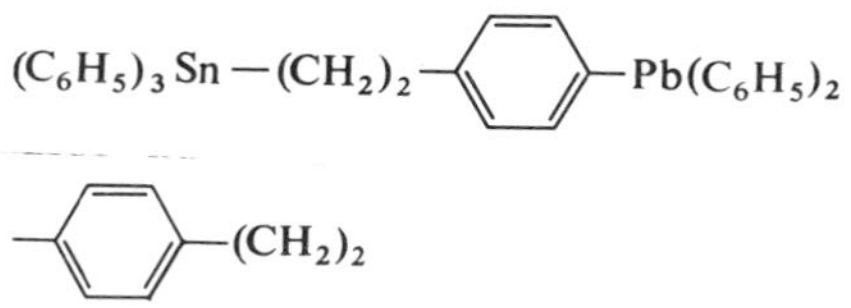

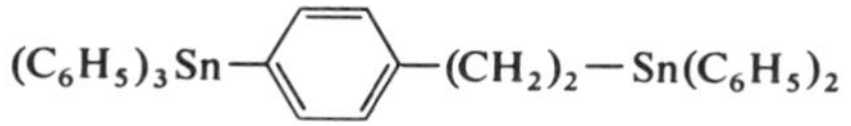

Continued

APPENDIX 23—*continued*

Ar in ArSn(CH$_3$)$_3$ 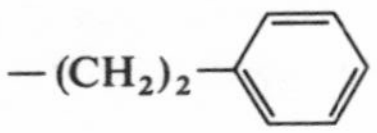	Important physical constants	Other properties
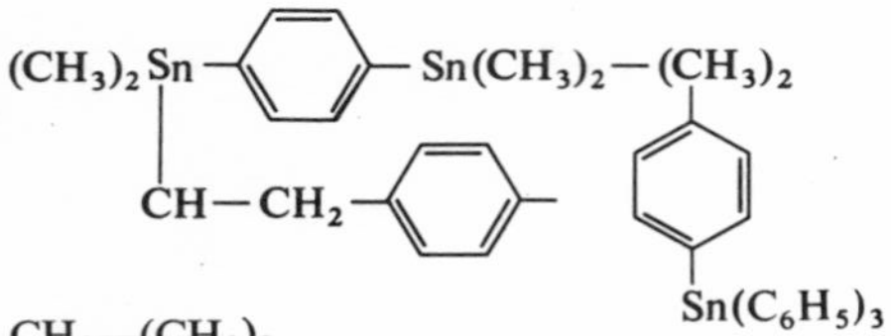	m: 124–126°C (*443*)	
(CH$_3$)$_2$Sn— with Sn(CH$_3$)$_2$—(CH$_3$)$_2$ and Sn(C$_6$H$_5$)$_3$, CH—CH$_2$	b$_3$: 250–255°C (*443*); n_D^{50}: 1.5530 (*443*); d_{50}: 1.096 (*443*); (*90*)	
CH$_3$—(CH$_2$)$_8$	m: 79–80°C (*443*)	
C$_6$H$_5$CO—(CH$_2$)$_2$ 1-Indenyl	m: 129–130°C (*443*)	
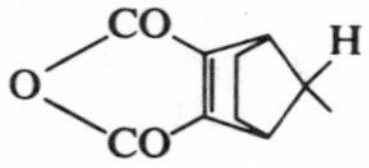	m: 144–145°C (*443*)	
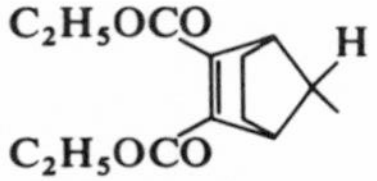	m: 109.5–111°C (*443*)	
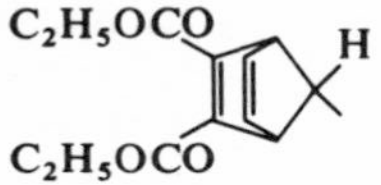	m: 107–109°C (*443*)	

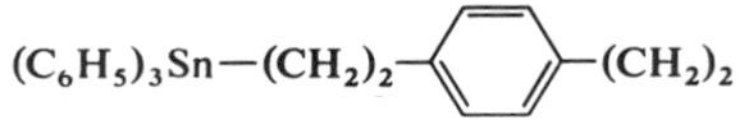

$(C_6H_5)_3Sn-(CH_2)_2-$[C₆H₄]$-(CH_2)_2$ m: 136–142°C *(443)*

$(C_6H_5)_2CH$
9-Fluorenyl   m: 138–139°C *(443)*
    m: 129–130°C *(443)*

[morpholine ring]—N—CH₂—[9H-fluorenyl]   m: 123–124°C *(443)*   ir *(443)*

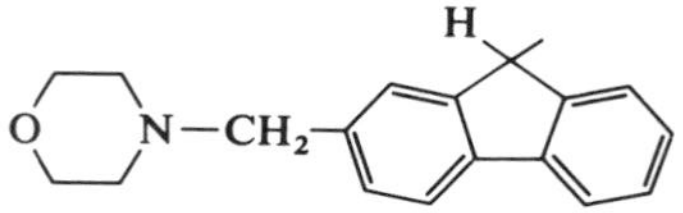

$(C_6H_5)_3C$ m: 272–273°C (dec) *(443)*   ir *(443)*
$CH_2=CH$ m: 45.2–45.4°C *(443)*   ir *(443)*
$CF_2=CF$ m: 68°C *(443)*   ir *(443)*
$C_2H_5O-CH=CH$ *(cis, trans)*   *(231)*   NMR *(231)*
$HOCH_2-CH=CH$ *(cis, trans)*   *(231)*   NMR *(231)*
$CH_2=C(CH_2OH)$ *(231)*   NMR *(231)*
$Cl_3C-CH=CH$ m: 132°C *(443)*   ir *(443)*; uv *(443)*
$CH_2=C=CH$ m: 55°C *(443)*   ir *(443)*
$(C_6H_5)_3Sn-CH=CH-CH=CH-CH$ m: 192–194°C *(443)*   NMR *(231)*
$CH_2=C=C(CH_3)$ *(443)*   ir *(443)*
$CH_3-(CH_2)_3-CH=CH$ *(cis, trans)*   *(231)*   NMR *(231)*
$C_6H_5-CH=CH$ *(cis, trans)*   *(231)*

$(C_6H_5)_3Sn-CH=CH-$[C₆H₄]$-CH=CH$ m: 253–254°C *(443)*   ir *(443)*

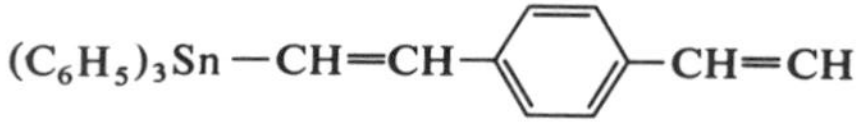

Continued

APPENDIX 23—continued

Ar in ArSn(C$_6$H$_5$)$_3$	Important physical constants	Other properties
HC≡C	m: 34°C (443)	
ClC≡C	m: 81–83°C (443)	
C$_6$H$_5$)$_3$Sn—C≡C	m: 153°C (443)	
CH$_3$—C≡C	m: 43°C, 74–75°C (443)	ir (443)
(C$_2$H$_5$O)$_2$CH—C≡C	m: 58–60°C (443)	ir (443); uv (443)
CH$_2$=CH—C≡C	m: 58°C (443)	ir (443); uv (443)
HC≡C—C≡C	m: 99°C (443)	ir (443); uv (443)
(C$_6$H$_5$)$_3$Sn—C≡C—C≡C	m: 245°C (dec) (443)	ir (443); uv (443)
CH$_3$—C≡C—C≡C	oil (443)	ir (443); uv (443)
CH$_2$=C(CH$_3$)—C≡C	m: 106°C (443)	ir (443); uv (443)
(C$_6$H$_5$)$_3$Sn—(C≡C)$_3$	m: 170°C (443)	ir (443); uv (443)
(C$_6$H$_5$)$_3$Sn—C≡C—(CH$_2$)$_3$—C≡C	m: 105°C (443)	
cycloC$_6$H$_{11}$—C≡C	m: 106°C (443)	
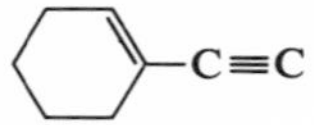 (cyclohexenyl)—C≡C	m: 64°C (443)	ir (443); uv (443)
C$_6$H$_5$—C≡C	m: 62°C (443)	
(C$_6$H$_5$)$_3$Sn—C≡C—(CH$_2$)$_4$—C≡C	m: 148°C (443)	ir (443); uv (443)
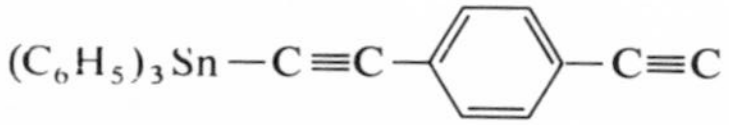 (C$_6$H$_5$)$_3$Sn—C≡C—(C$_6$H$_4$)—C≡C	m: 205°C (443)	

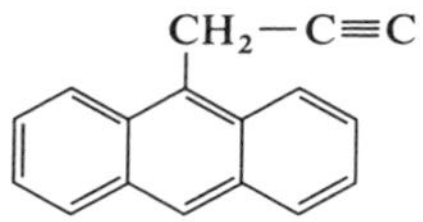

$CH_2-C\equiv C$ [anthracene structure]

m: 150°C (443)

ir (443)

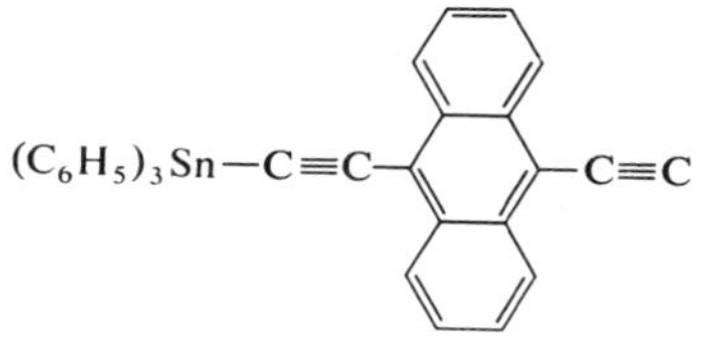

$(C_6H_5)_3Sn-C\equiv C$ [anthracene structure with $C\equiv C$]

m: 225°C (443)

ir (443)

APPENDIX 24

OTHER ALKYLTRIARYLTINS

R	$RSnAr_3$ Ar	Important physical constants	Other properties
CH_3	C_6F_5	(443)	NMR (212)
CH_3	$p\text{-}CH_3C_6H_4$	m: 155°C (212, 443)	NMR (212)
CH_3	$2,4,6\text{-}(CH_3)_3C_6H_2$	m: 133°C (212)	NMR (212)
CH_3	$3,4,5\text{-}(CH_3)_3C_6H_2$	m: 143.5°C (443)	
C_2H_5	$2,4,6\text{-}(CH_3)_3C_6H_2$	m: 130°C (443)	
$CH_3(CH_2)_2$	$2,4,6\text{-}(CH_3)_3C_6H_2$	m: 146.5°C (443)	
$(CH_3)_2CH$	$2,4,6\text{-}(CH_3)_3C_6H_2$	m: 118.5°C (443)	
$CH_3(CH_2)_3$	C_6F_5	$b_{1.1}$: 168–171°C (310); m: 62–64°C (310, 443)	ir (443)
$CH_3(CH_2)_3$	$2,4,6\text{-}(CH_3)_3C_6H_2$	m: 100°C (443) (impure)	
$(CH_3)_2CH\text{—}CH_2$	$p\text{-}CH_3C_6H_4$	m: 45.5–47°C (443)	
$CH_2\text{=}C(CH_3)\text{—}CH_2$	$2,4,6\text{-}(CH_3)_3C_6H_2$	m: 107°C (443)	
$i\text{-}C_5H_{11}$	$2,4,6\text{-}(CH_3)_3C_6H_2$	m: 115°C (443)	
$CH_3(CH_2)_5$	$o\text{-}CH_3C_6H_4$	m: 108–109°C (443)	
$C_6H_5CH_2$	$2,4,6\text{-}(CH_3)_3C_6H_2$	m: 104.5°C (443)	
$CH_3(CH_2)_7$	1-Naphthyl	m: 243–254°C (443)	ir (443)
9-Fluorenyl	2-Thienyl	(443)	
$CH_2\text{=}CH$	$p\text{-}CH_3C_6H_4$	m: 58–60°C (443)	
$CH_3\text{—}CH\text{=}CH$		m: 191°C (443)	ir (443)
$(p\text{-}ClC_6H_4)_3Sn\text{—}C\equiv C\text{—}Sn(p\text{-}ClC_6H_4)_3$		m: 143°C (443)	
$(o\text{-}CH_3C_6H_4)_3Sn\text{—}C\equiv C\text{—}Sn(o\text{-}CH_3C_6H_4)_3$			
$C_6H_5\text{—}C\equiv C$	$p\text{-}ClC_6H_4$	m: 132°C (443)	
$C_6H_5\text{—}C\equiv C$	$p\text{-}CH_3C_6H_4$	m: 106°C (443)	

APPENDIX 25

ARYLTRIPHENYLTINS

Ar in ArSn(C$_6$H$_5$)$_3$	Important physical constants	Other properties
o-HO—C$_6$H$_4$	m: 176–179°C, 201–203°C (443)	
m-HO—C$_6$H$_4$	m: 207–208°C (443)	
m-NaO—C$_6$H$_4$	(443)	
p-HO—C$_6$H$_4$	m: 201–203°C (443)	
o-CH$_3$O—C$_6$H$_4$	m: 129–130°C (443)	kinetics (36a, 103a)
p-CH$_3$O—C$_6$H$_4$	m: 156.5°C (443)	
m-C$_2$H$_5$O—CO—CH$_2$—O—C$_6$H$_4$	m: 97–98°C (443)	
p-H$_2$N—C$_6$H$_4$	m: 167–169°C (443)	
o-(CH$_3$)$_2$N—C$_6$H$_4$	m: 110–112°C (443)	
m-(CH$_3$)$_2$N—C$_6$H$_4$	m: 90–91°C (443)	
p-(CH$_3$)$_2$N—C$_6$H$_4$	m: 132–134°C (443)	
p-(CH$_3$)$_3$N—C$_6$H$_4$ (iodide)	m: 167–169°C (443)	
CH$_3$SO$_4$$^-$ p·(CH$_3$)$_3$N—C$_6$H$_4$	m: 240–243°C (443)	
3-(CH$_3$)$_2$N-6-(p-BrC$_6$H$_4$N$_2$)—C$_6$H$_3$	m: 199–200°C (443)	
3-(CH$_3$)$_2$N-6-(p-O$_2$NC$_6$H$_4$N$_2$)—C$_6$H$_3$	m: 205°C (443)	
3-(CH$_3$)$_2$N-6-(p-HOOC—C$_6$H$_4$N$_2$)—C$_6$H$_3$	m: 358°C (dec) (443)	
4-(CH$_3$)$_2$N-3-(p-ClC$_6$H$_4$N$_2$)—C$_6$H$_3$	m: 162–165°C (443)	
4-(CH$_3$)$_2$N-3-(p-BrC$_6$H$_4$N$_2$)—C$_6$H$_3$	m: 170–172°C (443)	
4-(CH$_3$)$_2$N-3-(p-O$_2$NC$_6$H$_4$N$_2$)—C$_6$H$_3$	m: 187–189°C (443)	
p-FC$_6$H$_4$	m: 171°C (443)	
C$_6$F$_5$	b$_{0.9}$: 208–210°C (310, 443); m: 82–84°C (310)	ir (310)
p-ClC$_6$H$_4$	m: 141°C (443)	
C$_6$Cl$_5$	m: 170–172°C (145)	uv (145)
p-BrC$_6$H$_4$	m: 133–135°C (443)	
p-IC$_6$H$_4$	m: 143°C (443)	

Continued

APPENDIX 25—*continued*

Ar in ArSn(C$_6$H$_5$)$_3$	Important physical constants	Other properties
p-(CH$_3$)$_3$Si—C$_6$H$_4$	m: 132–133.5°C (443)	ir (443)
p-(C$_6$H$_5$)$_3$Sn—C$_6$H$_4$	m: 313–315°C (443)	
o-CH$_3$C$_6$H$_4$	(443)	
p-CH$_3$C$_6$H$_4$	(443)	
o-HOCH$_2$—C$_6$H$_4$	m: 158–159°C (443)	
o-CH$_3$OCH$_2$—C$_6$H$_4$	m: 94.5–95.5°C (443)	
p-HOCH$_2$—C$_6$H$_4$	m: 98–100°C (443)	
p-HOOC—C$_6$H$_4$	m: 166–168°C (443)	
m-CF$_3$C$_6$H$_4$	m: 108–110°C (99, 443)	
2,6-(CH$_3$)$_2$C$_6$H$_3$	m: 118–119°C (443)	
2,4-(CH$_3$)$_2$C$_6$H$_3$	m: 113–115°C (443)	
2,5-(CH$_3$)$_2$C$_6$H$_3$	m: 97–99°C (443)	
p-C$_2$H$_5$—C$_6$H$_4$	(443)	
p-CH$_3$=CH—C$_6$H$_4$	m: 112–113°C (443)	ir (443)
2,4,6-(CH$_3$)$_3$C$_6$H$_2$	m: 157–158°C (443)	
p-CH$_2$=CH—CH$_2$—C$_6$H$_4$	m: 210°C (443)	
p-(CH$_3$)$_3$C—C$_6$H$_4$	m: 130°C (443)	
p-(cycloC$_6$H$_{11}$)—C$_6$H$_4$	m: 138°C (443)	
p-C$_6$H$_5$—C$_6$H$_4$	m: 302–303°C (443)	
p-(4-CH$_2$=CH—C$_6$H$_4$)—C$_6$H$_4$	m: 139–141°C (443)	
1-Naphthyl	m: 125–125.5°C (443)	
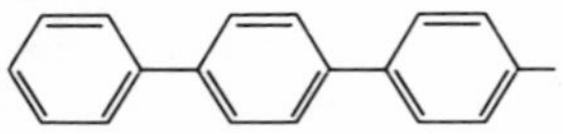	m: 150–152°C (443)	ir (443); uv (443)
2-Furyl	m: 158–159°C	
2-Pyridyl	m: 178–179°C (443)	
3-Pyridyl	m: 220°C (443) [methiodide: m: 183–184°C (443)]	
2-Thienyl	(443)	
Ferrocenyl	m: 130–132°C (299)	

APPENDIX 26

OTHER ArSnAr'₃

Ar	ArSnAr'₃ Ar'	Important physical constants	Other properties
C_6H_5	m-HOC_6H_4	m: 203–205°C (443)	
C_6H_5	C_6F_5	m: 97–99°C (310), 100–102°C (443); $b_{1.1}$: 189–190°C (310)	ir (443)
C_6H_5	m-$CF_3C_6H_4$	m: 109°C (443)	
C_6H_5	2,4,6-$(CH_3)_3C_6H_2$	m: 143°C (443)	
C_6H_5	p-$(CH_3)_3C$—C_6H_4	m: 190°C (443)	
C_6H_5	p-$cycloC_6H_{11}$—C_6H_4	m: 156°C (443)	
C_6H_5	o-C_6H_5—C_6H_4	m: 171.5–172.5°C (443)	
C_6H_5	2-Thienyl	(443)	
C_6H_5	p-$CH_3C_6H_4$	(443)	
C_6F_5	C_6F_5	(443)	
p-$CH_3C_6H_4$	p-C_6H_5—C_6H_4	m: 174.5°C (443)	
m-$CF_3C_6H_4$	p-$CH_3C_6H_4$	m: 133–134°C (99)	

APPENDIX 27

DIALKYLDIMETHYLTINS

R or $R_2Sn(CH_3)_2$	Important physical constants	Other properties
$H(CH_3)_2Si\!-\!CH_2$	b_{20}: 101°C; n_D^{25}: 1.4743; d_{25}: 1.108 (181, 443)	
$(CH_3)_3Si\!-\!CH_2$	b_{65}: 146.5-7.5°C; $b_{0.7}$: 55°C; n_D^{25}: 1.4644-1.4702; d_{25}: 1.073-1.0559 (181, 443)	
$C_2H_5O(CH_3)_2Si\!-\!CH_2$	b_5: 147°C; n_D^{25}: 1.4682; d_{25}: 1.053 (443)	
$H(C_6H_5)(CH_3)Si\!-\!CH_2$	b_{21}: 95°C; n_D^{25}: 1.4743; d_{25}: 1.203 (181, 443)	
$O[(CH_3)_2Si\!-\!CH_2]_2Sn(CH_3)_2$	(181)	MB (149)
$(\!-\!CH_2\!-\!Sn(CH_3)_2)_n$		
$ClCH_2$ $\overset{+}{(C_6H_5)_3P}\!-\!CH_2$	(181, 443)	
C_2H_5	b: 132°C; n_D^{19}: 1.4650; d_{19}: 1.2319 (173, 313); GLC (312, 443)	ir, Raman, NMR (181, 400, 443) MS (165)
$HCF_2\!-\!CF_2$	b: 124°C (443)	ir, NMR, F-NMR (443)
$CF_3\!-\!CF_2$	b_{89}; 62-3°C; GLC (443)	ir, F-NMR (r443)
C_2HF_3Br	b: 192°C (443)	ir, NMR (443)
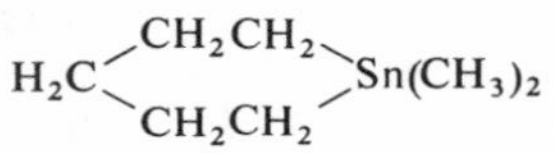 $H_2C\!\!<\!\!\overset{CH_2CH_2}{\underset{CH_2CH_2}{}}\!\!>\!\!Sn(CH_3)_2$	b_{15}: 63°C (181, 359)	
$CH_3CH_2CH_2$	GLC (312, 313)	
$HC\!\equiv\!C\!-\!CH_2$	b_5: 62°C (404)	ir (404) partly isomerized into allenic
$H(CH_3)_2Si\!-\!CH_2CH_2CH_2$	b_{15}: 146°C; n_D^{25}: 1.4730; d_{25}: 1.052 (181, 443)	ir (181, 443)
$O[(CH_3)_2Si(CH_2)_3]_2Sn(CH_3)_2$	b_{16}: 148°C; n_D^{25}: 1.4840; d_{20}: 1.147 (181, 443)	ir (181, 443)
$(CH_3)_2CH$	b_{29}: 68°C; n_D^{25}: 1.4621; d_{25}: 1.161 (181, 443); b_{16}: 26-8°C (14a)	MS (14a); NMR (14a)

Structure	Properties	Methods
$H_2C{<}{\scriptstyle CH_2CH_2 \atop CH-CH_2}{>}Sn(CH_3)_2$, HCl_2C	n_D^{25}: 1.5330 (359)	
$CH_3(CH_2)_3$	b_{44}: 70°C; n_D^{25}: 1.4640; d_{25}: 1.124 (9, 181, 443); GLC (312, 412) (443)	NMR (400)
$CH_3-CH{=}CH-CH_2$; CH_3CH_2CH with CH_3	$b_{5.5}$: 68°C; n_D^{25}: 1.4738; d_{25}: 1.43 (181, 443)	ir, NMR (443)
$CH_3-CH-CH_2$ with CH_3	$b_{16.5}$: 85°C (181, 443)	
$(CH_3)_3C$; $H(CH_3)_2Si-CH_2-CH-CH_2$ with CH_3	b_{40}: 84-85°C; n_D^{25}: 1.4662 (181, 443) (443)	
$CH_3(CH_2)_4$	b: 242°C; b_1: 68-70°C; n_D^{20}: 1.4676; d_{20}: 1.098 (9, 443); m: 177-8°C (443)	ir, Raman (443)
$(CH_3{-}\overset{\text{O}}{\underset{\|}{C}}{-})_2CH$	b_{29}: 119.5-120°C; n_D^{25}: 1.4870; d_{25}: 1.29 (181, 443)	
$(CH_3)_2(CH_3CH_2)C$	$b_{0.3}$: 76-7°C; n_D^{25}: 1.5109; d_{25}: 1.231 (181, 443)	
$_{CH_2CH_2 \atop CH_2CH_2}{>}CH$	$b_{0.001}$: 85°C (443)	NMR (443)
$_{CH=CH-CH_2 \atop CH=CH}{>}$	m: 105-7°C (154, 443)	
$(CO)Fe-C_5H_5$		

Continued

APPENDIX 27—continued

R or $R_2Sn(CH_3)_2$	Important physical constants	Other properties
$(CO)_3Mo-C_5H_5$	m: 155–60°C (153, 443)	
$H_2C\underset{CH_2CH_2}{\overset{CH_2CH_2}{<}}CH-$	$b_{0.5}$: 100–2°C; n_D^{25}: 1.5184; d_{25}: 1.208 (181, 443)	
$C_6H_5-CH_2$	(400)	NMR (400)
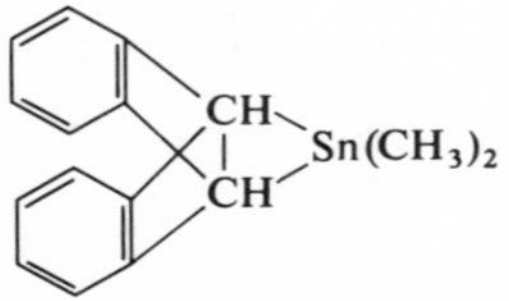	m: 218–21°C (107, 325)	
$CH_3(CH_2)_7$	$b_{0.2}$: 121–2°C; n_D^{25}: 1.4659 (181, 443)	
$CH_3(CH_2)_3CH-CH_2$ $\quad\quad\quad\quad\quad\mid$ $\quad\quad\quad CH_3-CH_2$	$b_{0.2}$: 101–2°C; n_D^{25}: 1.4715 (181, 443)	

APPENDIX 28

DIALKENYL- AND DIALKYNYLDIMETHYLTINS

R or $R_2Sn(CH_3)_2$	Important physical constants	Other properties
$CH_2=CH$	b: 120°C; n_D^{20}: 1.4701; (181,) (443)	ir (443)
$[CBr=CBr-Sn(CH_3)_2]_n$	(246, 246a)	
$[CBr=CBr-GeR_2-CBr=CBr-Sn(CH_3)_2]_n$	(246, 246a)	
$[CBr=CBr-SiR_2-CBr=CBr-Sn(CH_3)_2]_n$	(246, 246a)	
C_2H_2F	(29)	
$CHF=CH$	(29)	
$CHF=CF$	(29)	
$CF_2=CH$	(29)	
$CF_2=CF$	b_{38}: 58°C (29, 181, 443)	ir, NMR (443)
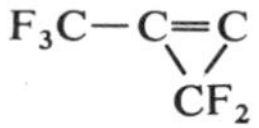 $F_3C-C=C$ $\backslash$ CF_2	(77)	ir, (F) NMR (77)
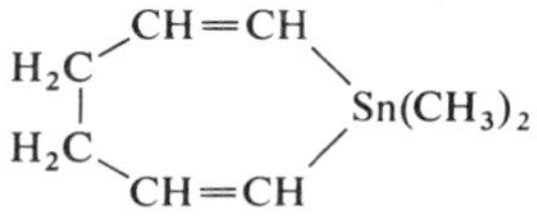 (structure: H_2C—$CH=CH$ / $CH=CH$—$Sn(CH_3)_2$)	$b_{0.2}$: 30–2°C; n_D^{20}: 1.5280 (443)	
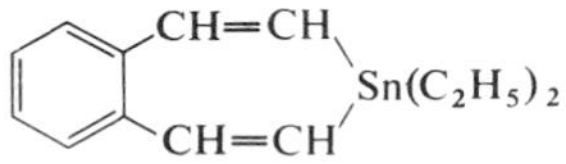 (structure: $CH=CH$ / $CH=CH$—$Sn(C_2H_5)_2$)	$b_{0.4}$: 88–90°C; m: 41–2°C (226)	
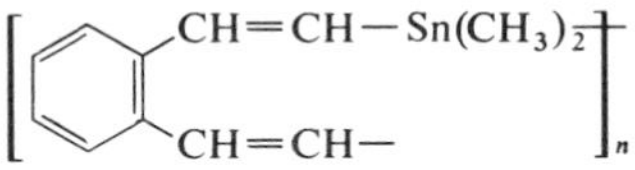 (structure: $[CH=CH-Sn(CH_3)_2]_2$ / $CH=CH-$)$_n$	(226)	

Continued

APPENDIX 28—*continued*

R or $R_2Sn(CH_3)_2$	Important physical constants	Other properties
$[-CBr{=}CBr-C_6H_4-CBr{=}CBr-Sn(CH_3)_2]_n$	(246, 246a)	
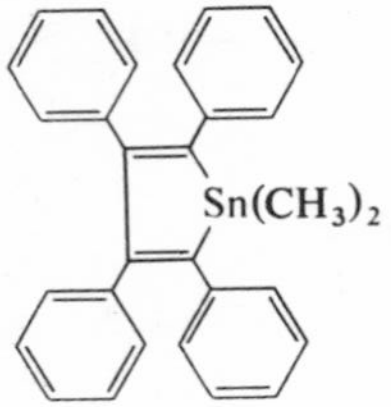	m: 192–3°C (219, 221, 443)	MB
N—C		
H—C≡C	m: 400°C (241) (245a)	ir (241)
$[-C{\equiv}C-Sn(CH_3)_2-]_n$	(246, 246a)	ir, NMR (246, 246a)
$[-C{\equiv}C-GeR_2-C{\equiv}C-Sn(CH_3)_2]_n$	(246, 246a)	ir, NMR (246, 246a)
$[-C{\equiv}C-SiR_2-C{\equiv}C-Sn(CH_3)_2]_n$	(246, 246a)	F—NMR, ir (77)
$F_3C-C{\equiv}C$	(77) $b_{0.2}$: 96°C; n_D^{18}: 1.5668 (85, 224, 443)	
$C_6H_5-C{\equiv}C$		
$[-C{\equiv}C-C_6H_4-C{\equiv}C-Sn(CH_3)_2]_n$	(246, 246a)	ir, NMR (246a)

APPENDIX 29

DIALKYL- DIALKENYL-, AND DIALKYNYLDIETHYLTINS

R or $R_2Sn(C_2H_5)_2$	Important physical constants	Other properties
CH_3	see Appendix 27	
$CH_3CH_2O-CH_2$	b_{16}: 110.9–11°C; n_D^{20}: 1.4688; d_{20}: 1.2114 *(222)*	
ICH_2	b_2: 96°C; d_{20}: 1.9890 *(443)*	
CH_3-CHCl	b_5: 114–5°C; n_D^{20}: 1.5083; d_{20}: 1.414 *(181, 443)*	
$CH_3O-\underset{\parallel}{\underset{O}{C}}-CH_2$	b_1: 109–11°C; n_D^{20}: 1.4932; d_{20}: 1.3771 *(443)*	
$C_2H_5O-\underset{\parallel}{\underset{O}{C}}-CH_2$	b_1: 106–8°C; n_D^{20}: 1.4850–8; d_{20}: 1.3007–12 *(443)*	
$C_3H_7O-\underset{\parallel}{\underset{O}{C}}-CH_2$	b_2: 134–6°C; n_D^{20}: 1.4820; d_{20}: 1.2370 *(443)*	
$\begin{array}{c} CH_2CH_2 \\ H_2C \diagdown \diagup CH_2CH_2 \end{array} Sn(C_2H_5)_2$	b_{14}: 95°C *(158, 181, 436, 444)*	ir *(443)*
$CH_3CH_2CH_2$	b: 205–7°C; $b_{10.11}$: 84.5°C *(181)*; GLC *(312)*	
$CH_2=CH-CH_2$	b_{17}: 99–100°C; n_D^{23}: 1.5086 *(181, 349, 443)*	
$N\equiv C-CH_2CH_2$	$b_{2.5}$: 144–7°C; n_D^{20}: 1.5088 *(443)*	
$HO-CH_2CH_2O-CH_2CH_2CH_2$	$b_{0.001}$: 170–7°C; n_D^{20}: 1.5025 *(443)*	
$CH_3O-\underset{\parallel}{\underset{O}{C}}-CH_2CH_2$	$b_{0.001}$: 150–6°C; n_D^{20}: 1.4849 *(443)*	
$(CH_3)_2CH$	b_5: 74–5°C; n_D^{20}: 1.4750; d_{20}: 1.1513 *(443)*	

Continued

APPENDIX 29—*continued*

R or $R_2Sn(C_2H_5)_2$	Important physical constants	Other properties
$CH_3(CH_2)_3$	b: 205–8°C; b_{10}: 112°C; n_D^{20}: 1.4734; d_{20}: 1.1035 (*181, 399, 401, 443*)	
$(CH_3)_2CH\!-\!CH_2$ $CH_3O\!-\!C\!-\!CH\!-\!CH_2$ $\quad\quad \overset{\parallel}{O}\quad \overset{\mid}{CH_3}$	$b_{0.03}$: 123–7°C; n_D^{20}: 1.4829 (*443*)	
$CH_3(CH_2)_4$ $(CH_3)_3C\!-\!CH_2$ $(CH_3)_2CH\!-\!CH_2CH_2$	b_{14}: 139–41 (*181, 443*) $b_{0.1}$: 66°C; n_D^{25}: 1.4710; d_{24}: 1.068 (*443, 461*) $b_{13.5}$: 131°C (*181*)	
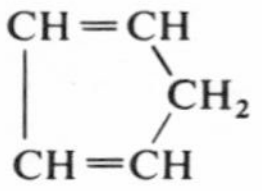 $CH\!=\!CH$ $\quad\quad CH_2$ $CH\!=\!CH$	$b_{2.5}$: 121.5–123°C: $b_{0.001}$: 90°C; n_D^{30}: 1.5890 (*443*)	NMR (*443*)
$(CO)_2Fe\!-\!C_5H_5$ $C_6H_5\!-\!CH_2$	m: 76°C (*36*) b_{20}: 223-4°C (*181, 443*)	ir, NMR (*36*)
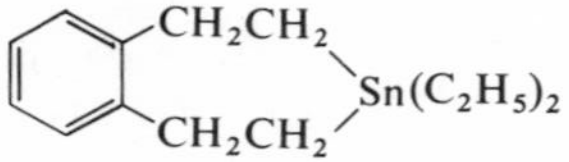 [benzene ring with two CH_2CH_2 groups joined to $Sn(C_2H_5)_2$]	$b_{0.08}$: 93–98°C (*226*)	
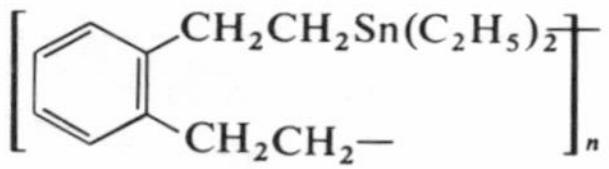 [benzene ring with $CH_2CH_2Sn(C_2H_5)_2$ and CH_2CH_2- bracketed]$_n$	(*226*)	
$CH_3(CH_2)_7$	b_8: 194-6°C (*448*)	

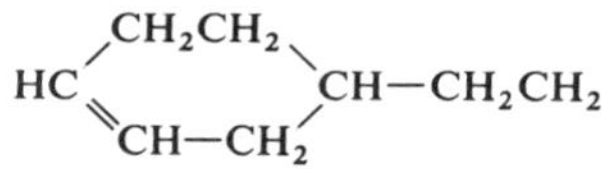

$\mathrm{HC} \overset{\displaystyle CH_2CH_2}{\underset{\displaystyle CH-CH_2}{\diagdown}} \overset{\displaystyle \diagup}{\underset{\displaystyle \diagdown}{}} CH-CH_2CH_2$

$b_{0.001}$: 100–1°C *(443)*

$CH_3(CH_2)_8$
$CH_3(CH_2)_9$
$CH_2=CH$
$CF_2=CF$

b_5: 195–200°C; n_D^{20}: 1.4690; d_{20}: 1.0023 *(443)*
b_5: 205–7°C; n_D^{20}: 1.4785; d_{20}: 1.0377 *(443)*
b_{765}: 168.5°C; n_D^{20}: 1.4860; d_{20}: 1.2356 *(443)*
b_{12}: 55–7°C; n_D^{25}: 1.4168; d_{25} 1.595 *(443)*

ir *(443)*; MB *(149)*
ir *(443)*

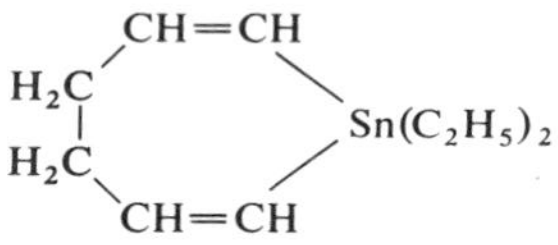

$\underset{\displaystyle H_2C}{\overset{\displaystyle CH=CH}{}} \diagdown \mathrm{Sn(C_2H_5)_2}$
$\underset{\displaystyle H_2C}{\overset{\displaystyle CH=CH}{}} \diagup$

b_5: 74–6°C; n_D^{20}: 1.5308 *(443)*

(benzene ring) $\overset{\displaystyle CH=CH}{\underset{\displaystyle CH=CH}{\diagdown \diagup}} \mathrm{Sn(C_2H_5)_2}$

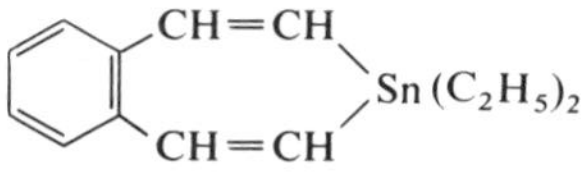

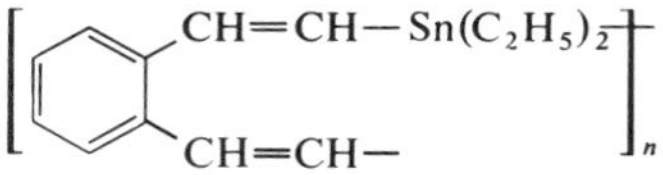

$b_{0.4}$: 95–6°C *(226)*

$\left[\text{(benzene ring)} \overset{\displaystyle CH=CH-\mathrm{Sn(C_2H_5)_2}}{\underset{\displaystyle CH=CH-}{\Big]}} \right]_n$

(226)

$N{\equiv}C$
$HC{\equiv}C$

m: 226°C *(241)*
b_1: 62°C; $b_{0.1}$: 32–5°C *(85)*; n_D^{20}: 1.4977; d_{20}: 1.2332 *(384, 443)*

ir *(241)*

$CH_3-C{\equiv}C$
$CH_2=CH-C{\equiv}C$
$CH_3CH_2CH_2-C{\equiv}C$
$CH_3(CH_2)_3-C{\equiv}C$
$C_6H_5-C{\equiv}C$

b_1: 62°C; n_D^{20}: 1.4977; d_{20}: 1.2332 *(85)*
b_1: 96°C; n_D^{20}: 1.5428; d_{20}: 1.2267 *(384)*
$b_{0.1}$: 66°C; n_D^{20}: 1.4969; d_{20}: 1.225 *(180)*
$b_{0.15}$: 101°C; n_D^{20}: 1.4888; d_{20}: 1.118 *(180)*
n_D^{20}: 1.5919 *(180)*

ir *(387)*

APPENDIX 30

DIALKYL-, DIALKENYL- AND DIALKYNYLDI-n-PROPYLTINS

R or $R_2Sn(CH_2CH_2CH_3)_2$	Important physical constants	Other properties
CH_3	see Appendix 27	
CH_3CH_2	see Appendix 29	
$CH_3O-C-CH_2$ $\parallel$ O	$b_{1.5}$: 121–2°C; n_D^{20}: 1.4909; d_{20}: 1.3088 (443)	
$C_2H_5O-C-CH_2$ $\parallel$ O	b_1: 135–7°C; n_D^{20}: 1.4823; d_{20}: 1.2407 (443)	
$CH_2=CH-CH_2$	b_{4-5}: 95–7°C; n_D^{20}: 1.4880; d_{20}: 1.1362 (443)	NMR (433)
$N\equiv C-CH_2CH_2$	$b_{0.0004}$: 113–7°C (181, 443)	NMR (433)
$CH_3O-C-CH_2CH_2$ $\parallel$ O	$b_{0.001}$: 119–21°C (181, 443)	
$NaO-C-CH_2CH_2$ $\parallel$ O	paper chrom. (181, 443)	
$(CH_3)_2CH$	b_5: 96–7°C; n_D^{20}: 1.4815; d_{20}: 1.1327 (443)	
$CH_3(CH_2)_3$	GLC (312, 399)	
$(CO)Ni-C_5H_4(CH_3)$	(443)	
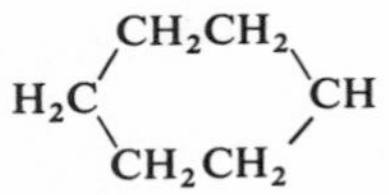 $\begin{array}{c} CH_2CH_2 \\ H_2C \quad CH \\ CH_2CH_2 \end{array}$	b_8: 204–5°C; n_D^{18}: 1.5170; d_{18}: 1.1540 (336)	
$C_6H_5-CH_2CH_2$	$b_{0.015}$: 172°C (181, 443)	

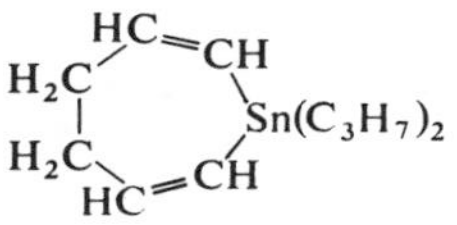

$$
\begin{array}{c}
\text{HC}=\text{CH} \\
\text{H}_2\text{C} \quad\quad\; \text{Sn(C}_3\text{H}_7)_2 \\
\text{H}_2\text{C} \quad\; \text{CH} \\
\text{HC}=\text{CH}
\end{array}
$$

$b_{0.02}$: 64–5°C; n_D^{20}: 1.5213 (443)

HC≡C

CH$_2$=CH—C≡C

CH$_3$CH$_2$CH$_2$—C≡C

CH$_3$CH$_2$CH$_2$CH$_2$—C≡C

C$_6$H$_5$—C≡C

b_2: 70°C; n_D^{20}: 1.4785; d_{20}: 1.1819 (384); b_2: 79 (85)

b_1: 102°C; n_D^{20}: 1.5343; d_{20}: 1.1840 (384)

$b_{0.15}$: 96°C; n_D^{20}: 1.4881; d_{20}: 1.143 (180)

$b_{0.15}$: 109–10°C; n_D^{20}: 1.4899; d_{20}: 1.137 (180)

$b_{0.09}$: 135°C (384); n_D^{20}: 1.5991 (180)

APPENDIX 31

DIALKYLDIISOPROPYLTINS

R or $R_2Sn[CH(CH_3)_2]_2$	Important physical constants	Other properties
CH_3	see Appendix 27	
CH_3CH_2	see Appendix 29	
$CH_3CH_2CH_2$	see Appendix 30	
$CH_2{=}CH{-}CH_2$	m: 281–2°C (443)	
$[CH_2CH_2{-}\underset{\|\|O}{C}{-}OCH_2CH_2{-}O{-}\underset{\|\|O}{C}{-}CH_2CH_2{-}Sn(isoC_3H_7)_2]_n$	(181)	
$CH_3(CH_2)_3$	b_3: 102°C; n_D^{25}: 1.4756; d_{25}: 1.074 (181, 443)	
$[CH(C_6H_5){-}CH_2{-}Sn(isoC_3H_7)_2]_n$	(181)	
$[CH_2CH_2{-}C_6H_4{-}CH_2CH_2{-}Sn(isoC_3H_7)_2]_n$	(181)	
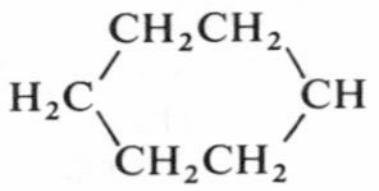 $H_2C\underset{CH_2CH_2}{\overset{CH_2CH_2}{<}}CH$	b_{13}: 190°C; n_D^{18}: 1.5245; d_{18}: 1.1700 (336)	

APPENDIX 32

DIALKYL-, DIALKENYL-, AND DIALKYNYLDI-*n*-BUTYLTINS

R or $R_2Sn(n\text{-}C_4H_9)_2$	Important physical constants	Other properties
CH_3	see Appendix 27	
$H(CH_3)_2Si-CH_2$	b_5: 130°C; n_D^{25}: 1.4810; d_{25}: 1.043 (181, 443)	
$(CH_3)_3Si-CH_2$	$b_{0.5}$: 98°C; n_D^{25}: 1.4777; d_{25}: 1.027 (181, 443)	
$C_2H_5O(CH_3)_2Si-CH_2$	b_{15}: 186°C; n_D^{25}: 1.4655; d_{25}: 1.056 (181, 443)	
$O[(CH_3)_2Si-CH_2]_2Sn(C_4H_9)_2$	b_{25}: 170°C; n_D^{25}: 1.4800; d_{25}: 1.113-6 (181, 443)	ir (443)
$[-CH_2-Sn(C_4H_9)_2-]_n$	(181)	
CH_3O-CH_2	$b_{20.5}$: 146.7-7.6°C; n_D^{20}: 1.4775; d_{20}: 1.1881 (222)	
CH_3CH_2	see Appendix 29	
HCF_2-CF_2	b: 124°C; (181, 443)	ir, NMR, F-NMR (443)
F_3C-CF_2	b_{89}: 62-3°C; GLC (443)	ir, F-NMR (443)
$CH_3CH_2CH_2$	see Appendix 30	
$CH_2=CH-CH_2$	b_{17}: 145-6°C; $b_{0.1}$: 93°C; n_D^{20}: 1.5023; d_{25}: 1.0999 (181, 288, 349, 443)	ir (443)
$HC\equiv C-CH_2$	(152)	uv, ir (mixture of isomers) (152)
$CH_3-\overset{\displaystyle O}{\underset{\displaystyle C_6H_5SO_2}{\overset{\|}{C}}}-CH$	m: 85-7°C (181, 443)	
$(CH_3)_2CH$	see Appendix 31	

Continued

APPENDIX 32—continued

R or $R_2Sn(n\text{-}C_4H_9)_2$	Important physical constants	Other properties
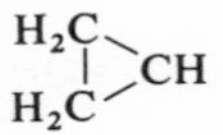 H_2C H_2C $>$CH—	$b_{0.4}$: 79°C; n_D^{25}: 1.4912 (367a, 443)	ir (443)
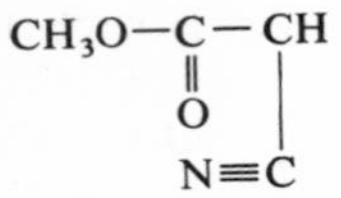 $CH_3O-\overset{\displaystyle O}{\underset{}{C}}-\overset{}{\underset{N\equiv C}{C}}H-$	(181, 443)	
$[C_2H_5O-\overset{\displaystyle O}{\underset{}{C}}]_2CH-$	n_D^{20}: 1.4665 (181, 443)	
$[C_4H_9O-\overset{\displaystyle O}{\underset{}{C}}]_2CH-$	n_D^{20}: 1.4544 (181, 443)	
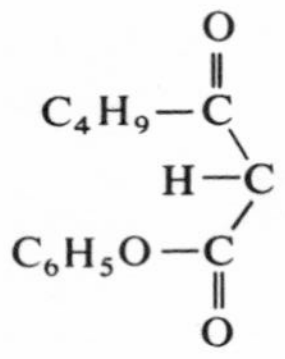 $O=\overset{C_4H_9}{\underset{C_6H_5}{}}C-\overset{H}{\underset{}{C}}-C=O$	(181)	
$[CH_3(CH_2)_3(C_2H_5)CH-CH_2-O-C]_2CH-$ $\|$ O	(181, 443)	

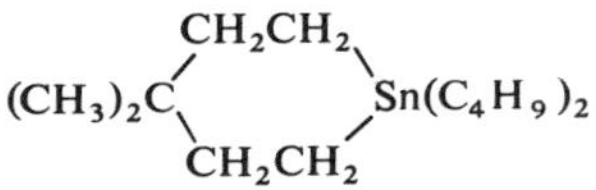

	$b_{0.0001}$: 71–77°C; n_D^{20}: 1.4948 (*315*, *317*, *318*, *443*)
$(CH_3)_2CH—CH_2$	(*345*)
$CH_2{=}CH(CH_3)—CH_2$	b_7. 142–3°C; n_D^{20}: 1.4986 (*349*, *443*)
$CH_3CH_2—CH(CH_3)$	(34)
	(*181*, *443*)
	(*181*, *443*)

Continued

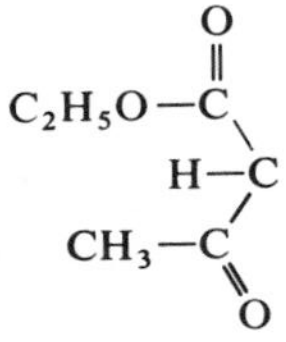

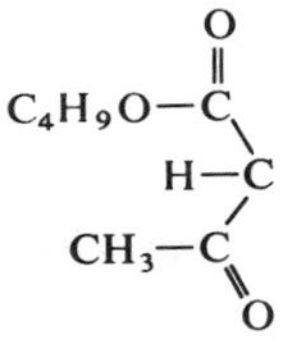

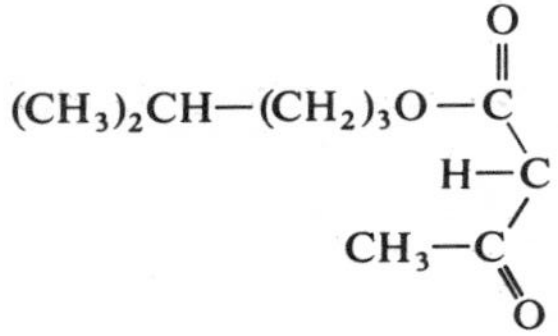

APPENDIX 32—*continued*

R or $R_2Sn(n\text{-}C_4H_9)_2$	Important physical constants	Other properties
$(CH_3)_3C$	b_{40}: 123–5°C; b_D^{25}: 1.4809; d_{25}: 1.0527 (*181, 345, 443*)	
$CH_3(CH_2)_4$ $CH_2{=}CH{-}CH_2CH_2CH_2$ $(CH_3)_2(C_2H_5)C$ $(CH_3{-}\overset{\|\,O}{C}{-})_2CH$	(*181*) $b_{0.5}$: 117–8°C; n_D^{25}: 1.4842; d_{25}: 1.050 (*443*) (*181*) (*181, 443*)	ir (*443*)
$(CH_3)_3C{-}CH_2$	$b_{0.1}$: 88°C; n_D^{25}: 1.4739; d_{27}: 1.0303 (*443, 461*)	
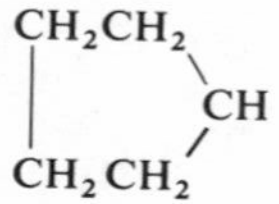 cyclopentane ring with two CH_2CH_2 arms bridged by CH	$b_{0.3}$: 128°C; n_D^{25}: 1.5067; d_{25}: 1.127 (*181, 443*)	
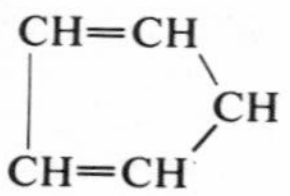 ring with $CH{=}CH$ / $CH{=}CH$ and CH	$b_{0.001}$: 105°C (*443*)	NMR (*443*)
$CH_3(CH_2)_5$	(*443*)	
$CH_2{=}C{-}CH{-}CH_2$ with H_3C CH_3	b_{12}: 181–5°C (*286*)	
$(CH_3)_2C{=}C{-}CH_2$ CH_3	b_{12}: 181–5°C (*286*)	

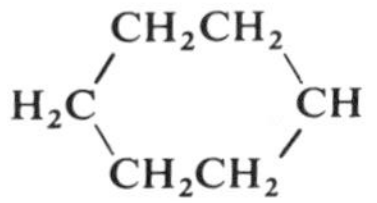	$b_{0.5}$: 143°C (*181*); b_7: 214–5°C (*336*); n_D^{25}: 1.5126 (*443*); n_D^{18}: 1.5132 (*336*); d_{25}: 1.119 (*443*); d_{18}: 1.1310 (*336*)
$(CH_3—\overset{\overset{O}{\Vert}}{C})_2(C_2H_5O—\overset{\overset{O}{\Vert}}{C})C$	(*181*, *443*)
$C_6H_5—CH_2$	(*443*)
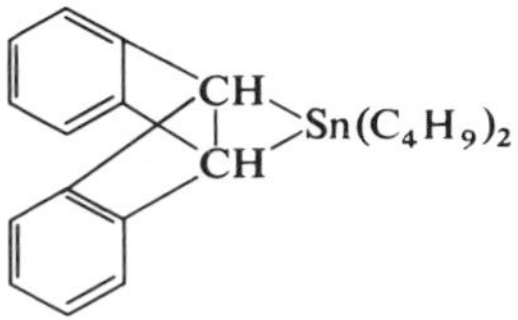	m: 225–235°C (*107*, *325*)
$(CH_3—\overset{\overset{O}{\Vert}}{C})(C_2H_5O—\overset{\overset{O}{\Vert}}{C})(CH_3CH_2CH_2)C$	(*181*, *443*)
$CH_3(CH_2)_7$	(*345*)
$CH_2{=}CH—(C_6H_{13\text{-}n})$	(*443*)
$CH_2{=}CH—(CH_2)_6$	$b_{0.001}$: 135°C; n_D^{20}: 1.4826 (*287*, *288*)
$CH_3(CH_2)_3CH(CH_3CH_2)—CH_2$	(*443*)
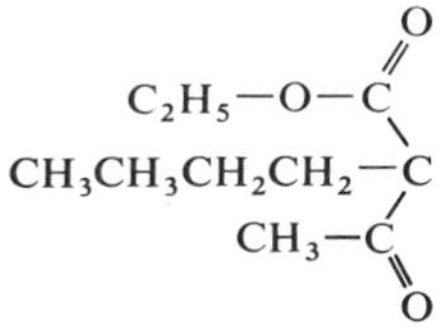	(*443*)

Continued

APPENDIX 32—*continued*

R or $R_2Sn(n\text{-}C_4H_9)_2$	Important physical constants	Other properties
 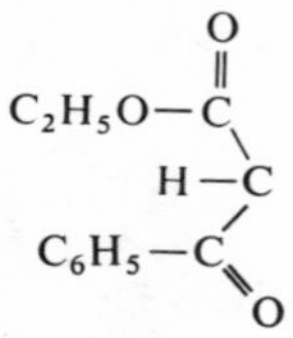 (indene structure)	(181, 443)	
$C_2H_5O-\overset{\displaystyle O}{\overset{\|}{C}}-\overset{\displaystyle H}{\underset{\|}{C}}-\overset{\displaystyle O}{\overset{\|}{C}}-C_6H_5$	(181, 443)	
$(C_2H_5O-\overset{\displaystyle O}{\overset{\|}{C}}-)_2(C_6H_5-CH_2-)C$	(181, 443)	
$(CH_3-\overset{\displaystyle O}{\overset{\|}{C}}-)_2(C_6H_5-CH_2-)C$	(443)	
$(CH_3-\overset{\displaystyle O}{\overset{\|}{C}}-)_2(C_6H_5-\overset{\displaystyle O}{\overset{\|}{C}}-)C$	(181, 443)	
$(CH_3-\overset{\displaystyle O}{\overset{\|}{C}}-)_2[CH_3(CH_2)_3CH(CH_3CH_2)-CH_2]C$	(181, 443)	
$CH_2=CH$	b_2: 78–80°C; $b_{0.4}$: 54–5°C; n_D^{25}: 1.4749; d_{25}: 1.122 (181, 439, 443, 447)	

Compound	Data	Reference
$[CBr=CBr-Sn(C_4H_9)_2]_n$	(246, 246a)	
$[CBr=CBr-GeR_2-CBr=CBr-Sn(C_4H_9)_2]_n$	(246, 246a)	
$[CBr=CBr-SiR_2-CBr=CBr-Sn(C_4H_9)_2]_n$	(246, 246a)	
$(C_4H_9)_3Sn-CH=CH$	$b_{0.02}$: 155–7°C; n_D^{20}: 1.5176 (279)	
$CF_2=CF$	$b_{0.4}$: 60–3°C; n_D^{25}: 1.4283; d_{25}:1.404 (443)	ir (443)
$CF_3-CH=C$ $\quad\quad\quad\;\; CF_3$	$b_{0.001}$: 61–3°C (75, 76)	
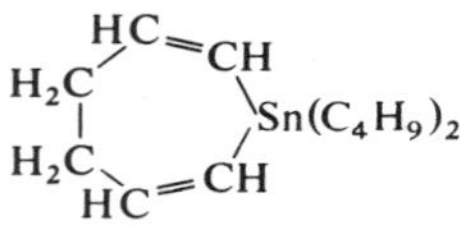 $\begin{array}{c} HC=CH \\ H_2C\quad\quad Sn(C_4H_9)_2 \\ H_2C\quad\quad CH \\ HC=CH \end{array}$	$b_{0.08}$: 90.2°C; n_D^{20}: 1.5174 (443)	ir (241)
$[CBr=CBr-C_6H_4-CBr=CBr-Sn(C_4H_9)_2]_n$	(246, 246a)	
$N\equiv C$	m: 220°C (241)	
$HC\equiv C$	(85, 443)	
$[-C\equiv C-Sn(C_4H_9)_2-]_n$	(246, 246a)	
$[-C\equiv C-GeR_2-C\equiv C-Sn(C_4H_9)_2]_n$	(246, 246a)	
$[-C\equiv C-SiR_2-C\equiv C-Sn(C_4H_9)_2]_n$	(246, 246a)	
$CH_2=CH-C\equiv C$	b_1: 108°C; n_D^{20}: 1.5188; d_{20}: 1.1352 (384)	
$CH_3CH_2CH_2-C\equiv C$	$b_{0.1}$: 99°C; n_D^{20}: 1.4884; d_{20}: 1.249 (180)	
$CH_3CH_2CH_2CH_2-C\equiv C$	$b_{0.15}$: 114°C; n_D^{20}: 1.4827; d_{20}: 1.063 (180)	
$C_6H_5-C\equiv C$	m: 14°C; n_D^{21}: 1.588 (443); n_D^{20}: 1.5878 (180)	ir; uv (151)
$[C\equiv C-C_6H_4-C\equiv C-Sn(C_4H_9)_2]_n$	(246, 246a)	

APPENDIX 33

DIALKYLDI-ISOBUTYLTINS

R in $R_2Sn[CH_2CH(CH_3)_2]_2$	Important physical constants	Other properties
CH_3	see Appendix 27	
CH_3CH_2	see Appendix 29	
$CH{=}CH{-}CH_2$	m: 245–6°C (288, 423)	
$N{\equiv}C{-}CH_2CH_2$	$b_{0.001}$: 146–50°C; n_D^{20}: 1.5012 (443)	
$CH_3O{-}\underset{\parallel O}{C}{-}CH_2CH_2$	$b_{0.001}$: 117–20°C; n_D^{20}: 1.4829 (443)	
$CH_3(CH_2)_3$	see Appendix 32	
$CH_3O{-}\underset{\parallel O}{C}{-}\underset{CH_3}{CH}{-}CH_2$	$b_{0.001}$: 102–3°C; n_D^{20}: 1.4812 (443)	
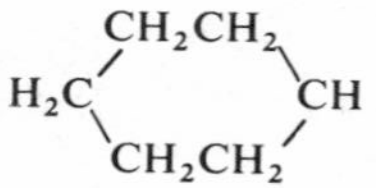 cyclohexyl (H_2C, CH_2CH_2, CH_2CH_2, CH)	m: 82°C (336)	
$H_2C{=}CH{-}(CH_2)_6$	$b_{0.001}$: 135°C; n_D^{20}: 1.4829 (287, 288)	
$C_6H_5{-}CH_2{-}CH_2$	$b_{0.001}$: 185–9°C; n_D^{20}: 1.5481 (443)	

APPENDIX 34
OTHER $R_2SnR'_2$

$R_2SnR'_2$	Important physical constants	Other properties
$(CH_3{-}CHCl)_2Sn(CH_2Cl)_2$ $[C_6H_5{-}C(CH_3)_2{-}CH_2]_2Sn(n{-}C_5H_{13})_2$	b_5: 141–2°C; n_D^{20}: 1.5478; d_{20}: 1.675 (181, 443) $b_{1.6}$: 135°C; n_D^{25}: 1.4742; d_{27}: 1.0118 (462)	
R in R_2Sn 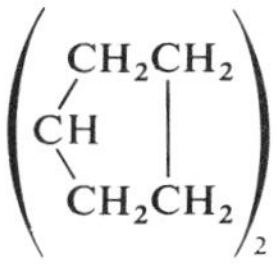 $\left(\begin{array}{c} CH_2CH_2 \\ CH{-} \\ CH_2CH_2 \end{array}\right)_2$		
CH_3 $CH_3(CH_2)_3$	see Appendix 27 see Appendix 32	
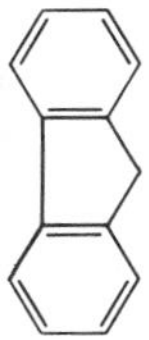 (fluorene structure)	m: 217–20°C (443)	
R in R_2Sn 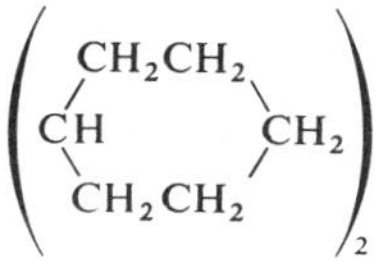 $\left(\begin{array}{c} CH_2CH_2{-}CH_2 \\ CH \\ CH_2CH_2 \end{array}\right)_2$		

Continued

APPENDIX 34—*continued*

$R_2SnR'_2$	Important physical constants	Other properties
CH_3	see Appendix 27	
$CH_3CH_2CH_2$	see Appendix 30	
$(CH_3)_2CH$	see Appendix 31	
$CH_3(CH_2)_3$	see Appendix 32	
$(CH_3)_2CH—CH_2$	see Appendix 33	
$CH_3(CH_2)_4$	b_7: 227–8°C; n_D^{18}: 1.5090; d_{18}: 1.1100 *(336)*	
$(CH_3)_2CHCH_2CH_2$	m: 45°C *(336)*	
$CH_3(CH_2)_n$ $n = 5$	*(338)*	
$n = 6$	*(338)*	
$n = 7$	*(338)*	
$n = 8$	*(338)*	
$n = 9$	*(338)*	
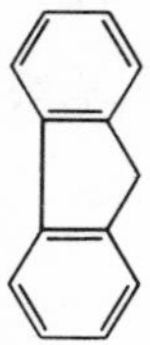	m: 235–40°C *(443)*	

$R_2SnR'_2$		
$[(CO)_4Ti—C_5H_5]_2Sn(CH_2—C_6H_5)_2$	*(443)*	

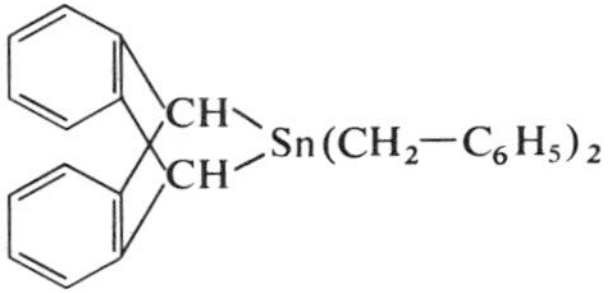

$CH\!-\!Sn(CH_2\!-\!C_6H_5)_2$ (with fused ring structure) (107)

$CH\!-\!Sn(C_8H_{17})_2$ (with fused ring structure) (107)

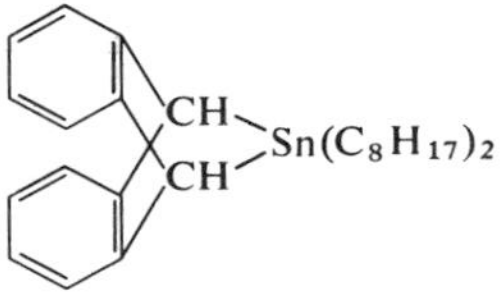

$[(CO)_3Cr\!-\!C_5H_5]_2Sn[C_5H_3(C_3H_7)(CH_3)]_2$ (153, 443)

$[(CO)_4Hf\!-\!C_5H_3(CH_3)_2]_2Sn(C_{16}H_{33})_2$ (443)

R in $R_2Sn(CH\!=\!CH_2)_2$

CH_3 see Appendix 28

CH_3CH_2 see Appendix 29

$CH_3(CH_2)_3$ see Appendix 32

$CH_2\!=\!CH\!-\!CH\!-\!CH_2$ (181)
       $|$
       CH_3

$R_2SnR'_2$

$CH\!-\!Sn(CH\!=\!CH_2)_2$ (with fused ring structure) (107)

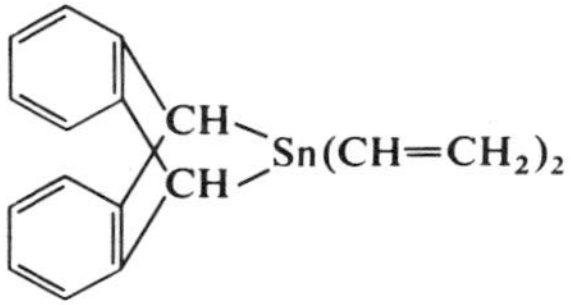

Continued

APPENDIX 34—continued

$R_2SnR'_2$	Important physical constants	Other properties
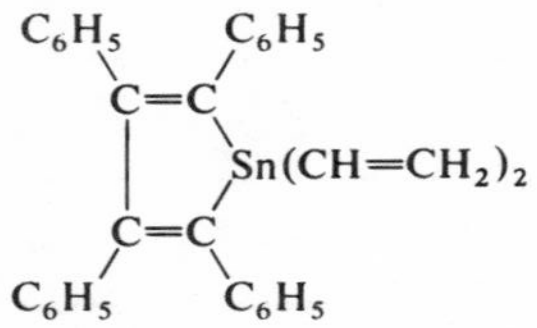	m: 158–9°C (*219, 443*)	MB
$(CH_2{=}CH{-}CH_2)_2Sn(C{\equiv}C{-}C_6H_4)_2$	n_D^{23}: 1.6073 (*443*)	

APPENDIX 35

DIALKYL-, DIALKENYL-, AND DIALKYNYLDIARYLTINS

R	R₂SnAr₂ Ar	Important physical constants	Other properties
CH₃	C_6H_5	m: 131–133°C (71)	NMR (212, 400)
CH₃	$Ar_2 = 2,2'\text{-}C_6F_4\text{—}C_6F_4$	b₂: 94–96°C (443), b₃: 126°C (310); n_D^{20}: 1.4912 (310)	ir (71)
CH₃	C_6F_5	$b_{0.2}$: 120–121°C (443); n_D^{20}: 1.5779 (443)	¹⁹F NMR (112); NMR (443)
CH₃	$p\text{-}CH_3C_6H_4$		NMR (212)
CH₃	$p\text{-}HOOC\text{—}C_6H_4$	m: 260–261°C (443)	
CH₃	$Ar_2 = CH_3N$ 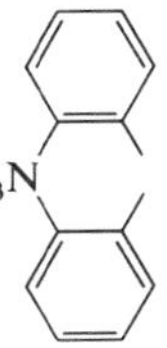	m: 133–134°C (213)	ir (213); uv (213); NMR (213)
CH₃	$Ar_2 = CH_3N$ 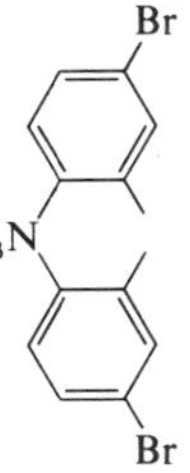	m: 122–123°C (213)	ir (213); uv (213); NMR (213)

Continued

APPENDIX 35—*continued*

R	R$_2$SnAr$_2$ Ar	Important physical constants	Other properties
CH$_3$	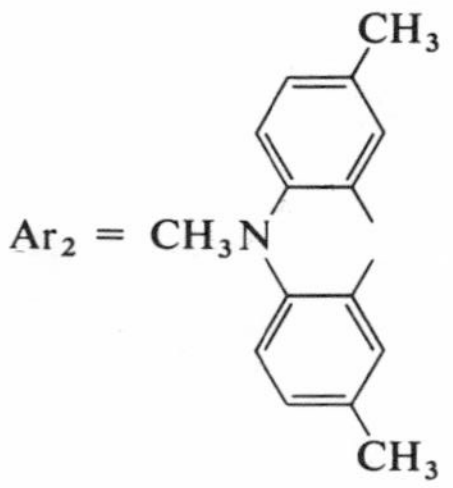 Ar$_2$ = CH$_3$N (di-2,4-dimethylphenyl structure with CH$_3$ groups)	m: 119–120°C (213)	ir (213); uv (213); NMR (213)
CH$_3$	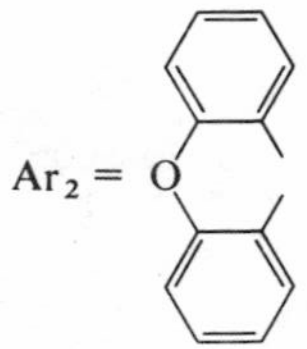 Ar$_2$ = (bis(2-methylphenyl) ether structure)	m: 259–260°C (214)	
CH$_3$	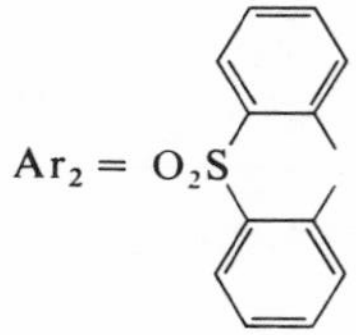 Ar$_2$ = O$_2$S (bis(2-methylphenyl) sulfone structure)	m: 164–165°C (214)	

CH_3	$Ar_2 =$ 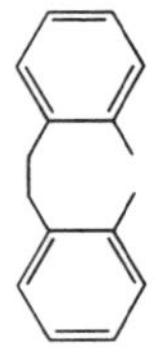	$b_{0.2}$: 130–135°C (207a); n_D^{25}: 1.6130 (207a)	
CH_3	p-OOC—C_6H_4. $\overset{+}{(C_{14}H_{29})_2NH_2}$	oil; n_D^{20}: 1.5010 (443)	
CH_3	2,4,6-$(CH_3)_3C_6H_2$	$b_{0.1}$: 170–172°C (212); m: 101°C (212)	NMR (212)
CH_3	3,4,5-$(CH_3)_3C_6H_2$	m: 56°C (212)	NMR (212)
CH_3	p-C_6H_5—C_6H_4	m: 173–174°C (443)	
$(CH_3)_3SiCH_2$	C_6H_5	$b_{0.35}$: 137°C, $b_{1.5}$: 138–140°C (443); n_D^{25}: 1.5425, 1.5499 (443); d_{25}: 1.1404, 1.149 (443)	
C_2H_5	C_6H_5	b_4: 154–156°C (443)	NMR (400); ^{1}H and ^{19}F NMR (443)
C_2H_5	C_6H_5		
C_2H_5	$Ar_2 =$ 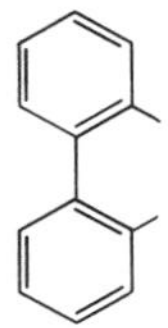	m: 73°C (125)	
C_2H_5	CH_2=CH—CH_2—C_6H_4	b_5: 183–186°C (443); n_D^{20}: 1.5844 (443); d_{20}: 1.3819 (443); surf. tens. (443)	

Continued

APPENDIX 35—continued

R₂SnAr₂		Important physical constants	Other properties
R	Ar		
$R_2 =$ C_6H_5—Si with CH_2—CH_2 / CH_2—CH_2 (spirocyclic), C_6H_5	C_6H_5	m: 134–135°C (443)	
$R_2 =$ —$(CH_2)_5$—	C_6H_5	$b_{0.1}$: 138–140°C ($23, 24$); n_D^{26}: 1.6007 ($23, 24$)	ir ($23, 24$)
$CH_3(CH_2)_2$	C_6H_5	b_3: 160–161°C (443)	
$CH_3(CH_2)_2$	$CH_2=CH$—CH_2—C_6H_4	$b_{4.5}$: 191–193°C (443); n_D^{20}: 1.5550 (443); d_{20}: 1.3034 (443)	
$CH_2=CH$—CH_2	C_6H_5	$b_{5.5}$: 173–174°C (443), $b_{0.05}$: 120–124°C (443); n_D^{20}: 1.608 (443)	
NC—CH_2—CH_2	C_6H_5	(331)	
CH_2OCH—CH_2O—$(CH_2)_3$	C_6H_5	(443)	
CH_3OOC—CH_2—CH_2	C_6H_5	$b_{0.003}$: 191–194°C (443)	
CH_3OOC—$CH(CH_3)$—CH_2	C_6H_5	$b_{0.01}$: 180–184°C (443); n_D^{20}: 1.5621 (443)	
$CH_3(CH_2)_3$	C_6H_5	$b_{0.2}$: 137°C (443), b_2: 164°C (443); n_D^{23}: 1.5605 (443)	
$CH_3(CH_2)_3$	C_6F_5	b_2: 139–141°C (310); n_D^{20}: 1.4912 (310)	ir (310)

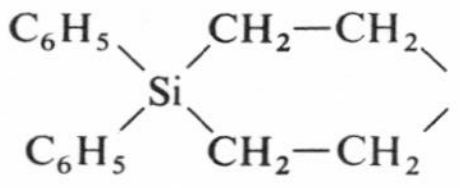

$CH_3(CH_2)_3$	$Ar_2 =$ 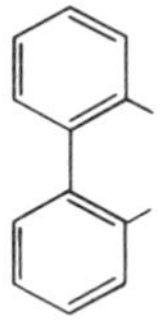	m: 56°C (125)	
$CH_3(CH_2)_3$	2-C_6H_5-carboranyl	(49)	
cycloC_5H_9	C_6H_5	m: 49–50°C (443)	
cyclopentadienyl	C_6H_5	m: 105–106°C (443)	NMR (443)
$CH=CH—(CH_2)_4$	C_6H_5	$b_{1.5}$: 173–175°C (443); n_D^{20}: 1.5598 (443)	
cycloC_6H_{11}	C_6H_5	m: 119–120°C (443)	
cycloC_6H_{11}	$Ar_2 = \ 90000$	m: 104°C (125)	
$CH_3(CH_2)_6$	C_6H_5	b_6: 251–252°C (443) n_D^{20}: 1.5354 (443); d_{20}: 1.078 (443)	
$C_6H_5CH_2$	C_6H_5	oil; d_{15}: 1.271 (443)	
$C_6H_5CH_2$	o-C_6H_5—C_6H_4	m: 142–143°C (364)	
$CH_3(CH_2)_7$	C_6H_5	b_4: 252°C (443); n_D^{20}: 1.5258 (443); d_{20}: 1.0670 (443)	
$CH_3(CH_2)_8$	C_6H_5	b_2: 241–242°C (443); n_D^{60}: 1.5160 (443); d_{60}: 1.032 (443)	
$(C_6H_5)_3Pb$——CH_2—$CH_2C_6H_5$ 		m: $\simeq 70$°C (443)	
1-Indenyl	C_6H_5	m: 116–117°C (443)	
$CH_3(CH_2)_9$	C_6H_5	$b_{4.5}$: 270–275°C (443); n_D^{20}: 1.5108 (443); d_{20}: 1.0330 (443)	
$(C_6H_5)_2CH$	C_2H_5	m: 175–177°C (443)	ir (443)
9-Fluorenyl	C_6H_5	m: 179°C (443)	ir (443)
9-Fluorenyl	1-Naphthyl	m: 288–292°C (443)	

Continued

APPENDIX 35—*continued*

R	Ar	Important physical constants	Other properties
$CH_2=CH$	C_6H_5	$b_{0.4}$: 121.5°C, b_5: 153–154°C (443); n_D^{25}: 1.5949 (443); d_{25}: 1.328, 1.334 (443)	ir (443)
$CH_2=CH$	C_6F_5	$b_{0.3}$: 107–109°C, b_1: 124–127°C (310); n_D^{20}: 1.5014 (310)	ir (443)
$CH_2=CH$ $CF_2=CF_2$	2-Thienyl C_6H_5	$b_{0.02}$: 75–80°C (443)	^{19}F NMR (443)
$R_2 = $ 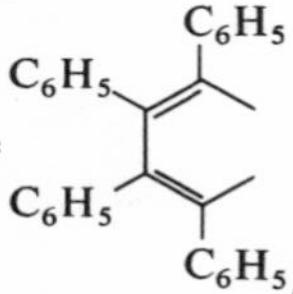	C_6H_5	m: 173°C (219), 176°C (48)	
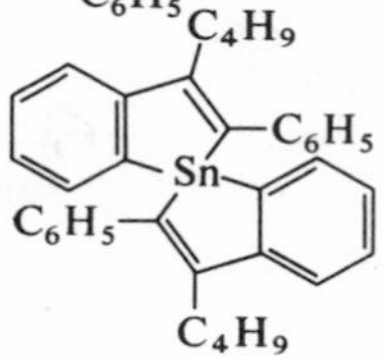		m: 141.8–142.5°C (326)	
$C_6H_5-C\equiv C$	C_6H_5	m: 82°C (443)	

APPENDIX 36

DIARYLDIPHENYLTINS

Ar in $Ar_2Sn(C_6H_5)_2$	Important physical constants	Other properties
$p\text{-}(CH_3)_2N\text{---}C_6H_4$	(443)	
$\overset{+}{p}\text{-}(CH_3)_3N\text{---}C_6H_4$ (iodide)	m: 164–168°C (dec) (443)	
$CH_3SO_4^- \cdot \overset{+}{p}\text{-}(CH_3)_3N\text{---}C_6H_4$	m: 125°C (dec) (443)	
$o\text{-}HO\text{---}C_6H_4$	m: 136–138°C (443)	
$m\text{-}HO\text{---}C_6H_4$	m: 189–190°C (443)	
$p\text{-}HO\text{---}C_6H_4$	m: 136–138°C (443)	
$p\text{-}CH_3O\text{---}C_6H_4$	m: 125–126°C (443)	
$p\text{-}C_6H_5O\text{---}C_6H_4$	(443)	
C_6F_5	b_5: 180–182°C (443); m: 84–86°C (443)	ir (443); ^{19}F NMR (112)
$p\text{-}(CH_3)_3Si\text{---}C_6H_4$	m: 95–96°C (443)	
C_6Cl_5	m: 237–240°C (145)	uv (145)
$p\text{-}CH_3C_6H_5$	m: 133–135°C (443)	
$p\text{-}CH_2\!=\!CH\text{---}C_6H_4$	m: 108–109°C (443)	ir (443)
$p\text{-}CH_2\!=\!CH\text{---}CH_2\text{---}C_6H_4$	m: 210°C (443)	
$p\text{-}(CH_3)_3C\text{---}C_6H_4$	m: 156°C (443)	
$p\text{-}cycloC_6H_{11}\text{---}C_6H_4$	m: 166°C (443)	
$Ar_2 = $ 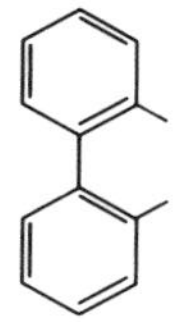	m: 141.5°C (125)	ir (125)

Continued

APPENDIX 36—continued

Ar in Ar$_2$Sn(C$_6$H$_5$)$_2$	Important physical constants	Other properties
Ar$_2$ = 2,2'-C$_6$F$_4$—C$_6$F$_4$		ir (71)
 Ar$_2$ 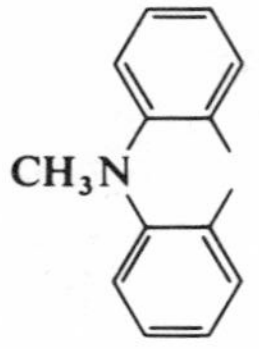 = CH$_3$N	m: 148.5–150°C (213)	ir (213); uv (213); NMR (213)
 Ar$_2$ 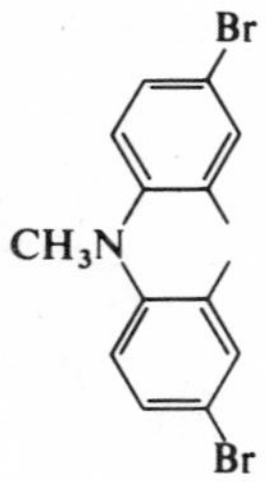 = CH$_3$N	m: 191–193°C (213)	ir (213); uv (213); NMR (213)
 Ar$_2$ 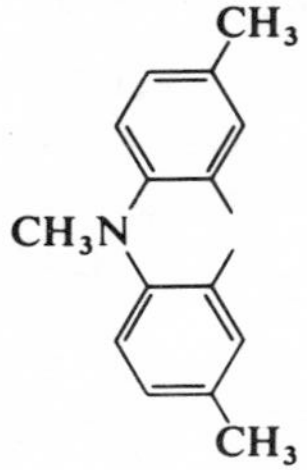 = CH$_3$N	m: 146–148°C (213)	ir (213); uv (213); NMR (213)

$Ar_2 = C_2H_5N$ m: 117–119°C (145a)

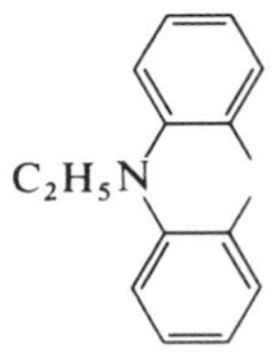

$Ar_2 = C_2H_5N$ m: 177–178°C (442)

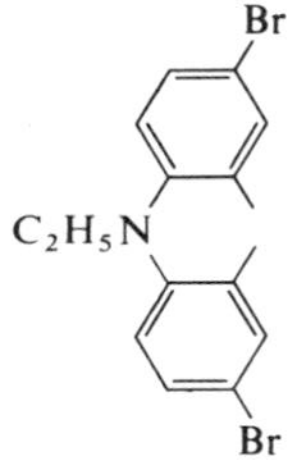

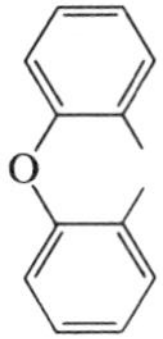

$Ar_2 = O$ m: 251–252°C (214)

$Ar_2 = O_2S$ m: 164–165°C (214)

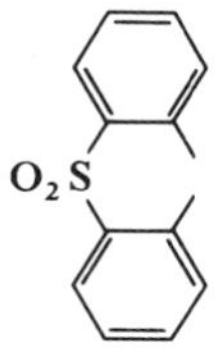

Continued

APPENDIX 36—*continued*

Ar in Ar$_2$Sn(C$_6$H$_5$)$_2$	Important physical constants	Other properties
Ar$_2$ 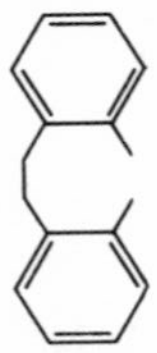 = ![structure]	m: 146–147°C (*207a*)	
1-Naphthyl	m: 209–210°C (*443*)	
o-C$_6$H$_5$—C$_6$H$_4$	m: 149.5°C (*125*)	
p-(C$_6$H$_5$)$_2$C(OH)—C$_6$H$_4$	m: 265–266°C (*443*)	
2-Thienyl	m: 202–210°C (*443*)	

APPENDIX 37

OTHER Ar$_2$SnAr$_2'$

Ar	Ar$_2$SnAr$_2'$ Ar'	Important physical constants	Other properties
p-CH$_3$O—C$_6$H$_5$	2-Thienyl	m: 89–93°C (*443*)	
p-CH$_3$O—C$_6$H$_5$	1-Naphthyl	(*443*)	
p-CH$_3$C$_6$H$_4$	C$_6$F$_5$	(*443*)	
p-CH$_3$C$_6$H$_4$	Ar$_2'$ 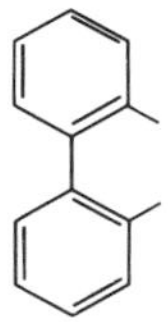 =	m: 108°C (*125*)	
2-Thienyl	1-Naphthyl	m: 145–146°C (*443*)	
o-C$_6$H$_5$—C$_6$H$_4$	Ar$_2'$ 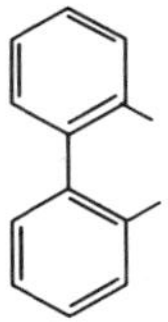 =	m: 196°C (*125*)	uv (*125*)

APPENDIX 38

TETRAORGANOTINS WITH THREE TYPES OF ALKYL GROUPS $R_2SnR'R''$

In $R_2Sn\begin{smallmatrix}R'\\R''\end{smallmatrix}$

R	R'	R''	Important physical constants	Other properties
CH_3	CH_3CH_2	$CH_3CH_2CH_2$	b: 153°C (181, 313) (409a)	NMR, MS (409a)
	$CH_3CH_2CH_2$	$(CH_3)_2CH$		MS (349a)
	$(CH_3)_2CH$	$CH_3(CH_2)_3$	GLC (349a)	
	$(CH_3)_2CH$	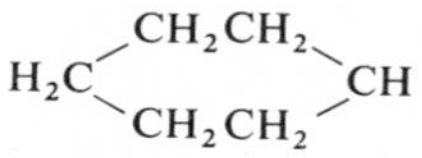 $H_2C{\begin{smallmatrix}CH_2CH_2\\ \\CH_2CH_2\end{smallmatrix}}CH$	$b_{1.7}$: 76.5°C (45)	MS, NMR (45)
	CH_2CH_3	$CH_2=CH$	b_{26}: 56–9°C; n_D^{25}: 1.5697 d_{25}: 1.222 (443)	
	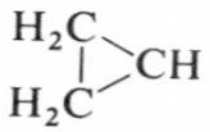 $H_2C{\begin{smallmatrix}\\ \\ \end{smallmatrix}}CH$ H_2C	$CH_2=CH$	n_D^{25}: 1.4844 (443)	ir (443)
CH_3CH_2	CH_3 CH_3	$CH_2=CH$	b_{26}: 56–9°C (181) $b_{1.5}$: 83–5°C; n_D^{20}: 1.4948;	
		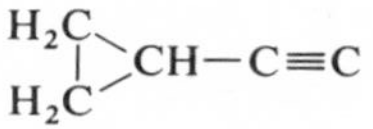 $H_2C{\begin{smallmatrix}\\ \\ \end{smallmatrix}}CH-C\equiv C$ H_2C	d_{20}: 1.1737 (85)	

CH₃CH₂CH₂	CH₃	$\overset{CH_2CH_2}{\underset{CH_2CH_2}{CH_2}}{\Big\rangle}CH-$ CH₃(CH₂)₃—	GLC (349a)	MS (349a)
CH₃CH₂CH₂	CH₃	CH₃CH₂	b; 183–4°C (181)	
$\overset{H_2C}{\underset{H_2C}{|}}{\Big\rangle}CH$	CH₃	CH₂=CH	(443)	ir (443)
CH₃(CH₂)₃	CH₃	(CH₃)₂CH	GLC (349a)	MS (349a)
	CH₃	cyclo-C₆H₁₁	GLC (349a)	MS (349a)
	CH₃CH₂	(CH₃)₂CH	GLC (349a)	MS (349a)
	CH₃CH₂	C₆H₅—CH₂	b₉: 175–80°C (181) (349a)	MS (349a)
	(CH₃)₂CH	$(CH_3)CH_2-\underset{CH_3}{\overset{|}{CH}}$		
	(CH₃)₂CH	$\overset{CH_2CH_2}{\underset{CH_2CH_2}{H_2C}}{\Big\rangle}CH$	b₀.₁: 98–100°C (349a); n_D^{20}: 1.495	MS (349a)
(CH₃)₂CH—CH₂CH₂	CH₃CH₂	CH₃CH₂CH₂	b₁₇: 141–2°C (181, 443)	
C₆H₅—CH₂	CH₃CH₂	CH₃CH₂CH₂	b₁₅: 220–5°C (181)	
	CH₃CH₂	CH₃CH₂CH₂CH₂	b₉: 207–9°C (181)	
CH₂=CH	CH₃	$\overset{H_2C}{\underset{H_2C}{|}}{\Big\rangle}CH$	(443)	ir (443)

APPENDIX 39

TETRAORGANOTINS WITH THREE TYPES OF LIGANDS AND AT LEAST ONE ARYL GROUP

R	$R_2R'SnC_6H_5$ R'	Important physical constants	Other properties
CH_3	C_2H_5		NMR (400)
CH_3	$CH_3(CH_2)_3$		NMR (400)
C_2H_5	CH_3		NMR (400)
$CH_3(CH_2)_3$	CH_3		NMR (400)
	$RR'Sn(C_6H_5)_2$		
CH_3	C_2H_5		NMR (400)
CH_3	$(CH_3)_2CH$	$b_{0.4}$: 118°C (225a)	NMR (225a)
CH_3	$CH_3-(CH_2)_3$	(443)	NMR (400)
$CH_3(CH_2)_3$	$CH_2=CH$		
$\begin{array}{c} COOC_2H_5 \\ | \\ -CH- \\ | \\ CO-CH_2-COOC_2H_5 \end{array}$	C_2H_5	(443)	
$\begin{array}{c} H_3C \\ \diagdown \\ Sn(1\text{-Naphthyl})_2 \\ \diagup \\ H_5C_6 \end{array}$		m: 127°C (225a)	NMR (225a)

APPENDIX 40

COMPOUNDS WITH FOUR DIFFERENT ALKYL GROUPS BOUND TO TIN

$$\begin{array}{c} R' \\ | \\ R{-}Sn{-}R'' \\ | \\ R''' \end{array}$$

R	R'	R''	R'''	Important physical constants	Other properties
CH_3	CH_3CH_2	$CH_3CH_2CH_2$	$(CH_3)_2CH$	$b_{0.2}$: 26.5°C; $b_{0.08}$: 14.5°C	NMR, MS (409a)
CH_3	CH_3CH_2	$(CH_3)_2CH$	$H_2C{<}\!\!\begin{smallmatrix}CH_2CH_2\\CH_2CH_2\end{smallmatrix}\!\!{>}CH$	$b_{0.7}$: 73.5°C (45)	NMR, MS (45)
CH_3	$CH_3CH_2CH_2$	$(CH_3)_2CH$	$CH_3(CH_2)_3$	$b_{0.15}$: 41.5–2.5°C; $b_{0.07}$: 41.5–2.5°C (409a)	NMR, MS (409a)
CH_3	$CH_3CH_2CH_2$	$(CH_3)_2CH$	$(CH_3)_2CHCHCH_3$	$b_{0.5}$: 54°C; $b_{0.12}$: 33.5–4°C	NMR, MS (409a)
CH_3	$CH_3CH_2CH_2$	$(CH_3)_2CH$	$CH_3CH_2CH{-}CH_3$	$b_{0.12}$: 44.5°C; $b_{0.12}$: 39.5°C	NMR, MS (409a)
CH_3	$CH_3CH_2CH_2$	$(CH_3)_2CH$	$(CH_3)_3C$	$b_{0.37}$: 37–7.5°C; (409a)	NMR, MS (409a)
CH_3	$(CH_3)_2CH$	$CH_3(CH_2)_3$	$H_2C{<}\!\!\begin{smallmatrix}CH_2CH_2\\CH_2CH_2\end{smallmatrix}\!\!{>}CH$	n_D^{20}: 1.494; GLC (349a)	NMR, MS (349a)
CH_3CH_2	$(CH_3)_2CH$	$CH_3(CH_2)_3$	$H_2C{<}\!\!\begin{smallmatrix}CH_2CH_2\\CH_2CH_2\end{smallmatrix}\!\!{>}CH$	n_D^{20}: 1.496; GLC (349a)	MS (349a)

APPENDIX 41

COMPOUNDS WITH FOUR DIFFERENT SUBSTITUENTS ATTACHED TO TIN AND AT LEAST ONE ARYL GROUP

R	$RR'R''Sn-C_6H_5$		Important physical constants	Other properties
	R'	R''		
CH_3	C_2H_5	$(CH_3)_2CH$	$b_{0.05}$: 45–46°C (144a)	
CH_3	$CH_3(CH_2)_2$	$(CH_3)_2CH$	$b_{0.03}$: 49–50°C (144a)	
CH_3	$(CH_3)_2CH$	$CH_3(CH_2)_3$	$b_{0.03}$: 56–60°C (144a)	
CH_3	$(CH_3)_2CH$	$(CH_3)_2CH-CH_2$	$b_{0.03}$: 51.5–54°C (144a)	
CH_3	$(CH_3)_2CH$	$C_2H_5-CH(CH_3)$	$b_{0.03}$: 55–59°C (144a)	
CH_3	$(CH_3)_2CH$	$p\text{-}CH_3O-C_6H_4$	$b_{0.025}$: 123.5°C (144a); n_D^{20}: 1.581 (144a)	

REFERENCES

1. M. H. Abraham and J. A. Hill, *J. Organometal. Chem.*, **7**, 11 (1967).

2. M. H. Abraham and T. R. Spalding, *Chem. Commun.*, 46 (1968).

2a. C. Alcais and J. Nasielski, *J. Chim. phys.*, **66**, 95 (1969).

3. A. Y. Aleksandrov, V. I. Bregadze, V. I. Goldanskii, P. I. Zakharkin, O. Y. Okhlobystin and V. V. Khrapov, *Applications of the Mössbauer Effect in Chemistry and Solid State Physics*, International Atomic Energy Agency, Vienna 1966 (Technical Reports Series No. 50), p. 168.

4. A. Y. Aleksandrov, O. Y. Okhlobystin, L. S. Polak, and V. S. Shpinel, *Dokl. Phys. Chem.*, **157**, 934 (1964); *English Transl.*, p. 768.

5. A. Y. Aleksandrov, V. I. Bregadze, V. I. Goldanskii, O. Y. Okhlobystin, and V. V. Khrapov, *Dokl. Akad. Nauk. SSSR*, **165**, 593 (1965); *Dokl. Phys. Chem., Proc. Acad. Sci. USSR*, **165**, 804 (1965).

6. Y. A. Aleksandrov and N. G. Sheyanov, *Zhur. Obshchei Khim.*, **36**, 953, (1966); through *CA*, **65**, 8955*E* (1966).

7. Y. A. Aleksandrov, B. A. Radbil, and V. A. Shushunov, *Zhur. Obshchei Khim.*, **37**, 208 (1967); through *CA*, **66**, 104491*Q* (1967).

8. E. Amberger, H. P. Fritz, C. G. Kreiter, and M. R. Kula, *Chem. Ber.*, **96**, 3270 (1963)

9. H. H. Anderson, *Inorg. Chem.*, **1**, 647 (1962).

10. D. G. Anderson, M. A. M. Bradney, B. A. Loveland, and D. E. Webster, *Chem. Ind.*, 505 (1964).

11. D. G. Anderson, M. A. M. Bradney, and D. E. Webster, unpublished results, quoted in Ref. (12).

12. D. G. Anderson, J. R. Chipperfield, and D. E. Webster, *J. Organometal. Chem.*, **12**, 323 (1968).

13. C. A. Aufdermarsh, *J. Org. Chem.*, **29**, 1994 (1964).

14. C. A. Aufdermarsh and R. Pariser, *J. Polymer Sci.* A2, 4727 (1964); through *CA*, **62**, 2896*B* (1965).

14a. J. Autin, S. Boue, J. Nasielski, and M. Gielen, unpublished results.

15. P. Baekelmans, M. Gielen, and J. Nasielski, *Ind. chim. belge*, **29**, 1265 (1964).

16. P. Baekelmans, M. Gielen, and J. Nasielski, *Tetrahedron Letters*, 1149 (1967).

17. P. Baekelmans, M. Gielen, P. Malfroid, and J. Nasielski, *Bull. soc. chim. Belges*, **77**, 85 (1968).

17a. P. Baekelmans, M. Gielen, and J. Nasielski, unpublished results.

18. G. Bähr and R. Gelius, *Chem. Ber.*, **91**, 812 (1958).

19. G. Bähr and R. Gelius, *Chem. Ber.*, **91**, 818 (1958).

20. G. Bähr and R. Gelius, *Chem. Ber.*, **91**, 825 (1958).

21. G. Bähr and R. Gelius, *Chem. Ber.*, **91**, 829 (1958).

22. L. I. Bai, A. Y. Yakubovich, and L. I. Muller, *Zh. Obshchei Khim.*, **34**, 3696 (1964).

23. F. J. Bajer and H. W. Post, *J. Org. Chem.*, **27**, 1422 (1962).

24. F. J. Bajer and H. W. Post, *J. Organometal. Chem.*, **11**, 187 (1968).

25. C. K. Banks, U.S. Pat. 3,297,732 (1967); through *CA*, **66**, 115807 *Y* (1967).

26. V. I. Baranovskii, B. E. Dzevitskii, L. M. Krizhanskii, and B. I. Rogozev, *Zhur. Strukt. Khim.*, **7**, 808 (1966).

27. K. C. Bass, *Lab. Practice*, **14**, 47 (1965).

28. K. C. Bass, *Lab. Practice*, **14**, 145 (1965).

28a. R. A. Benkeser, R. A. Hickner, D. I. Hoke, and D. H. Thomas, *J. Am. Chem. Soc.*, **80**, 5294 (1958).

29. A. D. Beveridge, H. C. Clark, and J. T. Kwon, *Can. J. Chem.*, **44**, 179 (1966).

30. A. D. Beveridge and H. C. Clark, *Inorg. Nucl. Chem. Letters*, 3, 95 (1967).
31. A. D. Beveridge and H. C. Clark, *J. Organometal. Chem.*, 11, 601 (1968).
32. R. E. J. Bichler, M. R. Booth, and H. C. Clark, *Inorg. Nucl. Chem. Letters*, 3, 71 (1967); through *CA*, 66, 95163*E* (1967).
33. Billiton, Neth. Appl.; 6,507,716 (1965); through *CA*, 64, P17640*A* (1966).
34. Billiton, M & T Chemische Industrie, Neth. Appl., 6,700,012 (1967); through *CA*, 68, 114745*F* (1968).
35. D. J. Blears, S. S. Danyluk, and S. Cawley, *J. Organometal. Chem.*, 6, 284 (1966).
36. F. Bonati and G. Wilkinson, *J. Chem. Soc.*, 179 (1964).
36a. R. W. Bott, C. Eaborn, and J. A. Waters, *J. Chem. Soc.*, 681 (1963).
37. R. W. Bott, C. Earborn, and T. W. Swaddle, *J. Chem. Soc.*, 2342 (1963).
38. R. W. Bott, C. Eaborn, and D. R. M. Walton, *J. Organometal. Chem.*, 2, 154 (1964).
39. R. W. Bott, C. Eaborn, and T. W. Swaddle, *J. Organometal. Chem.*, 5, 233 (1966).
40. S. Boué, M. Gielen, and J. Nasielski, *J. Organometal. Chem.*, 9, 443 (1967).
41. S. Boué, M. Gielen, and J. Nasielski, *J. Organometal. Chem.*, 9, 461 (1967).
42. S. Boué, M. Gielen, and J. Nasielski, *J. Organometal. Chem.*, 9, 481 (1967).
43. S. Boué, M. Gielen, and J. Nasielski, *Bull. Soc. chim. Belges*, 76, 559 (1967).
44. S. Boué, M. Gielen, and J. Nasielski, *Bull. soc. chim. Belges*, 77, 43 (1968).
45. S. Boué, M. Gielen, and J. Nasielski, *Tetrahedron Letters*, 1047 (1968).
45a. S. Boué, M. Gielen, J. Nasielski, J. Autin, and M. Limbourg, *J. Organometal. Chem.*, 15, 267 (1968).
46. I. N. Brago, L. V. Kaabak, and A. P. Tomilov, *Zhur. Vses. Khim. Obshchei*, 12, 472 (1967); through *CA*, 67, 104513*U* (1967).
47. J. Braun, *Compt. Rend.*, 260C, 218 (1965); through *CA*, 62, 14711*A* (1965).
47a. W. Braun, H. Kaltwasser, D. Kloetzer, G. Rulewicz, and V. Thust, East German Pat. 55,657 (1967); through *CA*, 68, 59725*X* (1968).
48. E. H. Braye, W. Hubel, and I. Caplier, *J. Am. Chem. Soc.*, 83, 4406 (1961).
49. V. I. Bregadze and O. Y. Okhlobystin, *Izv. Akad. Nauk. SSSR, Ser. Khim.*, 2084 (1967).
50. T. G. Brilkina and V. A. Shushunov, *Russ. Chem. Rev.*, 35, 613 (1966).
51. T. L. Brown and K. Stark, *J. Phys. Chem.*, 69, 2679 (1965).
52. O. Buchman, M. Grosjean, and J. Nasielski, *Bull. soc. chim. Belges*, 71, 467 (1962).
53. O. Buchman, M. Grosjean, and J. Nasielski, *Helv. Chim. Acta*, 47, 1679 (1964).
54. O. Buchman, M. Grosjean, J. Nasielski, and B. Wilmet-Devos, *Helv. Chim. Acta*, 47, 1688 (1964).
55. O. Buchman, M. Grosjean, and J. Nasielski, *Helv. Chim. Acta*, 47, 1695 (1964).
56. O. Buchman, M. Grosjean, and J. Nasielski, *Helv. Chim. Acta*, 47, 2037 (1964).
57. P. Cadiot and M. Le Quan, *Bull. soc. chim. France*, 35 (1965).
58. R. D. Chambers and T. Chivers, *Organometal. Chem. Rev.*, 1, 279 (1966).
59. D. B. Chambers, F. Glockling, J. R. C. Light, and M. Weston, *Chem. Commun.*, 281 (1966).
60. D. B. Chambers, F. Glockling, and M. Weston, *J. Chem. Soc. A*, 1759 (1967).
61. S. S. Chan and C. J. Willis, *Can. J. Chem.*, 46, 1237 (1968).
62. G. Chandra, T. A. George and M. F. Lappert, *Chem. Commun.*, 116 (1967).
63. J. Chatt and A. A. Williams; *J. Chem. Soc.*, 4403 (1954).
64. J. Chatt and A. A. Williams, *J. Chem. Soc.*, 688 (1956).
65. T. Chivers and B. David, *J. Organometal. Chem.*, 10, P35 (1967).
66. T. Chivers and B. David, *J. Organometal. Chem.*, 13, 177 (1968).
67. N. A. Chumaevskii and A. E. Borisov, *Dokl. Akad. Nauk. SSSR*, 161, 366 (1965); through *CA*, 63, 462g (1965).
68. H. C. Clark, J. D. Cotton, and J. H. Tsai, *Can. J. Chem.*, 44, 903 (1966).

69. H. C. Clark and J. H. Tsai, *Inorg. Chem.*, **5**, 1407 (1966).

70. J. Cochran, *Dissertation Abstr.*, **B28**, 2334 (1967).

71. S. C. Cohen and A. G. Massey, *J. Organometal. Chem.*, **10**, 471 (1967).

72. S. C. Cohen, M. L. M. Reddy, and A. G. Massey, *Chem. Commun.*, 451 (1967).

73. D. J. Colemann and H. A. Skinner, *Trans. Faraday Soc.*, **62**, 1721 (1966).

74. M. Cordey-Hayes, R. D. Peacock, and M. Vucelik, *J. Inorg. Nucl. Chem.*, **29**, 1177 (1967).

75. W. R. Cullen, D. S. Dawson, and G. E. Styan, *J. Organometal. Chem.*, **3**, 406 (1965).

76. W. R. Cullen and G. E. Styan, *J. Organometal. Chem.*, **6**, 117 (1966).

77. W. R. Cullen and M. C. Waldman, *Inorg. Nucl. Chem. Letters*, **4**, 205 (1968).

78. R. A. Cummins, *Australian J. Chem.*, **18**, 985 (1965).

79. C. W. N. Cumper, A. Melnikov, and A. I. Vogel, *J. Chem. Soc. A*, 242 (1966).

80. M. D. Curtis, *J. Am. Chem. Soc.*, **89**, 4241 (1967).

81. M. D. Curtis and A. L. Allred, *J. Am. Chem. Soc.*, **87**, 2554 (1965).

82. M. D. Curtis, R. L. Lee, and A. L. Allred; *J. Am. Chem. Soc.*, **89**, 5150 (1967).

83. M. Danzik, *Dissertation Abstr.*, **B24**, 4991 (1964).

84. M. Dao-Huy-Giao, *Compt. Rend.*, **260C**, 6937 (1965).

85. W. Davidsohn and M. C. Henry, *Chem. Rev.*, **67**, 95 (1967).

86. A. G. Davies, *Trans. N.Y. Acad. Sci.*, **26**, 923 (1964).

87. A. G. Davies and W. R. Symes, *J. Organometal. Chem.*, **5**, 394 (1966).

88. A. G. Davies and T. N. Mitchell, *J. Organometal. Chem.*, **6**, 568 (1966).

89. C. Deblandre, M. Gielen, and J. Nasielski, *Bull. soc. chim. Belges*, **73**, 214 (1964).

89a. M. De Clercq, M. Gielen, and J. Nasielski, unpublished results.

90. G. J. Del Franco, P. Resmick, and C. R. Dillard, *J. Organometal. Chem.*, **4**, 57 (1965).

91. A. Delhaye, J. Nasielski, and M. Planchon, *Bull. soc. chim. Belges*, **69**, 134 (1960).

92. H. J. De Liefde Meijer, J. W. G. van den Hurk and G. J. M. van der Kerk, *Rec. trav. Chim. Pays-Bas*, **85**, 1025 (1966).

93. J. J. De Ridder and G. Dijkstra, *Rec. trav. Chim. Pays-Bas*, **86**, 737 (1967).

94. Y. G. Dorfman, O. L. Lepedina, E. S. Finkelshtein, S. G. Durgaryan, and V. F. Mironov, *Zhur. Strukt. Khim.*, **7**, 200 (1966); *J. Struct. Chem. USSR*, **7**, 199 (1966).

95. R. S. Drago and N. A. Matwiyoff, *J. Organometal. Chem.*, **3**, 62 (1965).

96. R. S. Drago, *Rec. Chem. Prog.*, **26**, 157 (1965).

97. H. Dreeskamp, *Z. Phys. Chem.*, **38**, 121 (1963).

98. H. Dreeskamp, *Z. Naturforsch.*, **19A**, 139 (1964).

98a. C. Eaborn and R. C. Moore, *J. Chem. Soc.*, 3640 (1959).

99. C. Eaborn, H. L. Hornfeld, and D. R. M. Walton, *J. Organometal. Chem.*, **10**, 529 (1967).

100. C. Eaborn, H. L. Hornfeld, and D. R. M. Walton, *J. Chem. Soc. B*, 1036 (1967).

101. C. Eaborn and K. C. Pande, *J. Chem. Soc.*, 1566 (1960).

102. C. Eaborn, A. R. Thompson, and D. R. M. Walton, *J. Chem. Soc. C*, 1364 (1967).

103. C. Eaborn, J. A. Treverton, and D. R. M. Walton, *J. Organometal. Chem.*, **9**, 259 (1967).

103a. C. Eaborn and J. A. Waters, *J. Chem. Soc.*, 542 (1961).

104. Z. Eckstein and Z. Ejmocki, Polish Pat. 51,771 (1966); through CA, **68**, 49776*A* (1968).

105. Y. P. Egorov and G. G. Kirei, *Zhur. Obshchei. Khim.*, **34**, 3615 (1964); through *CA*, **62**, 7252*G*, (1965).

106. Y. P. Egorov and V. A. Khranovskii, *Teor. Eksp. Khim. Akad. Nauk. SSSR*, **2**, 175 (1966); through *CA*, **65**, 12092*E* (1966).

107. ESSO Research and Engineering Co., French Pat. 1,467,549 (1967); through *CA*, **68**, 49769*A*, (1968).

108. A. B. Evnin and D. Seyferth, *J. Am. Chem. Soc.*, **89**, 952 (1967).

109. S. Faleschini and G. Tagliavini, *Gazz. Chim. Ital.*, **97**, 1401 (1967).

110. *Reference deleted by author.*

111. A. F. Fentiman, R. E. Wyant, J. C. McFarling, and J. F. Kircher, *J. Organometal. Chem.*, **6**, 645 (1966).

112. D. E. Fenton, A. G. Massey, K. W. Jolley, and L. H. Sutcliffe, *Chem. Commun.*, 1097 (1967).

113. W. Findeiss, W. Davidsohn, and M. C. Henry, *J. Organometal. Chem.*, **9**, 435 (1967).

114. R. H. Fish, H. G. Kuivila, and I. J. Tyminski, *J. Am. Chem. Soc.*, **89**, 5861 (1967).

115. I. Földesi and P. Gömöry, *Acta Chim. Acad. Sci. Hung.*, **45**, 231 (1965).

116. I. Földesi, *Acta Chim. Hung.*, **45**, 237 (1965).

117. H. P. Fritz and C. G. Kreiter, *J. Organometal. Chem.*, **4**, 198 (1965).

118. H. P. Fritz and C. G. Kreiter, *J. Organometal. Chem.*, **4**, 313 (1965).

119. G. Garzo, J. Fekete, and M. Blazso, *Acta Chim. Acad. Sci. Hung.*, **51**, 359 (1967).

120. E. A. Gastilovich, D. N. Shigorin, and N. V. Komarov, *Trudy Komissii Spektrosk. Akad. Nauk. SSSR*, **3**, 70 (1964); through *CA*, **65**, 593*F* (1966).

121. H. Geissler and H. Kriegsmann, *Z. Chem.*, **4**, 354 (1964).

122. H. Geissler and H. Kriegsmann, *Z. Chem.*, **5**, 423 (1965).

123. H. Geissler and H. Kriegsmann, *J. Organometal. Chem.*, **11**, 85 (1968).

124. R. Gelius, *Angew. Chem.*, **72**, 322 (1960).

125. R. Gelius, *Chem. Ber.*, **93**, 1759 (1960).

126. T. A. George, K. Jones, and M. F. Lappert, *J. Chem. Soc.*, 2157 (1965).

127. M. Gielen and J. Nasielski, *Ind. Chim. Belge*, **26**, 1393 (1961).

128. M. Gielen and J. Nasielski, *Ind. Chim. Belge*, **29**, 767 (1964).

129. M. Gielen and J. Nasielski, *Bull. Soc. Chim. Belges*, **71**, 32 (1962).

130. M. Gielen and J. Nasielski, *Bull. Soc. chim. Belges*, **71**, 601 (1962).

131. M. Gielen and J. Nasielski, *J. Organometal. Chem.*, **1**, 173 (1963).

132. M. Gielen and J. Nasielski, *Rec. trav. Chim. Pays-Bas*, **82**, 228 (1963).

133. M. Gielen, J. Nasielski, J. E. Dubois, and M. Fresnet, *Bull. soc. chim. Belges*, **73**, 293 (1964).

134. M. Gielen and N. Sprecher, *Organometal. Chem. Rev.*, **1**, 455 (1966).

135. M. Gielen and J. Nasielski, *J. Organometal. Chem.*, **7**, 273 (1967).

136. M. Gielen, *Mécanismes de Rupture de la Liaison Carbone-Métal*, Free University of Brussels, 1966.

137. M. Gielen and J. Nasielski, *Bull. soc. chim. Belges*, **77**, 5 (1968).

138. M. Gielen and G. Mayence, *J. Organometal. Chem.*, **12**, 363 (1968).

139. M. Gielen, P. Lievin, and J. Nasielski, unpublished results.

140. M. Gielen, J. Nasielski, and E. van den Bulck, unpublished results.

141. M. Gielen, J. Nasielski, and J. van Bost, unpublished results.

142. M. Gielen, J. R. Taeymans, and M. Shames, unpublished results.

143. M. Gielen, F. Fremd, and M. Shames, unpublished results.

144. M. Gielen, G. Baron, and G. Eisendrath, unpublished results.

144a. M. Gielen, J. Nasielski, and J. Topart, *J. Organometal. Chem.*, to be published.

145. H. Gilman and S. Y. Sim, *J. Organometal. Chem.*, **7**, 249 (1967).

145a. H. Gilman and E. A. Zuech, *J. Am. Chem. Soc.*, **82**, 2522 (1960).

146. V. I. Goldanskii, V. V. Khrapov, and E. F. Makarov, *Rev. Mod. Phys.*, **36**, 461 (1964).

147. V. I. Goldanskii, I. P. Suzdalev, A. S. Plachinda, and J. G. Shtyrkov, *Dokl.*, **169**, 872 (1966); through *CA*, **65**, 16095*H* (1966).

148. V. I. Goldanskii and R. A. Stukan, *Zhur. Strukt. Khim.*, **8**, 875 (1967); through *CA*, **68**, 25168*C* (1968).

149. V. I. Goldanskii and V. V. Khrapov, ^{119}Sn-metal organic compounds. *Chemical Applications of Mössbauer Spectroscopy*, Chap. 6, 1968.

150. I. P. Goldstein, E. N. Guryanova, E. D. Delinskaya, and A. Kocheshkov, *Dokl. Akad. Nauk. SSSR*, **136**, 1079 (1968).

151. G. N. Gorshkova, M. A. Chubarova, A. M. Sladkov, L. K. Lunaev, and V. I. Kasatochkin, *Zhur. Fiz. Khim.*, **39**, 2695 (1965); through *CA*, **64**, 7540*A* (1965).

152. G. N. Gorshkova, M. A. Chubarova, A. M. Sladkov, L. K. Luneva, and V. I. Kasatochkin, *Zhur. Fiz. Khim.*, **40**, 1433 (1966); through *CA*, **65**, 17900*H* (1966).

153. R. D. Gorsich, U.S. Pat. 3,069,445 (1961); through *CA*, **58**, 10237*B* (1963).

154. R. D. Gorsich, U.S. Pat. 3,069,449 (1961); through *CA*, **58**, 10241*C* (1963).

155. D. Grant and J. R. van Wazer, *J. Organometal. Chem.*, **4**, 229 (1965).

156. V. V. Gravilenko, L. L. Ivavov, and L. I. Zakharkin, *Zhur. Obshchei Khim.*, **37**, 550 (1967); through *CA*, **67**, 21983*W* (1967).

157. V. S. Griffiths and G. A. W. Derwish, *J. Mol. Spectry*, **3**, 165 (1959).

158. G. Grüttner, E. Krause, and M. Wiernik, *Chem. Ber.*, **50**, 1549 (1917).

159. I. M. Gverdtsiteli and S. V. Adamiya, *Soobshcheniya Akad. Nauk. Gruzin. SSR*, **47**, 55 (1967); through *CA*, **68**, 29817*M* (1968).

160. H. Hartmann, B. Karbstein, and W. Reiss, *Naturwiss.*, **52**, 59 (1965).

161. H. Hartmann and K. Meyer, *Naturwiss.*, **52**, 303 (1965).

162. H. Hartmann and M. K. el Assam, *Naturwiss.*, **52**, 304 (1965).

163. H. Hashimoto and Y. Marimoto, *J. Organometal. Chem.*, **8**, 271 (1967).

164. K. Hayashi, J. Iyoda, and I. Shiihara, *J. Organometal. Chem.*, **10**, 81 (1967).

165. E. Heldt, K. Höppner, and K. H. Krebs, *Z. anorg. allgem. Chem.*, **347**, 95 (1966).

166. A. Henderson and A. K. Holiday, *J. Organometal. Chem.*, **4**, 377 (1965).

167. R. H. Herber and H. A. Stockler, *Trans. N.Y. Acad. Sci.*, **26**, 929 (1964).

168. R. H. Herber, H. A. Stöckler, and W. T. Reichle, *J. Chem. Phys.*, **42**, 2447 (1965).

169. R. H. Herber and G. I. Parisi, *Inorg. Chem.*, **5**, 769 (1966).

170. G. G. Hess, F. W. Lampe, and A. L. Yergey, *Ann. N.Y. Acad.Sci.*, **136**, 106 (1966).

171. J. M. Holmes, R. D. Peacock, and J. C. Tatlow, *Proc. Chem. Soc.*, 108 (1963).

172. K. Höppr.er, U. Proesch, and H. J. Zoepfl, *Abhandl. deut. Akad. Wiss. Berlin Kl. Chem. Geol., Biol.*, 393 (1966).

173. K. Höppner, *Proc. Tihany Symp. Radiat. Chem., 2nd, Tihany (Hung.) 1966*, p. 33 through *CA*, **67**, 59548W (1967).

174. H. H. Huang and K. M. Hui, *J. Organometal. Chem.*, **6**, 504 (1966).

175. H. H. Huang, K. M. Hui, and K. K. Chiu, *J. Organometal. Chem.*, **11**, 515 (1968).

176. D. K. Huggins and H. D. Kaesz, I.R. and Raman spectroscopy of organometallic compounds. *Progress in Solid State Chemistry* (H. Reiss, ed.), Vol. 1, Pergamon Press, Oxford, 1964, Chap. 11, p. 417.

177. D. K. Huggins and H. D. Kaesz, I.R. and Raman spectroscopy of organometallic compounds. *Progress in Solid State Chemistry* (H. Reiss, ed.), Vol. 1, Pergamon Press, Oxford, 1964, p. 427.

178. D. K. Huggins and H. D. Kaesz, I.R. and Raman spectroscopy of organometallic compounds. *Progress in Solid State Chemistry*, (H. Reiss, ed.), Vol. 1, Pergamon Press, Oxford, 1964, p. 494.

179. D. K. Huggins and H. D. Kaesz, I.R. and Raman spectroscopy of organometallic compounds. *Progress in Solid State Chemistry*, (H. Reiss, ed.), Vol. 1, Pergamon Press, Oxford, 1964, p. 502.

180. S. D. Ibekwe and M. J. Newlands, *J. Chem. Soc.*, 4608 (1965).

181. R. K. Ingham, S. D. Rosenberg, and H. Gilman, *Chem. Rev.*, **60**, 459 (1960).

182. Institute of Organic Chemistry, Siberian Dept. Acad. Sci., French Pat. 1,427,563 (1966); through *CA*, **65**, *P* 8962 (1966).

183. K. L. Jaura, L. K. Churamani, and K. K. Sharma, *Indian J. Chem.*, **4**, 329 (1966).

184. K. Jones and M. F. Lappert, *J. Organometal. Chem.*, 3, 295 (1965).

185. P. Jouve, *Compt. Rend.*, 262B, 815 (1966).

186. J. C. Jungers, L. Sajus, I. de Aguirre, and D. Decroocq, *Rev. Inst. Franç. Pétrole*, 21, 342 (1966).

187. L. V. Kaabak and A. P. Tomilov, *Zhur. Obshchei Khim.*, 33, 2808 (1963); *J. Gen. Chem. USSR*, 33, 2734 (1963); through *CA* 60, 5333 (1964).

188. A. N. Karasev, L. S. Polak, E. B. Shlikhter, and V. S. Shpinel, *Kinetika Kataliz*, 6, 710 (1965); through CA, 63, 15603C (1965).

189. A. N. Karasev, L. S. Polak, E. B. Shlikhter, and V. S. Shpinel, *Zhur. Fiz. Khim.*, 39, 3117 (1965); through *CA*, 64, 8961D (1966).

190. A. N. Karasev, Y. A. Kolbanovskii, L. S. Polak, and E. B. Shlikhter, *Kinetika Kataliz*, 8, 232 (1967); through *CA*, 67, 6014N (1967).

191. M. A. Kazankova, M. A. Belkina, and I. F. Lutsenko, *Zhur. Obshchei Khim.*, 37, 1710 (1967); through *CA*, 68, 13133Z (1968).

192. E. E. Kenaga, U.S. Pat. 3,264,177 (1966); through *CA*, 65, P14364H (1966).

193. V. V. Khrapov, V. I. Goldanskii, A. K. Prokofev, and R. G. Kostyanovskii, *Zhur. Obshchei Khim.*, 37, 3 (1967); *J. Gen. Chem. USSR*, 37, 1 (1967); through *CA*, 66, 109968K (1967).

194. G. Klose, *Ann. Physik*, 10, 391 (1963).

195. N. V. Komarov, M. F. Shostakovskii, I. S. Guseva, and V. K. Misyunas, USSR Pat. 173,758 (1965); through *CA*, 64, P3603D (1965).

196. N. V. Komarov and O. G. Yarosh, *Zhur. Obshchei Khim.*, 36, 101 (1966); through *CA*, 64, 14207F.

197. N. V. Komarov, I. S. Guseva, and F. P. Lvova, *Izv. Akad. Nauk. SSSR, Ser. Khim.*, 1479 (1966); through *CA*, 66, 65600C (1966).

198. N. V. Komarov and V. S. Misyunas, USSR Pat. 180,591 (1966); through *CA*, 65, P12240E (1966).

199. N. V. Komarov and O. G. Yarosh, *Zhur. Obshchei Khim.*, 37, 264 (1967); through *CA*, 66, 95126V.

200. N. V. Komarov and I. S. Guseva, British Pat. 1,084,522 (1967); through *CA*, 67, 108763Y (1967).

201. K. König and W. P. Neumann, *Tetrahedron Letters*, 495 (1967).

202. R. G. Kostyanovskii and A. K. Prokofev, *Izv. Akad. Nauk. SSSR, Ser. Khim.*, 175 (1965); through *CA*, 62, 11843D.

203. R. G. Kostyanovskii and A. K. Prokofev, *Dokl. Akad. Nauk. SSSR*, 164, 1054 (1965); through *CA*, 64, 2123C (1965).

204. R. G. Kostyanovskii and A. K. Prokofev, *Izv. Akad. Nauk. SSSR, Ser. Khim.*, 173 (1967); through *CA*, 67, 21982V (1967).

205. R. G. Kostyanovskii, *Tetrahedron Letters*, 2721 (1968).

206. K. Kramer and N. Wright, *Chem. Ber.*, 96, 1877 (1963).

207. H. G. Kuivila and J. A. Verdone, *Tetrahedron Letters*, 119 (1964).

207a. H. G. Kuivila and O. F. Beumel, *J. Am. Chem. Soc.*, 80, 3250 (1958).

208. H. G. Kuivila, W. Rahman and R. H. Fish, *J. Am. Chem. Soc.*, 87, 2835 (1965).

209. H. G. Kuivila and F. A. Pelczar, *3rd Intern. Symp. Organometal. Chem.*, München, 1967, p. 158.

210. H. G. Kuivila and R. Sommer, *J. Am. Chem. Soc.*, 89, 5616 (1967).

211. H. G. Kuivila and J. C. Cochran, *J. Am. Chem. Soc.*, 89, 7152 (1967).

212. M. R. Kula, E. Amberger, and K. K. Mayer, *Chem. Ber.*, 98, 634 (1965).

213. E. J. Kupchik and V. A. Pericante, *J. Organometal. Chem.*, 10, 181 (1967).

214. E. J. Kupchik, J. A. Ursino, and P. R. Bondjouk, *J. Organometal. Chem.*, 10, 269 (1967).

215. R. Kuschuk, H. Kaltwasser, and W. Braun, *Chem. Tech.*, 17, 749 (1965); through *CA*, 64, 9761*A* (1966).
216. F. W. Lampe and A. L. Yergey, *J. Am. Chem. Soc.*, 87, 4202 (1965).
217. H. G. Langer, *Tetrahedron Letters*, 43 (1967).
218. M. F. Lappert and J. Lorberth, Organometallic Diazoalkanes. *3rd Intern. Symp. Organometal. Chem., München,* 1967
219. F. C. Leavitt, T. A. Manuel, F. Johnson, L. U. Matternas, and D. S. Lehman, *J. Am. Chem. Soc.*, 82, 5099 (1960).
220. F. C. Leavitt, T. A. Manuel, and F. Johnson, *J. Am. Chem. Soc.*, 81, 3163 (1959).
221. F. C. Leavitt and F. Johnson, U.S. Pat. 3,116,307, (1963); through *CA*, 60, 6872*D* (1964).
222. M. Lefort, French Pat. 1,371,324 (1964); through *CA*, 62, *P* 4052*E* (1964).
223. M. Le Quan and P. Cadiot, *Compt. Rend.*, 254, 133 (1962).
224. M. Le Quan and P. Cadiot, *Bull. soc. chim. France*, 35 (1965).
225. M. Le Quan and P. Cadiot, *Bull. soc. chim. France*, 45 (1965).
225a. M. Le Quan, *Compt. Rend.*, 226C, 832 (1968).
225b. M. Le Quan and P. Cadiot, personal communication.
225c. M. Le Quan, P. Cadiot, and M. Gielen, unpublished results.
226. A. J. Leusink, J. G. Noltes, H. A. Budding, and G. J. M. van der Kerk, *Rec. trav. Chim. Pays-Bas*, 83, 1036 (1964).
227. A. J. Leusink, J. W. Marsman, H. A. Budding, J. G. Noltes, and G. J. M. van der Kerk, *Rec. trav. Chim. Pays-Bas*, 84, 567 (1965).
228. A. J. Leusink, J. W. Marsman and H. A. Budding, *Rec. trav. Chim. Pays-Bas*, 84, 689 (1965).
229. A. J. Leusink and J. G. Noltes, *Tetrahedron Letters*, 335 (1966).
230. A. J. Leusink and J. G. Noltes, *Tetrahedron Letters*, 2221 (1966).
231. A. J. Leusink, H. A. Budding, and J. W. Marsman, *J. Organometal. Chem.*, 9, 285 (1967).
232. A. J. Leusink, H. A. Budding, and W. Drenth, *J. Organometal. Chem.*, 9, 295 (1967).
233. A. J. Leusink, W. Drenth, J. G. Noltes, and G. J. M. van der Kerk, *Tetrahedron Letters*, 1263 (1967).
234. A. J. Leusink and H. A. Budding, *J. Organometal. Chem.*, 11, 533 (1968).
235. A. J. Leusink, H. A. Budding, and W. Drenth, *J. Organometal. Chem.*, 11, 541 (1968).
236. A. J. Leusink and H. A. Budding, *J. Organometal. Chem.*, 11, 553 (1968).
237. A. J. Leusink, H. A. Budding, and W. Drenth, *J. Organometal. Chem.*, 11, 541 (1968).
238. D. H. Lohmann, *J. Organometal. Chem.*, 4, 382 (1965).
239. P. Longi and R. Mazzocchi, *Chim. Ind.*, 48, 718 (1966); through *CA*, 65, 14431*E* (1966).
240. J. Lorberth and N. Nöth, *Chem. Ber.*, 98, 969 (1965).
241. J. Lorberth, *Chem. Ber.*, 98, 1201 (1965).
242. J. Lorberth and H. Vahrenkamp, *J. Organometal. Chem.*, 11, 111 (1968).
243. J. G. A. Luijten and G. J. M. van der Kerk, *Rec. trav. Chim. Pays-Bas*, 83, 295 (1964).
244. J. G. A. Luijten and F. Rijkens, *Rec. trav. Chim. Pays-Bas*, 83, 857 (1964).
245. L. Lunazzi and F. Faddei, *Boll. Sci. Fac. Chim. Ind. Bologna*, 23, 359 (1965); through *CA*, 64, 18736*C* (1966).
245a. L. K. Luneva, A. M. Sladkov, and V. V. Korshak, *Vysokomol. Soedin*, 7, 427 (1965); through *CA*, 63, 1879*E* (1966).
246. L. K. Luneva, *Usp. Khim.*, 36, 1140 (1967); *Russ. Chem. Rev.*, 36, 467 (1967); through *CA*, 68, 21975*R* (1968).
246a. L. K. Luneva, A. M. Sladkov, and V. V. Korshak, *Vysokomol. Soedin.*, A9, 895 (1967).

247. I. F. Lutsenko and S. V. Ponomarev, *Zhur. Obshchei. Khim.*, **31**, 2025 (1961).
248. I. F. Lutsenko, S.V. Ponomarev, and O. P. Petrii, *Zhur. Obshchei Khim.*, **32**, 896 (1962); *J. Gen. Chem. USSR*, **32**, 886 (1962).
249. I. F. Lutsenko, Y. I. Baukov, and B. N. Khasapov, *Zhur. Obshchei Khim.*, **33**, 2724 (1963).
250. G. E. Maciel, *J. Phys. Chem.*, **69**, 1947 (1965).
251. G. P. Mack and Z. Parker, U.S. Pat. 2,618,625; through *CA*, **47**, 4358 (1953).
252. J. C. Maire, *J. Organometal. Chem.*, **9**, 271 (1967).
253. J. Mangravite, *Dissertation Abstr.*, **26**, 7041 (1966).
254. D. F. Martin, P. C. Maybury, and R. D. Walton, *J. Organometal. Chem.*, **7**, 362 (1967).
255. D. F. Martin and R. D. Walton, *J. Organometal. Chem.*, **5**, 57 (1966).
256. P. L. Maxfield, *Dissertation Abstr.*, **26**, 7041 (1966).
256a. W. McFarlane, *J. Chem. Soc. A*, 528 (1967).
257. W. R. McWhinnie, R. C. Poller, and M. Thevarasa, *J. Organometal. Chem.*, **11**, 499 (1968).
258. J. Mendelsohn, A. Marchand, and J. Valade, *J. Organometal. Chem.*, **6**, 25 (1966).
259. H. Meyer, *J. Organometal. Chem.*, **11**, 525 (1968).
260. J. Michelet, Ph.D. Thesis, Free University of Brussels, 196 .
261. Y. Minoura, Y. Suzuki, Y. Sakanaka, and H. Doi, *Kogyo Kagaku Zasshi*, **69**, 345 (1966); through *CA*, **66**, 95414*N*.
262. V. F. Mironov and A. L. Kravchenko, *Zhur. Obshchei Khim.*, **34**, 1356 (1964); *J. Gen. Chem. USSR*, **34**, 1359 (1964).
263. A. G. Mirskov and V. M. Vlasov, *Zhur. Obshchei Khim.*, **36**, 166 (1966).
264. A. G. Mirskov and V. M. Vlasov, *Zhur. Obshchei Khim.*, **36**, 562 (1966); through *CA*, **65**, 744*B* (1966).
265. M. & T. Chemie, Neth. Appl. Pat. 6,505,520 (1965).
266. M. & T. Chemie; Neth. Appl. Pat. 6,601,352 (1966).
267. J. Nagy, J. Reffy, A. Kuszmann-Borbely, and K. Palossy-Becker, *J. Organometal. Chem.*, **7**, 393 (1967).
268. J. Nagy, J. Reffy, A. Borbely-Kuszmann, and K. Becker-Palossy, *Intern. Symp. Organosilicon Chem., Sci. Comm., Prague, 1964*, p. 241; through *CA*, **66**, 85308*S* (1967).
269. G. A. Nash, H. A. Skinner, and W. F. Stack, *Trans. Faraday Soc.*, **61**, 640 (1965).
270. J. Nasielski, O. Buchman, M. Grosjean, and E. Hannecart, *Bull. soc. chim. Belges*, **77**, 15 (1968).
271. J. Nasielski, O. Buchman, M. Grosjean, J. J. Schurter, and G. Vandendunghen, *Bull. soc. chim. Belges*, **77**, 349 (1968).
271a. J. Nasielski, O. Buchman, M. Grosjean, and M. Jauquet, *J. Organometal Chem.*, **19**, 353 (1969).
272. W. H. Nelson and D. F. Martin, *J. Inorg. Nucl. Chem.*, **27**, 89 (1965).
273. W. H. Nelson and D. F. Martin, *J. Organometal. Chem.*, **4**, 67 (1965).
274. A. N. Nesmeyanov and A. E. Borisov, *Dokl. Akad. Nauk. SSSR*, 6067 (1948).
275. A. N. Nesmeyanov and A. E. Borisov, *Tetrahedron*, **1**, 158 (1957).
276. A. N. Nesmeyanov, I. F. Lutsenko, and S. V. Ponomarev, *Dokl. Akad. Nauk. SSSR*, **124**, 133 (1959).
277. A. N. Nesmeyanov, I. F. Lutsenko, and S. V. Ponomarev, *Dokl. Akad. Nauk. SSSR*, **124**, 1073 (1959).
278. A. N. Nesmeyanov and A. E. Borisov, *Dokl.*, **174**, 96 (1967); through *CA*, **67**, 90903*G* (1967).

279. A. N. Nesmeyanov and A. E. Borisov, *Izv. Akad. Nauk. SSSR, Ser. Khim.*, 226 (1967); *Bull. Acad. Sci. USSR, Div. Chem. Sci.*, 227 (1967); through *CA*, **66**, 95147*C* (1967).
280. A. N. Nesmeyanov, A. E. Borisov, and N. V. Novikova, *Dokl. Akad. Nauk. SSSR*, **172**, 1329 (1967); through *CA*, **67**, 3127*R* (1967).
281. A. N. Nesmeyanov, A. E. Borisov, and S. H. Wang, *Izv. Akad. Nauk. SSSR, Ser. Khim.*, 1141 (1967); through *CA*, **68**, 29807*H* (1968).
282. W. P. Neumann, *Angew. Chem.*, **75**, 227 (1963).
283. W. P. Neumann and F. G. Kleiner, *Tetrahedron. Letters*, 3779 (1964).
284. W. P. Neumann, R. Sommer, and H. Lind, *Ann*, **688**, 14 (1965).
285. W. P. Neumann, B. Schneider, and R. Sommer, *Ann.*, **692**, 1 (1966).
286. W. P. Neumann and R. Sommer, *Ann.*, **701**, 28 (1967).
287. W. P. Neumann, H. Niermann, and B. Schneider, *Ann.*, **707**, 15 (1967).
288. W. P. Neumann and B. Schneider, *Ann.*, **707**, 20 (1967).
289. W. P. Neumann, H. J. Albert, and W. Kaiser; *Tetrahedron Letters*, 2041 (1967).
290. W. P. Neumann, *Die Organische Chemie des Zinns*, F. Enke Verlage, Stuttgart, 1967.
291. J. G. Noltes and G. J. M. van der Kerk, *Functionally Substituted Organotin Compounds*, Tin Research Institute, Greenford, Middlesex, 1958.
292. J. G. Noltes, H. M. J. C. Creemers and G. J. M. van der Kerk, *J. Organometal. Chem.*, **11**, *P*21 (1968).
293. H. Nöth and H. Vahrenkamp, *J. Organometal. Chem.*, **11**, 399 (1968).
294. Z. S. Novikova, M. V. Proskurnina, L. I. Petrovskaya, I. V. Bogdanova, N. P. Galitskova, and I. F. Lutsenko, *Zhur. Obshchei Khim.*, **37**, 2080 (1967); through *CA*, **68**, 78392*C* (1968).
295. V. Oakes, *CA*, **67**, 43925 (1967).
296. I. Omae, S. Matsuda, S. Kikkawa, and R. Sato, *Kogyo Kagaku Zasshi*, **70**, 705 (1967); through *CA*, **68**, 13107*U* (1968).
297. I. Omae, S. Ohnishi, and S. Matsuda, *Kogyo Kagaku Zasshi*, **70**, 1755 (1967); through *CA*, **68**, 87371*X* (1968).
298. M. E. Pedinoff and H. Seguin, *Rev. Sci. Instrum.*, **38**, 1342 (1967); through *CA*, **67**, 85208*E* (1967).
299. J. P. Pellegrini and I. J. Spilners, *CA*, **68**, 4831 (1968).
300. M. Pereyre and J. Valade, *Compt. Rend.*, **258**, 4785 (1964).
301. M. Pereyre and J. Valade, *Bull. soc. chim. France*, 2420 (1965).
302. M. Pereyre, G. Colin, and J. Valade, *Compt. Rend.*, **264C**, 1204 (1967).
303. M. Pereyre, B. Bellegarde, and J. Valade, *Compt. Rend.*, **265C**, 939 (1967).
304. M. Pereyre and J. Valade, *Bull. soc. chim. France*, 1928 (1967).
305. M. Pereyre, B. Bellegarde, J. Mendelsohn, and J. Valade, *J. Organometal. Chem.*, **11**, 97 (1968).
306. A. A. Petrov and V. S. Zavgorodnii, *Zhur. Obshchei Khim.*, **34**, 2806 (1964); through *CA*, **61**, 14701*E* (1964).
307. A. A. Petrov, N. V. Elsakov, V. S. Zavgorodnii, and V. B. Lebedev, *Teor. Eksp. Khim. Akad. Nauk. SSSR*, **1**, 697 (1965); through *CA*, **64**, 13581*C* (1965).
308. V. A. Petukhov, V. F. Mironov, and P. P. Shorygin, *Izv. Akad. Nauk. SSSR, Ser. Khim.*, 2203 (1964); *Bull. Acad. Sci. USSR, Div. Chem. Sci.*, 2099 (1964); through *CA*, **62**, 8973*A* (1964).
309. Pfizer and Co., Inc., British Pat. 1,089,428 (1967); through *CA*, **68**, 13889*A* (1968).
310. J. L. W. Pohlmann, F. E. Bruikmann, G. Tesi, and R. E. Donadio, *Z. Naturforsch.*, **20B**, 1 (1965).
311. F. H. Pollard, G. Nickless, and D. J. Cooke, *J. Chromatogr.*, **17**, 472 (1965).
312. F. H. Pollard, G. Nickless, and P. Uden, *J. Chromatogr.*, **19**, 28 (1965).

313. F. H. Pollard, G. Nickless, and D. N. Dolan, *Chem. Ind.*, 1027 (1965).

314. R. C. Poller, *Spectrochim. Acta*, **22**, 935 (1966).

315. R. Polster, *Ann.*, **654**, 21 (1962).

316. R. Polster, German Pat. 1,150,388 (1963) through *CA*, **60**, 553*D* (1964).

317. R. Polster, German Pat. 1,153,748 (1963); through *CA*, **60**, 551*F* (1964).

318. R. Polster, German Pat. 1,156,807 (1963); through *CA*, **60**, 4182*G* (1964).

319. S. V. Ponomarev, E. V. Machigin, and I. F. Lutsenko, *Zhur. Obshchei Khim.*, **36**, 548 (1966); through *CA*, **65**, 744*B* (1966).

320. S. V. Ponomarev, Z. M. Lisina, and I. F. Lutsenko, *Zhur. Obshchei Khim.*, **36**, 1818 (1966); *J. Gen. Chem. USSR*, **36**, 1810 (1966); through *CA*, **66**, 55564*E* (1967).

321. G. Pourcelot, M. le Quan, W. Chodkiewicz, and P. Cadiot, *XIXth IUPAC Congress, London, 1963*, Abstr. A, p. 177.

322. R. C. Putnam and H. Pu, *J. Gas Chromatogr.*, **3**, 160 (1965).

323. R. C. Putnam and H. Pu, *J. Gas Chromatogr.*, **3**, 289 (1965).

324. R. C. Putnam, *Can. J. Chem.*, **44**, 1343 (1966).

325. H. E. Ramsden, *U.S. Pat.* 3,240,795 (1966).

326. M. D. Rausch and L. P. Kemann, *J. Am. Chem. Soc.*, **89**, 5732 (1967).

327. G. A. Razuvaev, N. S. Vyazankin, and O. A. Shchepetkova, *Tetrahedron*, **18**, 667 (1962).

328. G. A. Razuvaev, N. S. Vyazankin, E. N. Gladyshev, and I. A. Borodavko, *Zhur. Obshchei Khim.*, **32**, 2154 (1962).

329. G. A. Razuvaev, N. S. Vyazankin, Y. I. Dergunov, and E. N. Gladyshev, *Izv.*, 848 (1964); *Bull. Acad. Sci. USSR, Div. Chem. Sci.*, 794 (1964).

330. W. T. Reichle, *Inorg. Chem.*, **5**, 87 (1966).

331. G. H. Reifenberg and W. J. Considine, *J. Organometal. Chem.*, **9**, 505 (1967).

331a. G. H. Reifenberg and W. J. Considine, *J. Organometal. Chem.*, **9**, 495 (1967).

332. G. H. Reifenberg and W. Considine, *J. Organometal. Chem.*, **10**, 285 (1967).

333. F. Rijkens, M. J. Janssen, W. Drenth, and G. J. M. van der Kerk, *J. Organometal. Chem.*, **2**, 347 (1964).

334. R. M. G. Roberts and F. El Kaissi, *J. Organometal. Chem.*, **12**, 79 (1968).

335. R. M. G. Roberts, *J. Organometal. Chem.*, **12**, 97 (1968).

336. G. F. Rubinchik and Z. M. Manulkin, *Zhur. Obshchei Khim.*, **36**, 261 (1966); through *CA*, **64**, 15918*E* (1966).

337. G. F. Rubinchik and Z. M. Manulkin, *Zhur. Obshchei Khim.*, **36**, 748 (1966).

338. G. F. Rubinchik and Z. M. Manulkin, *Zhur. Obshchei Khim.*, **36**, 1301 (1966); *J. Gen. Chem. USSR*, **36**, 1316 (1966).

339. R. E. Sacher, P. H. Lemmon, and F. A. Miller, *Spectrochim. Acta*, **23A**, 1169 (1967).

339a. A. V. Savitskii and Y. K. Syrkin, *Dokl. Phys. Chem.*, **146**, 700 (1962).

340. E. O. Schlemper and D. Britton, *Inorg. Chem.*, **5**, 507 (1966).

341. H. Schmidbaur and S. Waldmann, *Chem. Ber.*, **97**, 3381 (1964).

342. M. Schmidt, H. J. Dersin, and H. Schumann, *Chem. Ber.*, **95**, 1428 (1962).

343. M. Schmidt and H. Schumann, *Chem. Ber.*, **96**, 462 (1963).

344. M. Schmidt and H. Schumann, *Chem. Ber.*, **96**, 780 (1963).

345. B. Schneider and W. P. Neumann, *Ann.*, **707**, 7 (1967).

346. O. Schöllkopf and H. J. Tränckner, *J. Organometal. Chem.*, **5**, 300 (1966).

347. H. Schroeder, S. Papetti, R. P. Alexander, J. F. Sieckhaus, and T. L. Heying, *CA*, **68**, 1306 (1968).

348. H. Schroeder, S. Papetti, R. P. Alexander, J. F. Sieckhaus, and T. L. Heying, *CA*, **68**, 13463*G* (1968).

349. W. T. Schwartz, *Dissertation Abstr.*, **B27**, 1429 (1966).

349a. M. T. Sciot, S. Boue, M. Gielen, and J. Nasielski, unpublished results.

350. P. Selivokhin, *Gigiena Sanit.*, **31**, 68 (1966); through *CA*, **65**, 15973*G* (1966).
351. D. Seyferth and L. G. Vaughan, *J. Organometal. Chem.*, **1**, 138 (1963).
352. D. Seyferth, *J. Organometal. Chem.*, **1**, 201 (1964).
353. D. Seyferth, C. Sarafidis, and A. B. Evnin, *J. Organometal. Chem.*, **2**, 417 (1964).
354. D. Seyferth and L. G. Vaughan, *J. Am. Chem. Soc.*, **86**, 883 (1964).
355. D. Seyferth, *Rec. Chem. Prog.*, **26**, 87 (1965).
356. D. Seyferth, J.Y-P. Mui, M. E. Gordon, and J. M. Burlitch, *J. Am. Chem. Soc.*, **87**, 681 (1965).
357. D. Seyferth, G. Singh, and R. Suzuki, *Pure Appl. Chem.*, **13**, 159 (1966).
358. D. Seyferth, R. Suzuki, and L. G. Vaughan, *J Am. Chem. Soc.*, **88**, 286 (1966).
359. D. Seyferth and W. S. Washburne, *J. Organometal. Chem.*, **5**, 389 (1966).
360. D. Seyferth, F. M. Armbrecht, B. Prokai, and R. J. Cross, *J. Organometal. Chem.*, **6**, 573 (1966).
361. D. Seyferth and T. F. Jula, *J. Organometal. Chem.*, **8**, P13 (1967).
362. D. Seyferth, F. M. Armbrecht, and E. M. Hanson, *J. Organometal. Chem.*, **10**, P25 (1967).
363. D. Seyferth, A. B. Evnin, and D. R. Blank, *Inorg. Nucl. Chem. Lett.*, **3**, 181 (1967).
363a. D. Seyferth, G. Singh, and R. Suzuki, *Pure Appl. Chem.*, **13**, 159 (1966).
364. D. Seyferth and A. B. Evnin, *J. Am. Chem. Soc.*, **89**, 1468 (1967).
365. D. Seyferth and F. M. Armbrecht, *J. Am. Chem. Soc.*, **89**, 2790 (1967).
366. D. Seyferth, H. Dertouzos, R. Suzuki, and J. Y-P. Mui, *J. Org. Chem.*, **32**, 2980 (1967).
367. D. Seyferth, J. Y-P. Mui, and J. M. Burlitch, *J. Am. Chem. Soc.*, **89**, 4953 (1967).
367a. D. Seyferth, U.S. Pat. 3,347,888 (1967); through *CA*, **68**, 59726*Y* (1968).
368. D. Seyferth and K. V. Darragh, *J. Organometal. Chem.*, **11**, P10 (1968).
369. D. Seyferth, T. F. Jula, H. Dertouzos, and M. Pereyre, *J. Organometal. Chem.*, **11**, 63 (1968).
370. D. Seyferth, A. B. Evnin, and D. R. Blank, *J. Organometal. Chem.*, **13**, 25 (1968).
371. D. Seyferth and T. F. Jula, *J. Am. Chem. Soc.*, **90**, 2938 (1968).
372. L. G. Sharanina, V. S. Zavgorodnii, and A. A. Petrov, *Zhur. Obshchei Khim.*, **36**, 1154 (1966); through *CA*, **65**, 10617*G* (1966).
373. N. I. Shergina, N. I. Golovanova, R. G. Mirskov, and V. M. Vlasov, *Izv. Akad. Nauk. SSSR, Ser. Khim.*, 1378 (1967); *Bull. Acad. Sci. USSR, Div. Chem. Sci.*, 1334 (1967).
374. K. Shiina, T. Brennan, and H. Gilman, *J. Organometal. Chem.*, **11**, 471 (1968).
375. P. P. Shorygin, V. A. Petukhoc, O. M. Nefedov, S. P. Kolesnikov, and V. I. Shiryaev, *Teor. Eksp. Khim. Akad. Nauk. SSSR*, **2**, 190 (1966); through *CA*, **65**, 14660*G* (1966).
376. M. F. Shostakovskii, N. V. Komarov, I. S. Guseva, and V. K. Misyunas, *Dokl.*, **158**, 918 (1964); through *CA*, **62**, 2788*E* (1964).
377. M. F. Shostakovskii, V. M. Vlasov, and R. G. Mirskov, *Dokl.*, **159**, 869 (1964); through *CA*, **62**, 7788*D* (1964).
378. M. F. Shostakovskii, N. V. Komarov, V. K. Misyunas, and M. K. Zainchkovskaya, *Izv. Akad. Nauk. SSSR, Ser. Khim.*, 1102 (1964); *Bull. Acad. Sci. USSR, Div. Chem. Sci.*, 1018 (1964).
379. M. F. Shostakovskii, V. M. Vlasov, R. G. Mirskov, and I. E. Loginova, *Zhur. Obshchei Khim.*, **34**, 3178 (1964); through *CA*, **62**, 4046*H* (1964).
380. M. F. Shostakovskii, V. M. Vlasov, and R. G. Mirskov, USSR Pat. 165, 454 (1964); through *CA*, **62**, *P* 6513*D* (1964).
380a. M. F. Shostakovskii, V. M. Vlasov, R. G. Mirskov, and V. N. Petrova, USSR Pat. 172,782 (1965); through *CA*, **64**, *P* 757*F* (1966).
381. M. F. Shostakovskii, V. M. Vlasov, and R. G. Mirskov, USSR Pat. 173,757 (1965); through *CA*, **64**, 5138*G* (1966).

382. M. F. Shostakovskii, V. M. Vlasov, R. G. Mirskov, and V. N. Petrova, USSR Pat. 173,760 (1965); through *CA*, **64**, *P* 3602*E* (1965).

383. M. F. Shostakovskii, V. M. Vlasov, R. G. Mirskov, and V. N. Petrova, *Zhur. Obshchei Khim.*, **35**, 47 (1965); through *CA*, **62**, 13169*B* (1965).

384. M. F. Shostakovskii, N. V. Komarov, V. K. Misyunas, and A. M. Sklyanova, *Dokl.*, **161**, 370 (1965); through *CA*, **63**, 624*B* (1965).

385. M. F. Shostakovskii, N. V. Komarov, I. S. Guseva, V. K. Misyunas, A. Sklyanova, and T. D. Burnashova, *Dokl.*, **163**, 390 (1965); through *CA*, **63**, 11601*F* (1965).

386. M. F. Shostakovskii, V. M. Vlasov, R. G. Mirskov, and I. M. Korotaeva, *Zhur. Obshchei Khim.*, **35**, 401 (1965); *J. Gen. Chem. USSR*, **35**, 403 (1965); through *CA*, **62**, 13167*C* (1965).

387. M. F. Shostakovskii, N. I. Shergina, N. I. Golovanova, N. V. Komarov, E. I. Brodskaya, and V. K. Misyunas, *Zhur. Obshchei Khim.*, **35**, 1768 (1965); through *CA*, **64**, 1927*F* (1965).

387a. M. F. Shostakovskii, G. I. Kagan, R. G. Mirskov, and V. M. Vlasov, *Zhur. Prikl. Spektrosk.*, *Akad. Nauk. Belorussk. SSR*, **4**, 46 (1966); through *CA*, **64**, 18700*G* (1966).

388. M. F. Shostakovskii, N. V. Komarov, Y. V. Maroshin, and F. P. Lvova, *Zhur. Obshchei Khim.*, **37**, 567 (1967); *J. Gen. Chem. USSR*, **37**, 531 (1967).

389. M. F. Shostakovskii, R. G. Mirskov, V. M. Vlasov, and S. J. Tarpishchev, *Zhur. Obshchei Khim.*, **37**, 1738 (1967); through *CA*, **68**, 13103*Q* (1968).

389a. M. F. Shostakovskii, N. V. Komarov, and V. K. Misyunas, *Dokl. Akad. Nauk. SSSR*, **173**, 843 (1967); *Proc. Acad. Sci. USSR*, **173** (1967).

390. M. F. Shostakovskii, N. V. Komarov, A. M. Sklyanova, and A. V. Suvorora, *Dokl.*, **176**, 356 (1967); through *CA*, **68**, 29824*M* (1968).

391. M. F. Shostakovskii, A. S. Atavin, E. P. Vyalykh, B. A. Trofimov, and R. D. Yakubov, *Izv. Akad. Nauk. SSSR*, 2118 (1967); *Bull. Acad. Sci. USSR, Div. Chem. Sci.*, 2045 (1967); through *CA*, **68**, 29812*F* (1968).

392. M. F. Shostakovskii, N. V. Komarov, A. M. Sklyanova, and A. V. Suvorora, *Dokl. Akad. Nauk. SSSR*, **176**, 356 (1967); *Proc. Acad. Sci. USSR*, **176**, 821 (1967).

393. M. F. Shostakovskii, N. V. Komarov, and A. M. Sklyanova, German Pat. 1,235,917 (1967); through *CA*, **67**, 22014*T* (1967).

394. M. F. Shostakovskii, N. V. Komarov, and A. M. Stepanovich, British Pat. 1,092,036 (1967); through *CA*, **68**, 22059*G* (1968).

395. J. M. Sichel and M. A. Whitehead, *Theoret. Chim. Acta*, **5**, 35 (1966).

396. M. P. Simonnin, *J. Organometal. Chem.*, **5**, 155 (1966).

397. M. P. Simonnin, *Bull. soc. chim. France*, 1774 (1966).

398. K. Sisido, S. Kozima, and K. Takizawa, *Tetrahedron Letters*, 33 (1967).

399. K. Sisido, S. Kozima, and F. Isibasi, *J. Organometal. Chem.*, **10**, 439 (1967).

400. K. Sisido, T. Miyanisi, K. Nabika, and S. Kozima, *J. Organometal. Chem.*, **11**, 281 (1968).

401. K. Sisido and S. Kozima, *J. Organometal. Chem.*, **11**, 503 (1968).

402. K. Sisido and S. Kozima, *J. Organometal. Chem.*, **11**, 503 (1968).

403. H. A. Skinner, *Adv. Organometal. Chem.*, **2**, Academic Press (1964).

404. A. M. Sladkov and L. K. Luneva, *Zhur. Obshchei Khim.*, **36**, 553 (1966); through *CA*, **65**, 744*g* (1966).

405. G. W. Smith, *J. Chem. Phys.*, **42**, 4229 (1965).

406. G. W. Smith, *Liquids, Struct. Properties, Solid Interactions, Proc. Symp. Warren, Mich., 1963*, p. 219; through *CA*, **64**, 16864*B* (1966).

407. S. P. Solodovnikov and E. A. Chernyshev, *Trudy Soveshch. Fiz. Metodam. Issled. Organ. Soedin. Khim. Protessov, Akad. Nauk. Kirg. SSR, Inst. Organ. Khim. Frunze, 1962*, p. 196; through *CA*, **62**, 4804*a* (1964).

408. Solvay and Co., French Pat. 1,449,872 (1966); through *CA*, **66**, 95200*L* (1966).

409. R. Sommer and H. G. Kuivila, *J. Org. Chem.*, **33**, 802 (1968).

409a. R. Spielman, M. Gielen, and J. Nasielski, unpublished results.

410. J. J. Spijkerman, *Adv. Chem. Ser. No.* 68, 105 (1967); through *CA*, **68**, 24253*B* (1968).

411. W. Steingross and W. Zeil, *J. Organometal. Chem.*, **6**, 109 (1966).

412. R. D. Steinmeyer, A. F. Fentiman, and E. J. Kahler, *Anal. Chem.*, **37**, 520 (1965).

413. H. A. Stöckler and H. Sano, *Phys. Letters*, **25A**, 550 (1967).

414. H. A. Stöckler, H. Sano, and R. H. Herber, *J. Chem. Phys.*, **47**, 1567 (1967).

415. W. Sundermeyer and W. Verbeek, *Angew. Chem. Intern. Ed.*, **5**, 1 (1966).

416. W. Sundermeyer and W. Verbeek, German Pat. 1,239,687 (1967); through *CA*, **68**, 2989*G* (1968).

417. G. Tagliavini, G. Pilloni, and G. Plazzogna, *Ric. Sci.*, **36**, 114 (1966).

418. Y. Takami, *Kogyo Shiken sho Hokoku*, **57**, 234 (1962); through *CA*, **62**, 2826*C* (1965).

419. C. Tamborski, E. J. Soloski, and S. M. Dec, *J. Organometal. Chem.*, **4**, 446 (1965).

420. V. I. Telnoi and I. B. Rabinovich, *Zhur. Fiz. Khim.*, **39**, 2122 (1965); *Russ. J. Phys. Chem.*, **39**, 1108 (1965).

421. V. I. Telnoi and I. B. Rabinovich, *Zhur. Fiz. Khim.*, **39**, 2314 (1965); *Russ. J. Phys. Chem.*, **39**, 1239 (1965).

422. V. I. Telnoi and I. B. Rabinovich, *Zhur. Fiz. Khim.*, **40**, 1556 (1966); through *CA*, **65**, 15209*G* (1966).

423. K. S. Tillyaev and Z. M. Manulkin, *Dokl. Akad. Nauk. SSSR*, **22**, 45 (1965); through *CA*, **63**, 5668*C* (1965).

424. P. M. Treichel and R. A. Goodrich, *Inorg. Chem.*, **4**, 1424 (1965).

425. C. L. Tseng, J. H. Cho, and S. C. Ma, *K'o Hsueh T'ung Pao*, **17**, 77 (1966); through *CA*, **60**, 28862*U* (1966).

426. W. P. Tucker, *Inorg. Nucl. Chem. Letters*, **4**, 83 (1968).

427. E. van den Bulck, M. Gielen, and J. Nasielski, unpublished results.

428. G. J. M. van der Kerk and J. G. Noltes, *J. Appl. Chem.*, **9**, 106 (1959).

429. L. G. Vaughan and D. Seyferth, *J. Organometal. Chem.*, **5**, 295 (1966).

430. L. Verdonck and G. P. van der Kelen, *Ber. Bunsenges Phys. Ges.*, **69**, 478 (1965).

431. L. Verdonk and G. P. van der Kelen, *J. Organometal. Chem.*, **5**, 532 (1966).

432. L. Verdonck and G. P. van der Kelen, *Bull. soc. chim. Belges*, **76**, 258 (1967).

433. L. Verdonck and G. P. van der Kelen, *J. Organometal. Chem.*, **11**, 491 (1968).

434. T. Vladimirov and E. R. Malinovski, *J. Chem. Phys.*, **42**, 440 (1965).

435. V. M. Vlasov, R. G. Mirskov, and V. N. Petrova, *Zhur. Obshchei Khim.*, **37**, 954 (1967); *J. Gen. Chem. USSR*, **37**, 902 (1967); through *CA*, **68**, 13114*U* (1968).

436. A. I. Vogel, W. T. Cresswell, and J. Leicester, *J. Phys. Chem.*, **58**, 174 (1954).

437. N. S. Vyazankin, G. A. Razuvaev, and T. N. Brevnova, *Dokl.*, **163**, 1389 (1965); through *CA*, **63**, 16379*C* (1965).

438. N. S. Vyazankin, T. N. Brevnova, and G. A. Razuvaev, *Zhur. Obshchei Khim.*, **37**, 204 (1967); through *CA*, **66**, 94533*P* (1967).

439. R. Waack, U.S. Pat. 3,305,388 (1967); through *CA*, **66**, 97827*Y* (1967).

440. J. L. Wardell, *J. Organometal. Chem.*, **9**, 89 (1967).

441. J. L. Wardell, *J. Organometal. Chem.*, **10**, 53 (1967).

442. D. Wasserman, R. E. Jones, S. A. Robinson, and J. D. Garber, *J. Org. Chem.*, **30**, 3248 (1965).

443. R. W. Weiss, *Organometallic Compounds—Methods of Synthesis, Physical Constants and Chemical Reactions* (M. Dub, ed.) Vol. II: Compounds of Ge, Sn and Pb including biological activity and commercial application, Springer Verlag, New York. 1967, 2nd ed.

444. R. West and E. G. Rochow, *J. Am. Chem. Soc.*, **74**, 2490 (1952).

445. E. Wiberg, E. Amberger, and H. Cambensi, *Z. anorg. allgem. Chem.*, **351**, 164 (1967).
446. B. Woitkowiak and R. Queignec, *Compt. Rend.*, **262B**, 811 (1966).
447. A. Work and S. Digiovanni, *Anal. Chem.*, **38**, 742 (1966); through *CA*, **65**, 2985*F* (1966).
448. J. Yamazaki, S. Kidooka, and M. IIda, Japanese Pat. 4,650 (1967), through *CA*. **67**, 32779*K* (1967).
449. A. L. Yergey and F. W. Lampe, *J. Am. Chem. Soc.*, **87**, 4204 (1965).
450. L. I. Zakharkin, V. I. Bregadze, and O. Y. Okhlobytsin, *J. Organometal. Chem.*, **4**, 211 (1965).
451. V. S. Zabgorodnii and A. A. Petrov, *Zhur. Obshchei Khim.*, **35**, 760 (1965); through *CA*, **63**, 5666*H* (1965).
452. V. S. Zavgorodnii and A. A. Petrov, *Zhur. Obshchei Khim.*, **35**, 931 (1965); through *CA*, **63**, 7033*C* (1965).
453. V. S. Zavgorodnii and A. A. Petrov, *Zhur. Obshchei Khim.*, **35**, 1313 (1965); *J. Gen. Chem. USSR*, **35**, 1319 (1965); through *CA*, **63**, 11601*E* (1965).
454. V. S. Zavgorodnii and A. A. Petrov, *Zhur. Obshchei Khim.*, **36**, 1480 (1966); through *CA*, **66**, 2624*P* (1966).
455. V. S. Zavgorodnii, B. I. Ionin, and A. A. Petrov, *Zhur. Obshchei Khim.*, **37**, 949 (1967); *J. Gen. Chem. USSR*, **37**, 898 (1967).
456. V. S. Zavgorodnii, L. G. Sharanina, and A. A. Petrov, *Zhur. Obshchei Khim.*, **37**, 1548 (1967); *J. Gen. Chem. USSR*, **37**, 1469 (1967); through *CA*, **68**, 39755*D* (1968).
457. J. G. Zavistoski and J. J. Zuckerman, in press.
458. H. Ziegler and H. Lehmkuhl, German Pat. 1,212,085 (1966); through *CA*, **64**, *P* 19675*B* (1966).
459. H. Zimmer and H. W. Sparmann, *Chem. Ber.*, **87**, 645 (1954).
460. H. Zimmer and H. Gold, *Chem. Ber.*, **89**, 712 (1956).
461. H. Zimmer, I. Hechenbleikner, O. A. Homberg, and M. Danzik, *J. Org. Chem.*, **29**, 2632 (1964).
462. H. Zimmer, O. A. Homberg, and M. Jayawant, *J. Org. Chem.*, **31**, 3857 (1966).
463. J. J. Zuckermann, *J. Inorg. Nucl. Chem.*, **29**, 2191 (1967).
464. M. Gielen, C. Dehouck and B. De Poorter, *Chem. Weekbl.*, in press.
465. F. R. Jensen and D. D. Davis, *J. Am. Chem. Soc.*, **93**, (1971), 4047, 4048.
466. H. C. Brown and C. F. Lane, *Chem. Comm.* (1971), 521.

10. ORGANOTIN COMPOUNDS WITH Sn–Sn BONDS

ALBERT K. SAWYER

Department of Chemistry
College of Technology
University of New Hampshire
Durham, New Hampshire

I. Introduction 823
II. Preparation and Properties 826
   A. Organoditins and Other Organopolytins without Functional Substituents 826
   B. Organoditins and Other Organopolytins with Functional Substituents 845
III. Reactions 854
   A. Introduction 854
   B. Homolytic Dissociation 856
   C. Thermal Behavior 858
   D. Reactions with Halogens 860
   E. Reactions with Oxygen and Other Group VI Elements 862
   F. Reactions with Other Oxidizing Agents 865
   G. Reactions with Metals 867
   H. Reactions with Hydrides and Other Nucleophilic Reagents... 868
   I. Reactions with Acids 869
   J. Insertion Reactions 871
   K. Reactions with Organic Halides 872
   L. Reactions with Other Organotin Compounds 874
   M. Miscellaneous 875
References 876

I. Introduction

There have been several summaries of organotin compounds containing tin-tin bonds. One of the earlier ones, covering the literature up to 1937, was contained in a book by Krause and von Grosse (51).

A review article by Ingham et al. (*41*) appeared in 1960. Later, Gilman et al. (*32*) surveyed the catenated compounds of silicon, germanium, tin and lead, through the middle of 1965. This survey was updated in 1967 by Atwell and Gilman (*8*).

In 1967, also, a book written by Neumann (*64*) appeared containing a chapter on organotin compounds with tin-tin bonds. A recent thesis by Creemers (*20*) in 1967 dealt in detail with hydrostannolysis as a general method for creating tin-metal bonds, but it dealt particularly with tin-tin bonds. Note should also be made of the recent survey of organometallic compounds of germanium, tin, and lead by Dub and Weiss (*28*). In 1969 the chain compounds of silicon, germanium, tin, and lead were reviewed by MacKay and Watt (*60*). Yearly surveys are made covering all aspects of organotin chemistry in Organometallic Reviews B. Mention should also be made of the continuing series by MacDiarmid (*59*) on organometallic compounds of Si, Ge, Sn, and Pb. Very recently a book by Poller (*81b*) appeared, with a chapter on tin-metal bonds.

Because of these existing recent surveys, no attempt at completeness has been made in this chapter particularly with respect to older work. Instead, more attention has been placed on newer developments. However, tables have been included containing all organotin compounds with tin-tin bonds reported up to 1969. A number of references will also be made to other sections of this book dealing with particular aspects which have been treated by the other authors.

Historically, the first known organotin compound, a diethyltin polymer containing tin-tin bonds, was described by Lowig (*58*) in 1852. It was later variably described by different individuals, and only recently has the "divalent" organotin situation been clarified by Neumann et al. (*66, 67, 72*).

The first organopolytin compound suggested to have a branched chain structure, tetrakis (triphenylstannyl) tin, was obtained by Boeseken and Rutgers (*12*) in 1923, but it was not completely characterized until recently by Gilman and Cartledge (*33*).

Another landmark in organopolytin chemistry was the work of Kraus et al. (*46–49*), who, starting in 1925, synthesized the first organotritin, tetratin and pentatin using organotin sodium compounds prepared in liquid ammonia. Krause and von Grosse listed approximately twenty compounds containing tin-tin bonds which had been prepared up to 1937. These included a few R_2Sn compounds, a few hexaorganoditins, and four higher polystannanes. The review article on organotin compounds by Ingham et al. in 1960, still listed only approximately 29 tin-tin bond containing compounds consisting of about 16 R_2Sn compounds, about 19 hexaorganoditins, 4 higher polystannanes, and no functionally substituted organopolytins (except for the possible inclusion of several organopolytin sodium compounds which were prepared in liquid ammonia).

About 1960, there was a marked increase in interest in organotin chemistry which was reflected by a large increase in the number of publications in this field. In the area of organopolytins this can also be seen by comparing about 140 tin-tin bond-containing compounds now listed in this article with the much smaller number (about 30) known in 1960. Over 40 of these organotin compounds contain functional substituents, whereas about 70 of them are organotritins or higher polytins. These figures particularly point out two areas of recent activity, i.e., the attempt to prepare and characterize catenated compounds containing more than two tin atoms in a chain, and the preparation of organotin compounds with functional substituents.

Without attempting to be complete, attention is called in this final paragraph to some of the work which has contributed greatly to this increase since about 1960. At that time Kuivila and co-workers had just completed some studies on group IV organometallic compounds of tin involving preparation and reactions of diphenyltin, reductions with organotin hydrides which led to organotin products containing tin-tin bonds, and reactions leading to the formation of functionally substituted organoditins. Neumann and co-workers studied the so-called "divalent" tin problem, R_2Sn, showing that such compounds are polymeric substances which, prepared under differing conditions, may be linear with end groups, may have branched chains, or may be cyclic. Gilman et al., followed by Creemers et al., investigated branched chain polystannanes.

The great increase in the number and variety of organotin hydrides and their reactions has lead to an increase in the number of known organopolytins. Several groups of investigators, including Neumann et al., van der Kerk et al., and Sawyer et al., have carried out decompositions of organotin hydrides either with or without catalysts to give compounds containing tin-tin bonds. These groups have also made use of the hydrostannolyis reaction to obtain ditins, tritins, and other higher polytins. The mechanism of this reaction and the often accompanying exchange reaction has also been studied. Creemers has further used this reaction to prepare organotin compounds containing metal-metal bonds with tin bonded to other metals. These compounds will be described in another chapter.

Sawyer et al. have prepared a number of di-functionally substituted ditins, whereas Creemers et al. have prepared a number of monofunctionally substituted ditins. Although about 33 such functionally substituted ditins are listed in Table 2 there are only about 10 higher polytins containing functional substituents so listed. One may anticipate increased activity in this area as routes to these interesting compounds now appear available.

II. Preparation and Properties

A. ORGANODITINS AND OTHER ORGANOPOLYTINS WITHOUT FUNCTIONAL SUBSTITUENTS

1. *Linear*

a. Organoditins. Many hexaorganoditins are known either as a result of their direct preparation or by their formation as by-products in other reactions. The review article in 1960 by Ingham et al. (*41*) listed nineteen hexaalkyl and hexaaryl ditins, five of which were unsymmetrical. In a more recent survey by Gilman et al. (*32*) in 1966, twenty-four hexaorganoditins were listed. A listing of hexaorganoditins and other organopolytins without functional substituents, is found in the Table 1.

The hexaorganoditins with small alkyl groups tend to be liquids which can be distilled at reduced pressure without decomposition. For example, 1,1,1-triethyl-2,2,2-trimethylditin shows no dissociation during heating at 170°C for several hours (*76*). Hexaphenylditin and other ditins containing aryl groups tend to be solids at room temperature.

The Sn—Sn bond energy in hexaethylditin has been reported to be 50 kcal/mole based on its heat of reaction with benzoyl peroxide (*82c*). This is to be compared with a Ge—Ge bond energy of 62 kcal/mole calculated from the heat of combustion of hexaethyldigermane (*82b*).

The first reported hexaorganoditin, hexaethylditin, was obtained by reaction of ethyl iodide with a tin-sodium alloy (*58*). Although most of the earlier methods of preparation involved organotin halides and/or organotin alkali metal derivatives, later methods have involved organotin hydrides. Many of the earlier methods led only to symmetrical hexaorganoditins. Recent work, mainly involving hydrostannolysis reactions, leads not only to symmetrical but to unsymmetrical hexaorganoditins as well. This work has been extended to the formation of compounds containing tin–other element bonds (*20*) for example:

$$R_3SnNEt_2 + Ph_3GeH \longrightarrow R_3Sn—GePh_3 + Et_2NH \qquad (R = Et, Ph)$$

The following reactions are illustrative of the methods just noted:

$$2\,Me_3SnBr + 2\,Na \longrightarrow Me_3Sn—SnMe_3 + 2\,NaBr$$

$$Me_3SnBr + Ph_3SnNa \longrightarrow Me_3Sn—SnPh_3 + NaBr$$

Often the reactions have been carried out in liquid ammonia although other solvents such as benzene, toluene, xylene, and diethyl ether have also been used. Organotin hydrides react with organotin oxides, alkoxides, amines, halides, formyl amines, and hydrazines under suitable conditions to give compounds containing tin-tin bonds. The name hydrostannolysis has been given to this general reaction:

$$2\,Bu_3SnH + (Bu_3Sn)_2O \xrightarrow{100°} 2\,Bu_3Sn\text{---}SnBu_3 + H_2O$$

$$R_3SnH + R_3SnOR' \longrightarrow R_3Sn\text{---}SnR_3 + R'OH$$

$$R_3SnH + R_3SnNR'_2 \longrightarrow R_3Sn\text{---}SnR_3 + R'_2NH$$

By varying R groups in the two reactants unsymmetrical compounds may be produced.

$$R_3SnN(Ph)CHO + Ph_3SnH \longrightarrow R_3SnSnPh_3 + HN(Ph)CHO$$

Using this latter reaction, for example, Creemers (*20*) has prepared R_3Sn—$SnPh_3$ compounds where R = Me, Et, *n*-Bu, *n*-Hex, and *n*-Oct. He has also studied the mechanism of the hydrostannolysis of the Sn—N and Sn—O bond in detail, as well as the often accompanying exchange reaction.

Catalytic decompositions of triorganotin hydrides, which occur less readily than with diorganotin dihydrides, produce hexaorganoditins (*64*):

$$2\,R_3SnH \xrightarrow{\text{catalyst}} R_3Sn\text{---}SnR_3 + H_2$$

A number of specific reactions leading to the well-known compound hexaphenylditin are also indicated in the following diagram.

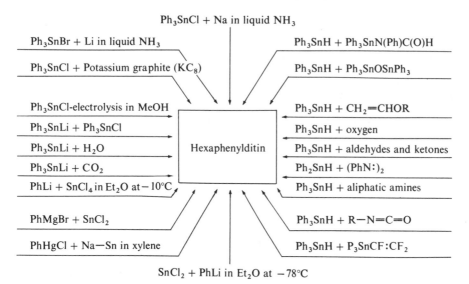

b. Organotritins. Although in 1925 Kraus and Greer (*47*) reported the first example of an organotritin, 1,3-diethyl-1,1,2,2,3,3-hexamethyltritin, by the reaction of 1 mole of hexamethyltritin 1,3-disodium with 2 moles of ethyl bromide, it was not until recently that other examples of octaorganotritins were reported from reactions involving organotin hydrides:

$$\underset{\underset{\displaystyle CH_3\ CH_3\ CH_3}{|\quad|\quad|}}{\overset{\overset{\displaystyle CH_3\ CH_3\ CH_3}{|\quad|\quad|}}{Na-Sn-Sn-Sn-Na}} + 2\ CH_2H_5I \longrightarrow \underset{\underset{\displaystyle CH_3\ CH_3\ CH_3}{|\quad|\quad|}}{\overset{\overset{\displaystyle CH_3\ CH_3\ CH_3}{|\quad|\quad|}}{C_2H_5-Sn-Sn-Sn-C_2H_5}} + 2\ NaI$$

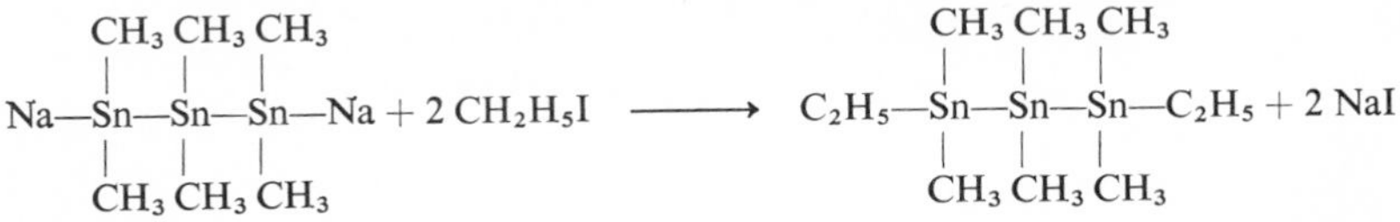

Reactions of organotin oxides with organotin hydrides at about 100°C have been used to produce both symmetrical organotritins and those having fixed organic groups. For example, triethyltin hydride and diethyltin oxide yielded octaethyltritin (78). Octa-*n*-butyltritin was obtained by the reaction of tri-*n*-butyltin hydride with di-*n*-butyltin oxide using a 2:1 mole ratio as shown by the equation below (89, 90):

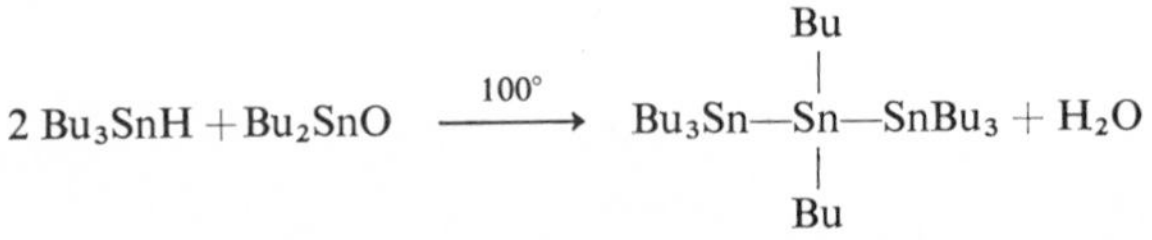

$$2\ Bu_3SnH + Bu_2SnO \xrightarrow{\ 100°\ } \underset{\underset{\displaystyle Bu}{|}}{\overset{\overset{\displaystyle Bu}{|}}{Bu_3Sn-Sn-SnBu_3}} + H_2O$$

Although the reaction between di-*n*-butyltin dihydride and bis-(tri-*n*-butyltin) oxide in a 1:1 mole ratio at 100°C also yielded octa-*n*-butyltritin, it was found that, on mixing the reactants at room temperature, a rapid exchange occurred producing

$$(Bu_3Sn)_2O + Bu_2SnH_2 \longrightarrow 2\ Bu_3SnH + Bu_2SnO$$

the reactants of the previous equation. In numerous such cases hydrostannolysis to form tin-tin bonds may be observed to be preceded by exchange of electronegative groups. The hydrostannolysis reaction, both as to scope and mechanism as well as exchange reactions involving organotin hydrides and other organotin-element bonds are reviewed in considerable detail in Sec. IV of the chapter on organotin hydrides.

Hydrostannolysis involving organotin oxides and organotin hydrides has also produced the following organotritins with mixed organic groups:

(*n*-Bu)₃Sn—SnPh₂—Sn—(*n*-Bu)₃	(from tri-*n*-butyltin hydride and diphenyltin oxide) (90)
(*iso*-Bu)₃Sn—SnPh₂—Sn(*iso*-Bu₃)	(from triisobutyltin hydride and diphenyltin oxide) (104)

Triethyltin methoxide and diphenyltin dihydride in a 2:1 mole ratio has led to $Et_3Sn-SnPh_2-SnEt_3$ (20).

Hydrostannolysis was not observed to occur with bis(triorganotin)sulfides and triorganotin hydrides (20).

The condensation of organotin dihydrides with organotin amines has also been used to produce octaorganotritins (*78, 103, 104*):

$$2 \; R_3'Sn—NEt_2 + H—\overset{\displaystyle R}{\underset{\displaystyle R}{\overset{|}{\underset{|}{Sn}}}}—H \longrightarrow R_3'Sn—\overset{\displaystyle R}{\underset{\displaystyle R}{\overset{|}{\underset{|}{Sn}}}}—SnR_3' + 2 \; Et_2NH$$

When $R = R' =$ methyl, ethyl, *n*-butyl, and isobutyl symmetrically substituted compounds were obtained. Compounds with mixed organic groups were obtained when $R = $ *n*-butyl and $R' = $ ethyl, and where $R = $ isobutyl and $R' = $ ethyl, phenyl, and cyclohexyl, respectively. Likewise organotritins were obtained in some cases by the following reaction, where $R = R' =$ methyl, ethyl, and *n*-butyl and where $R' = $ ethyl and $R = $ *n*-butyl, methyl, and isobutyl, respectively (*103, 104*):

$$2 \; R_3'SnH + R_2Sn(NEt_2)_2 \longrightarrow R_3'Sn—\overset{\displaystyle R}{\underset{\displaystyle R}{\overset{|}{\underset{|}{Sn}}}}—SnR_3' + 2 \; Et_2NH$$

As with oxides in certain cases ligand redistribution on tin was observed to occur.

Octamethyl-, octaethyl-, and octa-*n*-butyltritins have been obtained from the corresponding pentaorganoditin monohydrides (*20, 21*).

Mixed aliphatic-aromatic tritins and octaphenyltritin have been prepared by Creemers et al. (*20, 21*) from organotin hydrides and (*N*-phenylformamido) tin drivatives:

$$2 \; R_3SnN(Ph)C \,(OH) + Ph_2SnH_2 \longrightarrow R_3Sn—SnPh_2—SnR_3 + 2 \; PhNHC(O)H$$
$$(R = \text{methyl, ethyl, } n\text{-butyl, } n\text{-hexyl, and } n\text{-octyl})$$

$$R_2Sn[N(Ph)C(O)H]_2 + 2 \; Ph_3SnH \longrightarrow Ph_3Sn—SnR_2—Ph_3 + 2 \; PhNHC(O)H$$
$$(R = \text{ethyl, } n\text{-butyl and phenyl})$$

An example of condensation brought about by an amine has been reported by Neumann et al. (*104*) in which di-*n*-butyltin dibromide and triethylamine in a 1 : 2 mole ratio were mixed with 2 moles of triphenyltin hydride to obtain triethylamine hydrochloride and 1,1,1,3,3,3-hexaphenyl-2,2-di-*n*-butyltritin. 1,1,1-Triethyl-2,2,2-triphenylditin was also prepared in the same manner

$$Ph_3SnH + Et_3SnCl \xrightarrow[\text{exothermic}]{Et_3N} Ph_3Sn—SnEt_3 + Et_3N \cdot HCl$$

Octaphenyltritin has been obtained from triphenyltin sodium and diphenyltin dichloride in ethylene glycol dimethyl ether (*72*).

c. Organotetratins. In 1929, Kraus and Neal (*48*) reported the formation of decamethyltetratin by the reaction of tetramethylditin 1,2-disodium in liquid ammonia with trimethyltin bromide in a 1 : 2 mole ratio.

Creemers and Noltes (*20, 21*) have recently reported the formation of decaethyl-, deca-*n*-butyl-, and decaphenyltetratins by catalytic decomposition of the corresponding pentaorganoditin monohydrides:

$$2\,R_3Sn\text{—}SnR_2H \longrightarrow R_3Sn\text{—}SnR_2\text{—}SnR_2\text{—}SnR_3 + H_2$$

In addition 1,1,1,4,4,4-hexaethyl-2,2,3,3-tetraphenyltetratin

$$(Et_3Sn\text{—}SnPh_2\text{—}SnPh_2\text{—}SnEt_3)$$

was prepared by catalytic decomposition of $Et_3Sn\text{—}SnPh_2H$.

Sommer et al. (*104*) have also reported the formation of tetratins of the type $R_3'Sn\text{—}SnR_2\text{—}SnR_2\text{—}SnR_3'$ by the hydrostannolysis of tetraorganoditin 1,2-dihydrides with trialkylstannyldiethylamines:

$$2\,R_3'SnNEt_2 + H\underset{\underset{\displaystyle R}{|}}{\overset{\overset{\displaystyle R}{|}}{Sn}}\underset{\underset{\displaystyle R}{|}}{\overset{\overset{\displaystyle R}{|}}{Sn}}H \longrightarrow R_3'Sn\underset{\underset{\displaystyle R}{|}}{\overset{\overset{\displaystyle R}{|}}{Sn}}\underset{\underset{\displaystyle R}{|}}{\overset{\overset{\displaystyle R}{|}}{Sn}}SnR_3' + 2\,Et_2NH$$

Examples were given where R = isobutyl, and R′ = methyl, ethyl, phenyl, and cyclohexyl, respectively, and where R = *n*-butyl and R′ = methyl.

d. Organopentatins. Dodecamethylpentatin was prepared in 1925 from hexamethyltritin 1,3-disodium in liquid ammonia, and two moles of trimethyltin bromide (*47*):

$$NaMe_2Sn\text{—}SnMe_2\text{—}SnMe_2Na + 2\,Me_3SnBr$$
$$\longrightarrow Me_3Sn\text{—}SnMe_2\text{—}SnMe_2\text{—}SnMe_2\text{—}SnMe_3 + 2\,NaBr$$

Docecaethylpentatin has been obtained by the reaction of the phenylisocyanate adduct of pentaethylditin monohydride with diethyltin dihydride in a 2 : 1 mole ratio (*20, 21*).

$$Et_3Sn\text{—}SnEt_2H + PhNCO \longrightarrow Et_3Sn\text{—}SnEt_2\text{—}N(Ph)C(O)H$$
$$2\,Et_3Sn\text{—}SnEt_2\text{—}N(Ph)C(O)H + Et_2SnH_2$$
$$\longrightarrow Et_3Sn\text{—}SnEt_2\text{—}SnEt_2\text{—}SnEt_2\text{—}SnEt_3$$
$$+ 2\,PhNHC(O)H$$

An example of a linear pentatin with mixed organic groups was obtained from the phenyl isocyanate adduct of penta-*n*-butylditin monohydride and diphenyltin dihydride yielding $Bu_3Sn\text{—}SnBu_2\text{—}SnPh_2\text{—}SnBu_2\text{—}SnBu_3$ (*20*).

It was suggested that organopentatins should also result from the reaction of organotritin monohydrides with the phenylisocyanate adducts of organoditin monohydrides although no specific examples were given (*20*).

e. Organohexatins. Tetradecaethylhexatin, $Et_{14}Sn_6$, has been produced by

Creemers and Noltes via catalytic decomposition of heptaethyltritin mono-hydride (*20, 21*):

$$2 \text{ Et}_3\text{Sn—SnEt}_2\text{—SnEt}_2\text{H} \xrightarrow[-\text{H}_2]{\text{Et}_2\text{NH}} \text{Et}_3\text{Sn—SnEt}_2\text{—SnEt}_2\text{—SnEt}_2\text{—SnEt}_2\text{—SnEt}_3$$

2. Branched

The first branched chain organopolytin compound was obtained by Boeseken and Rutgers (*12*) in 1923 along with tetraphenyltin and hexaphenyl-ditin in the reaction of phenylmagnesium bromide with stannous chloride in a 6 : 1 mole ratio. Of several possible structures it was thought to be tetrakis (triphenylstannyl)tin, $(\text{Ph}_3\text{Sn})_4\text{Sn}$.

Gilman and Cartledge (*33*) prepared this same compound by Böesekens method and by several other methods involving a triphenyltin compound. The compounds obtained from all of these reactions were identical and were shown by the method of preparation, x-ray studies, and chemical reactions to be tetrakis(triphenylstannyl)tin. The intermediate tris(triphenylstannyl)tin lithium in one of these reactions was characterized by reaction with chloro-triphenylgermane to give tris(triphenylstannyl)-(triphenylgermyl)tin:

$$3 \text{ Ph}_3\text{SnLi} + \text{SnCl}_2 \longrightarrow [(\text{Ph}_3\text{Sn})_3\text{SnLi}] \xrightarrow{\text{Ph}_3\text{SnCl}} (\text{Ph}_3\text{Sn})_4\text{Sn}$$
$$[(\text{Ph}_3\text{Sn})_3\text{SnLi}]$$

$$\xrightarrow{\text{ClGePh}_3} (\text{Ph}_3\text{Sn})_3\text{SnGePh}_3$$

Williamsens and van der Kerk (*119, 120*) in a study of compounds of the general formula $(\text{Ph}_3\text{M})_4\text{M}'$ (where M and M′ are Ge, Sn, or Pb in all possible combinations) prepared $(\text{Ph}_3\text{Sn})_4\text{Sn}$ from triphenyltin lithium and stannic chloride:

$$4 \text{ Ph}_3\text{SnLi} + \text{SnCl}_4 \longrightarrow (\text{Ph}_3\text{Sn})_4\text{Sn} + 4 \text{ LiCl}$$

Tris(trialkyltin)phenyltin compounds of the type $(\text{R}_3\text{Sn})_3\text{SnPh}$ were obtained by Creemers et al. (*20, 23*) by reactions of trialkyl(*N*-phenylforma-mido)tin with phenyltin trihydride.

$$3 \text{ R}_3\text{SnN(Ph)C(O)H} + \text{PhSnH}_3 \longrightarrow (\text{R}_3\text{Sn})_3\text{SnPh} + 3 \text{ PhNHC(O)H}$$
$$(\text{R} = \text{ethyl, } n\text{-butyl, and } n\text{-octyl})$$

Catalytic decomposition of 1,1,1,3,3,3-hexa-*n*-butyl-2-phenyltritin-2-hydride has resulted in an organohexatin with branched chains, namely, 1,1,1,4,4,4-hexa-*n*-butyl-2,3-diphenyl-2,3-di(tri-*n*-butylstannyl)tetratin (*20*):

$$2 \underset{\underset{\text{H}}{|}}{\overset{\overset{\text{Ph}}{|}}{\text{Bu}_3\text{Sn—Sn—SnBu}_3}} \xrightarrow{\text{Et}_2\text{NH}} \underset{\underset{\text{Ph}}{|}}{\overset{\overset{\text{Ph}}{|}}{\text{Bu}_3\text{Sn—Sn—SnBu}_3}} + \text{H}_2$$

Irradiation of both tetraethyltin and hexaethylditin by ultraviolet radiation as well as the action of aluminum chloride has been shown by Razuvaev and coworkers (*83–85*) to yield dark red polymeric organotin compounds. Studies of these compounds indicated the presence of branching and the mechanism of its production was suggested. These compounds are highly reactive toward oxygen.

Neumann (*66*) has surveyed the "dialkyltin" problem and has determined that many of the preparations reported in the literature involving colored products, both with dialkyltins and with diphenyltin, consist of partially branched tin chains. The degree of branching was determined by halogenation at $-70°C$ to give cleavage of the Sn—Sn bonds only. The presence of only R_2SnCl_2 in the product indicated cyclic organotin polymers, the presence of R_3SnCl indicated end groups, and the presence of $RSnCl_3$ indicated branching. Catalytic dehydrogenation of diorganotin dihydrides with appropriate catalysts gave cyclic organotin compounds. These compounds reacted with "aluminum chloride, boron fluoride, ferric chloride, ethyl magnesium bromide and other substances to give yellow or red oils with open and sometimes branched tin chains".

Kuivila and Beumel (*52*) have carried out reductions of aldehydes and ketones with butyltin trihydride and phenyltin trihydride, respectively, and as a tin containing by-product obtained the first reported example of a compound analyzing for $(RSn)_n$. In the case of the reaction of butyltin trihydride with acetone a red solid, pyrophoric in air, was isolated with a formula indicating it to be butyltin $(BuSn)_n$.

When butyltin trihydride was allowed to decompose thermally, or in the presence of a catalyst, NMR spectra taken at intervals indicated the presence of intermediate hydrides whose proportions changed with time. These hydrides eventually disappeared resulting in a product showing the same properties as those above (*94*). Presumably these intermediates are polytin hydride species such as

$$
\begin{array}{ccc}
 & Bu & \\
Bu & | & Bu \\
\diagdown Sn-Sn-Sn \diagup & \\
H \diagup \;|\;\;\;|\;\;\;| \diagdown H & \\
\;\;\; H\;\; H\;\; H &
\end{array}
\qquad
\left[\begin{array}{c} Bu \\ | \\ Sn \\ | \\ H \end{array}\right]_n
\quad,\ etc.
$$

When exposed to air, this product was converted to butylstannonic acid. Because of its extreme reactivity, accurate molecular weights were not obtained but preliminary osmometric determinations and its ready solubility in common organic solvents such as benzene, toluene, methylene chloride, chloroform, and carbon tetrachloride, indicated a low degree of polymerization. Authentic R_2Sn compounds have been shown, in reality, to be cyclic polymers containing tetravalent tin. If it is assumed that tin is tetravalent in

RSn compounds and if multiple bonding is ruled out, these compounds must contain tin chains with considerable branching. The specific structure and the type of bonding in these compounds remains to be determined.

3. *Cyclic*

Although compounds with the empirical formula R_2Sn have been known for some time, until recently their real structure was not recognized.

The first reported dialkyltin, diethyltin, was obtained by Lowig (*58*) in 1852 as one of several products in the reaction of ethyl iodide with a sodium-tin alloy. The review of organotin compounds in 1960 by Ingham et al. (*41*) listed 16 such compounds.

In 1961, Kuivila (*54*) and co-workers prepared some modifications of diphenyltin. This was followed by a series of excellent papers by Neumann and co-workers (*65, 66, 68, 70, 71, 73–75*) shedding light on the structure of R_2Sn compounds. Many of these were shown to have end groups and/or branched chains. But particularly, they were able to show that numerous compounds were clearly cyclic in nature. This was shown by reactions with halogen (X_2) at low temperature followed by isolation of only R_2SnX_2, as well as by NMR studies. Brown and Morgan (*15*) in 1963 reported, based on NMR and molecular weight studies, that they had obtained cyclic hexamers of dimethyltin. Farrar and Skinner (*29*) in 1969 also reported the formation of octa-*tert*-butylcyclotetratin. That it was a cyclic polymer was shown by its reaction with one mole of I_2 to yield octa-*tert*-butyltetratin 1,4-diiodide. Although it seems that six-membered rings predominate, cyclic compounds varying from four to nine tin atoms in the ring have been obtained depending on the R group and on the method of preparation. Small differences in reaction conditions and catalysts seem to markedly affect the degree of poly-merization. No organocyclotritins have been reported. The structure of dodecaphenylcyclohexatin has been determined by X-ray analysis (*81*). An excellent recent critical survey of these compounds may be found in Chap. 14 of " Die Organische Chemie des Zinns " by Prof. Dr. Wilhelm Neumann (*64*). A listing of organocyclotins may be found in the Table 1. A brief discussion of some individual organocyclotins follows.

a. Organocyclotetratins.

```
        R   R
        |   |
    R—Sn—Sn—R
        |   |
    R—Sn—Sn—R
        |   |
        R   R
```

Octa-*tert*-butylcyclotetratin was obtained by Farrar and Skinner (*29*) when di-*tert*-butyltin dichloride reacted with an excess of *tert*-butylmagnesium

TABLE 1

ORGANODITINS AND OTHER ORGANOPOLYTINS WITHOUT FUNCTIONAL SUBSTITUENTS

M.p. and b.p. have been separated by a comma, and b.p.'s have pressures alongside ( ) expressed in torr.

Compounds	m.p. (°C) b.p. (°C)	References
Organoditins		
$R_3Sn—SnR_3$		
Hexamethylditin	23°C, 182°C (756 torr)	(39, 45, 46, 48, 49, 79)
Hexaethylditin	84–87°C (0.07 torr), 160°C (23 torr)	(20, 30, 78, 79)
	n_D^{20} 1.5380, $n_D^{17.8}$ 1.53738	
Hexa-n-propylditin	143.6°C (15 torr)	(37)
	$n_D^{19.5}$ 1.52583	
Hexa-n-butylditin	156–160°C (0.025 torr)	(78, 79, 90a)
	n_D^{25} 1.5990	
Hexaisobutylditin	56°C, 130°C (0.15 torr)	(79, 103)
Hexaneopentylditin	275–277°C	(124)
Hexacyclohexylditin	—	(79)
Hexaphenylditin	237°C	(78, 79)
Hexa-p-chlorophenylditin	224–226°C	(36a, 63a)
Hexakis(m-trifluoromethylphenyl)ditin	100.6–101.9°C	(104a)
Hexa-p-tolylditin	145°C, 251–252°C	(14)
Hexa-o-tolylditin	298–300°C, 208–210°C	(36a, 63)
Hexabenzylditin	147–148°C	(57a)
Hexa-p-xylylditin	196°C	(50)

Hexa-2-biphenylyldiltin	170°C, 288–289°C	(9)
Hexacyanoethyldiltin	—	(111)
R₃Sn—SnR₃'		
1,1,1-Trimethyl-2,2,2-triethylditin	235°C (748 torr)	(76, 79)
1,1,1-Trimethyl-2,2,2-tri-*n*-butylditin	—	(90a)
1,1,1-Triethyl-2,2,2-tri-*n*-propylditin	88–89°C (907 torr) n_D^{20} 1.5219	(20)
1,1,1-Triethyl-2,2,2-tri-*n*-butylditin	109°C (0.2 torr), n_D^{20} 1.5230	(20, 79, 103)
1,1,1-Triethyl-2,2,2-triisobutylditin	117°C (0.3 torr)	(78, 79, 103)
1,1,1-Trimethyl-2,2,2-tricyclohexylditin		(79)
1,1,1-Triisobutyl-2,2,2-tricyclohexylditin		(79)
1,1,1-Trimethyl-2,2,2-triphenylditin	108–110°C, 107–108.5°C	(20, 79)
1,1,1-Triethyl-2,2,2-triphenylditin	16°C, n_D^{20} 1.6327	(20, 23, 78, 79)
1,1,1-Tri-*n*-propyl-2,2,2-triphenylditin	37–39°C	(20)
1,1,1-Tri-*n*-butyl-2,2,2-triphenylditin	n_D^{20} 1.5978	(20, 79)
1,1,1-Triisobutyl-2,2,2-triphenylditin	79°C	(79, 103)
1,1,1-Tri-*n*-hexyl-2,2,2-triphenylditin	n_D^{20} 1.5776	(20)
1,1,1-Tricyclohexy-2,2,2-triphenylditin		(79)
1,1,1-Tri-*n*-octyl-2,2,2-triphenylditin	n_D^{20} 1.5599	(20)
1,1,1-Trimethyl-2,2,2-tri-*p*-tolylditin	139.5–141°C	(14)
1,1,1-Triethyl-2,2,2-tri-*p*-tolylditin	88–98°C (0.07 torr), n_D^{20} 1.5219	(20, 22)
R₂Sn—SnR₂' R' | R'		
1,2-Di-*n*-propyltetraethylditin	165.8°C (15 torr), $n_D^{15.3}$ 1.53541	(37)
1,2-Diisobutyltetraethylditin	179°C (15.5 torr), $n_D^{19.8}$ 1.5271	(37)
1,2-Bis(cyanoethyl)tetraisobutylditin	173–175°C (0.005 torr), n_D^{20} 1.539	(64)
1,2-Bis(γ-aminopropyl)tetraisobutylditin	—	(75)
1,2-Bis(acetoxyethyl)tetraisobutylditin	148–150°C (10⁻⁴torr) n_D^{20} 1.521	(64)

Continued

TABLE 1—*continued*

Compounds	m.p. (°C) b.p. (°C)	References
Organotritins		
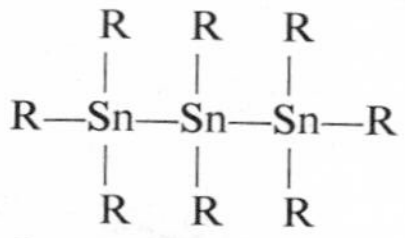 $\begin{array}{ccc} R & R & R \\ \| & \| & \| \\ R-Sn-Sn-Sn-R \\ \| & \| & \| \\ R & R & R \end{array}$		
Octamethyltritin	50–52°C (3.10 × 10⁻⁵ torr), 66–68°C (10⁻⁴ torr), n_D^{20} 1.5983, 1.5898	(*14, 20, 104*)
Octaethyltritin	124–127°C (10⁻⁴ torr), 118°C (10⁻³ torr), n_D^{20} 1.5894, 1.5802	(*20, 21, 78, 103, 104*)
Octa-*n*-butyltritin	175–177°C (10⁻⁴ torr), 165°C	(*103, 104,*)
Octaisobutyltritin	(10⁻³ torr), n_D^{20} 1.5342, 1.5380	(*20, 21, 90, 103, 104*)
	−7°C 169–172°C (10⁻⁴ torr), 170°C (10⁻³ torr), n_D^{20} 1.5431	(*103, 104*)
Octaphenyltritin	156–158°C dec., 280°C dec.	(*70, 72*)
Octabenzyltritin	163–165°C dec.	(*75*)
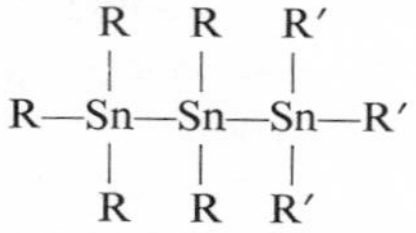 $\begin{array}{ccc} R & R & R' \\ \| & \| & \| \\ R-Sn-Sn-Sn-R' \\ \| & \| & \| \\ R & R & R' \end{array}$		
1,1,1,2,2-Pentaethyl-3,3,3-triphenyltritin	n_D^{20} 1.6516	(*23*)
1,1,1,2,2-Penta-*n*-butyl-3,3,3-triphenyltritin	n_D^{20} 1.6002	(*20, 21*)
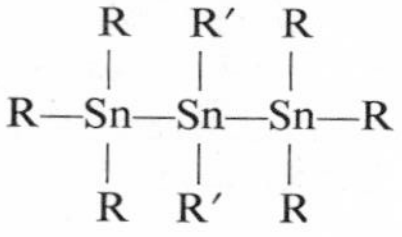 $\begin{array}{ccc} R & R' & R \\ \| & \| & \| \\ R-Sn-Sn-Sn-R \\ \| & \| & \| \\ R & R' & R \end{array}$		

1,1,1,3,3,3-Hexaethyl-2,2-dimethyltritin	113–117°C (10^{-4} torr), 114°C (0.001 torr), n_D^{20} 1.5821	(103, 104)
1,1,1,3,3,3-Hexaethyl-2,2-di-n-butyltritin	139–141°C (10^{-4} torr), 140°C (0.001 torr), n_D^{20} 1.5641	(78, 103, 104)
1,1,1,3,3,3-Hexaethyl-2,2-diisobutyltritin	136°C (0.001 torr)	(103)
1,1,1,3,3,3-Hexacyclohexyl-2,2-diisobutyltritin	168°C	(104)
1,1,1,3,3,3-Hexamethyl-2,2-diphenyltritin	n_D^{20} 1.6624	(23)
1,1,1,3,3,3-Hexaethyl-2,2-diphenyltritin	n_D^{20} 1.6202	(23)
1,1,1,3,3,3-Hexa-n-butyl-2,2-diphenyltritin	n_D^{20} 1.5886	(20, 23, 90)
1,1,1,3,3,3-Hexaisobutyl-2,2-diphenyltritin	28°C, n_D^{20} 1.5840	(104)
1,1,1,3,3,3-Hexa-n-octyl-2,2-diphenyltritin	n_D^{20} 1.5420	(23)
1,1,1,3,3,3-Hexaphenyl-2,2-di-n-butyltritin	83°C, n_D^{20} 1.6452	(20, 23, 104)
1,1,1,3,3,3-Hexaphenyl-2,2-diisobutyltritin	111°C	(104)

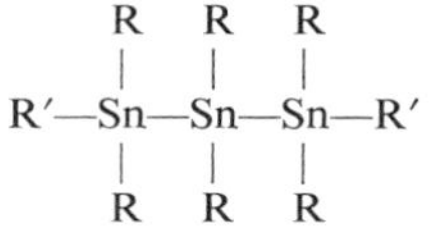

```
        R   R
        |   |
R'—Sn—Sn—R'
        |   |
        R   R
```

1,1,2,2,3,3-Hexamethyl-1,3-diethyltritin	—	(47)

Organotetratins

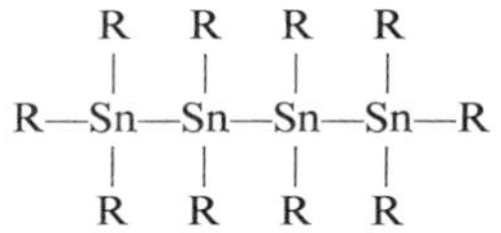

```
          R   R   R
          |   |   |
R—Sn—Sn—Sn—Sn—R
          |   |   |
          R   R   R
```

R			
Methyl	Decamethyltetratin	—	(48)
Ethyl	Decaethyltetratin	n_D^{20} 1.6283	(20, 21, 104)
n-Butyl	Deca-n-butyltetratin	n_D^{20} 1.5543	(21)
Phenyl	Decaphenyltetratin	170–172°C	(20)

Continued

TABLE 1—continued

Compounds	m.p. (°C) b.p. (°C)	References

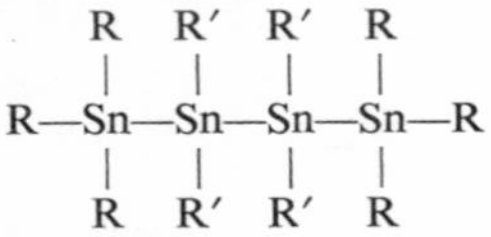

```
      R    R'   R'    R
      |    |    |     |
  R—Sn—Sn—Sn—Sn—R
      |    |    |     |
      R    R'   R'    R
```

R	R'		
Methyl	n-Butyl	161–164°C (10⁻⁴ torr), n_D^{20} 1.5785	(104)
Methyl	Isobutyl	~90°C, 150–155°C (10⁻⁴ torr)	(104)
Ethyl	Isobutyl	172–175°C (10⁻⁴ torr), n_D^{20} 1.5842	(104)
Cyclohexyl	Isobutyl	207°C	(104)
Phenyl	Isobutyl	114°C	(104)
Ethyl 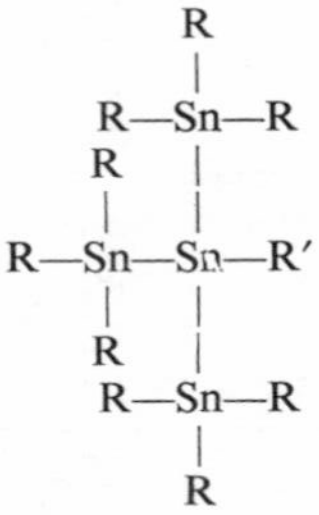	Phenyl	n_D^{20} 1.6877	(104)

```
          R
          |
      R—Sn—R
          |
  R—Sn—Sn—R'
          |
      R—Sn—R
          |
          R
```

R	R'		
Methyl	Methyl	—	(117a)
Phenyl	Methyl	181–188°C	(20, 23)
Ethyl	Phenyl	n_D^{20} 1.6648	(20)
n-Butyl	Phenyl	n_D^{20} 1.5721	(20, 23)
Octyl	Phenyl	n_D^{20} 1.5345	

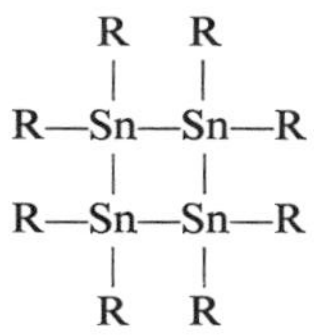

tert-Butyl	Octa-tert-butylcyclotetratin	205°C dec.	(29, 75)
Benzyl	Octabenzylcyclotetratin	226–228°C dec.	(69, 75)

Organopentatins

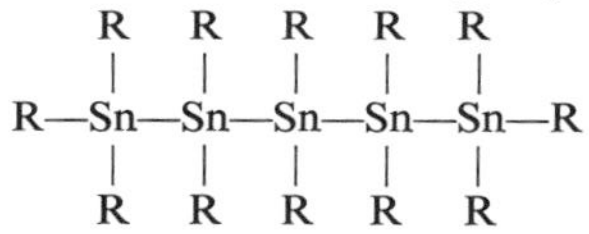

Methyl	Dodecamethylpentatin	—	(47)
Ethyl	Dodecaethylpentatin	n_D^{20} 1.6433	(20, 21)
n-Butyl / Phenyl	3,3-Diphenyldeca-n-butylpentatin	n_D^{20} 1.6085	(20)

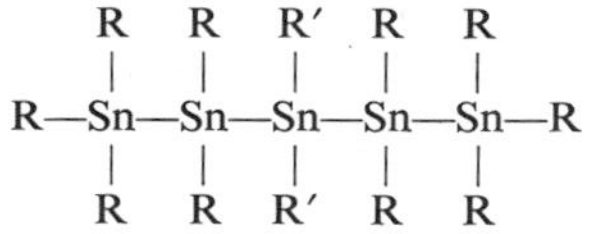

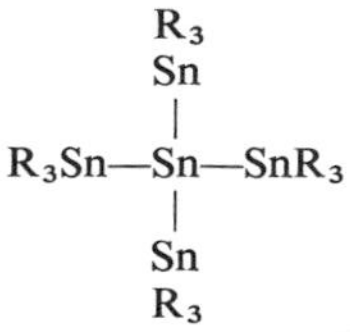

$$R_3Sn\!-\!Sn\!-\!SnR_3$$

Continued

TABLE 1—*continued*

Compounds	m.p. (°C) b.p. (°C)	References
R Ph Tetrakis(triphenylstannyl)tin	280°C dec.	(12, 33, 119, 120)
R Cyclohexyl Decacyclohexylcyclopentatin Phenyl Decaphenylcyclopentatin	185°C dec.	(75) (68, 70)

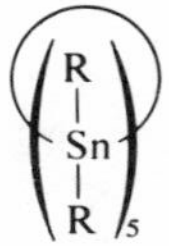

Organohexatins

$$R-Sn-Sn-Sn-Sn-Sn-R$$

with R groups on each Sn.

Tetradecaethylhexatin R Ethyl	n_D^{20} 1.678	(20, 21)
$R_3Sn-Sn-SnR_3$ R' $R_3Sn-Sn-SnR_3$ R'		
R n-Butyl R' Phenyl 1,1,1,4,4,4-Hexa-*n*-butyl-2,3-diphenyl-2,3-di(tri-*n*-butylstannyltetratin)	n_D^{20} 1.6258	(20)

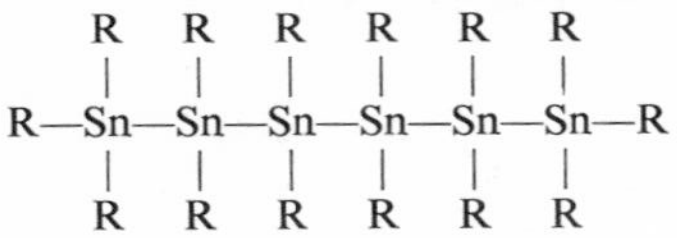

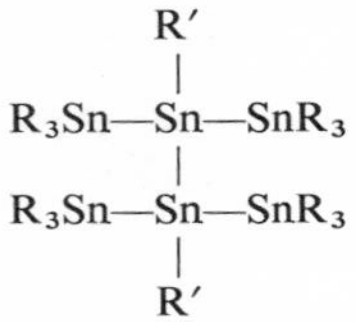

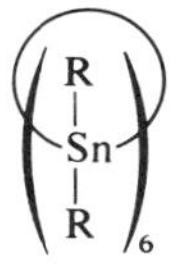

$(R—Sn—R)_6$

R			
Methyl	Dodecamethylcyclohexatin	—	(14)
Ethyl	Dodecaethylcyclohexatin	—	(65, 73)
n-Butyl	Dodeca-n-butylcyclohexatin		(75)
Isobutyl	Dodecaisobutylcyclohexatin	—	(67, 75)
Phenyl	Dodecaphenylcyclohexatin	270°C dec.	(68, 70, 81)
p-Tolyl	Dodeca-p-tolylcyclohexatin	260–270°C dec.	(71)
p-Ethoxyphenyl	Dodeca-p-ethoxyphenylcyclohexatin	235–240°C dec.	(71)
p-Biphenylyl	Dodeca-p-biphenylylcyclohexatin		(71)
α-Naphthyl	Dodeca-α-naphthylcyclohexatin	305°C dec.	(71)
β-Naphthyl	Dodeca-β-naphthylcyclohexatin*	270°C dec.	(71)

Other Organopolytins

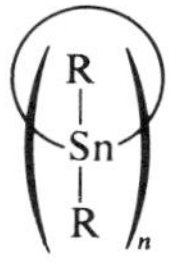

$(R—Sn—R)_n$

n	R			
7	Ethyl	Tetradecaethylcycloheptatin		(65, 73)
9	Ethyl	Octadecaethylcyclononatin		(65, 73)
9	Isobutyl	Octadecaisobutylcyclononatin		(75)

* Not specifically shown to be a cyclic hexamer.

chloride in boiling tetrahydrofuran. X-ray analysis indicated that the degree of polymerization must be four or less. Reaction with a cold solution of iodine in benzene yielded a compound whose analysis and molecular weight corresponded to octa-*tert*-butyltetratin 1,4-diiodide.

The same compound was obtained by Neumann et al. (*75*) by hydrostannolysis involving di-*tert*-butyltin dihydride and di-*tert*-butyltin diethylamine.

Octabenzylcyclotetratin was prepared by Neumann and Konig (*69*) by the catalytic decomposition of dibenzyltin dihydride in dimethylformamide with dibenzyltin dichloride as a cocatalyst.

Thermal decomposition of di-*n*-butyltin dihydride in the presence of pyridine only at 105°C has given a quantitative yield of hydrogen and a product, over 96% pure by iodine titration, whose degree of polymerization determined osmometrically in toluene was 4.06. Although not proven by these experiments, it is likely that this also is a cyclic tetramer of di-*n*-butyltin (*93*). Other modifications of di-*n*-butyltin prepared by Neumann et al. (*75*) by slightly different methods were cyclic hexamers.

b. Organocyclopentatins.

$$\begin{array}{c} \text{R} \quad \text{R} \\ \text{R}_{\diagdown}\overset{|}{\underset{}{\text{Sn}}}-\overset{|}{\underset{}{\text{Sn}}}-\text{R} \\ \diagup \qquad \diagdown \\ \text{R}-\text{Sn}_{\diagdown}\quad_{\diagup}\text{Sn}-\text{R} \\ \diagup \quad \text{Sn} \quad \diagdown \\ \text{R} \diagup \quad \diagdown \text{R} \\ \text{R} \qquad \text{R} \end{array}$$

Diphenyltin dihydride decomposes in dimethylformamide to give decaphenylcyclopentatin (*70*).

Decacylohexylcyclopentatin has been obtained by hydrostannolysis involving dicyclohexyltin dihydride and dicyclohexyltin diethylamine (*75*).

c. Organocyclohexatins.

$$\begin{array}{c} \text{R} \quad \text{R} \qquad \text{R} \quad \text{R} \\ \text{R}_{\diagdown}\quad_{\diagdown}\text{Sn}\diagup\quad_{\diagup} \\ \diagdown \qquad \diagup \\ \text{R}-\text{Sn} \qquad \text{Sn}-\text{R} \\ | \qquad\qquad | \\ \text{R}-\text{Sn}_{\diagdown}\quad_{\diagup}\text{Sn}-\text{R} \\ \diagup \quad \text{Sn} \quad \diagdown \\ \text{R} \quad \text{R} \qquad \text{R} \quad \text{R} \end{array}$$

Dodecamethylcyclohexatin has been obtained by Brown and Morgan (*15*) from polydimethyltin resulting from the reaction of dimethyltin dichloride with sodium in liquid ammonia. They also prepared it by treatment of the dimethyltin dichloride triethylamine adduct with lithium aluminum hydride in ether at 0°. The two products above were essentially identical. A combination of NMR and molecular weight studies indicated that these substances were cyclic hexamers of dimethyltin.

Dodecaethylcyclohexatin has been reported by Neumann and co-workers from decomposition of diethyltin dihydride with various catalysts (*65, 73*).

Dodeca-*n*-butylcyclohexatin has been prepared in several different ways by Neumann and co-workers (*75*). These methods include the decomposition of di-*n*-butyltin dihydride in the presence of ether, pyridine, and di-*n*-butyltin dichloride, or by sodium methoxide in tetrahydrofuran. Hydrostannolysis of di-*n*-butyltin dihydride with di-*n*-butyltin diethylamine or di-*n*-butyltin dimethoxide also produced the cyclic hexamer.

Dodecaisobutylcyclohexatin has been obtained by the reaction of di-isobutyltin dichloride with magnesium in tetrahydrofuran followed by treatment with methanol (*67, 75*).

Diphenyltin has been known for some time and has been prepared in various ways. Its physical properties are reported to vary greatly. Kuivila et al. (*54*) surveyed this situation and reported new preparations of diphenyltin from diphenyltin dihydride. One of these colorless forms obtained by decomposition of the dihydride in dimethylformamide has since been found to be dodecaphenylcyclohexatin (*68, 70*). The colorless crystalline compound obtained by the decomposition of the dihydride in methanol has been shown to be linear dodecaphenylhexatin 1,2-dihydride (*68, 70*). When these crystals were dissolved in dimethylformamide the previous modification was obtained (*54*). An X-ray study was made by Olsen and Rundle (*81*) on single crystals prepared by this latter method. This modification was shown to have a cyclic six membered ring with a chair configuration as shown in the following diagram.

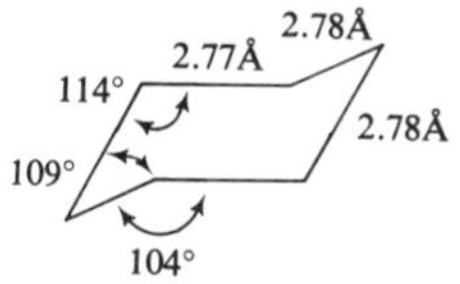

The reactions just discussed are outlined below:

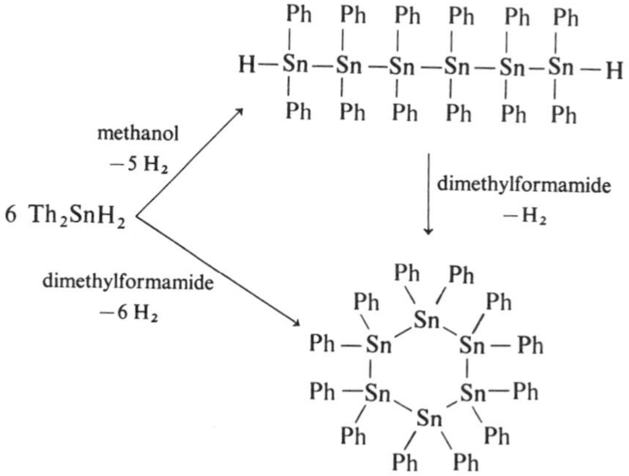

Neumann et al. (*68, 70*) have shown that with pyridine as a catalyst the hexamer is the main product, whereas with dimethylformamide the pentamer may also be obtained depending on the conditions. They have also prepared the cyclic hexamer by reaction of diphenyltin dichloride with naphthalene sodium in tetrahydrofuran (*70*).

Neumann and Konig (*71*) have prepared several other "diaryltins" by catalytic decomposition of the corresponding diaryltin dihydrides:

$$6 \ Ar_2SnH_2 \xrightarrow{\text{catalyst}} 6 \ H_2 \ + \ \text{[cyclic hexamer]}$$

In most, but not all, cases they are believed to be cyclic hexamers.

Ar =

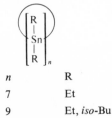

Di-*p*-biphenylyltin was also obtained from the diiodide with naphthalene-sodium in tetrahydrofuran.

d. Other Organocyclopolytins.

$$\left[\begin{array}{c} R \\ | \\ Sn \\ | \\ R \end{array}\right]_n$$

n	R
7	Et
9	Et, *iso*-Bu

Tetradecaethylcycloheptatin has been obtained by catalytic decomposition of diethyltin dihydride with finely divided tin as a catalyst. The degree of polymerization (n) varied from 6 to 9 depending on the conditions. Organic bases such as pyridine or aniline were also used as catalysts with the reaction being complete in several hours at 20–50°C. Octadecaethylcyclononatin was obtained in 94% yield by decomposition of diethyltin dihydride using $(C_2H_5)_2SnCl_2 \cdot 2$ pyridine as a catalyst (*65, 73*):

$$\text{Et}_2\text{SnH}_2 \xrightarrow[\text{or Et}_2\text{SnCl} \cdot 2 \text{ pyridine}]{\text{Tin}} \text{cyclo(Et}_2\text{Sn)}_9$$

Octadecaisobutylcyclononatin was formed by the decomposition of diisobutyltin dihydride with pyridine and diisobutyltin dichloride. It has also been obtained from hydrostannolysis of the dihydride with the corresponding organotin diethylamine, and from hydrostannolysis of the tetraorganoditin dihydride with the organotin diethylamine (*75*).

B. Organoditins and Organopolytins with Functional Substituents

Historically, Kraus and Greer (*47*) in 1925 prepared tetramethylditin 1,2-disodium by the reaction of dimethyltin dibromide with sodium in liquid ammonia. Dimethyltin was also found to react with sodium in liquid ammonia to give tetramethylditin 1,2-disodium. An analogous reaction has been carried out starting with diethyltin to yield tetraethylditin 1,2-disodium (*40*). It has also been determined that dimethyltin reacts with dimethyltin disodium to form tetramethylditin 1,2-disodium (*47*). Hexamethyltritin 1,3-disodium was produced by the reaction of dimethyltin disodium with dimethyltin dibromide in a 2 : 1 mole ratio in liquid ammonia as shown by its reaction with ethyl bromide to give the corresponding octaorganotritin. It was also converted to an organopentatin by reaction with trimethyltin bromide. Tetramethylditin 1,2-disodium has been converted to decamethyltetratin by reaction with trimethyltin bromide in a 1 : 2 mole ratio (*48*). Treatment of dimethyltin dihydride with sodium in liquid ammonia (*45*) is also believed to have produced tetramethylditin 1,2-disodium from the fact that, upon addition of methyl iodide, hexamethylditin was obtained.

Since then, starting about 1960, a number of organopolytins have been isolated bearing one or more functional substituents including carboxylate, halide, and hydride groups. These compounds are treated in this section and are listed in Table 2.

1. Organoditins with Functional Substituents

a. Tetraorganoditin 1,2-dicarboxylates. Tetraorganoditin 1,2-dicarboxylates have been prepared by the action of organic acids on diorganotin

TABLE 2

Organoditins and Other Organopolytins with Functional Substituents

Compound	Melting point (°C) [Boiling point °C (torr)	References
Organoditins		
Tetramethylditin 1,2-dichloride	186°C dec.	(12)
Tetraisobutylditin 1,2-dichloride	n_D^{20} 1.550	(74, 104)
Tetraisobutylditin 1,2-dihydride	109–112°C (10^{-3} torr) n_D^{20} 1.518	(74, 104)
Tetra-*n*-butylditin 1,2-dichloride	25–27°C	(31, 92, 96)
Tetra-*n*-butylditin 1,2-dihydride	122–124°C (10^{-3} torr), n_D^{21} 1.5205	(74, 96, 104)
Tetra-*n*-butylditin 1,2-diacetate	−7 to −4°C, n_D^{106} 1.5060	(95–98)
Tetra-*n*-butylditin 1,2-dibenzoate	31.5–32.5°C	(95, 97)
Tetra-*n*-butylditin 1,2-di-*o*-chlorobenzoate	65–66.5°C	(95, 97)
Tetra-*n*-butylditin 1,2-di-*p*-chlorobenzoate	75–77°C	(95, 97)
Tetra-*n*-butylditin 1,2-dilaurate	—	(97)
Tetraphenylditin 1,2-trifluoroacetate	165°C	(95, 97)
Tetraphenylditin 1,2-trichloroacetate	170°C	(95, 97)
Tetraphenylditin 1,2-dichloroacetate	169°C	(95, 97)
Tetraphenylditin 1,2-monochloroacetate	150°C	(95, 97)
Tetraphenylditin 1,2-diacetate	152°C	(95, 97)
Tetraphenylditin 1,2-dibenzoate	184–185°C	(34, 95, 97)
Tetraphenylditin 1,2-di-*o*-chlorobenzoate	161°C	(95, 97)
Tetraphenylditin 1,2-di-*o*-hydroxybenzoate	197°C	(95, 97)
Tetraphenylditin 1,2-dihexanoate	85–87°C	(95, 97)
Tetraphenylditin 1,2-dioctanoate	86–88°C	(95, 97)
Tetraphenylditin 1,2-diferrocenate	180–182°C	(55)
Tetraphenylditin 1,2-furoate	184–186°C dec.	(117)
Tetraphenylditin 1,2-thenoate	177–178°C dec.	(117)
Pentamethylditin monohydride	—	(20)
Pentaethylditin monohydride	n_D^{20} 1.5876	(20, 21)
Penta-*n*-butylditin monohydride	—	(20, 21)
Pentaphenylditin monohydride	—	(20, 21)
2,2,2-Triethyl-1,1-diphenylditin 1-hydride	—	(20, 21)
Penta-*n*-butylditin acetate	—	(20)
Penta-*n*-butylditin chloride	—	(20)
Pentaethylditin chloride	—	(20)
Pentaethylditin hydroxide	200°C dec.	(20)
1,2-Diphenylditin 1,1,2,2-tetrabromide	—	(30)
Organotritins		
Heptaethyltritin monohydride	—	(20, 21)
Et$_3$Sn—Et$_2$Sn—Et$_2$Sn—H		
1,1,1,3,3,3-Hexa-*n*-butyl-2-phenyltritin 2-hydride	n_D^{20} 1.5712	(20, 21)

$$\begin{array}{c} \text{Ph} \\ | \\ n\text{-Bu}_3\text{Sn—Sn—Sn-}n\text{-Bu}_3 \\ | \\ \text{H} \end{array}$$

TABLE 2—*continued*

Compound	Melting point (°C) Boiling point °C (torr)	References
Hexa-*n*-propyltritin 1,3-dichloride Cl—(*n*-Pr$_2$Sn)$_3$—Cl	122°C	(*123*)
Organotetratins		
Octaethyltetratin 1,4-dichloride Cl—(Et$_2$Sn)$_4$—Cl	179–182°C	(*123*)
Octa-*tert*-butyltetratin 1,4-diiodide I—(*tert*-Bu$_2$Sn)$_4$—I	160°C	(*31*)
Organopentatins		
Decabutylpentatin 1,5-dichloride Cl—(*n*-Bu$_2$Sn)$_5$—Cl	165–166°C	(*123*)
Organohexatins		
Dodecaphenylhexatin 1,6-dihydride H—(Ph$_2$Sn)$_6$—H	—	(*54, 68, 70*)
Dodecaethylhexatin 1,6-dibromide Br—(Et$_2$Sn)$_6$—Br	—	(*73*)
Organononatins		
Octadecaethylnonatin 1,9-dihydride H—(Et$_2$Sn)$_9$—H	—	(*73*)
Octadecaethylnonatin 1,9-diiodide I—(Et$_2$Sn)$_9$—I	—	(*73*)

dihydrides (*95, 97*). In the case of diphenyltin dihydride, irrespective of the hydride-acid ratio, the product isolated was the ditin dicarboxylate. With di-*n*-butyltin dihydride, the main product obtained depended on the hydride-acid ratio, yielding the ditin dicarboxylate in a 1 : 1 mole ratio and the monotin dicarboxylate in a 1 : 2 mole ratio:

$$2\,R_2SnH_2 + 2\,R'COOH \longrightarrow \underset{\underset{R'OCO}{|}}{R_2Sn}\!\!-\!\!\!-\!\!\!-\!\!\underset{\underset{OCOR'}{|}}{SnR_2} + 3\,H_2$$

In the case of di-*n*-butyltin dihydride with acetic acid, di-*n*-butyltin acetate hydride was found to be an intermediate in the reaction (*98*). In fact, mixing di-*n*-butyltin dihydride with di-*n*-butyltin diacetate also rapidly produced the same equilibrium mixture containing di-*n*-butyltin acetate hydride. This hydride slowly decomposed in both cases with the formation of hydrogen and tetra-*n*-butylditin 1,2-diacetate:

$$2\,Bu_2SnH_2 + 2\,HOAc \longrightarrow 2\,Bu_2Sn(OAc)H + 2\,H_2$$
$$Bu_2SnH_2 + Bu_2Sn(OAc)_2 \rightleftharpoons Bu_2Sn(OAc)H$$
$$2\,Bu_2Sn(OAc)H \longrightarrow \underset{\underset{AcO}{|}}{Bu_2Sn}\!\!-\!\!\!-\!\!\underset{\underset{OAc}{|}}{SnBu_2} + H_2$$

Tetra-*n*-butylditin 1,2-dihydride has been converted to the 1,2-diacetate by reaction with acetic acid (*96*).

Vyazankin and Bychov (*114*) have obtained tetra-*n*-butylditin-1,2-dibenzoate from the reaction of di-*n*-butyltindihydride with benzoyl peroxide.

$$2 \, Bu_2SnH_2 + (C_6H_5COO)_2 \longrightarrow 2 \, H_2 + Bu_2(C_6H_5COO)Sn{-}Sn(OCOC_6H_5)Bu_2$$

When a 1 : 1 mole rato is used di-*n*-butyltin dibenzoate and hydrogen are produced instead. They have also obtained the same ditin dibenzoate by reaction of polymeric di-*n*-butyltin with benzoic acid in a 1 : 1 mole ratio (*115*).

The reaction of diphenyltin with benzoyl peroxide produced tetraphenylditin 1,2-dibenzoate in 81% yield (*95*). This same ditin was apparently obtained by Gilman and Eisch (*34*) as a product in the reaction of triphenyltin hydride with benzoyl peroxide. Weber and Becker (*117*) noted its identity and also reported its formation in the reaction of triphenyltin hydride with benzoic acid. Triphenyltin hydride with acetic and propionic acids gave only the corresponding triphenyltin carboxylates. However, with furoic and thenoic acids it gave both the triphenyltin carboxylate and the tetraphenylditin 1,2-dicarboxylates in varying yield depending on the hydride-acid ratio.

Allan (*6*) has studied the polarographic behavior of a number of organotin compounds and has speculated that the first reduction wave of R_2SnCl_2 involves one electron as shown:

$$R_2SnCl_2 + e \longrightarrow \begin{array}{c} R_2Sn\cdot + Cl^- \\ | \\ Cl \end{array}$$

$$2 \begin{array}{c} R_2Sn\cdot \\ | \\ Cl \end{array} \longrightarrow \begin{array}{c} R_2Sn{-}SnR_2 \\ | \quad | \\ Cl \quad Cl \end{array}$$

and that the second reduction wave involves two electrons:

$$R_2SnCl_2 + 2 \, e \longrightarrow R_2Sn + 2 \, Cl^-$$

Dessey et al. (*25*) have made a more thorough study of the polarographic reduction of diphenyltin dichloride. Reduction was reported to occur in two steps. The first involved one electron forming tetraphenylditin 1,2-dichloride, which was identified by conversion using silver benzoate to the known compound, tetraphenylditin 1,2-dibenzoate. The second reduction step involved two electrons and produced an anionic species of diphenyltin:

$$Ph_2SnCl_2 \xrightarrow[-1.6 \, V]{e} 0.5 \begin{array}{c} Ph_2Sn{-}SnPh_2 \\ | \quad | \\ Cl \quad Cl \end{array} \xrightarrow[-2.7 \, V]{e} (Ph_2\overset{..}{Sn}\!:^-)_x$$

Di-*n*-butyltin dichloride showed similar electrochemical behavior.

Kupchik and Kiesel (*55*) have also carried out reactions of triphenyltin hydride with a variety of carboxylic acids (1-apocamphane carboxylic acid,

1-norbornanecarboxylic, 1-triptycenecarboxylic acid, and 1-pyrrole-2-car-boxylic acid), obtaining the corresponding triphenyltin esters irrespective of the hydride-acid ratio. However, the reaction with ferrocene carboxylic acid gave triphenyltin ferrocenate or tetraphenylditin 1,2-diferrocenate depending on the hydride-acid ratio. They also prepared the same ditin by allowing ferrocene carboxylic acid to react with diphenyltin dihydride by the method of Sawyer and Kuivila (*95, 97*). An attempt to prepare tetraphenyl-ditin 1,2-dipicolinate by this method gave a good yield of diphenyltin dipicolinate instead of the ditin. (See Sec. III.G of the chapter on Organotin Hydrides.)

Plassogna et al. (*81a*) from infrared spectra of 1,1,2,2-tetra-phenyl-1, 2-diacyloxyditin compounds, $Ph_4Sn_2(OCOR^1)_2$ (when $R^1 = CH_3$, CH_2Cl, $CHCl_2$, CCl_3 or CF_3) have concluded that they are polymers in the solid state with bridging carboxylate groups, and that in solution carboxylate ligands bridge the two tin atoms, which are thus five-coordinated in a trigonal bipyramidal structure.

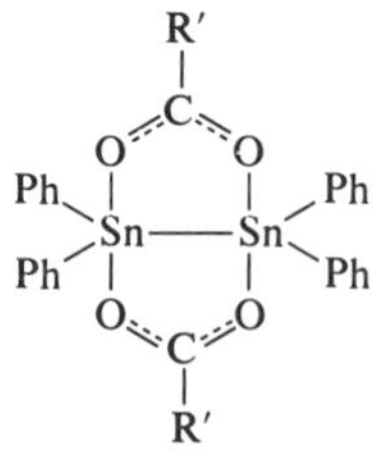

The compounds were found to be monomeric in benzene and chloroform and to be nonconducting in benzene-ethanol solution.

b. Tetraorganoditin 1,2-dichlorides. Tetra-*n*-butylditin 1,2-dichloride has been obtained by treatment of tetra-*n*-butylditin 1,2-diacetate with hydrogen chloride in ether (*31, 96*).

Thermal decomposition of di-*n*-butyltin chloride hydride also has been shown to give this same ditin in over 90% yield (*92*).

Neumann et al. have also prepared tetraalkylditin 1,2-dichlorides from dialkyltin chloride hydrides by catalytic decomposition with amines (*74, 104*).

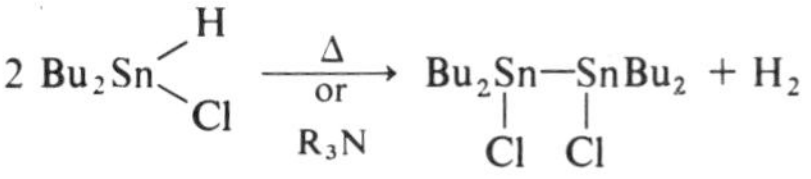

Tetramethylditin 1,2-dichloride has been produced by the reaction of di-methyltin dichloride with sodium in xylene (*122*).

Substances originally reported (*43, 44*) as tetraorganoditin 1,2-dihalides by the reactions of organic amines with organotin halides in ethanol have been shown instead to be bis(dialkylhalotin) oxides (*7, 31, 42*).

Indirectly tetraphenylditin 1,2-dichloride was shown to be formed in the polarographic reduction of diphenyltin dichloride (see the previous section). Its synthesis has not yet been reported. An attempt to obtain this compound by decomposition of diphenyltin chloride hydride resulted in only a small fraction of the expected hydrogen being evolved. Instead, a substantial yield of benzene and triphenyltin chloride were obtained along with other unidentified products (*93*).

c. Tetraorganoditin 1,2-dihydrides. Tetra-*n*-butylditin 1,2-dihydride has been formed by reduction of tetra-*n*-butylditin 1,2-dichloride with lithium aluminum hydride in ether (*96*), without substantial cleavage of the Sn—Sn bond.

Neumann et al. (*74, 104*) have reported the formation of the same organoditin dihydride as well as tetraisobutylditin 1,2-dihydride by reduction of the corresponding ditin dichlorides with lithium aluminum hydride in ether, and their recovery in 45% yield by vacuum distillation.

A reaction sequence involving some of these functionally substituted ditins is shown in the diagram below:

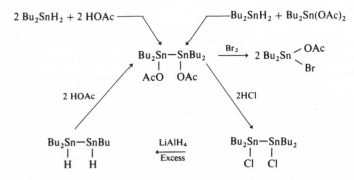

d. Pentaorganoditin monohydrides and other pentaorganoditin compounds. Pentaorganoditin monohydrides have been shown to be very useful in the planned synthesis of organopolytins. Creemers and Noltes (*20, 21*) first reported the formation and use of these hydrides in preparing linear tri-, tetra-, penta-, and hexatin compounds. The hydrides were prepared by the reaction of a trialkyl (*N*-phenylformamido) tin with an equimolar quantity of a dialkyl- or diaryltin dihydride:

$$R_3SnN(Ph)C(O)H + R_2'SnH_2 \longrightarrow R_3SnSnR_2'H + PhNHC(O)H$$

Included among these were compounds of the types:

$$
\begin{array}{c}
R \\
| \\
R_3Sn{-}Sn{-}H \\
| \\
R
\end{array}
\quad \text{(where R = Me, Et, Bu, and Ph),}
$$

$$
\begin{array}{c}
R' \\
| \\
R_3Sn{-}Sn{-}H \\
| \\
R'
\end{array}
\quad \text{(where R = Et and R' = Ph).}
$$

An attempt to prepare an asymmetrical organoditin dihydride:

$$
\begin{array}{c}
R' \\
| \\
R_3Sn{-}Sn{-}H \\
| \\
H
\end{array}
\quad \text{(where R = Bu and R' = Ph)}
$$

by the reaction of one mole of tributyl (*N*-phenylformamido) tin with one mole of phenyltin trihydride gave instead an organotritin monohydride by the following reaction:

$$
2\ Bu_3SnN(Ph)C(O)H + PhSnH_3 \longrightarrow
\begin{array}{c}
Ph \\
| \\
Bu_3Sn{-}Sn{-}SnBu_3 \\
| \\
H
\end{array}
+ 2\ PhNHC(O)H
$$

When pentabutylditin monohydride was reacted with one mole of acetic acid in diethyl ether, the expected amount of hydrogen was obtained. The product formed took up one mole of bromine and gave tributyltin bromide and dibutyltin bromide acetate suggesting that the following reaction had occurred:

$$
Bu_3SnSnBu_2H + HOAc \longrightarrow Bu_3SnSnBu_2OAc + H_2
$$

However, the product isolated from carrying out this reaction was tributyltin acetate. It was suggested that the intermediate pentabutylditin acetate rearranges to form tributyltin acetate and dibutyltin. From an analogous reaction between pentaethylditin hydride and hydrogen chloride in ether, triethyltin chloride was obtained. Likewise bromination of the freshly prepared product yielded triethyltin bromide and diethyltin bromide chloride. These results also indicated that pentaethylditin chloride was first formed followed by rearrangement to give triethyltin chloride and diethyltin. Hydrolysis of the freshly prepared reaction product with 30% sodium hydroxide solution gave a solid analyzing for pentaethylditin hydroxide. Triethyltin oxide formed by secondary rearrangement was also found as a product of this reaction.

2. *Other Organopolytins with Functional Substituents*

a. Organotritins. In the previous section the formation of an organotritin monohydride, 1,1,1,3,3,3-hexa-*n*-butyl-2-phenyltritin 2-hydride:

$$
\begin{array}{c}
\text{Ph} \\
| \\
\text{Bu}_3\text{Sn—Sn—SnBu}_3 \\
| \\
\text{H}
\end{array}
$$

was noted.

Phenylisocyanate adducts of pentaorganoditin monohydrides were found to react with dialkyltin dihydrides in a 1 : 1 mole ratio to give linear tritin monohydrides (*20, 21*):

$$\text{R}_3\text{Sn—SnR}_2\text{N(Ph)C(O)H} + \text{R}_2\text{SnH}_2 \longrightarrow \text{R}_3\text{Sn—SnR}_2\text{—SnR}_2\text{H} + \text{PhNHC(O)H}$$

These hydrides, which were generally not isolated, were decomposed to yield fully alkylated hexatin derivatives. In one specific case the phenyliso-cyanate adduct of pentaethylditin monohydride was treated in a 1 : 1 mole ratio with diethyltin dihydride to give heptaethyltritin monohydride (*20, 21*).

Hexa-*n*-propyltritin 1,3-dichloride has been obtained from di-*n*-propyltin dichloride with sodium in xylene (*123*).

b. Organotetratins. Octaethyltetratin 1,4-dichloride has also been obtained from diethyltin dichloride with sodium in xylene (*123*).

Octa-*tert*-butylcyclotetratin has been cleaved by one mole of iodine under mild conditions to give octa-*tert*-butyltetratin 1,4-diiodide (*29*). This was the first reported conversion of a cyclic $(\text{R}_2\text{Sn})_n$ compound to the corresponding functionally substituted linear compound using a limited amount of halogen. The quantitative yield of product

$$
\begin{array}{c}
\text{R} \quad \text{R} \\
| \quad | \\
\text{R—Sn—Sn—R} \\
| \quad | \quad + \text{I}_2 \\
\text{R—Sn—Sn—R} \\
| \quad | \\
\text{R} \quad \text{R}
\end{array}
\longrightarrow
\begin{array}{c}
\text{R} \quad \text{R} \quad \text{R} \quad \text{R} \\
| \quad | \quad | \quad | \\
\text{I—Sn—Sn—Sn—Sn—I} \\
| \quad | \quad | \quad | \\
\text{R} \quad \text{R} \quad \text{R} \quad \text{R}
\end{array}
$$

$$(\text{R} = \text{tert-Butyl})$$

suggests that this may be an attractive route to some functionally substituted polytins. Neumann (*73*), starting with well-defined cyclic $(\text{R}_2\text{Sn})_n$ compounds, has since carried out some reactions of this kind.

c. Organopentatins. Deca-*n*-butylpentatin 1,5-dichloride has been reported to be formed in the reaction of dibutyltin dichloride with sodium in xylene (*123*).

d. Organohexatins. Several forms of diphenyltin have been reported (*54*). One of these forms, obtained as colorless crystals by the decomposition of diphenyltin dihydride in methanol, has since been shown by Neumann and co-workers to be dodecaphenylhexatin 1,6-dihydride (*68, 70*).

$$6 \, Ph_2SnH_2 \xrightarrow{\quad CH_3OH \quad} H(Ph_2Sn)_6H + 5 \, H_2$$

Its decomposition in the presence of pyridine yielded diphenyltin:

$$H(Ph_2Sn)_6H \xrightarrow{\quad pyridine \quad} cyclo(Ph_2Sn)_6 + H_2$$

Neumann and Pedain (*73*) have noted the reaction of dodecaethylcyclo-hexatin with bromine in a 1 : 1 mole ratio at 5°C forming dodecaethylhexatin 1,6-dibromide.

$$cyclo(Et_2Sn)_6 \xrightarrow[5°C]{+ Br_2} Br-(Et_2Sn)_6-Br$$

e. Organononatins. Neumann and Pedain (*73*) have indicated also that the catalytic decomposition of diethyltin dihydride may occur in stages first yielding octadecaethylnonatin 1,9-dihydride followed by loss of hydrogen forming octadecaethylcyclononatin. The latter compound is said to react with iodine in a 1 : 1 mole ratio at 5°C to give octadecaethylnonatin 1.9-diiodide:

$$cyclo(Et_2Sn)_9 \xrightarrow[5°C]{I_2} I-(Et_2Sn)_9-I$$

f. Other Polymeric Compounds $(RSnX)_n$. Although numerous compounds of the type $(R_2Sn)_n$ and SnX_2 are known there have been relatively few examples reported of compounds of the type RSnX. Presumably they would be polymeric and contain Sn—Sn bonds.

Smith (*102*) reduced stannic chloride by diisobutyl aluminum hydride to give a solid which, when dissolved and recovered from chloroform at reduced pressure, showed the formula 4 $(BuSnCl)\cdot CHCl_3$.

Fritz and Scheer (*30*) obtained a yellow polymer of composition $(EtSnBr)_n$ by the decomposition of ethyltin dihydride bromide:

$$EtSnH_3 + HBr(g) \xrightarrow{\quad -78°C \quad} EtSnH_2Br + H_2$$

$$n \, EtSnH_2Br \xrightarrow{\quad above \, -65°C \quad} (EtSnBr)_n + n \, H_2$$

Similarly a phenyltin bromide polymer appeared to be formed:

$$Ph_3SnH + HBr(g) \xrightarrow{\quad -78°C \quad} Ph_2SnHBr + C_6H_6$$

$$n \, Ph_2SnHBr \xrightarrow{\quad at \, room \, temp. \quad} n \, C_6H_6 + (PhSnBr)_n$$

They reported also the following reactions leading to 1,2-diphenyl-1,1,2,2,-tetrabromoditin:

$$Ph_3SnH + 2\,HBr \xrightarrow{\ -78^\circ C\ } PhSnHBr_2 + 2\,C_6H_6$$

$$PhSnHBr_2 \xrightarrow[\text{(ether)}]{\text{at room temp}} Ph\!-\!\!\underset{\underset{Br\ \ Br}{\diagdown}}{\overset{\diagup}{Sn}}\!-\!\!\underset{\underset{Br\ \ Br}{\diagdown}}{\overset{\diagup}{Sn}}\!-\!Ph$$

Recently Tombe et al. (*110*) in order to explain the products obtained in the reactions of triphenyltin chloride with a zinc-copper couple in refluxing THF or in MeOH have postulated the formation of Ph_2Sn followed by its reactions to form $PhSnCl$.

It may be expected that in the future more attention will be turned to the preparation and structure of these polymeric compounds containing functional groups. It seems that a likely route to these compounds will be through reactions involving appropriate monoorganotin hydrides.

III. Reactions

A. Introduction

It has been noted by Gilman et al. that "organopolytin compounds with functional groups attached to tin have been prepared only recently, so that most of the chemistry of the organopolytins involves scission of the Sn—Sn bond" (*32*).

Many common reagents usually cause cleavage of the Sn—Sn bond including halogens, oxygen, peroxides, silver nitrate, potassium permanganate, and other oxidizing agents. Likewise, many reducing agents such as sodium in liquid ammonia, lithium in tetrahydrofuran, sodium amide in liquid ammonia, and phenyllithium, also cause cleavage. Although under mild conditions the tin—tin bond resists cleavage by lithium aluminum hydride, more vigorous conditions do result in substantial cleavage. In many cases the cleavage is homolytic whereas in some cases, particularly thermally or catalytically, disproportionation occurs. A few reactions in which the Sn—Sn bond is preserved are noted in the following paragraphs.

Sawyer and Kuivila (*96*) have described a sequence of reactions involving conversion of tetra-*n*-butylditin-1,2-diacetate to the 1,2-dichloride by dry hydrogen chloride in ether, then conversion of the 1,2-dichloride to the 1,2-dihydride by lithium aluminum hydride in ether followed by conversion by glacial acetic acid back to the starting compound. (See the diagram illustrating this sequence in Sec. II.B.1.c.)

Although Noltes and van der Kerk (*80*) reported the reductive cleavage by lithium aluminum hydride of tetra-*n*-butylditin-1,2-dichloride (prepared by the Johnson and Fritz (*43*) reaction) to give di-*n*-butyltin dihydride, it is now understood that the reported ditin was in reality bis(di-*n*-butylchlorotin)-oxide, and that cleavage of the Sn—O bond rather than the Sn—Sn bond had in fact occurred (*10*).

It has been reported recently by Wiberg and Behringer (*118*) that hexaphenylditin reacts with glacial acetic acid at 120°C to form hexaacetoxyditin. This compound may be subsequently converted by hydrogen chloride at −100°C to hexachloroditin which, upon treatment with phenyllithium, gives the starting ditin. These reactions are outlined on page 266 of the chapter on organotin compounds with Sn—O bonds.

Sommer et al. (*104*) have also reduced tetra-*n*-butylditin 1,2-dichloride and tetraisobutylditin 1,2-dichloride with lithium aluminum hydride to give the corresponding tetra-butylditin 1,2-dihydrides in 45% yield.

In the photo-initiated oxidation of hexaethylditin one mechanism is indicated to be the following (*2*), in which cleavage of the Sn—Sn bond does not occur:

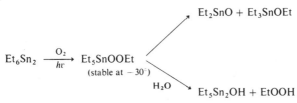

The other mechanism involves formation and decomposition of the peroxide:

$$Et_6Sn_2 \xrightarrow[hv]{O_2} Et_3SnOOSnEt_3 \longrightarrow Et_2SnO + Et_3SnOSnEt_3$$

Other reactions which might well come under the heading of those which do not involve scission of the tin—tin bond are a number of reactions of functionally substituted ditins or other polytins leading to higher polytins. As examples might be the reaction of hexamethyltritin 1,3-disodium with trimethyltin bromide yielding dodecamethylpentatin (*47*),

$$Na—Me_2Sn—Me_2Sn—Me_2Sn—Na$$
$$\xrightarrow{Me_3SnBr} Me_3Sn—Me_2Sn—Me_2Sn—Me_2Sn—SnMe_3$$

catalytic decompositions of organotin hydrides, as well as hydrogenolyses involving functionally substituted ditins or polytins, leading to the formation of new Sn—Sn bonds, examples of which are found elsewhere in this chapter.

B. Homolytic Dissociation

In the past there has been considerable controversy and conflicting evidence as to whether or not organoditins dissociate into free radicals in the sense of the following equation:

$$-\overset{|}{\underset{|}{Sn}}-\overset{|}{\underset{|}{Sn}}- \;\rightleftharpoons\; 2 -\overset{|}{\underset{|}{Sn}}\cdot$$

The absence of color in these ditins has often been cited as evidence against their dissociation into free radicals. Ladenburg (56) in 1869 found that the vapor density measurements of hexaethylditin at 225°C corresponded to the formula Et_6Sn_2.

Although molecular weight determinations based on boiling point measurements of hexamethylditin in benzene were claimed by Kraus and Sessions (49) to indicate its extensive dissociation, magnetic susceptibility measurements by Morris and Selwood (62) gave no evidence of such dissociation. Morris et al. (63) made magnetic measurements on hexa-o-tolylditin with similar results. In an effort to determine why the molecular weight measurements and magnetic data were contradictory, they also made ebulliometric measurements on benzene solutions of hexamethylditin. The rapid and continuing change in boiling point elevation with time indicated that decomposition of hexamethylditin was occurring and pointed to the unreliability of ebulliometric measurements for studying its dissociation. Neumann et al. (76) have recently determined molecular weights by thermistor vapor pressure osmometer for hexacyclohexyl and hexaphenylditin. They both showed the calculated values even at concentrations as low as 10^{-3} M in benzene, thus excluding appreciable dissociation in the sense of the equation above. However, molecular weights determined ebullioscopically also showed anomolous results. Electron spin resonance measurements on these solutions showed the absence of free radicals.

Using gas chromatography as a tool they have reported that the unsymmetrical ditin, 1,1,1-triethyltrimethylditin shows no dissociation even at 170°C for several hours. Above 190°C decomposition begins to take place in which in addition to the symmetrical ditins, tetraethyltin, tetramethyltin and tin are found.

Hague and Prince (38) have recently obtained further evidence by studying the kinetics of the iodination of hexaphenylditin. The reaction is reported to display second-order kinetics and to be radical free. Other methods including flash photolysis, electron spin resonance of solutions irradiated by ultraviolet light and reaction with 1,1-diphenyl-2-picrylhydrazyl showed no detectable tendency to form triphenylstannyl radicals from hexaphenylditin. Likewise, the presence of hexaphenylditin did not induce polymerization of methyl methacrylate. They have pointed out that whereas there is some circumstantial evidence for the presence of small concentrations of free radicals in several reactions, no attempts to detect such radicals have been successful.

Doretti and Tagliavini (*26*) have recently studied the reversible redox systems R_6Sn_2/R_3Sn^+ on platinized platinum electrodes. They determined standard E_0 potentials for systems where R = Me, Et, Bu, and Ph in methanol and methanol-benzene solutions:

$$R_3Sn\text{—}SnR_3 \rightleftharpoons 2\,R_3Sn^+ + 2e$$

The system was also studied using the biamperometric technique. The reversibility of these systems is rationalized in terms of the formation of $R_3Sn\cdot$ radicals through the catalytic activity of the platinum black in a rate-determining step followed by electron transfer:

$$2\,R_2Sn\cdot \rightleftharpoons 2\,R_3Sn^+ + 2\,e$$

The following electrolytic reaction has been brought about in a cell consisting of a silver electrode immersed in an alcoholic solution of silver nitrate and a metallic electrode dipped in an alcoholic solution of R_6Sn_2 (*106*). The reaction was not reversible in the presence of mercury or smooth platinum electrodes but was reversible with a platinized platinum electrode:

$$R_3Sn\text{—}SnR_3 + 2\,Ag^+ \rightleftharpoons 2\,R_3Sn^+ + 2\,Ag$$

Likewise, reversibility was shown for the redox couple Ph_6Pb_2/Ph_3Pb^+ at a platinized platinum electrode (*27*). "Isotopic exchange between tagged hexaphenyldilead and triphenyllead ions supports the hypothesis of the formation of $Ph_3Pb\cdot$ radicals at the surface of a platinized platinum foil."

Dessey et al. (*25*) in a study of hexaphenylditin, the triphenyltin anion (Ph_3Sn^-) and the triphenyltin cation (Ph_3Sn^+) by triangular voltametry have postulated the existence of triphenyltin radicals to account for the electrochemical results:

Reduction

$$Ph_3Sn^+ \underset{-1\,e}{\overset{+1\,e}{\rightleftharpoons}} Ph_3Sn\cdot \underset{-1\,e}{\overset{+1\,e}{\rightleftharpoons}} Ph_3Sn:^-$$

Oxidation

It thus appears that, although there is some reason to believe that short-lived, organotin free radicals may exist under certain conditions, there is no good evidence to support substantial formation of stable organotin free radicals by facile homolytic dissociation of organoditins.

Schmidt et al. (*99*) have obtained triisobutyl and triphenyltin radicals by photolysis of the corresponding organotin hydrides with homolytic fission of the Sn—H bond. The radicals were collected on a cold finger and were studied by electron spin resonance methods. Similar experiments involving ditins have not been reported.

The photochemical behavior of hexaphenylditin has recently been re-investigated by Wilputte-Steinert and Nasielski, (12aa) who explain their results in terms of the formation of "hot" triphenyltin radicals, whose decomposition into diphenyltin and phenyl radicals competes with re-combination and disproportionation.

Very recently Bulten, Budding, and Noltes (15a) have reported the base catalyzed disproportionation of hexaalkylditins under polar conditions even at room temperature. Thus, the following reaction between hexamethylditin and hexaethylditin in the presence of hexamethylphosphoric triamide reaches equilibrium in less than one hour to give about 50% $Me_3SnSnEt_3$. In tetrahydrofuran and in acetonitrile at room temperature the reaction occurs only in the presence of a catalytic amount of base such as sodium methodide or methylmagnesium bromide.

$$Me_6Sn_2 + Et_6Sn_2 \rightleftharpoons 2Me_3SnSnEt_3$$

C. Thermal Behavior

The known polytins have been stated to be reasonably stable to heat (*32*). Hexamethylditin is reported to distil at 182°C and 756 torr without decomposition. Even a number of octaorganotritins have been distilled at reduced pressure (0.001 torr) at temperatures under 200°C. 1,1,1-Triethyl-2,2,2-trimethylditin is stable at 170°C but decomposes at 190°C (*76*). A number of Lewis acids such as aluminum chloride effect disproportionation of hexa-organoditins at much lower temperatures (*32*) (see Sec. III.F).

The thermal decomposition of hexaethylditin at 275°C has been studied (*83*). The first step is suggested to involve the formation of tetraethyltin and diethyltin:

$$Et_3SnSnEt_3 \longrightarrow Et_4Sn + \frac{1}{n}(Et_2Sn)_n$$

with diethyltin then decomposing into tin and two ethyl radicals. Two mechanisms for the decomposition of hexaethylditin have been proposed (*87*):

$$Et_3Sn-SnEt_3 \begin{cases} \xrightarrow{\text{thermal decomposition}} Et_4Sn + Sn + 2\,Et \\ \xrightarrow{\text{disproportionation}} Et_4Sn + Sn \end{cases}$$

Hexaphenylditin has been refluxed in tetrahydrofuran for 21 h with 98% of the ditin recovered unchanged (*10*). Although most of the tetra-*n*-butyl 1,2-diacyloxyditins appeared to have normal melting points, usually below

100°C, most of the tetraphenyl 1,2-diacyloxyditins decompose at their melting points, usually between 150–200°C. In the case of tetraphenylditin 1,2-diacetate the decomposition products have been identified (97):

$$\underset{\substack{| \quad | \\ \text{AcO} \quad \text{OAc}}}{\text{Ph}_2\text{Sn—SnPh}_2} \xrightarrow[\text{3 h}]{153-161°C} \underset{(68\%)}{\text{Ph}_4\text{Sn}} + \underset{(43\%)}{\text{Sn(OAc)}_2}$$

Pentaethylditin monhydride has been reported to decompose when distilled at reduced pressure (20).

$$\text{Et}_3\text{SnSnEt}_2\text{H} \xrightarrow{\Delta} \text{Et}_3\text{SnH} + \frac{1}{n}(\text{Et}_2\text{Sn})_n$$

Disproportionation of diethyltin to tin and tetraethyltin is well documented (32). Diphenyltin has been earlier observed to decompose to tin and hexa-phenylditin (12, 50).

A detailed study of the pyrolysis of diethyltin and of di-*n*-butyltin has recently been carried out by Sisido et al. (101a). Disproportionation of di-*n*-butyltin occurred much less readily than

$$(\text{Et}_2\text{Sn})_n \xrightarrow[\text{15 h}]{160°C} \underset{(12.9\%)}{\text{Et}_4\text{Sn}} + \underset{(4.8\%)}{\text{Et}_3\text{SnSnEt}_3} + \underset{(12.5\%)}{\text{Et}_3\text{Sn—}} + \underset{(28.6\%)}{\text{Et}_2\text{Sn—}}$$

$$+ \underset{(\text{trace})}{\text{EtSn—}} + \underset{(38.1\%)}{\text{Sn}}$$

$$(\text{Bu}_2\text{Sn})_n \xrightarrow[\text{15 h}]{160°C} \underset{(0.2\%)}{\text{Bu}_4\text{Sn}} + \underset{(—)}{\text{Bu}_3\text{SnSnBu}_3} + \underset{(6.6\%)}{\text{Bu}_3\text{Sn—}} + \underset{(85.6\%)}{\text{Bu}_2\text{Sn—}}$$

$$+ \underset{(4.5\%)}{\text{BuSn—}} + \underset{(\text{trace})}{\text{Sn}}$$

with diethyltin. However, Vyazankin and Bychkov (116) found that di-*n*-butyltin at 220°C for 20 h gave high yields of tin and hexa-*n*-butylditin.

$$(\text{Bu}_2\text{Sn})_n \xrightarrow[\text{20 h}]{220°C} \underset{(97\%)}{\text{Sn}} + \underset{(48\%)}{\text{Bu}_6\text{Sn}_2}$$

Below 200°C diphenyltin is quite stable thermally, but when heated to about 250°C it disproportionates into tetraphenyltin and metallic tin (53). This disproportionation occurred at a much lower temperature under the influence of boron trifluoride:

$$(\text{Ph}_2\text{Sn})_n \xrightarrow[\text{benzene—room temperature}]{\text{BF}_3} \underset{(68\% \quad (93.5\%)}{\text{Ph}_4\text{Sn} + \text{Sn}}$$

Diphenyltin is said to yield tetraphenyltin when heated in carbon tetra-chloride with *N*-nitrosoacetanilide but to yield hexaphenylditin when heated in carbon tetrachloride with phenylazotriphenylmethane (*82d*).

Kulheim and Neumann (*51b*) obtained a mass spectrum of dodecaphenyl-cyclohexatin, $(Ph_2Sn)_6$, which showed peaks corresponding to only one or two tin atoms. In contrast the analogous silicon and germanium compounds, $(R_2Si)_6$ and $(R_2Ge)_6$, showed peaks corresponding to moieties containing from six down to one metal atom in each case. Ridder and Noltes (*87a*) have recently suggested that the mass spectrum above may be a combination of those of hexaphenylditin and tetraphenyltin. These comments were based on observing that thermal decomposition of $(Ph_2Sn)_6$ occurs when it is heated up to the ion source temperature (220–250°C). The products found were Sn, $SnPh_4$, Sn_2Ph_6, and minor amounts of Sn_3Ph_8.

D. REACTIONS WITH HALOGENS

Reactions of halogens with the tin—tin bond are well known (*32, 41*). Also see Sec. II.C of the chapter on Organotin Halides.

The basic reactions may be illustrated as follows:

$$R\underset{\underset{R}{|}}{\overset{\overset{R}{|}}{-}}Sn\underset{\underset{R}{|}}{\overset{\overset{R}{|}}{-}}Sn-R + X_2 \longrightarrow 2\,R_3SnX$$

$$(R_2Sn)_n + n\,X_2 \longrightarrow n\,R_2SnX_2$$

In some cases the reactions have been used to characterize compounds by quantitatively titrating the Sn—Sn bond with bromine or iodine solutions under appropriate conditions. For example, bromine quantitatively reacts with tetra-*n*-butylditin 1,2-diacetate (*97*).

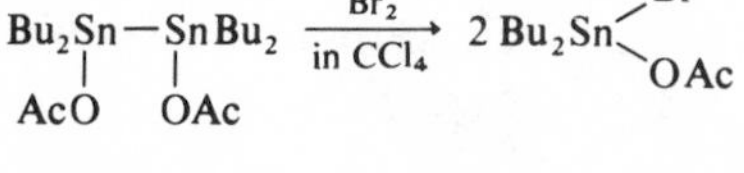

$$\underset{\underset{AcO}{|}}{Bu_2Sn}-\underset{\underset{OAc}{|}}{SnBu_2} \xrightarrow[\text{in } CCl_4]{Br_2} 2\,Bu_2Sn\overset{Br}{\underset{OAc}{\diagdown}}$$

Neumann (*65, 68, 73*) has used the reaction with halogens at low tem-perature to show the presence or absence of organocyclopolytins. For example, cyclic compounds result in the sole formation of diorganotin dihalides. The formation of triorganotin halides comes from cleavage of end groups and organotin trihalides arise where there is branching (see Sec. II.A.3).

The syntheses of functionally substituted polytins has been accomplished using controlled amounts of halogen at low temperatures. Farrar and Skinner (*29*) carried out the reaction of a limited amount of a cold solution of iodine in benzene to cleave one tin-tin bond in octa-*tert*-butylcyclotetratin giving octa-*tert*-butyl-tetratin 1,4-diiodide:

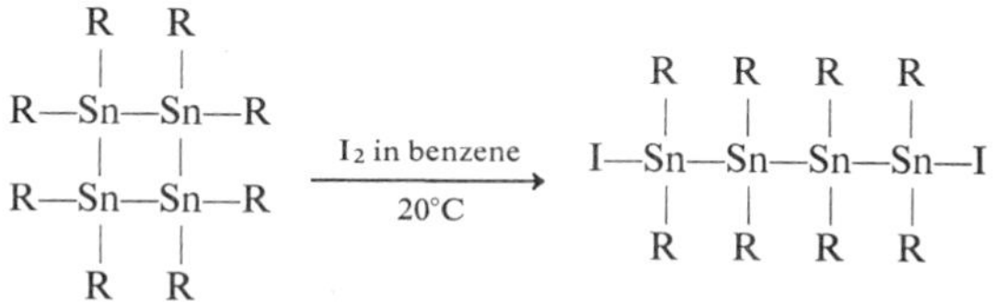

$$R_2Sn(SnR_2)_2SnR_2 \xrightarrow[20°C]{I_2 \text{ in benzene}} I-SnR_2-SnR_2-SnR_2-SnR_2-I$$

(R = *tert*-Bu)

Upon further addition of iodine di-*tert*-butyltin diiodide was formed. Neumann (73) has reported similar reactions of cyclic diethyltin polymers with bromine and iodine at 5°C in a 1–1 mole ratio to give the linear organopolytin dihalides.

Hague and Prince (38) have studied the kinetics of iodination of hexaphenylditin (see Sec. III.C). The reaction in cyclohexene is second order and may be interpreted to occur via a cyclic intermediate.

Results obtained by Boué et al. (12a) in the reaction of iodine with hexamethylditin and hexabutylditin in acetone are considered to be due to the formation of an intermediate complex formed by electrophilic attack by iodine on one of the tin atoms in the ditin.

The rates of cleavage of a number of hexaorganoditins by iodine have been measured in alcoholic solvents by Tagliavini et al. (106a). Organoditins, $R_3Sn-SnR_3$, were used where R = Me, Et, *n*-Bu, Ph, and *p*-tolyl. Mixed ditins were used, $R_3Sn-SnR'_3$, where R = Ph and R' = Me and Et. Alcohols included methanol, ethanol, 1-propanol, 2-propanol and a 50–50 vol. benzene-ethanol mixture it was concluded that a polar transition state rather than a cyclic four-center one was operative, consisting of an acyclic four-center transition state, formed after attachment of the solvent in a fast preliminary step:

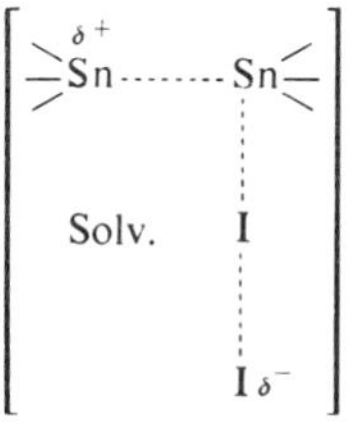

$$\left[\begin{array}{c} \overset{\delta^+}{\underset{|}{\searrow}}Sn\cdots\cdots Sn\underset{\diagdown}{\diagup} \\ \\ Solv. \quad | \\ \\ \underset{\delta^-}{I} \end{array} \right]$$

Using a coulometric titration method (104b) Plazzogna, Peruzzo, and Tagliavini (81a) have recently confirmed the stoichiometry previously reported (53) for the bromination of tetraphenyl 1,2-diacyloxyditins,

$$Ph_2S\text{-}SnnPh_2 \xrightarrow{Br_2} 2Ph_2Sn(OAc)Br$$
$$\underset{AcO\ OAc}{|\ |}$$

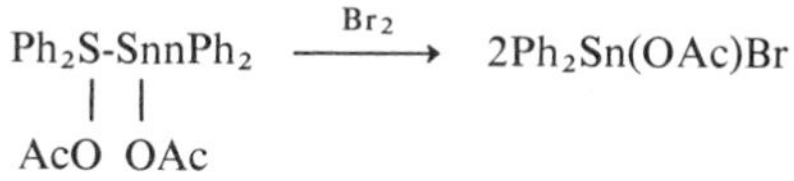

and have shown that these compounds can also be quantitatively titrated with one mole of iodine or two moles of silver ions. They studied the rates of reaction of 1,1,2,2-tetraphenyl-1,2,-diacyloxyditins with iodine in chloroform in which the reaction appears to involve electrophilic attack of iodine at a tin atom.

The Sn—Sn bond is more rapidly cleaved by halogen than is the Sn—C bond. However, in some cases it has been noted that both are observed to occur under the conditions used (*45a*):

$$n\text{-Bu}_6\text{Sn}_2 \xrightarrow{\text{Cl}_2} n\text{-Bu}_3\text{SnCl} + n\text{-Bu}_2\text{SnCl}_2$$

E. Reactions with Oxygen* and Other Group VI Elements

Because of the high reactivity of the Sn—Sn bond in most organoditins and other polytins to oxygen, it is necessary to handle most of these compounds in an inert atmosphere. Typical reactions with oxygen are illustrated below:

$$\text{Bu}_3\text{Sn—SnBu}_3 \xrightarrow{\text{oxygen}} \text{Bu}_3\text{Sn—O—SnBu}_3$$

$$(\text{Bu}_2\text{Sn})_n \xrightarrow{\text{oxygen}} \text{Bu}_2\text{SnO}$$

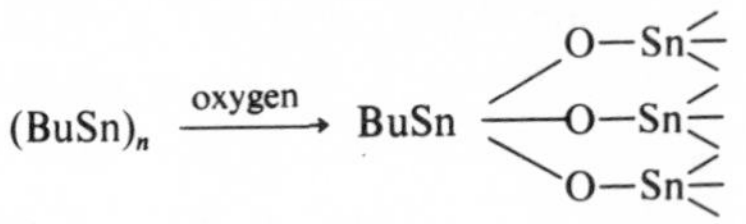

$$(\text{BuSn})_n \xrightarrow{\text{oxygen}} \text{BuSn} \begin{array}{c} \diagup \text{O—Sn} \diagup \\ \diagdown \text{O—Sn} \diagdown \\ \diagdown \text{O—Sn} \diagdown \end{array}$$

$$\underset{\underset{\text{Cl}}{|}\ \underset{\text{Cl}}{|}}{\text{Bu}_2\text{Sn—SnBu}_2} \xrightarrow{\text{oxygen}} \underset{\underset{\text{Cl}}{|}\ \underset{\text{Cl}}{|}}{\text{Bu}_2\text{Sn—O—SnBu}_2}$$

$$\underset{\underset{\text{AcO}}{|}\ \underset{\text{OAc}}{|}}{\text{Bu}_2\text{Sn—SnBu}_2} \xrightarrow{\text{oxygen}} \underset{\underset{\text{AcO}}{|}\ \underset{\text{OAc}}{|}}{\text{Bu}_2\text{Sn—O—SnBu}_2}$$

$$\underset{\underset{\text{H}}{|}\ \underset{\text{H}}{|}}{\text{Bu}_2\text{Sn—SnBu}_2} \xrightarrow{\text{oxygen}} \text{Bu}_2\text{SnO}$$

Several examples of air oxidation of hexaalkylditins have been noted (*41*). The product obtained is either the oxide or the

$$\text{R}_3\text{Sn—SnR}_3 \xrightarrow{\text{O}_2} \text{R}_3\text{Sn—O—SnR}_3$$

* Special note is made here of a recent book (*13*) on "Reactions of Organometallic Compounds with Oxygen and Peroxides," by Brilkina and Shushunov (USSR Translation edited by Alwyn Davies) dealing with reactions and mechanisms and including chapters on group IV metals as well as organopolymetallic compounds in their reactions with oxygen and peroxides.

hydroxide, R_3SnOH, depending on which is more stable in the presence of moisture in the air.

The hexaalkylditins undergo oxidation more readily than the hexaaryl-ditins. Although hexamethylditin is oxidized by air (*49*) 1,1,1-trimethyltri-phenylditin is unaffected (*46*). Hexaphenylditin is unaffected even by un-diluted oxygen (*36a*). Oxidation of hexaethylditin has been studied by several workers (*1–3, 39, 88*). Its oxidation in *n*-nonane is postulated to occur by formation of the peroxide followed by conversion to bis(triethyltin)oxide (*5*). In the photo-initiated oxidation of hexaethylditin two mechanisms have been observed, one involving O_2 insertion into the Sn—Sn bond and the other O_2 insertion into the Sn—C bond (*2*).

Tsai and Lehn (*112*) have studied reactions of hexaphenylditin with a variety of oxidizing agents. Whereas no reaction occurred in air, with sodium methoxide and air in THF a 92% yield of Ph_3SnOH was obtained. Further investigation of the mechanistic aspects of this reaction resulted in the conclusion that sodium methoxide provides an active peroxide which starts a free-radical chain reaction. Addition of ethyl bromide to the reaction mixture resulted in the formation of some ethyltriphenyltin, presumably via free triphenyltin radicals:

$$Ph_3Sn \cdot + EtBr \longrightarrow Ph_3SnBr + Et \cdot$$
$$Et \cdot + Ph_3SnSnPh_3 \longrightarrow Ph_3SnEt + Ph_3Sn \cdot$$

They have also summarized a number of reactions of hexaphenylditin, most of which are indicated in the following diagram.

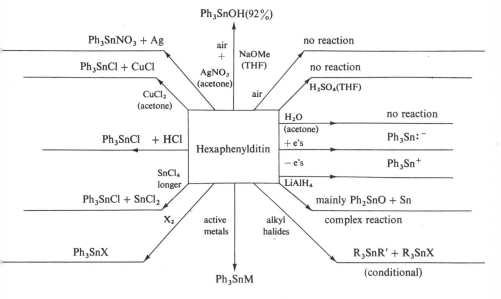

The ease of oxidation varies with the nature of both the organic group and the functional substituent in functionally substituted ditins. Tetra-*n*-butylditin 1,2-diacetate lost 12% of its ditin content on exposure to air for one day whereas over the same period of time, tetra-*n*-butylditin 1,2-dichloride had lost 76% of its ditin content. On the other hand, tetraphenylditin 1,2-diacetate showed no measurable loss over forty-eight days *(91, 95, 97)*. Although hexaphenylditin as well as tetraphenyl-1,2-diacyloxyditins have shown resistance to air oxidation, polymeric diphenyltin is readily oxidized to diphenyltin oxide *(53)*. Numerous examples of air oxidation of $(R_2Sn)_n$ compounds have been summarized earlier *(41)*:

$$(R_2Sn)_n \quad \xrightarrow{O_2} \quad n\,R_2SnO$$

Oxidation occurs more readily in solution, and in the solid state, a few $(R_2Sn)_n$ compounds, di-2,5-xylyltin *(50)* and di-9-phenanthryltin *(9)*, appear to be stable to oxidation.

Kuivila and Beumel *(52)* have observed the pyrophoric nature of $(BuSn)_n$ in air. The product of air oxidation of this compound has been found by the author to be butylstannonic acid *(94)*.

Sulfur and selenium have been found to react in some cases with compounds containing tin-tin bonds to give the corresponding sulfides and selenides. Hexamethylditin and sulfur in benzene at room temperature yielded bis(trimethyltin)sulfide *(49)*. Likewise, hexaethylditin or hexabutylditin in refluxing benzene gave the corresponding bis(triorganotin)sulfides *(20)*:

$$R_3Sn\text{---}SnR_3 \quad \xrightarrow[85^\circ C]{\text{sulfur}} \quad (R_3Sn)_2S$$

Hexaethylditin also reacted with selenium forming bis(triethyltin)selenide *(113)*. With hexaarylditins more strenuous conditions are needed. Hexaphenyl or hexabenzylditin with sulfur in refluxing benzene showed no reaction *(82)*. Hexaphenylditin, however, when heated with sulfur in a 1 : 1 mole ratio for $2\frac{1}{2}$ h at 170°C, gave bis(triphenyltin)sulfide in 83% yield. When a similar reaction was carried out using a 1 : 2 mole ratio of ditin to sulfur at 225°C, trimeric diphenyltin sulfide was obtained as a result of phenyl group cleavage by excess sulfur:

$$Ph_3SnSnPh_3 + 3\,S \quad \xrightarrow{220^\circ C} \quad 2/3\,(Ph_2SnS)_3 + Ph_2S$$

Diphenyltin and sulfur in toluene react rapidly at refluxing temperature, but only after several days at room temperature, with the formation of diphenyltin sulfide *(53)*:

$$3\,(Ph_2Sn)_n \quad \xrightarrow{\text{sulfur}} \quad n\,(Ph_2SnS)_3$$

F. Reactions with Other Oxidizing Agents

The tin-tin bond has been cleaved homolytically by a variety of oxidizing agents other than molecular oxygen (*41*). Razuvaev et al. (*86*), have reported the homolytic cleavage of the tin-tin bond in hexaethylditin by dibenzoyl peroxide, acetyl benzoyl peroxide, as well as by cyclohexyl percarbonate, nitrosoacetanilide, and lead tetraacetate. No reaction was found by Tsai and Lehn (*112*) between 30% hydrogen peroxide in acetone and hexaphenylditin. Neumann and Rübsamen (*77*) obtained the following reaction between hexa-*n*-butylditin and di-*tert* butyl peroxide;

$$Bu_3Sn—SnBu_3 \xrightarrow{\text{\textit{tert}-Butyl peroxide}} 2Bu_3Sn—O—\textit{tert}.\ Bu$$

More recently cleavage of the tin-tin bond in di-*n*-butyltin was reported by Vyazanzin and Bychkov (*115*). A number of these reactions are indicated below:

$$(Bu_2Sn)_n \xrightarrow[\text{(room temp.)}]{\text{benzoyl peroxide}} \underset{\underset{\text{PhCOO}}{|} \quad \underset{\text{OCOPh}}{|}}{Bu_2Sn—SnBu_2}\ (84\%)$$

$$(Bu_2Sn)_n \xrightarrow[\text{(130–135°C for 15 h)}]{\text{\textit{tert}–butyl peroxide}} Bu_2Sn(O\text{-}t\text{-Bu})_2\ (36\%)$$

Earlier diphenyltin was shown to undergo a similar reaction (*53*):

$$(Ph_2Sn)_n \xrightarrow[\text{(in benzene at room temp.)}]{\text{benzyl peroxide}} \underset{\underset{\text{PhCOO}}{|} \quad \underset{\text{OCOPh}}{|}}{Ph_2Sn—SnPh_2}\ (81\%)$$

However, with diethyltin and benzoyl peroxide diethyltin dibenzoate was obtained (*116*).

$$(Et_2Sn)_n \xrightarrow{\text{benzoyl peroxide}} Et_2Sn(OCOPh)_2$$

tert-Butyl hydroperoxide and di-*n*-butyltin reacted to give dibutyltin oxide and *t*-butyl alcohol (*115*):

$$(Bu_2Sn)_n \xrightarrow[\text{(room temp.)}]{\text{t-BuOOH}} Bu_2SnO\ (72\%) + t\text{-BuOH}\ (80\%)$$

With diphenyltin and 30% hydrogen peroxide diphenyltin oxide was produced (*53*):

$$(Ph_2Sn)_n \xrightarrow[\text{(room temp.)}]{\text{H}_2\text{O}_2} Ph_2SnO\ (97\%)$$

Organic disulfides, the sulfur analogs of organic peroxides, have been reported to react only with hexaalkylditins and mixed aliphatic-aromatic ditins (*20*). Hexa-*n*-butylditin or hexaethylditin with diphenyl disulfide gave the corresponding thiophenoxides. Triethyltriphenylditin and diphenyl disulfide gave a mixture of triethyl and triphenylthiophenoxide:

$$Et_3Sn\!-\!SnPh_3 \xrightarrow[\text{(reflux—dry benzene)}]{PhSSPh} Et_3SnSPh + Ph_3SnSPh$$

When dimethyl disulfide was used the reaction did not go to completion. Diphenyltin and dibenzyl disulfide yields diphenyltin dithiobenzylate (53):

$$Ph_2Sn + PhCH_2SSCH_2Ph \longrightarrow 2\ Ph_2Sn(SCH_2Ph)_2$$

Some triorganostibine sulfides are reported to react with hexaorganoditins to give bis(triorganotin)sulfides (82):

$$R_3SbS + R'_3Sn\!-\!SnR'_3 \longrightarrow R_3Sb + R'_3Sn\!-\!S\!-\!SnR'_3$$
$$(R = Me;\ R' = Ph\ or\ benzyl\ and\ R = Ph,\ R' = Ph)$$

The formation of silver in the reactions of ditins with silver nitrate solution has been used as a qualitative test for ditins, for example (112):

$$Ph_3Sn\!-\!SnPh_3 \xrightarrow[\text{(in acetone)}]{AgNO_3} Ag + Ph_3SnNO_3\ (90\%)$$

Creemers (20) has carried out oxidations of some symmetrical hexaorganoditins with potassium permanganate,

$$R_3Sn\!-\!SnR_3 \xrightarrow[\text{(in acetone)}]{KMnO_4} R_3SnOSnR_3$$
$$(R = Bu\ and\ Ph)$$

and has further noted that a mixed trialkyl-triarylditin does not produce a mixed trialkyl-triaryltin oxide but yields instead a mixture of symmetrical oxides.

$$2\ Et_3Sn\!-\!SnPh_3 \xrightarrow[\text{(KMnO}_4\text{ in acetone)}]{2\ (O)} (Et_3Sn)_2O + (Ph_3Sn)_2O$$

A number of metal halides cause oxidative cleavage of the tin-tin bond but in other cases disproportionation is effected.

Tsai and Lehn (112) have carried out reactions with hexaphenylditin and several metal halides.

$$Ph_3Sn\!-\!SnPh_3 \xrightarrow[\text{(in acetone)}]{CuCl_2} CuCl + Ph_3SnCl\ (99\%)$$

Mercuric chloride also caused cleavage with formation of Ph_3SnCl (15%) but the initial cleavage was complicated by other reactions. No reaction occurred using stannous chloride or zinc chloride in acetone. Stannic chloride in benzene, however, reacted as follows:

$$Ph_3Sn\!-\!SnPh_3 \xrightarrow[\text{(benzene)}]{SnCl_4} SnCl_2 + Ph_3SnCl\ (32\%)$$

Gold chloride has also been found to cleave hexamethylditin forming trimethyltin chloride along with some dimethyltin dichloride (*105*).

Creemers (*20*) has reported reactions of hexa-*n*-butylditin with tin tetrachloride and with germanium tetrachloride. In both cases the organotin compounds recovered were tri-*n*-butyltin chloride and di-*n*-butyltin dichloride. It was concluded from the experiments that the first step in these reactions was an oxidative cleavage of the tin-tin bond by the halide with its subsequent reduction:

$$Bu_3Sn—SnBu_3 + SnCl_4 \longrightarrow Bu_3SnCl + Bu_2SnCl_2 + SnCl_2$$

rather than alkyl-halogen exchange as is found in the case of the corresponding germanium compounds. Similar reactions with hexaethylditin (*87*) and triethyltributylditin (*20*) have been reported.

Diphenyltin has been reported to react with stannic chloride:

$$(Ph_2Sn)_n \xrightarrow{SnCl_4} SnCl_2 + Ph_2SnCl_2 \, (76\%)$$

and with mercuric chloride yielding mercury and diphenyltin dichloride (58%) (*53*).

Disproportionation during thermal decomposition of hexaorganoditins is said to be catalyzed by a number of metal salts which act as Lewis acids (*32*). Some of these include aluminum (III) bromide (*87*), aluminum (III) chloride (*84*), tin (II) chloride (*87*), tin (IV) chloride (*83, 87*), titanium (IV) chloride (*83*), and zirconium (IV) chloride (*83*):

$$Et_6Sn_2 \xrightarrow[70°C—1\,h]{AlCl_3} Et_4Sn + \frac{1}{n}(Et_2Sn)_n$$

In a number of these cases free tin was also formed.

G. Reactions with Metals

A number of metals react with the tin-tin bond to give the corresponding organotin-metal derivatives. The earliest example of this type of reaction was that of Kraus et al. (*49*), in the reaction of hexamethylditin with sodium in liquid ammonia to yield trimethyltin sodium:

$$Me_3Sn—SnMe_3 \xrightarrow[\text{(in liquid NH}_3)]{Na} Me_3SnNa$$

This same ditin has also been reduced using a sodium-potassium alloy in ethylene glycol dimethyl ether yielding trimethyltin potassium (*14*):

$$Me_3Sn—SnMe_3 \xrightarrow[\substack{\text{(in ethylene glycol} \\ \text{dimethyl ether)}}]{K–Na} Me_3SnK$$

The mono-sodium adduct of naphthalene has been found to react with hexaphenylditin giving triphenyltin sodium (62):

$$Ph_3Sn—SnPh_3 \xrightarrow{\text{Naphthalene–sodium}} Ph_3SnNa$$

Lithium in tetrahydrofuran has reduced both hexaphenylditin (35, 107) and hexa-n-butylditin (108) to the corresponding organotin lithium compounds:

$$R_3Sn—SnR_3 \xrightarrow[\text{(R = Ph and n–Bu)}]{\text{Li in THF}} R_3SnLi$$

Magnesium in tetrahydrofuran also has been found to cleave hexaphenylditin (109). This reaction was initiated by a small amount of ethyl bromide:

$$Ph_3Sn—SnPh_3 \xrightarrow[\text{(small amount of EtBr)}]{\text{Mg in THF}} (Ph_3Sn)_2Mg$$

Sodium in liquid ammonia is said to catalyze the addition of vinylacetylene to hexaethylditin (121):

$$Et_3SnSnEt_3 + HC≡C—CH=CH_2 \xrightarrow[\text{(in liq. NH}_3\text{)}]{\text{Mg in THF}} Et_3SnC≡C—CH=CH_2$$

Polymeric dimethyltin, $(Me_2Sn)_n$, reacts with sodium forming tetramethylditin disodium of which the tin-tin bond is cleaved upon further addition of sodium yielding dimethyltin disodium (47):

$$(Me_2Sn)_n \xrightarrow[\text{(liq. NH}_3\text{)}]{\text{Na}} \underset{\overset{|}{Na} \; \overset{|}{Na}}{Me_2Sn—SnMe_2} \xrightarrow[\text{(liq. NH}_3\text{)}]{\text{Na}} Me_2SnNa_2$$

Diethyltin reacts with sodium in a similar manner (40).

H. REACTIONS WITH HYDRIDES AND OTHER NUCLEOPHILIC REAGENTS

The tin-tin bond has been shown under suitable conditions to resist cleavage by lithium aluminum hydride (96, 104). Baum and Considine (10) carried out a detailed study of the reaction of hexa-n-butylditin with a large excess of lithium aluminum hydride under varying conditions of temperature, contact time, and solvent. At lower temperatures cleavage was not extensive and the main cleavage product was found to be tri-n-butyltin hydride. For example, from ether at 35°C after 18 h, 90% of the ditin was recovered. In tetrahydrofuran, at 64°C, even after 168 h, 71% of the ditin did not react. The data point to an equilibrium reaction for which the first step has been postulated as:

$$(C_4H_9)_3Sn—Sn(C_4H_9)_3 \underset{}{\overset{H^-}{\rightleftharpoons}} (C_4H_9)_3SnH + (C_4H_9)_3Sn^-$$

Even at 100°C, in dioxane, after 3 h, 85% of the starting ditin was recovered. As the temperature was raised or as the contact time was increased, more complex changes occurred lowering the percentage of ditin recovered and resulting in the formation of tars and even tin metal. In the case of hexaphenylditin, complex reactions occurred in which little if any starting material was found, and with diphenyltin oxide and tin being the main products.

Diborane is said to be an effective catalyst for the disproportionation of hexamethylditin (16):

$$Me_3SnSnMe_3 \longrightarrow Me_4Sn + \frac{1}{n}(Me_2Sn)_n$$

Both hexa-n-butylditin and (triphenylgermyl) triethyltin appear to be hydrolytically stable upon reflux for 6 h in an oxygen free 70% dioxane-water mixture (20).

Hexamethylditin reacts with sodium amide in liquid ammonia (48a):

$$Me_3Sn—SnMe_3 + NaNH_2 \xrightarrow{\text{liquid } NH_3} Me_3SnNa + Me_3SnNH_2$$

Hot alcoholic potassium hydroxide does not affect hexaphenylditin although it is suggested that lack of solution is probably a hindrance to this reaction (32). Moist hot piperidine with hexaphenylditin results in homogeneous cleavage with the formation of bis(triphenyltin)oxide (32). Phenyllithium also cleaves hexaphenylditin with the formation of tetraphenyltin (89%) (36). Ethylmagnesium bromide is found to cleave hexaphenylditin as indicated by the hydrolysis products (20):

$$Ph_3Sn—SnPh_3 + EtMgBr \longrightarrow Ph_3SnEt + Ph_3SnMgBr$$
$$\downarrow H_2O$$
$$Ph_3SnH + Mg(OH)Br$$

Cleavage can also be brought about using organomercury compounds such as diphenyl mercury or phenyl mercuric chloride (45b):

$$Et_3Sn—SnEt_3 \xrightarrow[\text{at } 60°C]{Ph_2 Hg} Et_3SnPh + Hg$$
$$\xrightarrow[\text{at } 150°C]{PhHgCl} Et_3SnPh + Et_3SnCl$$

However, a different reaction was obtained using thienylmercury chloride (20):

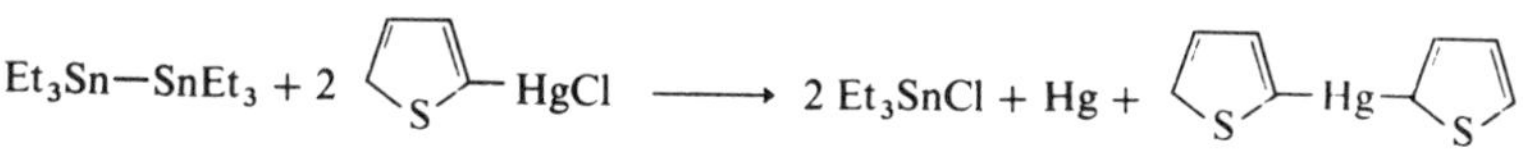

$$Et_3Sn—SnEt_3 + 2 \underset{S}{\bigcirc}—HgCl \longrightarrow 2 Et_3SnCl + Hg + \underset{S}{\bigcirc}—Hg—\underset{S}{\bigcirc}$$

I. REACTIONS WITH ACIDS

Very little work has been reported on the reactions of acids with compounds containing a tin-tin bond, but, such evidence as exists indicates that under mild conditions the tin-tin bond is quite stable to reaction with both organic and inorganic acids. Under some conditions this bond has been shown to remain intact in the presence of acids, but, in other cases cleavage has been reported to occur.

Hexamethylditin in methanol at 25°C has been reported to react with hydrogen chloride to give trimethyltin chloride (*105*). Hydrobromic acid also reacted with hexamethylditin forming trimethyltin bromide (*49*). Hexaethylditin, however, reacted with hydrogen chloride forming diethyltin dichloride, ethane, and hydrogen (*57*):

$$Et_6Sn_2 + 4\,HCl \longrightarrow 2\,Et_2SnCl_2 + 2\,C_2H_6 + H_2$$

Hexaethylditin also reacted with glacial acetic acid at about 135°C forming ethane, triethyltin acetate, hydrogen, and a small amount of diethyltin diacetate (*115*).

Hexaphenylditin with sulfuric acid in THF is reported to show no reaction (*112*). On the other hand, with hydrogen chloride in THF, hydrogen and triphenyltin chloride (60%) were produced. With nitric acid, a mixture was obtained which was not purified but the presence of triphenyltin hydroxide and nitrate was indicated. Hexaphenylditin with acetic acid at 120°C is converted to hexaacetoxyditin (*118*). The latter compound with hydrogen chloride in ether yields $Cl_2(AcO)SnSn(OAc)Cl_2$ but liquid HCl at $-100°C$ gives hexachloroditin.

Recently, di-*n*-butyltin has been observed to react with benzoic acid under relatively mild conditions forming hydrogen and tetra-*n*-butylditin 1,2-dibenzoate:

$$2\,[n\text{-}Bu_2Sn]_n + 2n\,PhCOOH \xrightarrow[\substack{(40-50\ min \\ in\ benzene)}]{60-70°C} \begin{array}{c} n\text{-}Bu_2Sn\!-\!Sn\!-\!n\!=\!Bu_2 \quad (90\%) \\ \ \ \ |\qquad\quad | \\ PhOCO\quad OCOPh \\ +\,n\,H_2(100\%) \end{array}$$

In the reaction of di-*n*-butyltin with inorganic acids, however, di-*n*-butyltin dihalides resulted (*115*):

$$(Bu_2Sn)_n \xrightarrow[(X=Br,\,I)]{HX} Bu_2SnX_2 + H_2$$

Tetra-*n*-butylditin 1,2-diacetate was converted by hydrogen chloride in ether to tetra-*n*-butylditin 1,2-dichloride (*31*, *96*). Likewise, the tin-tin bond remained intact when tetra-*n*-butylditin 1,2-dihydride reacted rapidly with a 100% excess of glacial acetic acid to give a quantitative yield of hydrogen and tetra-*n*-butylditin 1,2-diacetate (*96*). In another reaction when tetra-*n*-butylditin 1,2-diacetate was allowed to stand with glacial acetic acid, no gas evolution was observed even after several days (*98*). Likewise, di-*n*-butyltin and an excess of glacial acetic acid showed no gas evolution over several days at room temperature (*91*).

J. INSERTION REACTIONS

Beg and Clark (*11*) have described the first instance of direct addition of olefins to Sn—Sn bonds. Tetrafluoroethylene reacted with hexamethylditin in carbon tetrachloride upon ultraviolet irradiation giving the insertion compound containing the —Sn—CF_2—CF_2—Sn— grouping:

$$Me_3Sn\text{—}SnMe_3 + F_2C{=}CF_2 \longrightarrow Me_3Sn\text{—}CF_2\text{—}CF_2\text{—}SnMe_3$$

Clark and Tsai (*19*) subsequently reported that hexamethylditin and perfluoropropene reacted for eight hours in a sealed silica tube at 70°C under ultraviolet radiation to give mainly the insertion product:

$$Me_3Sn\text{—}SnMe_3 + CF_3\text{—}CF{=}CF_2 \longrightarrow Me_3Sn\underset{\underset{\textstyle CF_3}{|}}{\text{—}CF}\text{—}CF_2\text{—}SnMe_3$$

The authors suggested a free radical mechanism from the facts that the reactions also occur slowly under ultraviolet irradiation at 20°C, are accelerated by raising the temperature, but do not occur by heating alone.

Clark et al. (*18*) reacted a series of fluorinated olefins with hexamethylditin under conditions favoring the formation of trimethyltin radicals. Insertion products were obtained with tetrafluoromethylene, perfluoropropene, trifluoroethylene and 1,1-difluoroethylene. Reactions of dimethyltin and diphenyltin with tetrafluoroethylene showed some addition but the products were of indeterminate composition.

Cullen et al. (*24*) have found that hexafluoro-2-butyne reacts with hexamethylditin under ultraviolet radiation to give an unstable insertion product:

$$Me_3Sn\text{—}SnMe_3 + F_3CC{\equiv}CCF_3 \xrightarrow{uv} Me_3Sn\underset{\underset{\textstyle CF_3}{|}}{\overset{\overset{\textstyle CF_3}{|}}{\text{—}C}}{=}C\text{—}SnMe_3$$

The ^{19}F NMR spectrum indicated that there was only one isomer and the ir spectrum suggested that it was the *trans* isomer. Its thermal decompositon at 150°C yielded a mixture of products:

$$(CH_3)_3Sn\underset{\underset{\textstyle CF_3}{|}}{\overset{\overset{\textstyle CF_3}{|}}{\text{—}C}}{=}C\text{—}Sn(CH_3)_3$$

$$\xrightarrow{150°C} (CH_3)_4Sn + (CH_3)_3SnSn(CH_3)_3 + (CH_3)_3Sn\underset{\underset{\textstyle CF_3}{|}}{\overset{\overset{\textstyle CF_3}{|}}{C}}{=}CH + \ ?$$

The only compound isolated from a similar reaction involving hexabutylditin and hexafluoro-2-butyne was dibutylbis(1,1,1,4,4,4-hexafluoro-2-butenyl-2)tin, $(C_4H_9)_2Sn[C(CF_3){=}C(CF_3)H]_2$.

Seyferth and co-workers (*100, 101*) have reported the first examples of dihalocarbene insertion into the Sn—Sn bond using organomercury compounds:

$$Me_3Sn{-}SnMe_3 \xrightarrow{PhHgCCl_2Br} Me_3SnCCl_2SnMe_3(53\%) + PhHgBr$$

$$Me_3Sn{-}SnMe_3 \xrightarrow{PhHgCBr_2Cl} Me_3SnClBrClSnMe_3(39\%) + PhHgBr$$

$$Me_3Sn{-}SnMe_3 \xrightarrow{PhHgCCl_2F} Me_3Sn{-}CClF{-}SnMe_3(36\%)$$
$$Me_3Sn{-}CCl_2{-}SnMe_3\ (8\%)$$

Carey and Clark (*17*) have also carried out reactions of sulfur dioxide with hexamethylditin and hexaphenylditin. The tin-tin bond was cleaved in each case giving compounds of the type $R_3Sn \cdot SO_2$. Where R is phenyl $R_3Sn \cdot 2SO_2$ was also obtained. The evidence suggests that 5 coordinate tin atoms are present in the products and that SO_2 has been inserted into the tin-tin bond.

Recently, Bulten, Budding and Noltes (*15a*) have carried out reactions of hexamethylditin and hexaethylditin with unsaturated systems under polar conditions. Hexamethylditin and diphenylacetylene in hexamethylphosphoric triamide (HMPT) in the presence of sodium methoxide gave 1,2-bis(trimethylstannyl)-1,2-diphenylethylene which was indicated to be the trans isomer. The ethyl analog was similarly obtained.

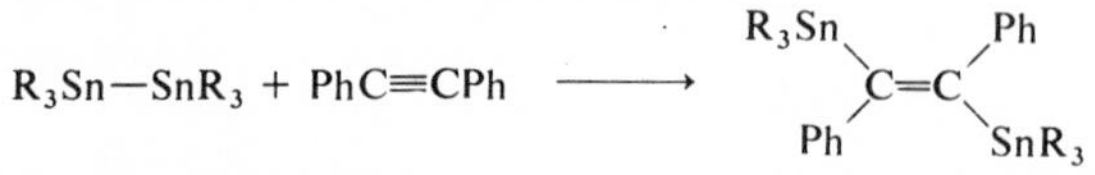

$$R_3Sn{-}SnR_3 + PhC{\equiv}CPh \longrightarrow \begin{array}{c} R_3Sn \\ \diagdown \\ Ph \end{array} C{=}C \begin{array}{c} Ph \\ \diagup \\ SnR_3 \end{array}$$

$$(R = Me\ and\ Et)$$

Additional reactions were carried out of hexamethylditin with various unsaturated species in solvents of different polarity to give addition products with phenylacetylene, diphenylbutadiyne, and diethyl azodicarboxylate (the latter in HMPT without a catalyst.)

K. Reactions with Organic Halides

Kaesz et al. (*44a*) have carried out reactions showing that the tin-tin bond in hexaorganoditins is readily cleaved by perfluoroalkyl iodides forming the corresponding organoperfluoroalkyltin derivatives:

$$R_3Sn{-}SnR_3 + C_nF_{2n+1}I \xrightarrow[\text{or heat}]{uv} R_3SnC_nF_{2n+1} + R_3SnI$$
$$(n = 1\ and\ R = Me,\ Et\ and\ Ph;\ n = 2\ and\ R = Me)$$

Clark and Willis (*19a*) also reported a similar reaction in the liquid phase in the absence of light:

$$Me_3Sn\!-\!SnMe_3 + CF_3I \xrightarrow[\text{liquid phase}]{\text{absence of light}} Me_3SnCF_3 + MeSnI$$

They considered homolytic dissociation of hexamethylditin unlikely as the first step in the mechanism of the reaction, and considered also the possibility of the formation of an intermediate complex of the two reactants. Subsequently, preparations by Chambers et al. (*17a*) using highly purified hexamethylditin gave erratic and sometimes no results under the conditions previously used. Irradiation of the reaction mixture with ultraviolet light under mild conditions caused a rapid reaction for which the following reaction scheme was suggested:

$$Me_3SnSnMe_3 \xrightarrow{\text{uv}} 2\,Me_3Sn\cdot$$
$$Me_3Sn\cdot + CF_3I \longrightarrow Me_3SnCF_3 + I$$
$$I + Me_3Sn\!-\!SnMe_3 \longrightarrow Me_3SnI + Me_3Sn\cdot \text{ etc.}$$

Note is made in the previous section (Sec. III.J) of reactions of a series of fluorinated olefins with hexamethylditin. In addition to the insertion products a second type of product was found, namely, $Me_3SnCF_2CF(R)H$. These two types of products are rationalized in terms of the formation of an intermediate radical $Me_3SnCF_2CF(R)$ which may either abstract H or form the insertion product, $Me_3SnCF_2CF(R)SnMe_3$.

Cleavage of hexaethylditin in carbon tetrachloride when carried out in the presence of a free radical initiator results in the formation of Et_3SnCl (*86*).

There are several examples of reactions which have been carried out between $(R_2Sn)_n$ compounds and organic halides (*51a, 82a*), for example:

$$Et_2Sn + EtI \longrightarrow Et_3SnI$$

A rather detailed study (*101a*) has recently been done of reactions of a number of alkyl halides with dialkyltins, $(R_2Sn)_n$ at 140°C for 3 h. From $(R_2Sn)_n$ and R'X the two main kinds of products obtained were R_3SnX and $R_2R'SnX$ types of compounds. Alkyl bromides gave both $R_2R'SnBr$ and R_3SnBr compounds, and alkyl chlorides gave only R_3SnCl compounds. A similar study (*101b*) with diphenyltin $(Ph_2Sn)_n$ and alkyl halides, (RX) resulted mainly in the formation of Ph_2RSnX and Ph_3SnX, and usually small amounts of $PhRSnX_2$, PhR_2SnX and Ph_2SnX_2. The same workers found only a slight cleavage of hexaphenylditin by methyl iodide at 140°C:

$$Ph_3SnSnPh_3 \xrightarrow[\text{140°C—3 h}]{\text{MeI}} Ph_3SnI\ (6\%)$$

L. Reactions with Other Organotin Compounds

This section deals with a few reactions in which the tin-tin bond in organotin compounds reacts with other organotin compounds.

Apparently tin-tin bonds are cleaved by organotin halides as indicated by several reactions. Kuivila and Jakusik (*53*) attempted the following reactions of polymeric diphenyltin with diphenyltin dichloride:

$$\frac{1}{n}(Ph_2Sn)_n + Ph_2SnCl_2 \longrightarrow \underset{\overset{|}{Cl}}{Ph_2Sn} - \underset{\overset{|}{Cl}}{SnPh_2}$$

Instead, they obtained the reaction noted below, in which the tin-tin bonds in polymeric diphenyltin were cleaved:

$$\frac{1}{n}(Ph_2Sn)_n + 2\,Ph_2SnCl_2 \xrightarrow[3\,h]{130°C} Ph_3SnCl + SnCl_2$$

Later it was found that even at room temperature in boiling benzene or methylene chloride high yields of triphenyltin chloride were obtained (*54a*).

Recently, Sisido et al. (*101b*), carried out the reaction of excess polymeric diphenyltin with diphenyltin diiodide:

$$2/n\,(Ph_2Sn)_n + Ph_2SnI_2 \xrightarrow[10\,h]{140°C} \underset{53\%}{2\,Ph_3SnI} + \underset{35\%}{Sn}$$

With di-*n*-butyltin diiodide a mixture of products was obtained in which nearly all of the tin-tin bonds were cleaved:

$$(Ph_2Sn)_n + Bu_2SnI_2 \xrightarrow[10\,h]{140°C} \begin{array}{l} PhBu_2SnI\text{---}42\% \\ PhBuSnI_2\text{---}5\% \\ Ph_3SnI\text{---}6\% \\ Ph_2SnI_2\text{---}5\% \\ Ph_3Sn\text{---}SnPh_3\text{---}7\% \end{array}$$

They also found that di-*n*-butyltin reacted with di-*n*-butyltin dichloride (*101a*).

$$(Bu_2Sn)_n + Bu_2SnCl_2 \xrightarrow[160°C-15\,h]{Et_3N} \underset{30\%}{Bu_3SnCl} + \underset{43\%}{Sn}$$

With di-*n*-butyltin and diethyltin dichloride in a 2 : 1 mole ratio all of the diethyltin dichloride was used up and the tin-tin bonds in the dialkyltin chain were broken:

$$(Bu_2Sn)_2 + Et_2SnCl_2 \xrightarrow[\text{160°C—15 h}]{\text{Et}_3\text{N}} Bu_2EtSnCl\ (12.4\%)$$

$$Bu Et_2SnCl\ (7.3\%)$$
$$Bu_3SnCl\quad (5\%)$$
$$Et_3SnCl\quad (1.3\%)$$
$$Sn\qquad\quad (48\%)$$

Molecular weight studies of mixtures of dibutyltin and di-*n*-butyltin dihalides (X = Cl, Br and I) in toluene at 37°C clearly show that reactions occur in each case but the results are not clear as to the nature of the reactions (*93*).

Although no reaction seems to take place between tributyltin hydride and di-*n*-butyltin, some reaction occurs using di-*n*-butyltin dihydride as indicated by new substantial infrared absorption appearing at about 1780 cm^{-1} (previously reported for polytin hydride species) (*93*).

Similarly, a reaction occurs with di-*n*-butyltin hydride chloride. As the $Bu_2Sn(H)Cl/Bu_2Sn$ ratio is increased, infrared spectral data indicated increased formation of di-*n*-butyltin dihydride. However, absorption at 1780 cm^{-1} due to polytin hydrides appeared at a 2–1 mole ratio and was predominant at a 3–1 mole ratio and higher (*93*).

M. MISCELLANEOUS

An inclusion compound containing hexaphenylditin and tetraphenyltin in a 1.75 : 1 mole ratio has been reported to be formed in the reaction of 2-pyridylmagnesium bromide with a benzene solution of triphenyltin chloride (*61*). The same compound was obtained upon refluxing hexaphenylditin and tetraphenyltin in nitromethane.

Hexamethylditin has been reported by Cotton et al. (*19b*) to react with triruthenium dedecacarbonyl and by Akhtar and Clark (*5b*) to react with tetrakis(triphenylphosphine)platinum to form compounds containing tin-ruthenium and tin-platinum bonds respectively. More recently Abel and Morehouse (*5a*) have shown that hexamethylditin reacts with a number of transitional metal compounds containing metal-metal bonds to give compounds containing tin-transitional metal bonds.

$$Me_3Sn\text{—}SnMe_3 + Co_2(CO)_8 \longrightarrow 2Me_3SnCo(CO)_4$$
$$\text{''}\qquad + Mn_2(CO)_{10} \longrightarrow 2Me_3SnMn(CO)_5$$
$$\text{''}\qquad + Re_2(CO)_{10} \longrightarrow 2Me_3SnRe(CO)_5$$

Similar reactions are observed with a number of dimeric cyclopentadienyl metal carbonyls, with the metals being Ni, Fe, Mo, and W., e.g.,

$$Me_3Sn\text{—}SnMe_3 + [(\pi\text{-}C_5H_5)Ni(CO)]_2 \longrightarrow 2(\pi\text{-}C_5H_5)Ni(CO)SnMe_3$$

It is suggested that these reactions may involve fission of the transitional metal-metal bond and the formation of free radicals.

REFERENCES

1. Yu A. Aleksandrov, T. G. Brilkina, and V. A. Shushnov, *Trudy Khim. Tekhnol.*, **4**, 3 (1961); through *CA*, **56**, 492 (1962).

2. Yu A. Alexsandrov and B. A. Radbil, *Zhur. Obshchei Khim.*, **36**, 543 (1966).

3. Yu A. Alexsandrov, B. A. Radbil, and V. A. Shushnov, *Trudy Khim. Khim. Tekhnol.*, 3, 381 (1960); through *CA*, **55**, 27023 (1961).

4. Yu A. Alexandrov and B. V. Suldin, *Zhur. Obshchei Khim.*, **37**, 2350 (1966).

5. Yu A. Alexsandrov and N. N. Vyshinskii, *Trudy Khim. Khim. Tekhnol.*, **4**, 656 (1962); through *CA*, **58**, 3453 (1963).

5a. E. W. Abel and S. Moorhouse, *J. Organometal. Chem.*, **24**, 687 (1970).

5b. M. Akhtar and H. C. Clark, *J. Organometal. Chem.*, **22**, 233 (1970).

6. R. B. Allan, Dissertation, University of New Hampshire, 1959.

7. D. L. Alleston and A. G. Davies, *Chem. Ind.*, 949 (1961).

8. W. H. Atwell and H. Gilman, *Intern. Symp. Decomposition Organometallic Compounds*, Air Force Materials Labaratory, Wright-Patterson Air Force Base, Dayton, Ohio, 1967.

9. G. Bahr and R. Gelius, *Chem. Ber.*, **91**, 829 (1958).

10. G. A. Baum and W. J. Considine, *J. Org. Chem.*, **29**, 1267 (1964).

11. M. A. A. Beg and H. C. Clark, *Chem. Ind.*, 140 (1962).

12. J. Böeseken and J. J. Rutgers, *Rec. trav. Chim.*, **42**, 107 (1923).

12a. S. Boué, M. Gielen, and J. Nasielski, *Bull. Soc. chim. Belges*, **73**, 864 (1964).

13. T. C. Brilkina, and V. A. Shushunov, " Reactions of Organometallic Compounds with Oxygen and Perioxides " U.S.S.R. transl. edited by Alwyn G. Davies, Chemical Rubber Co., Cleveland, Ohio, 1969.

14. M. P. Brown and G. W. Fowles, *J. Chem. Soc.*, 2811 (1958).

15. T. L. Brown and G. L. Morgan, *Inorg. Chem.*, **2**, 736 (1963).

15a. E. J. Bulten, H. A. Budding and J. G. Noltes, *J. Organometal. Chem.*, **22**, C5 (1970).

16. A. B. Burg and T. R. Spielman, *J. Am. Chem. Soc.*, **83**, 2667 (1961).

17. N. A. D. Carey and H. C. Clark, *Can. J. Chem.*, **46**, 643 (1968).

17a. R. D. Chambers, H. C. Clark, and C. F. Willis, *Chem. Ind.*, 76 (1960).

18. H. C. Clark, J. D. Cotton, and J. H. Tsai, *Can. J. Chem.*, **44**, 903 (1966).

19. H. C. Clark and J. H. Tsai, *Chem. Commun.*, 111 (1965).

19a. H. C. Clark and C. J. Willis, *J. Am. Chem. Soc.*, **82**, 1888 (1960).

19b. J. D. Cotton, S. A. R. Knox and F. G. A. Stone, *J. Chem. Soc. A*, 2758 (1968).

20. H. M. J. C. Creemers, Doctoral Dissertation, Utrecht, 1967.

21. H. M. J. C. Creemers and J. G. Noltes, *Rec. trav. Chim.*, **84**, 382 (1965).

22. H. M. J. C. Creemers and J. G. Noltes, *Rec. trav. Chim.* **84**, 590 (1965).

23. H. M. J. C. Creemers, J. G. Noltes, and G. J. M. van der Kerk, *Rec. trav. Chim.*, **83** 1284 (1964).

24. W. R. Cullen, D. S. Dawson, and G. E. Styan, *J. Organometal. Chem.*, **3**, 406 (1965).

25. R. E. Dessey, W. Kitching, and T. Chivers, *J. Am. Chem. Soc.*, **88**, 453 (1966).

26. L. Doretti and G. Tagliavini, *J. Organometal Chem.*, **12**, 203 (1968).

27. L. Doretti and G. Tagliavini, *J. Organometal. Chem.*, **13**, 195 (1968).

28. M. Dub and R. W. Weiss, *Organometallic Compounds*, Vol. II, Springer Verlag, New York (1967).

29. W. V. Farrar and H. A. Skinner, *J. Organometal. Chem.*, **1**, 434 (1964).

30. H. P. Fritz and H. Scheer, *Z. Naturforsch.*, **19b**, 537 (1964); *Z. anorg. allgem. Chem.* **338**, 1 (1965).

31. A. J. Gibbons, A. K. Sawyer, and A Ross, *J. Org. Chem.*, **26**, 2304 (1961).

32. H. Gilman, W. H. Atwell, and F. K. Cartledge, *Adv. Organometal. Chem.*, **4**, 1 (1966).

33. H. Gilman and F. K. Cartledge, *Chem. Ind.*, 1231 (1964).

33a. H. Gilman and F. K. Cartledge, *J. Organometal. Chem.*, **5**, 48 (1966).

34. H. Gilman and J. Eisch, *J. Org. Chem.*, **20**, 763 (1955).

35. H. Gilman, O. L. Mans, and S. Y. Sim, *J. Org. Chem.*, **27**, 4232 (1962).

36. H. Gilman and S. D. Rosenberg, *J. Org. Chem.*, **18**, 680 (1953).

36a. H. Gilman and S. D. Rosenberg, *J. Org. Chem.*, **18**, 1554 (1953).

37. G. Gruttner, *Ber.* **50**, 1808 (1917).

38. D. N. Hague and R. H. Prince, *J. Inorg. Nucl. Chem.*, **28**, 1039 (1966).

39. T. Harada, *Bull. Chem. Soc. Japan*, **15**, 481 (1940).

40. T. Harada, *Sci. Papers Inst. Phys. Chem. Res., Tokyo*, **35**, 290 (1939); through *CA*, **33**, 5387 (1939).

41. R. K. Ingham, S. D. Rosenberg, and H. Gilman, *Chem. Rev.*, **60**, 459 (1960).

42. O. H. Johnson, *J. Org. Chem.*, **25**, 2262 (1960).

43. O. H. Johnson and H. E. Fritz, *J. Org. Chem.*, **19**, 74 (1954).

44. O. H. Johnson, H. E. Fritz, , D. O. Halvorsan, and R. L. Evans, *J. Am. Chem. Soc.* **77**, 5857 (1955).

44a. H. D. Kaesz, J. R. Phillips, and F. G. A. Stone, *J. Am. Chem. Soc.*, **82**, 6228 (1960).

45. S. F. A. Kettle, *J. Chem. Soc.*, 2936 (1959).

45a. G. J. M. van der Kerk and J. G. A. Luijten, *J. Appl. Chem.*, **4**, 301 (1954).

45b. K. A. Kocheschkov, A. N. Nesmeyanow, and W. P. Pusyruva, *Ber.*, **69**, 1639 (1936).

46. C. A. Kraus and R. H. Bullard, *J. Am. Chem. Soc.*, **48**, 2131 (1926).

47. C. A. Kraus and W. N. Greer, *J. Am. Chem. Soc.*, **47**, 2568 (1925).

48. C. A. Kraus and A. M. Neal, *J. Am. Chem. Soc.*, **51**, 2403 (1929).

48a. C. A. Kraus and A. M. Neal, *J. Am. Chem. Soc.*, **52**, 695 (1930).

49. C. A. Kraus and W. V. Sessions, *J. Am. Chem. Soc.*, **47**, 2361 (1925).

50. E. Krause and R. Becker, *Ber.*, **53**, 173 (1920).

51. E. Krause and A. von Grosse, *Die Chemie der Metallorganischen Verbindungen* Borntraeger, Berlin (1937).

51a. E. Krause and R. Pohland, *Ber.*, **57**, 532 (1924).

51b. K. Kulheim and W. P. Neumann, *J. Organometal. Chem.*, **14**, 317 (1968).

52. H. G. Kuivila and O. F. Beumel, Jr., *J. Am. Chem. Soc.*, **83**, 1246 (1961).

53. H. G. Kuivila and E. R. Jakusik, *J. Org. Chem.*, **26**, 1430 (1961).

54. H. G. Kuivila, A. K. Sawyer, and A. G. Armour, *J. Org. Chem.*, **26**, 1426 (1961).

54a. H. G. Kuivila and A. K. Sawyer, unreported observations.

55. E. J. Kupchik and R. J. Kiesel, *J. Org. Chem.*, **31**, 456 (1966).

56. A. Ladenburg, *Ann.*, Suppl., **8**, 69 (1869).

57. A. Ladenburg, *Ber.*, **3**, 647 (1870).

57a. K. K. Law, *J. Chem. Soc.*, 3243 (1926).

58. C. Lowig, *Ann.*, **84**, 308 (1852).

59. A. G. MacDiarmid, *Organometallic Compounds of the Group IV Elements*, Marcel Dekker, New York (1968).

60. K. M. MacKay and R. Watt, *Organometal Chem. Rev.*, **A4**, 137 (1969).

61. W. R. McWhinnie, R. C. Poller, and M. Thevarasa, *J. Organometal. Chem.*, **11**, 499 (1968).

62. H. Morris and P. W. Selwood, *J. Am. Chem., Soc.*, **63**, 2509 (1941).

63. H. Morris, W. Beyerly, and P. W. Selwood, *J. Am. Chem. Soc.*, **64**, 1727 (1942).

63a. M. M. Nad and K. A. Kocheschkov, *Zhur. Obshchei. Khim.*, **8**, 42 (1938); through *CA*, **32**, 5387 (1938).

64. W. P. Neumann, *Die Organische Chemie des Zinns*, Ferdinand Enke Verlag, Stuttgart, 1967.

65. W. P. Neumann, *Angew. Chem.*, **74**, 122 (1962).

66. W. P. Neumann, *Angew. Chem.*, **75**, 225 (1963).
67. W. P. Neumann, *Angew. Chem.*, **75**, 679 (1963).
68. W. P. Neumann and K. Konig, *Angew. Chem.*, **74**, 215 (1962).
69. W. P. Neumann and K. Konig, *Angew. Chem.*, **76**, 892 (1964); *Angew. Chem. Intern. Ed.*, **3**, 751 (1964).
70. W. P. Neumann and K. Konig, *Ann.*, **667**, 1 (1964).
71. W. P. Neumann and K. Konig, *Ann.*, **677**, 12 (1964).
72. W. P. Neumann, K. Konig, and G. Burkhardt, *Ann.*, **677**, 18 (1964).
73. W. P. Neumann and J. Pedain, *Ann.*, **672**, 34 (1964).
74. W. P. Neumann and J. Pedain, *Tetrahedron Letters*, 2461 (1964).
75. W. P. Neumann, J. Pedain, and R. Sommer, *Ann.*, **694**, 9 (1966).
76. W. P. Neumann, E. Petersen, and L. Sommer, *Angew. Chem. Intern. Ed.*, **4**, 599 (1965).
77. W. P. Neumann and K. Rubsamen, cited in Ref. (*64*).
78. W. P. Neumann and B. Schneider, *Angew. Chem.*, **76**, 891 (1964); *Angew. Chem. Intern. Ed.*, **3**, 751 (1964).
79. W. P. Neumann, B. Schneider, and R. Sommer, *Ann.*, **692**, 1 (1966).
80. J. Noltes and G. J. M. van der Kerk, *Functionally Substituted Organotin Compounds*, Tin Research Institute, Greenford, England, 1958, p. 43.
81. D. H. Olsen and R. E. Rundle, *Inorg. Chem.*, **2**, 1310 (1963).
81a. G. Plazzogna, V. Peruzzo and G. Tagliavini, *J. Organometal. Chem.*, **24**, 667 (1970).
81b. R. C. Poller, "The Chemistry of Organotin Compounds," Academic Press, New York 1970.
82. J. Otera, T. Kadowaki, and R. Okawara, *J. Organometal. Chem.*, **19**, 213 (1969).
82a. P. Pfeiffer, *Ber.*, **44**, 1269 (1911).
82b. I. B. Rabinovich, V. I. Tel'noi, N. V. Karakin, and G. A. Razuveav, *Dokl. Akad. Nauk. SSSR*, **149**, 324 (1963); through *CA*, **59**, 3367 (1963).
82c. I. B. Rabinovich, V. I. Tel'noi, P. N. Nikolaev, N. V. Karakin, and G. A. Razuveav, *Dokl. Akad. Nauk. SSSR*, **138**, 852 (1961); through *CA.*, **55**, 23024 (1961).
82d. G. A. Razuveav and E. I. Fedotova, *Zhur. Obschchei. Khim.*, **21**, 1118 (1951); through *CA*, **46**, 5006 (1952).
83. G. A. Razauaev, N. S. Vyazankin, Yu. I. Dergunov, and N. N. Vyshinskii, *Zhur. Obshchei Khim.*, **31**, 1712 (1961); through *CA*, **55**, 24546 (1961).
84. G. A. Razauaev, N. S. Vyazankin, Yu. I. Dergunov, and O. S. D'yachkovskaya, *Dokl. Akad. Nauk. SSSR*, **132**, 364 (1960); through *CA*, **54**, 20937 (1960).
85. G. A. Razuvaev, N. S. Vyazankin, and O. A. Shchepetkova, *Tetrahedron*, **18**, 667 (1962).
86. G. A. Razuvaev, N. S. Vyazankin, and O. A. Shchepetkova, *Zhur. Obshchei. Khim.*, **30**, 2498 (1960); through *CA*, **55**, 14290 (1961).
87. G. A. Razuvaev, N. S. Vyazankin, and O. A. Shchepetkova, *Zhur. Obshchei. Khim.*, **31**, 3762 (1961); through *CA*, **57**, 8597 (1962).
87a. J. J. De Ridder and J. Noltes, *J. Organometal. Chem.*, **20**, 287 (1969).
88. L. Rugheimer, *Ann.*, **364**, 51 (1909).
89. A. K. Sawyer, *J. Am. Chem. Soc.*, **87**, 537 (1965).
90. A. K. Sawyer, U.S. Pat. 3,347,889 (1967); through *CA*, **68**, 4830 (1968).
90a. A. K. Sawyer, U.S. Pat. 3,322,801 (1967); through *CA*, **67**, 22001 (1967).
91. A. K. Sawyer, unreported observations.
92. A. K. Sawyer, J. E. Brown, and E. L. Hanson, *J. Organometal. Chem.*, **3**, 464 (1965).
93. A. K. Sawyer and E. L. Hanson, unreported observations.
94. A. K. Sawyer and M. Jefferson, unreported observations.
95. A. K. Sawyer and H. G. Kuivila, *J. Am. Chem. Soc.*, **82**, 5958 (1960).
96. A. K. Sawyer and H. G. Kuivila, *J. Am. Chem. Soc.*, **85**, 1010 (1963).

97. A. K. Sawyer and H. G. Kuivila, *J. Org. Chem.*, **27**, 610 (1962).
98. A. K. Sawyer and H. G. Kuivila, *J. Org. Chem.*, **27**, 837 (1962).
99. D. Schmidt, K. Kabitzke, K. Merku, and W. P. Neumann, *Ber.*, **98**, 3827 (1965).
100. D. Seyferth and F. M. Ambrecht, Jr., *J. Am. Chem. Soc.*, **89**, 2790 (1967).
101. D. Seyferth and K. V. Darragh, *J. Organometal. Chem.*, **11**, P9 (1968).
101a. K. Sisido, S. Kozima, and T. Isibasi, *J. Organometal. Chem.*, **10**, 439 (1967).
101b. K. Sisido, T. Miyanisi, K. Nabika, and S. Kozima, *J. Organometal. Chem.*, **11**, 281 (1968).
102. T. D. Smith, *Nature*, **199**, 374 (1963).
103. R. Sommer, W. P. Neumann, and B. Schneider, *Tetrahedron Letters*, **51**, 3875 (1964).
104. R. Sommer, B. Schneider, and W. P. Neumann, *Ann.*, **692**, 12 (1966).
104a. A. Stern and E. I. Becker, *J. Org. Chem.*, **29**, 3221 (1964).
104b. G. Tagliavini, *Anal. Chim. Acta*, **34**, 24 (1966).
105. G. Tagliavini, U. Belluco, and G. Pilloni, *Ric. Sci. Rend.*, **3**, 889 (1963); through *CA*, **60**, 15900 (1964).
106. G. Tagliavini, S. Faleschini, and E. Genero, *Ric. Sci.*, 717 (1966).
106a. G. Tagliavini, S. Faleschini, G. Pilloni, and G. Plazzongna, *J. Organometal. Chem.*, **5**, 136 (1966).
107. C. Tamborshi, F. E. Ford, and E. J. Soloski, *J. Org. Chem.*, **28**, 181 (1963).
108. C. Tamborski, F. E. Ford, and E. J. Soloski, *J. Org. Chem.*, **28**, 237 (1963).
109. C. Tamborski and E. J. Soloski, *J. Am. Chem. Soc.*, **83**, 3734 (1961).
110. F. J. A. Tombe, G. J. M. van der Kerk, and J. G. Noltes, *J. Organometal. Chem.*, **13**, P9 (1968).
111. A. P. Tomilov, Yu. D. Smirnov, and S. L. Varshavskii, *Zhur. Obshchei. Khim.*, **35**, 391 (1965).
112. T. T. Tsai and W. L. Lehn, *J. Org. Chem.*, **31**, 2981 (1966).
113. N. S. Vyazankin, M. N. Bochkarev, and L. P. Sanina, *Zhur. Obshchei. Khim.*, **36**, 166 (1966); through *CA*, **64**, 14212 (1966).
114. N. S. Vyazankin and V. T. Bychkov, *Zhur. Obshchei. Khim.*, **35**, 684 (1965).
115. N. S. Vyazankin and V. T. Bychkov, *Zhur. Obshchei. Khim.*, **36**, 1684 (1966); through *CA*, **66**, 46460 (1967).
116. N. S. Vyazankin, G. A. Razuvaev, and S. P. Kornea, *Zhur. Obshchei. Khim.*, **33**, 1041 (1963).
117. S. Weber and E. I. Becker, *J. Org. Chem.*, **27**, 1258 (1962).
117a. W. L. Wells, and T. L. Brown, *J. Organometal. Chem.*, **11**, 271 (1965).
118. E. Wiberg and H. Behringer, *Z. anorg. allgem. Chem.*, **329**, 290 (1964).
119. L. C. Williamsens and G. J. M. van der Kerk, *Investigations in the Field of Organolead Chemistry*, Inst. Organic Chem., T.N.O. Utrecht, Holland, 1965.
120. L. C. Williamsens and G. J. M. van der Kerk, *Organometal. Chem.*, **2**, 260 (1964).
120a. L. Wilputte-Steinert and J. Nasielski, *J. Organometal. Chem.*, **24**, 113 (1970).
121. V. S. Zavgorodnii and A. A. Petrov, *Zhur. Obschei. Khim.*, **33**, 2791 (1963); through *CA*, **59**, 15297 (1963).
122. N. N. Zemlyanski, E. M. Panov, and K. A. Kocheskov, *Dokl. Akad. Nauk. SSSR*, **146**, 1335 (1962); through *CA*, **58**, 9110 (1963).
123. S. N. Zhivukkin, E. D. Dudikova, and A. N. Kotov, *Zhur. Obshchei. Khim.*, **33**, 3274 (1963); through *CA*, **60**, 4169 (1964).
124. H. Zimmer, I. Hechenblaikner, O. A. Hemberg, and M. Dangiz, *J. Org. Chem.*, **29**, 2632 (1964).

11. ORGANOTIN COMPOUNDS WITH TIN—OTHER METAL BONDS

M. J. NEWLANDS

Department of Chemistry

Memorial University of Newfoundland
St. John's, Newfoundland, Canada

I.	Introduction	881
II.	Compounds Containing Tin—Typical Element Bonds	882
	A. General	882
	B. Between Tin and the Elements of Groups IA, IIA, IIB, and IIIA	882
	C. Between Tin and the Other Elements of Group IVA	889
III.	Compounds Containing Tin—Transition Metal Bonds	895
	A. General	895
	B. Methods of Preparation	896
	C. Chemical Properties	911
	D. Physical Properties	918
IV.	Postscript	924
References	....	924

I. Introduction

At the time of the publication of Ingham, Gilman, and Rosenberg's review (*135*), the knowledge of tin–metal bonds was largely restricted to bonds to Group IV elements and to the alkali metals. Since that time there has been an awakening of interest in metal–metal bonding in general, an interest which is evidenced by the large number of review articles on this subject which have been produced in the last few years. Because of the ready availability and ease of handling of the Group IV organometallic halides and hydrides, compounds containing Group IV–other metal bonds are very much the largest group of M—M' compounds; for example, Vyazankin's review lists some 830 compounds containing M—M' bonds—in all but about 50 of these compounds a Group IV element is involved (*224*).

The present chapter surveys the literature to the end of 1969 and includes some material from 1970 and 1971. No attempt has been made to obtain complete coverage since this would duplicate in large measure the excellent reviews by Vyazankin, Razuvaev, and Kruglaya (*224*); Mackay and Watt (*162*); and Baird (*5*). In addition there are several recent reviews on compounds containing tin–metal bonds by Poller (*194*), Neumann (*177*), Brooks and Cross (*28*), Belluco et al. (*7*), Spiro (*205*), and Davis and Gray (*69*).

The definition of a metal has been stretched somewhat in the present chapter to include boron and silicon, which would not otherwise have been covered in the present book. Finally, some compounds are included which do not contain tin–carbon bonds. These substances are direct analogs of the organotin compounds and their properties may provide important indications of those of hitherto unknown organotin derivatives.

II. Compounds Containing Tin—Typical Element Bonds

A. GENERAL

There has been relatively little study of compounds containing bonds between tin and the highly reactive elements of groups IA, IIA, and IIIA, although many reactions for the preparation of tetraorganotin and hexaorganoditin compounds have been discussed in terms of the intermediate formation of tin–lithium, tin–sodium, and tin–magnesium bonds. On the other hand, a reasonably detailed study has been made of the much more covalent tin–silicon, tin–germanium, and tin–lead compounds. These two groups of compounds will be discussed separately.

B. BETWEEN TIN AND THE ELEMENTS OF GROUPS IA, IIA, IIB, AND IIIA

1. Preparation

Since Kraus and his co-workers first prepared trimethyltin sodium, a number of methods have been developed for the preparation of tin–alkali metal compounds in solution (*152, 153*). The most convenient of these, so far as aryl derivatives are concerned, is the direct reaction of a triaryltin halide with lithium in tetrahydrofuran (*105, 210, 211*):

$$Ph_3SnCl + 2Li \xrightarrow{\text{THF}} Ph_3SnLi + LiCl$$

The method has also been used to prepare trimethyltin lithium in high yield (*212*).

$$Me_3SnX + 2Li \xrightarrow{\text{THF}} Me_3SnLi + LiX \quad (X = Cl, Br)$$

Kraus' original method was to treat an organotin halide with sodium in liquid ammonia (*153*):

$$R_3SnX + 2Na \xrightarrow{\text{NH}_3(l)} R_3SnNa + NaX \quad (R = Me, Ph)$$

Treatment of diorganotin dihalides gave the corresponding disodium derivative (*152*). Apparently the initial product is polydimethyltin, $(Me_2Sn)_n$, which reacts with further sodium to give 1,1,2,2-tetramethylditin disodium and then dimethyltin disodium. The presence of the ditin derivative was shown by reaction with methyl iodide which gave hexamethylditin:

$$Me_2SnBr_2 + 2Na \xrightarrow{NH_3(l)} (Me_2Sn)_n + 2NaBr$$

$$(Me_2Sn)_n + n\,Na \longrightarrow NaMe_2Sn \cdot SnMe_2Na \xrightarrow{MeI} Me_3Sn \cdot SnMe_3$$

$$NaMe_2Sn \cdot SnMe_2Na + 2Na \longrightarrow Me_2SnNa_2$$

Eméleus and Kettle (*83, 144*) have prepared similar sodium and disodium derivatives from stannane itself. These compounds are stable only at low temperatures.

Lithium, sodium, and potassium derivatives have been prepared by scission of tin–tin bonds in liquid ammonia, diglyme, or tetrahydrofuran (*29, 105, 154, 155, 210, 211*)

$$R_6Sn_2 + 2M \longrightarrow 2R_3SnM \quad (R = Me, Ph; M = K, Li)$$

Similarly, triphenyltinsodium can be prepared conveniently by the reaction of sodium-naphthalene on hexaphenylditin, triphenyltin bromide, or tetraphenyltin in 1,2-dimethoxyethane (*17*):

$$Ph_6Sn_2 + 2Na^+C_{10}H_8^- \longrightarrow 2Ph_3SnNa + 2C_{10}H_8$$

$$Ph_3SnBr + 2Na^+C_{10}H_8^- \longrightarrow Ph_3SnNa + NaBr + 2C_{10}H_8$$

$$Ph_4Sn + 2Na^+C_{10}H_8^- \longrightarrow Ph_3SnNa + PhNa + 2C_{10}H_8$$

Two related reactions have been widely used for the preparation of triorganotin lithium compounds. In the first reaction one mole of an organolithium is added to the corresponding poly(diorganotin) in ether (*232, 233*):

$$n\,RLi + (R_2Sn)_n \longrightarrow n\,R_3SnLi$$

while in the second reaction three moles of an organolithium are added to tin(II) chloride in ether, usually below room temperature (*17, 101–103*). The disadvantage of this method is that the product is frequently in equilibrium with poly(diorganotin) and organolithium (*17*):

$$3RLi + SnCl_2 \longrightarrow R_2Sn + RLi \rightleftharpoons R_3SnLi \quad (R = Et, Bu)$$

This problem does not arise when R = Ph (*17, 104*).

The formation of compounds containing tin–magnesium bonds is still a matter of some controversy. The intermediate formation of tin analogs of Grignard reagents has frequently been postulated to account for the formation of ditins from the reaction of Grignard reagents with tin(IV) halides (*156*) and with triorganotin halides (*167, 236*). Reaction schemes of the following type were invoked:

$$3RMgX + SnX_4 \longrightarrow R_3SnX + 3MgX_2 \qquad \textbf{(a)}$$
$$R_3SnX + Mg \longrightarrow R_3SnMgX \qquad \textbf{(b)}$$
$$R_3SnX + RMgX \longrightarrow R_3SnMgX + RX \qquad \textbf{(c)}$$
$$R_3SnMgX + R_3SnX \longrightarrow R_3Sn\cdot SnR_3 + MgX_2 \qquad \textbf{(d)}$$

Glockling and his co-workers (*44, 109*) have provided evidence for reaction **(b)** in the analogous reaction of a phenylmagnesium halide with germanium tetrachloride. In this case, the yield of the digermane is sharply reduced if the Grignard reagent solution is freed from excess magnesium metal before addition of the germanium tetrachloride.

Creemers, Noltes, and van der Kerk have reported the preparation of triphenyltin magnesium bromide from triphenylstannane and ethyl–magnesium bromide (*65*):

$$EtMgBr\cdot NEt_3 + Ph_3SnH \xrightarrow[-15°]{Et_2O} Ph_3SnMgBr\cdot NEt_3 \qquad (oil)$$
$$2Ph_3SnMgBr\cdot NEt_3 \xrightarrow[vacuum]{high} (Ph_3SnMgBr)_2 + 2Et_3N$$

and Creemers described the corresponding complex with N,N,N^1,N^1-tetramethylethylenediamine, $Ph_3SnMgBr\cdot TMED$ (*63*).

Ashby (*3*) cited his own unpublished work on the reaction of tributylstannane with *n*-butylmagnesium bromide, which was said to give tributyltin magnesium bromide and butane:

$$n\text{-}Bu_3SnH + n\text{-}BuMgBr \longrightarrow n\text{-}Bu_3SnMgBr + C_4H_{10}$$

However, Lahournère and Valade (*158*) have disputed Ashby's results. The French workers have been unable to detect any reaction of primary alkyl Grignard reagents with tributylstannane. No deuterated tributylstannane was produced on deuteriolysis of the reaction mixture. With sterically hindered Grignard reagents, on the other hand, alkane was liberated and deuteriolysis of the reaction mixture gave good yields (66–73 %) of deuterated tributylstannane:

$$n\text{-}Bu_3SnH + RMgX \longrightarrow [n\text{-}Bu_3SnMgX] + RH(g)$$
$$(R = i\text{-}Pr, s\text{-}Bu, t\text{-}Bu, C_6H_{11})$$
$$[n\text{-}BuSnMgX] + D_2O \longrightarrow n\text{-}Bu_3SnD + Mg(OD)X$$

The intermediate Grignard reagent was also detected by its reactions with chlorotrimethylsilane and alkyl chloride.

Tamborski and Sokolski (*209*) have apparently obtained *bis*-(triphenyltin)magnesium by treatment of triphenyltin chloride or hexaphenylditin with magnesium in tetrahydrofuran containing a small amount of ethyl bromide. Hydrolysis of the reaction mixture gave triphenylstannane:

$$2Ph_3SnCl + Mg \longrightarrow (Ph_3Sn)_2Mg \xrightarrow{H_2O} 2Ph_3SnH + Mg(OH)_2$$

While mercury, and to a lesser extent, zinc and cadmium derivatives of silicon and germanium are well authenticated (see for example, Refs. *224* and *229*), the analogous compounds of tin do not appear to have been reported until very recently. Neumann and Blankaut (*180*) have prepared symmetrical *bis*(triorganotin)mercurials by the treatment of di-*t*-butylmercury with triorganostannanes.

$$(t\text{-Bu})_2Hg + 2R_3SnH \longrightarrow (R_3Sn)_2Hg + 2C_4H_{10}$$

The known mercurials are listed in Table 1.

Tin–boron compounds are also far more difficult to prepare than the corresponding silicon–boron and germanium–boron derivatives. Nöth and Hermannsdörfer (*180*) prepared compounds stabilized by B—N bonds via a tin–lithium derivative

$$Et_3SnLi + ClB(NMe_2)_2 \longrightarrow Et_3Sn \cdot B(NMe_2)_2 + LiCl$$
$$Et_3SnLi + Cl_2BNMe_2 \longrightarrow Et_3Sn \cdot BClNMe_2 + LiCl$$
$$2Et_3SnLi + Cl_2BNMe_2 \longrightarrow (Et_3Sn)_2BNMe_2 + 2LiCl$$

Reactions of either triethyltin lithium (*180*) or triphenyltin lithium (*181*) with boron trichloride, organoboron dichlorides, or diorganoboron monohalides gave the corresponding ditins and no compounds containing Sn—B bonds.

However, Nöth and his colleagues (*181*) have made Sn—B bonds unsupported by B—N bonds, using bis(diphenyboryl)-bis[1,2-bis(diphenyphosphino)ethane]cobalt as a source of diphenylboron groups:

$$(LL)_2Co(BPh_2)_2 + Me_nSnBr_{4-n} \longrightarrow Me_nSn(BPh_2)_{4-n} + (LL)_2CoBr_2$$
$$(LL = Ph_2PCH_2CH_2PPh_2; n = 0, 1, 2, \text{ or } 3)$$

A fascinating tin–boron compound which has been recently reported (*220*) is 1-stanna-2,3-dicarbaclosodecarborane (*83*) in which a tin atom occupies one apex of an icosahedron with three boron and two carbon atoms as nearest neighbors:

$$SnCl_2 \text{ or } R_2SnCl_2 + B_9C_2H_{11}{}^{2-} \longrightarrow SnB_9C_2H_{11}$$

The tin atom is displaced by treatment with methanolic potassium hydroxide.

The known Sn—B compounds are listed in Table 1.

TABLE 1

COMPOUNDS CONTAINING TIN–TYPICAL ELEMENT BONDS[a]

Compound	Physical Properties	References
Sn—B		
$Et_3SnB(NMe_2)_2$	bp 31–35°/10^{-3}	(*180*)
$Et_3SnBCl(NMe_2)$	bp 26–28°/10^{-3}	(*180*)
$(Et_3Sn)_2BNMe_2$	bp 91–93°/10^{-3}	(*180*)
$Sn(BPh_2)_4$	mp 119–124° 76%	(*181*)
$MeSn(BPh_2)_3$	mp 112–118° 69%	(*181*)
$Me_2Sn(BPh_2)_2$	mp 118–121°d 79%	(*181*)
Me_3SnBPh_2	mp 110–115°d 61%	(*181*)
1-stanna-2,3-dicarbaclosodecaborane(II)	discolors at 210° and chars at 265°	(*220*)
Sn—Si		
$(Me_3Sn)_nSiH_{4-n}$	$n = 1, 3, 4$. No mp. or bp. data given	(*2*)
$Me_3SnSiMe_3$	bp 144–146°	(*199*)
$Ph_3Sn—SiMe_3$	bp 94°/1	(*2*)
$Ph_3SnSiMe_3$	mp 119°	(*104*)
$(Ph_3Sn)_2SiMe_2$	mp 172° 30%	(*2*)
$Sn(SiMe_3)_4$	mp 235–236°	(*36*)
$Me_3SnGeMe_3$	bp 154°	(*199*)
$Ph_3SnGeBu_3$	mp 24–25° 68%	(*43*)
$Ph_3SnGePh_3$	282–286°	(*63, 64*)
$XPh_2SnGePh_3$	X = C≡CPh, OH, NEt$_2$	(*63, 64*)
$(Ph_3Sn)_2GePh_2$	mp 169–170° 63%	(*63, 64*)
$EtSn(GePh_3)_3$	mp > 330° 3%	(*63, 64*)
Sn—Pb		
$Et_3SnPbPh_3$	not isolated	(*63, 64*)
$Ph_3SnPbPh_3$	mp 110°d 54%	(*200, 231*)
$(Ph_3Sn)_4Pb$	mp 200°d 55%	(*200, 231*)
$Sn(PbPh_3)_4$	mp 160°d 54%	(*200, 231*)
Ge—Si—Sn		
$(Ph_3Ge)_3SiSnPh_3$	mp 340–342° 16%	(*100*)
$Et(Et_3Ge)_2SiSnEt_3$		(*106*)
Sn—Hg		
$(Me_3Sn)_2Hg$	red crystals, d below −10°	(*178*)
$(Et_3Sn)_2Hg$	yellow liquid, d below −10°	(*178*)
$(n\text{-}Bu_3Sn)_2Hg$	yellow liquid, d below −10°	(*178*)

[a] Only representative examples of Sn—Si and Sn—Ge compounds are given. A complete listing is to be found in Table 30 of Mackay and Watt's review (3).

Tin–aluminium compounds appear to be unknown. An attempt by Amberger and his co-workers (*157*) to prepare such a compound by the reaction of diethylaminotriorganotins with an aluminium hydride gave the products of amine exchange:

$$R_3Sn \cdot NEt_2 + Bu_2AlH \longrightarrow R_3SnH + Bu_2AlNEt_2$$

2. Physical Properties

Very little has been reported on the physical properties of this group of compounds. Trimethyltin sodium (*153*) and triphenyltin sodium (*49*) are unstable yellow compounds. Triphenyltin lithium is also yellow and can be crystallized from dioxane (*232*).

Ammoniacal solutions of triphenyltin sodium and trimethyltin sodium have the conductivity properties of strong electrolytes (*154, 155*) but Flitcroft and Kaesz (*88*) report that ^{1}H NMR spectra of trimethyltin lithium and dimethyltin dilithium in methylamine indicate that the free anions Me_3Sn^- and Me_2Sn^{2-} are not present.

Wells and Brown (*228*) have studied the NMR spectrum of trimethyltin lithium in tetrahydrofuran (THF) solution. $^1J(^{13}C-^{119}Sn)$ is 5.2 Hz which is reasonable if the Sn—C bonds have high p-character, because most of the s-character is concentrated on the Me_3Sn^- electron pair. There is no apparent exchange with methyllithium. Removal of solvent gave $(Me_3Sn)_3SnLi$ with $^1J(^{13}C-^{119}Sn)$ of 33 Hz and $^2J(^{13}C-Sn-^{119}Sn)$ of 2.3 Hz.

Gol'danskii and his co-workers (*110, 111*) have studied triphenyltin lithium in dipolar aprotic solvents by Mössbauer spectroscopy and have demonstrated that both contact ion pairs and solvent-separated ion pairs can occur. In THF and THF/DMSO mixtures both types exist, while in pure DMSO only the solvent-separated ion pairs are found.

3. Chemical Properties

The reactions of tin–alkali metal and tin–magnesium compounds with elements of Groups VA and VIA are discussed in detail in Chaps. 8 and 6, respectively.

As mentioned above, trialkyltin lithium compounds appear to exist in equilibrium with poly(dialkyltin) and alkyllithium (*16, 19*):

$$R_3SnLi \rightleftharpoons R_2Sn + RLi$$

Consequently, some reactions give products derived from the alkyl lithium rather than from the triorganotin lithium, e.g. (*17*):

$$Bu_3SnLi + Me_3SiCl \longrightarrow (Bu_2Sn)_n + BuSiMe_3$$
$$Bu_3SnLi + CO_2/H_2O \longrightarrow (Bu_2Sn)_n + Bu_2CO + BuCO_2H$$

Some reactions recently reported by Creemers, Noltes, and van der Kerk (*65*) could be interpreted in the same way:

$$Ph_3SnMgBr + MeI \longrightarrow Ph_2SnMeI$$

$$Ph_3SnMgBr + Co_2(CO)_8 \longrightarrow Ph_2Sn[Co(CO)_4]_2$$

In both reactions the tin-containing product could have arisen from incipient or actual formation of 'diphenyltin.'

In general, however, alkali metal derivatives of tin react by metathesis with organic halides and with halides of the transition elements (see below); and those of the elements of Groups IVA (see below), VA (see Chap. 8), and VIA (see Chap. 6). A few examples of coupling reactions with organic halides follow:

$$2Me_3SnNa + p\text{-}C_6H_4Cl_2 \longrightarrow p\text{-}C_6H_4(SnMe_3)_2 + 2NaCl \quad (153)$$

$$Ph_3SnLi + EtBr \longrightarrow Ph_3SnEt + LiBr \quad (17)$$

$$Ph_3SnLi + PhCH_2Cl \longrightarrow Ph_3SnCH_2Ph + LiCl \quad (17)$$

Gilman and Rosenberg (*94, 101, 102*) reported that tetraphenyltin was an important product in the reaction of triphenyltin lithium with organic halides. This was not confirmed by the Durham workers (*17*).

Coupling reactions with the tin–alkali metal compounds are frequently complicated by two competing reactions: reduction and metal–halogen exchange. The latter is discussed in more detail in Sec. II.C below.

Typical reductions by triphenyltin sodium have been reported by Blake, Coates, and Tate (*17*). For example, the sodium compound reduced benzophenone to the corresponding ketyl and the final hydrolysis products included approximately equal weights of benzophenone and diphenylmethanol, a trace of benzpinacol, and about 75% of hexaphenylditin.

$$2Ph_3SnNa + 2Ph_2CO \rightleftharpoons Ph_6Sn_2 + 2Ph_2CO^-Na^+$$

With benzoyl chloride the final product was *cis*-stilbenediol dibenzoate:

$$2PhCOCl + 2Ph_3SnNa \longrightarrow Ph_6Sn_2 + Ph \cdot C(O^-) \cdot C(O^-)Ph + 2Na^+$$

$$PhC(O^-) \cdot C(O^-)Ph + 2PhCOCl \longrightarrow PhC(OOCPh) \cdot C(OOCPh)Ph + 2Cl^-$$

Oxygen, carbon dioxide, and sulfur dioxide were reduced to peroxide, oxalate, and dithionite, respectively:

$$2Ph_3SnNa + O_2 \longrightarrow Ph_6Sn_2 + Na_2O_2 \quad (50\%)$$

$$2Ph_3SnNa + 2CO_2 \longrightarrow Ph_6Sn_2 + Na_2C_2O_4 \quad (98\%)$$

$$2Ph_3SnNa + 2SO_2 \longrightarrow Ph_6Sn_2 + Na_2S_2O_4 \quad (75\%)$$

With diphenyl disulfide, the tin–sodium compound gave both the ditin and triphenyl(phenylthio)tin:

$$Ph_3SnNa + PhS \cdot SPh \longrightarrow Ph_6Sn_2 + Ph_3Sn \cdot SPh + PhSNa$$

Similar studies have been carried out by Gilman and Rosenberg (*94, 101, 102*) and by Tamborski, Ford, and Sokolski (*211, 212*).

Gilman and his co-workers (*95*) have studied the relative stability of silicon, germanium, and tin lithium compounds to storage in tetrahydrofuran. The stabilities lie in the orders

$$Si > Ge \sim Sn \quad \text{and} \quad Ph_3Sn > Ph_2MeSn > Bu_3Sn.$$

Nöth and Hermannsdörfer (*180*) found that the tin–boron bond is readily broken by water, halogen, and heat.

$$Et_3Sn \cdot B(NMe_2)_2 + 3H_2O \longrightarrow Et_3SnH + B(OH)_3 + 2Me_2NH$$

$$Et_3Sn \cdot B(NMe_2)_2 + X_2 \longrightarrow Et_3SnX + XB(NMe_2)_2$$

$$2Et_3Sn \cdot B(NMe_2)_2 \xrightarrow{\Delta} Et_6Sn_2 + (Me_2N)_2BB(NMe_2)_2$$

$$(Et_3Sn)_2BNMe_2 \xrightarrow{\Delta} Et_6Sn_2 + B_4(NMe_2)_6 + \text{other products}$$

An interesting observation was that gaseous hydrogen chloride split the B—N bond before the B—Sn bond. The compounds $Me_nSn(BPh_2)_{4-n'}$, reported in a later paper (*181*), had low thermal stability and were very sensitive to oxygen.

C. BETWEEN TIN AND THE OTHER ELEMENTS OF GROUP IVA

Mackay and Watt (*162*) and Vyazankin, Razuvaev, and Kruglaya (*224*) have reviewed this area of chemistry in considerable detail. Consequently no attempt is made here to give comprehensive coverage.

1. *Preparation*

There are two principal methods of preparation, reaction of an alkali metal derivative with a halide:

$$R_3MM'' + R'_3M'X \longrightarrow R_3MM'R'_3 + M''X$$

and elimination of an amine from a dialkylamino compound and a hydride:

$$R_3M \cdot NR''_2 + R'_3M'H \longrightarrow R_3M \cdot M'R''_3 + R'_2NH$$

The first of these methods is frequently used to monitor the formation of a tin–alkali metal compound [e.g., (*210, 211*)], since the reaction with chlorotrimethylsilane is usually fast and high in yield (but see Ref. *17*), e.g.:

$$Ph_3SnLi + ClSiMe_3 \longrightarrow Ph_3Sn \cdot SiMe_3 + LiCl$$

However, the general reaction is frequently complicated by metal–halogen exchange, so that a mixture of three very similar compounds is obtained. Such mixtures can be exceedingly difficult to separate, e.g. (*96*):

$$Ph_3GeK + ClSiPh_3 \longrightarrow Ph_6Ge_2 + Ph_3Ge \cdot SiPh_3 + Ph_6Si_2$$

Willemsens and van der Kerk (97) found that the tendency for lithium–halogen exchange decreased from germanium lithium to lead lithium. Gilman and his co-workers have made detailed studies of the effects of solvent, alkali metal, and direction of addition on metal–halogen exchange (97–99), while Wiberg and his co-workers (229) have shown that metal–halogen exchange increased with increasing temperature. Hence, the best conditions for a good yield of an M—M′ compound appear to be slow addition of the alkali metal derivative to the halide at a temperature of 0° or below.

Amberger and Mülhofer (2) have used an analogous method to make trimethytin derivatives of silane. Here metal hydrogen exchange was probably responsible for the production of the byproducts, $(Me_3Sn)_3SiH$ and $(Me_4Sn)_4Si$.

Vyazankin and his co-workers (221–223) have found that triethylgermyl lithium reacts with triethylstannane to give triethylgermyltriethylstannane:

$$Et_3GeLi + Et_3SnH \longrightarrow Et_3Ge \cdot SnEt_3 + LiH$$

The second method for preparing $Sn—M^{IV}$ bonds cannot be used to prepare $Sn—Si$ bonds, but has been used successfully, mainly by Creemers (63, 64) and by Neumann (179, 202), to produce $Sn—Ge$ compounds. This reaction seems to be free from competing side reactions so far as $Sn—Ge$ bonds are concerned.

The known compounds containing $Sn—Si$, $Sn—Ge$, and $Sn—Pb$ bonds are listed in Table 1.

2. *Physical Properties*

Apart from such parameters as melting point, boiling point, and refractive index (see Table 1), the physical properties of compounds containing $Sn—M^{IV}$ bonds have been very little studied. Thus, while the bond energies of homo-nuclear metal–metal bonded compounds of the Group IVA elements have been studied in some detail (see Ref. 162, pp. 140–3), there are as yet no published values for $Sn—M^{IV}$ bonds. Similarly, there are no detailed vibrational spectroscopic studies in which force constants for $Sn—M^{IV}$ bonds have been found, nor are there any determinations of $Sn—M^{IV}$ bond lengths by diffraction methods.

Bürger and Goetz (36) and Chambers and Glockling (48) have assigned the frequencies of the M—Si skeleta of the compounds $(Me_3Si)_4M$. For M = Sn they assigned a vibration at 311 cm^{-1} to v_1 and one at 330 cm^{-1} to v_3. Carey and Clark (43) have studied a number of compounds of the types $R_3Ge \cdot SnR'_3$ and $R_3Sn \cdot SnR'_3$ and have assigned bands in the 225–240 cm^{-1} region to the Ge—Sn stretch (cf. 194–208 cm^{-1} for v_{Sn-Sn}). Schumann and Ronecker (199) have assigned a frequency of 322 cm^{-1} to the Si—Sn stretch in the spectrum of $Me_3Si \cdot SnMe_3$. Vyazankin and his co-workers (79) have

TABLE 2

^{1}H NMR DATA FOR COMPOUNDS CONTAINING Sn—Si BONDS

Compound	Chemical shifts (τ)			Coupling constants (Hz)				References
	HC	HSi	^{29}Si	H−C−Si−^{119}Sn	H−C−Si−^{117}Sn	H−C−^{117}Sn	H−C−^{119}Sn	
Me$_3$SnSiH$_3$[a]	10.302	7.077				52.2	50.6	(2)
(Me$_3$Sn)$_3$SiH	9.740					47.2	45.2	(2)
(Me$_3$Sn)$_4$Si	9.737					48.6		(2)
(Me$_3$Si)$_4$Sn[b]	10.29		6.7 ± 0.1	22.2 ± 0.2	21.5 ± 0.2			(36)

[a] $J_{\text{H−Si−}^{119}\text{Sn}}$ 52.9 Hz; $J_{\text{H−Si−}^{117}\text{Sn}}$ 51.6 Hz.
[b] $J_{\text{H−}^{13}\text{C}}$ 120.7 ± 0.5 Hz.

studied a series of more complicated compounds containing M−M' bonds, including $Et(Et_3Ge)_2SiSnEt_3$.

Some NMR studies have been made on compounds of this group. Nöth and his co-workers (*181*) report the ^{11}B and ^1H (phenyl) spectra of $Me_nSn(BPh_2)_{4-n}$. The phenyl resonances vary from $\delta - 7.19$ to -7.38 ppm with respect to tetramethylsilane. Amberger and Mülhofer (*2*) report ^1H spectra of $(Me_3Sn)_nSiH_{4-n}$ including ^{119}Sn and ^{117}Sn coupling constants (Table 2). Bürger and Goetze (*36*) have similarly reported chemical shifts and coupling constants for $(Me_4Si)_4Sn$ (Table 2).

Mössbauer spectroscopy appears to have been applied relatively little to organotin compounds containing $Sn−M^{IV}$ bonds. Greenwood and Gibb (*93*) have obtained spectra for the compounds $(Ph_3Sn)_4M^{IV}$, where M^{IV} is germanium, tin, or lead (Table 3). None of the compounds showed quadrupole

TABLE 3

TIN MÖSSBAUER SPECTRA OF COMPOUNDS CONTAINING TIN−M^{IV}
BONDS (*58*)

Compound	Isomer shift (mm sec^{-1})	Quadrupole splitting (mm sec^{-1})	Line width (mm sec^{-1})
$(Ph_3Sn)_4Ge$	−0.97	0.0	0.30
$(Ph_3Sn)_4Sn$	−0.77	0.0	0.30
$(Ph_3Sn)_4Pb$	−0.71	0.0	0.30

splitting (line widths ~ 0.30 mm sec^{-1}) and the isomer shifts were 1.13, 1.33, and 1.39 ± 0.10 mm sec^{-1}, respectively, relative to $\alpha - SnO_2$. Measurements were taken at 80°K. Perhaps the most surprising feature of these results is that the compound $(Ph_3Sn)_4Sn$ shows but a single line despite the two different tin environments.

Van der Kerk and his colleagues (*74*) have examined the ultraviolet spectra of a number of compounds containing $Sn−M^{IV}$ bonds (Table 4). The absorption is ascribed to a $\sigma - \sigma^*$ transition of the $Sn−M^{IV}$ bonds.

TABLE 4

ULTRAVIOLET ABSORPTION SPECTRA OF COMPOUNDS
CONTAINING TIN−M^{IV} BONDS

Compound	λ (nm)	ε	Solvent	Reference
$(Ph_3Sn)_4Ge$	276	73000	$CHCl_3$	(*74*)
$(Ph_3Sn)_4Sn$	277	79000	$CHCl_3$	(*74*)
$(Ph_3Sn)_4Pb$	298	59500	$CHCl_3$	(*74*)
$(Ph_3Pb)_4Sn$	319	67000	C_6H_6	(*74*)

It is quite clear that considerably more study is needed of the physical properties of organotin compounds containing $Sn-M^{IV}$ bonds.

3. Chemical Properties

a. Reactions with Retention of the $Sn-M$ *Bond.* Wiberg and his co-workers (*230*) showed that phenyl groups of the compounds $Ph_3Sn \cdot MPh_3$ could be replaced by acetate groups by treatment with refluxing glacial acetic acid in the absence of air:

$$Ph_3Sn \cdot MPh_3 + 6CH_3COOH \longrightarrow (CH_3COO)_3Sn \cdot M(OOCCH_3)_3$$

The compound $Ph_3Ge \cdot Sn(OOCCH_3)_3$ was isolated as an intermediate from $Ph_3Ge \cdot SnPh_3$. In the presence of air the product was the corresponding metalloxane $(CH_3COO)_3Sn \cdot O \cdot M(OOCCH_3)_3$.

The hexaacetates containing $Sn-M$ bonds could be converted to the corresponding hexachlorides and hexahydrides at low temperatures:

$$(CH_3COO)_3Sn \cdot M(OOCCH_3)_3$$

HCl / −100 to −105°   \ LiAlH₄, Et₂O / −80 to −90°

$$Cl_3Sn \cdot MCl_3 \xrightarrow[-85°]{LiAlH_4, \, Et_2O} H_3Sn \cdot MH_3$$

↓ 0°   ↓ 0°

$$MCl_4 + SnCl_2 \qquad MH_4 + H_2 + Sn$$

The hexaacetates themselves did not melt below 360°, but the hexachlorides and hexahydrides pyrolysed with $Sn-M$ bond scission below 0°. The hexaacetates underwent $Sn-M$ scission with iodine.

Creemers and Noltes (*64*), in their detailed study of formation of $Sn-Ge$ bonds via hydrogenolysis of germanium–nitrogen and tin–nitrogen bonds, have carried out a number of reactions in which $Sn-Ge$ bonds are retained. The equations below summarize some of their results.

Conversion of $Sn-H$ *to* $Sn-Sn$

$$Bu_3GeNMe_2 + Bu_2SnH_2 \longrightarrow Bu_3GeSnBu_2H + Me_2NH$$

↓ base catalysis

$$Bu_3Ge \cdot SnBu_2 \cdot SnBu_2 \cdot GeBu_3$$

Typical Reactions of Sn—NEt$_2$ *Compounds*

Ph$_3$GeH + Et$_2$Sn(NEt$_2$)$_2$ $\longrightarrow$ Ph$_3$Ge·SnEt$_2$(NEt$_2$)

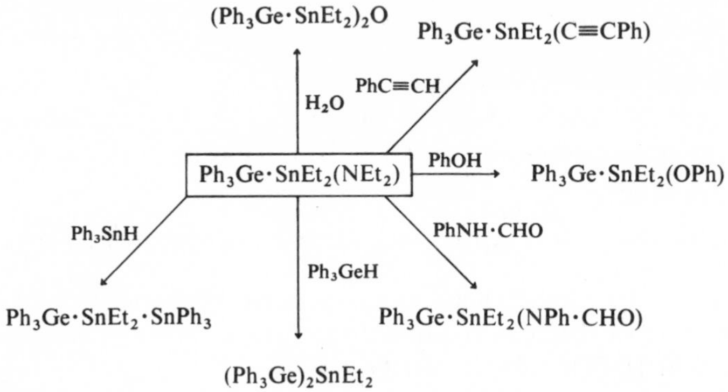

(Ph$_3$Ge·SnEt$_2$)$_2$O   Ph$_3$Ge·SnEt$_2$(C≡CPh)

$$
\begin{array}{ccc}
 & \text{H}_2\text{O} & \text{PhC≡CH} \\
\end{array}
$$

Ph$_3$Ge·SnEt$_2$(NEt$_2$) $\xrightarrow{\text{PhOH}}$ Ph$_3$Ge·SnEt$_2$(OPh)

Ph$_3$SnH   PhNH·CHO

Ph$_3$GeH

Ph$_3$Ge·SnEt$_2$·SnPh$_3$ Ph$_3$Ge·SnEt$_2$(NPh·CHO)

(Ph$_3$Ge)$_2$SnEt$_2$

Similar series of reactions were carried out starting with ethyltris(diethylamino)tin and triphenylgermane to give compounds containing up to seven metal atoms, e.g.:

Ph$_3$Ge·SnEt$_2$(NPhCHO) $\xrightarrow[\text{2 : 1 molar ratio}]{+ \text{R}_2\text{SnH}_2}$ Ph$_3$Ge·SnEt$_2$·SnR$_2$·SnEt$_2$·GePh$_3$

$+ \text{R}_2\text{SnH}_2$ $\Big\downarrow$ (1 : 1 molar ratio)

Ph$_3$Ge·SnEt$_2$·SnR$_2$·SnR$_2$·SnEt$_2$·GePh$_3$

Ph$_3$Ge·SnEt(NPhCHO)$_2$ + 2Ph$_3$SnH $\longrightarrow$ (Ph$_3$Sn)$_2$·SnEt·GePh$_3$

and

EtSn(NEt$_3$)$_2$ $\xrightarrow[\text{(1 : 2 molar ratio)}]{\text{PH}_3\text{GeH}}$ (Ph$_3$Ge)$_2$SnEt(NEt$_2$) $\xrightarrow{\text{HN(H}_5\text{)C(O)H}}$

(Ph$_3$Ge)$_2$SnEt(NPhCHO) $\xrightarrow[\text{(2 : 1 molar ratio)}]{\text{R}_2\text{SnH}_2}$ (Ph$_3$Ge)$_2$SnEt·SnR$_2$·SnEt(GePh$_3$)$_2$

These two studies indicate that relatively mild displacements can be made at tin without scission of the Sn—M bond.

b. Reactions with Scission of the Sn—M *Bond.* Kraus and Foster (*150*) reported that trimethyl(triphenylgermyl)tin was unaffected by oxygen in boiling benzene. However, observation by Wiberg et al. (*230*) that the reactions of Ph$_3$Sn·MPh$_3$ with glacial acetic acid differed in the presence and absence of air indicates that a Sn—M bond somewhere in the reaction scheme is affected by oxygen:

Ph$_3$Sn·MPh$_3$ + 6CH$_3$COOH $\xrightarrow[\text{N}_2]{\text{reflux,}}$ (CH$_3$COO)$_3$Sn·M(OOCCH$_3$)$_3$

$\Big\downarrow$ reflux, air

(CH$_3$COO)$_3$Sn·O·M(OOCCH$_3$)$_3$

It has been fairly generally observed that Sn—M bonds are split by halogens (*98, 150, 151, 230*)

$$Ph_3Ge \cdot SnPh_3 + I_2 \xrightarrow[\text{temp}]{\text{room}} Ph_3GeI \text{ (no tin cpd identified)} \qquad (98)$$

$$Ph_3Ge \cdot SnMe_3 + Br_2 \longrightarrow Ph_3GeBr + Me_3SnBr \qquad (150)$$

$$Ph_3Si \cdot SnMe_3 + Br_2 \longrightarrow Ph_3SiBr + Me_3SnBr \qquad (151)$$

The Sn—M bond is susceptible to nucleophilic attack; for example, tetrakis(trimethylsilyl)tin gave hexamethyldisiloxane and tin on treatment with potassium hydroxide (*36*):

$$(Me_3Si)_4Sn + 2H_2O \xrightarrow{\text{KOH}} 2(Me_3Si)_2O + Sn + 2H_2$$

and a tin–germanium bond has been split by organolithium reagents (*98*):

$$Ph_3Ge \cdot SnPh_3 + PhLi \longrightarrow Ph_4Ge + Ph_4Sn$$

$$Ph_3Ge \cdot SnPh_3 \xrightarrow[\text{(ii) CO}_2]{\text{(i) BuLi}} Ph_3GeCO_2H + Ph_6Ge_2$$

The products of the first reaction were not well characterized and no pure tin compound was obtained from the second reaction.

Both Kraus (*151*) and Gilman (*98*) have reported scission of Sn—M bonds by alkali metals:

$$Me_3Sn \cdot SiPh_3 \xrightarrow[\text{NH}_3(1)]{\text{Na}} Me_3SnNa + Ph_3SiNa \xrightarrow{\text{MeI}} Me_4Sn + Ph_3SiMe \qquad (62)$$

$$Ph_3Sn \cdot GePh_3 \xrightarrow[\text{THF}]{\text{Na/K}} Ph_3SnK + Ph_3GeK \xrightarrow{\text{PrBr}} Ph_3SnPr + Ph_3GePr \qquad (44)$$

Dessy's studies of electrochemistry of metal–metal bonded compounds (*70, 71*) have shown that hexaphenyldisilane was not reducible at the dropping mercury electrode, while (triphenysilyl)-triphenyltin underwent a one-electron reduction at a half-wave potential of 3.1 V:

$$Ph_3Sn \cdot SiPh_3 + e^- \longrightarrow Ph_3Sn^- + Ph_3Si \cdot (\longrightarrow Ph_3SiH)$$

and hexaphenylditin underwent a two-electron reduction at 2.9 V:

$$Ph_3Sn \cdot SnPh_3 + 2e^- \longrightarrow 2Ph_3Sn^-$$

Dessy's work also showed that the triphenylgermyl anion was a better nucleophile than the triphenyltin anion.

III. Compounds Containing Tin–Transition Metal Bonds

A. GENERAL

This area of chemistry has aroused very considerable interest in the last ten years and the literature has been surveyed in some detail recently in the monograph by Coates, Green, and Wade (*54*); in wide ranging reviews of metal–metal bonded compounds, especially those by Vyazankin, Razuvaev and Kruglaya (*224*) and Baird (*5*); and in specific reviews of compounds, containing transition metal–Group IVA bonds by Kolobova, Antonova, and Anisimov (*149*) and by Young (*235*). There have been many other reviews on metal–metal bonded compounds in the last few years, but those cited are the most useful for the present purpose.

B. Methods of Preparation

Compounds containing tin–transition metal bonds are normally prepared by one of four general methods:

1. metathetical reactions involving an alkali metal derivative,
2. insertions reactions,
3. oxidative addition reactions, and
4. elimination of small covalent molecules.

[This classification appears to have been used first by Stone (*206*)]. In addition, some compounds have been made by special methods. These five groups of reactions are discussed in turn below.

1. *Metathetical Reactions Involving Alkali Metal Derivatives*

The general reaction can be written in the form:

$$L_nMM' + XM''L'_m \longrightarrow L_nM \cdot M''L + M'X$$

This type of reaction can start either from a tin halide, e.g.:

$$Ph_3SnCl + NaFe(CO)_2Cp \longrightarrow Ph_3Sn \cdot Fe(CO)_2Cp + NaCl \qquad (118, 119)$$

or from a transition metal halide:

$$Ph_3SnLi + PtCl_2(PPh_3)_2 \longrightarrow Ph_3Sn \cdot PtCl(PPh_3)_2 + LiCl \qquad (4, 160)$$

$$Ph_3SnLi + Cp_2TiCl_2 \longrightarrow Cp_2TiCl(SnPh_3) + LiCl \qquad (61)$$

$$2Ph_3SnLi + Cp_2TiCl_2 \longrightarrow Cp_2Ti(SnPh_3)_2 + 2LiCl \qquad (61)$$

Compounds made by these two routes are listed in Table 5.

In some cases partial replacement of halogen has been obtained, e.g.:

$$Me_2SnCl_2 + NaMn(CO)_5 \longrightarrow Me_2SnCl[Mn(CO)_5] + NaCl$$

and this has permitted the preparation of compounds with three different metals linked by metal–metal bonding (*187*):

$$(CO)_5Mn \cdot SnMe_2Cl + M(CO)_3Cp^- \longrightarrow (CO)_5Mn \cdot SnMe_2 \cdot M(CO)_3Cp$$
$$(M = Mo, W)$$

TABLE 5

COMPOUNDS CONTAINING TIN–TRANSITION ELEMENT BONDS PREPARED VIA ALKALI–METAL DERIVATIVES

Product	Tin starting material	mp (bp)	Yield (%)	References
Sn—Ti				
$Ph_3Sn \cdot TiCp_2 \cdot THF$	Ph_3SnLi	80°d		(61)
$[(Ph_3Sn)_2TiCp_2]^-$	Ph_3SnLi	Not isolated		(142)
$Ph_3Sn \cdot TiCp_2Cl$	Ph_3SnLi	177–180°d		(61)
$(Ph_3Sn)_2TiCp_2$	Ph_3SnLi	80°d		(61)
Sn—Zr				
$n\text{-}C_8H_{17}Sn[Zr(CO)_4(MeBuC_5H_3)]_3$	$n\text{-}C_8H_{17}SnCl_3$	Isolated impure		(114)
$Ph_3Sn \cdot ZrCp_2Cl$	Ph_3SnLi			(61)
Sn—Hf				
$(o\text{-}MeC_6H_4)_3Sn \cdot Hf(CO)_4(indenyl)$	$(o\text{-}MeC_6H_4)_3SnCl$			(114)
Sn—V				
$[(C_{12}H_{25})_2Sn[V(CO)_3(Et_2C_5H_3)]]$	$(C_{12}H_{25})_2SnCl_2$			(114)
Sn—Nb				
None recorded				
Sn—Ta				
$[(Mesityl)_2Sn[Ta(CO)_3(CetylC_5H_4)]]$	$(Mesityl)_2SnCl_2$			(114)
Sn—Cr				
$Ph_3Sn \cdot Cr(CO)_3Cp$	Ph_3SnCl	219–221°, 220–222°	46	(170, 186)
$(EtPrC_5H_3)_2Sn[Cr(CO)_3Cp]_2$	$(EtPrC_5H_3)_2SnCl_2$			(114)

Continued

TABLE 5 (*Continued*)

Product	Tin starting material	mp (bp)	Yield (%)	References
Sn—Mo				
$Me_3Sn \cdot Mo(CO)_3Cp$	Me_3SnCl			(186)
$Me_2ClSn \cdot Mo(CO)_3Cp$	Me_2SnCl_2			(186)
$Me_2Sn[Mo(CO)_3Cp]_2$	Me_2SnCl_2	89–90°	50	(114, 186)
$Ph_3Sn \cdot Mo(CO)_3Cp$	Ph_3SnCl	156–159°d	57	(72, 163, 170, 186)
$Ph_2Sn[Mo(CO)_3Cp]_2$	Ph_2SnCl_2	211–214°d	39	(170, 186)
$ClSn[Mo(CO)_3Cp]_3$	$SnCl_4$	190–191.5°		(173)
Sn—W				
$Me_3Sn \cdot W(CO)_3Cp$	Me_3SnCl	119–120°	90	(186)
$Ph_3Sn \cdot W(CO)_3Cp$	Ph_3SnCl	229–230.5°	57	(170, 186)
$Ph_2Sn[W(CO)_3Cp]_2$	Ph_2SnCl_2	207–209°		(170)
$PhClSn[W(CO)_3Cp]_2$	$PhSnCl_3$	183–184°		(173)
$ClSn[W(CO)_3Cp]_3$	$SnCl_4$	198°		(173)
Sn—Mn				
$Me_3Sn \cdot Mn(CO)_5$	Me_3SnCl	29.5°(47° 0.001)	80	(50, 51, 136)
$Me_3Sn \cdot Mn(CO)_4 \cdot AsMe_3$	Me_3SnCl			(115)
$Me_2Sn[Mn(CO)_5]_2$	Me_2SnCl_2	102–104°	86–98	(116, 117, 119, 213, 214)
$MeSn[Mn(CO)_5]_3$	$MeSnCl_3$	120–155°d		(213)
$(CH_2:CH)_3Sn \cdot Mn(CO)_4(PMe_3)$	$(CH_2:CH)_3SnCl$	120–140°d		(117)
$(CH_2:CH)Sn[Mn(CO)_5]_3$	$(CH_2:CH)SnCl_3$	150–152°	85	(213)
$Ph_3Sn \cdot Mn(CO)_5$	Ph_3SnCl			(24, 37, 72, 113, 116, 117, 119, 136, 213)

Compound	Reagent	M.p.	Yield	References
$Ph_2Sn[Mn(CO)_5]_2$	Ph_2SnCl_2	137–139°	82	(116, 117, 119, 214)
$PhSn[Mn(CO)_5]_3$	$PhSnCl_3$	130–140° (90), 166–167° (83)		(173, 213)
$Ph_2ClSn \cdot Mn(CO)_5$	Ph_2SnCl_2	102–103.5°	85	(113)
$Me_3Sn \cdot Mn(CO)_4Tdp$	Me_3SnCl			(146)
$Et_2ClSn \cdot Mn(CO)_4AsPr_3$	Et_2SnCl_2			(115)
$n\text{-}BuSn[Mn(CO)_5]_3$	$n\text{-}BuSnCl_3$	143–145°		(214)
$(EtC_5H_4)_3Sn \cdot Mn(CO)_5$	$(EtC_5H_4)_3SnCl$			(116, 117)
$CH_2{:}CHCH_2Sn[Mn(CO)_5SbPh_3]_3$	$CH_2{:}CHCH_2SnCl_3$			(115)
$PhSn[Mn(CO)_4 \cdot As(C_6H_4Me \cdot O)_3]_3$	$PhSnCl_3$			(115)
$m\text{-}EtC_6H_4Sn[Mn(CO)_4 \cdot Sb(C_6H_4Et\text{-}m)_3]_3$	$m\text{-}EtC_6H_4SnCl_3$			(115)
Sn—Tc				
None recorded				
Sn—Re				
$Me_3Sn \cdot Re(CO)_5$	Me_3SnCl	51–58°		(136, 214)
$Me_2Sn[Re(CO)_5]_2$	Me_2SnCl_2	119–121°		(214)
$MeSn[Re(CO)_5]_3$	$MeSnCl_3$	160–165°d		(214)
$Et_3Sn \cdot Re(CO)_5$	Et_3SnCl			(116, 117)
$CH_2{:}CHSn[Re(CO)_5]_3$	$CH_2{:}CHSnCl_3$	175–200°d		(214)
$n\text{-}BuSn[Re(CO)_5]_3$	$n\text{-}BuSnCl_3$	165–166°		(214)
$Ph_3Sn \cdot Re(CO)_5$	Ph_3SnCl	144.5–146°	77	(24, 136, 176)
$Ph_2Sn[Re(CO)_5]_2$	Ph_2SnCl_2	139°	51	(176, 214)
$PhSn[Re(CO)_5]_3$	$PhSnCl_3$	189°		(173, 176, 214)
$(Me_2C_5H_3)_3Sn \cdot Re(CO)_5$	$(Me_2C_5H_3)_3SnCl$			(116, 117)
$(EtPrC_5H_3)_3Sn \cdot Re(CO)_5$	$(EtPrC_5H_3)_3SnCl$			(116)
$(EtPrC_5H_3)_2Sn[Re(CO)_5]_2$	$(EtPrC_5H_3)_2SnCl_2$			(117)
Sn—Fe				
$(Me_3Sn)_2Fe(CO)_4$	Me_3SnCl	~8°	47–70	(59, 138, 139)
$(Ph_3Sn)_2Fe(CO)_4$	Ph_3SnOH	145–150°d	32	(127)

Continued

TABLE 6 (*Continued*)

Product	Tin starting material	mp(bp)	Yield (%)	References
[Me$_2$SnFe(CO)$_4$]$_2$	Me$_2$SnCl$_2$, MeSnCl$_3$			(138, 207)
[Bu$_2$SnFe(CO)$_4$]$_2$	Bu$_2$SnCl$_2$	112–113°	<32	(130, 131, 138)
[Ph$_2$SnFe(CO)$_4$]$_2$	Ph$_3$SnOH		46	(59, 127)
Me$_4$Sn$_3$[Fe(CO)$_4$]$_4$	MeSnCl$_3$	198–200°d		(59, 137, 207)
Et$_4$Sn$_3$[Fe(CO)$_4$]$_4$	EtSnCl$_3$			(59)
Me$_3$Sn·Fe(CO)$_2$Cp	Me$_3$SnCl			(41, 42, 187)
Me$_2$Sn[Fe(CO)$_2$Cp]$_2$	Me$_2$SnCl$_2$	105–107°	78	(118)
Et$_2$Sn[Fe(CO)$_2$Cp]$_2$	Et$_2$SnCl$_2$	87–89°	60	(171)
Ph$_2$Sn[Fe(CO)$_2$Cp]$_2$	Ph$_2$SnCl$_2$	148–150°	60	(118, 171)
I$_2$Sn[Fe(CO)$_2$Cp]$_2$	SnI$_4$	180°d	86	(87)
PhSn[Fe(CO)$_2$Cp]$_3$	PhSnCl$_3$	243–245°d	50	(171)
Sn[Fe(CO)$_2$Cp]$_4$	SnCl$_4$	275°d		(171)

Sn—Ru

Product	Tin starting material	mp(bp)	Yield (%)	References
(Me$_3$Sn)$_2$Ru(CO)$_4$	Me$_3$SnCl			(57, 58)
(Et$_3$Sn)$_2$Ru(CO)$_4$	Et$_3$SnCl			(57, 58)
(n-Pr$_3$Sn)$_2$Ru(CO)$_4$	n-Pr$_3$SnCl			(57, 58)
(n-Bu$_3$Sn)$_2$Ru(CO)$_4$	n-Bu$_3$SnCl			(57, 58)
(Ph$_3$Sn)$_2$Ru(CO)$_4$	Ph$_3$SnCl			(57, 58)
[(PhCH$_2$)$_3$Sn]$_2$Ru(CO)$_4$	(PhCH$_2$)$_3$SnCl			(57, 58)
[Me$_2$Sn·RuC(O)$_4$]$_2$	Me$_2$SnCl$_2$			(148)

Sn—Os

None recorded

Sn—Co

Product	Tin starting material	mp(bp)	Yield (%)	References
Me$_3$Sn·Co(CO)$_4$	Me$_3$SnCl	74.5°	95	(8, 25, 42, 83, 214)
Et$_3$Sn·Co(CO)$_4$	Et$_3$SnCl			(140, 207)

Compound	Reactant	M.p.	Yield	Ref.
$n\text{-}Bu_3Sn\cdot Co(CO)_4$	$n\text{-}BuSnCl_3$	Oil	80–99	(130, 131)
$Ph_3Sn\cdot Co(CO)_4$	Ph_3SnCl	123°		(8, 18, 24, 25, 127, 189)
$n\text{-}Bu_2Sn[Co(CO)_4]_2$	$n\text{-}Bu_2SnCl_2$	Oil		(130, 131)
$Ph_2Sn[Co(CO)_4]_2$	Ph_2SnCl_2	139–141°		(127, 140, 191)
$MeSn[Co(CO)_4]_3$	$MeSnCl_3$	69–71°	53	(189, 191, 192, 214)
$CH_2{:}CH\cdot Sn[Co(CO)_4]_3$	$CH_2{:}CHSnCl_3$	57–60°		(191, 192)
$n\text{-}BuSn[Co(CO)_4]_3$	$n\text{-}BuSnCl_3$	60–62°	60	(191, 192)
$PhSn[Co(CO)_4]_3$	$PhSnCl_3$	90–92°	67	(173, 191, 192)
$(Acac)_2Co_2(CO)_7$	$(acac)_2SnCl_2$			(193)

Sn—Rh

Compound	Reactant	M.p.	Yield	Ref.
$Me_3Sn\cdot Rh(CO)_2(PPh_3)_2$	Me_3SnCl			(56)

Sn—Ir

Compound	Reactant	M.p.	Yield	Ref.
$Me_3Sn\cdot Ir(CO)_3PPh_3$	Me_3SnCl			(56)
$Ph_3Sn\cdot Ir(CO)_3PPh_3$	Ph_3SnCl			(56)
$Me_2Sn[Ir(CO)_3PPh_3]_2$	Me_2SnCl_2			(56)

Sn—Ni

None reported

Sn—Pd

None reported

Sn—Pt

Compound	Reactant	M.p.	Yield	Ref.
$Ph_3SnPtCl(PPh_3)_2$	Ph_3SnLi	278–282°	55	(4, 160)

Sn—Cu, Sn—Ag, Sn—Au

None reported

Nesmeyanov and his co-workers (*171*) made similar materials by a slightly different approach:

$$2CpFe(CO)_2^- + Ph_2SnCl_2 \longrightarrow [CpFe(CO)_2]_2SnPh_2 + 2Cl^-$$

$$[CpFe(CO)_2]_2SnPh_2 + 2HCl \longrightarrow [CpFe(CO)_2]_2SnCl_2 + 2C_6H_6$$

$$[CpFe(CO)_2]_2SnCl_2 + M(CO)_5^- \longrightarrow [CpFe(CO)_2]_2SnCl[M(CO)_5] + Cl^-$$
$$(M = Mn, Re)$$

and Dighe and Orchin (*73*) prepared substances in which tin atoms were directly bonded to four other metal atoms:

$$[CpFe(CO)_2]_2Sn[Mo(CO)_3Cp]_2 \quad \text{and} \quad [CpFe(CO)_2]_2Sn[Co(CO)_4]_2$$

This type of metathetical reaction sometimes fails or is complicated because of competing side reactions. Metal–halogen exchange has been mentioned as a complication in attempts to prepare $Sn-M^{IV}$ bonds (Sec. II.C.1 above). Dessy's extensive studies on the electrochemistry and nucleophilicity of carbonyl anions and R_3M^- ions provide an excellent guide to the likelihood of metal–halogen exchange (Refs. *70* and *71*, and references cited therein).

A second side reaction is reduction of one of the reactants. This has been observed in reactions of triphenyltin potassium with titanium(IV) compounds:

$$Cp_2TiCl_2 + Ph_3SnK(excess) \xrightarrow{(MeOCH_2)_2} [Cp_2Ti(SnPh_3)_2]^- + 2KCl \qquad (142)$$

As can be seen from Table 5, this method has been used to prepare compounds containing tin bound to most transition metals.

More complex compounds are sometimes obtained as a result of secondary reactions. For example, Hieber and Breu (*130, 131*) found that reactions of triorganotin halides with tetracarbonylferrate(–2) gave products in which only two methyl groups were attached to tin:

$$R_3SnCl + Fe(CO)_4^{2-} \longrightarrow [R_2Sn \cdot Fe(CO)_4]_2$$

Physical data indicate that the dimeric products have structure (**I**).

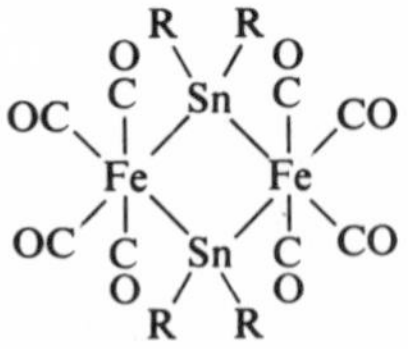

I

Similar reactions with methyltin trichloride have given the spirocyclic compound (**II**) in addition to (**I**) (*207*):

$$MeSnCl_3 + Fe(CO)_4^{2-} \xrightarrow{THF} [Me_2Sn \cdot Fe(CO)_4]_2 + Me_4Sn_3Fe_4(CO)_{16} \textbf{(II)}$$

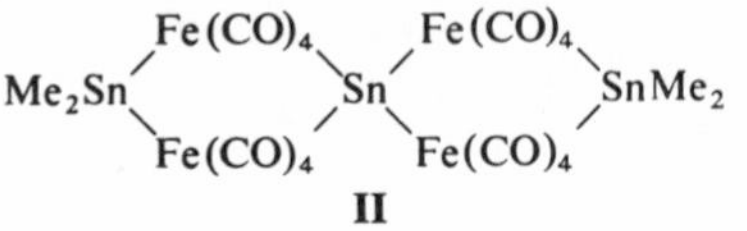

II

A compound of ruthenium, which presumably has a structure analogous to (**I**), arose from the reaction of trimethylsilyltetracarbonylruthenate(–1) and dimethyltin dichloride (*148*):

$$[Me_3Si \cdot Ru(CO)_4]^- + Me_2SnCl_2 \longrightarrow [Me_2SnRu(CO)_4]_2$$

This result was somewhat surprising since the same anion with trimethyltin chloride gave a normal product:

$$[Me_3Si \cdot Ru(CO)_4]^- + Me_3SnCl \longrightarrow Me_3Si \cdot Ru(CO)_4 \cdot SnMe_3 + Cl^-$$

The reaction between *bis*(pentane-2,4-dionato)dichlorotin and tetracarbonylcobaltate(–1) gave a heptacarbonyldicobalt derivative (**III**) rather than the octacarbonyldicobalt expected (*193*):

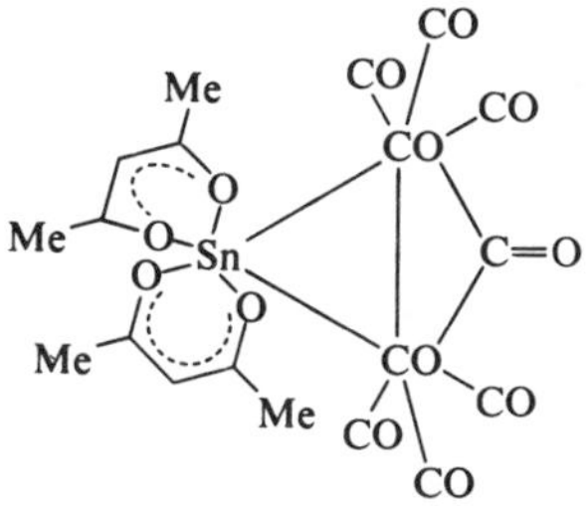

III

It has been suggested that $(acac)_2Sn[Co(CO)_4]_2$ may form initially and that this compound then loses carbon monoxide with formation of a cobalt–cobalt bond to give (**III**). It is interesting to note that the compounds $RSn[Co(CO)_4]_3$ show no tendency to lose carbon monoxide to form a $SnCo_3$ tetrahedron (*191, 192*) analogous to that from the reaction of carbon tetrachloride with dicobalt octacarbonyl (**IV**):

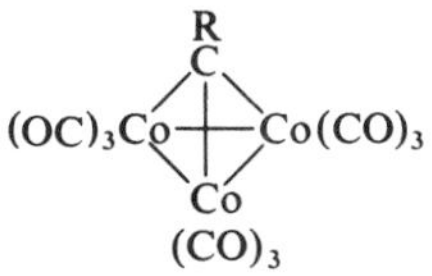

$$(OC)_3Co \underset{\underset{\displaystyle (CO)_3}{\overset{|}{Co}}}{\overset{\overset{\displaystyle \underset{C}{R}}{\diagup \diagdown}}{\quad}} Co(CO)_3$$

IV

It is possible that this difference in behavior arises from the large expected difference in Co—Sn—Co bond angle (and hence in Co—Co distance) in the two intermediates: $(acac)_2Sn[Co(CO)_4]_2$ has an octahedrally coordinated tin atom so that LCo—Sn—CO $\sim 90°$, whereas $RSn[Co(CO)_4]_3$ has a tetrahedrally coordinated tin atom with LCo—Sn—CO $\sim 109°$.

Very recently Burlitch and Ulmer have prepared manganese and iron analogs of Grignard reagents (*37*) and have used these to prepare manganese–tin and iron–tin bonds:

$$(CO)_5MnBr + Mg \xrightarrow{\text{THF}} (CO)_5MnMgBr \xrightarrow{\text{Ph}_3\text{SnCl}} (CO)_5Mn \cdot SnPh_3$$

$$CpFe(CO)_2Cl + Mg \xrightarrow{\text{THF}} CpFe(CO)_2MgBr \xrightarrow{\text{Ph}_3\text{SnCl}} CpFe(CO)_2 \cdot SnPh_3$$

$$Mn_2(CO)_{10} + Mg \xrightarrow[\text{THF}]{\text{BrCH}_2\text{CH}_2\text{Br}} (CO)_5MnMgBr \xrightarrow{\text{Ph}_3\text{SnCl}} (CO)_5Mn \cdot SnPh_3$$

2. Insertion Reactions

Tin(II) halides insert into some metal–metal bonds and many metal–halogen bonds. In this respect the tin(II) compounds behave rather like carbenes (see Refs. *169* and *219*).

$$[CpRu(CO)_2]_2 + SnX_2 \longrightarrow CpRu(CO)_2 \cdot SnX_2 \cdot Ru(CO)_2Cp \quad (16)$$

$$CpRu(CO)_2Cl + SnCl_2 \longrightarrow CpRu(CO)_2SnCl_3 \quad (16)$$

Insertion into transition metal–transition metal bonds appears to occur most readily with compounds containing bridging carbonyl groups (*190*), e.g., $Co_2(CO)_8$, $[CpFe(CO)_2]_2$, and $[CpNi(CO)]_2$. However, insertions into $[Co(CO)_3(PPh_3)]_2$ (*190*) and into $Mn_2(CO)_{10}$ [under forcing conditions (*132*)] have been observed. Neither of these substances has bridging carbonyls in the solid state. Insertion occurs under mild conditions (methylene chloride, room temperature) with the anions $M_2(CO)_{10}^{2-}$ (M = Cr, W) which also lack bridging carbonyl groups (*197*).

Tin(II) halides do not appear to have been inserted into a metal–metal bond containing two different metals, but tin(II) chloride does react with an asymmetrically substituted metal–metal bond (*126*):

$$[CpFe(CO)_2]_2 + L \xrightarrow[\text{reflux}]{\text{benzene}} Cp_2Fe_2(CO)_3L \xrightarrow{\text{SnCl}_2}$$

$$CpFe(CO)_2 \cdot SnCl_2 \cdot Fe(CO)LCp + CpFe(CO)_2 \cdot SnCl_2 \cdot Fe(CO)_2Cp$$

$$[L = (PhO)_3P, Et_3P, (i\text{-}PrO)_3P]$$

The products still contain tin–halogen bonds which can be readily alkylated or arylated.

Insertion of tin(II) halides into metal–halide bonds has been less commonly used to prepare tin–metal bonds, except for the water soluble complexes of the 2nd and 3rd series Group VIII metals. With these metals, the $SnCl_3^-$ complexes are intensely colored and provide a convenient colorimetric method of estimation. This particular group of compounds, which lies outside the range of the present chapter, has been reviewed in some detail by Baird (*5*) and Young (*67*).

It was originally suggested (*164*) that it was possible to prepare mixed tin halides by the insertion reaction:

$$CpFe(CO)_2I + SnCl_2 \longrightarrow CpFe(CO)_2SnCl_2I$$

but more recent studies (*166*) have shown that halogen interchange is very rapid and that only homohalogenated compounds are formed.

$$CpFe(CO)_2SnCl_3 + SnX_2 \longrightarrow CpFe(CO)_2SnX_3 + SnCl_2 \quad (X = Br, I)$$

An unusual compound made in this way is derived from cobaloxime, a model compound for vitamin B_{12} (*198*):

$$CoL_2L^1Cl + SnCl_2 \longrightarrow CoL_2L^1(SnCl_3) \ (L = \text{dimethylglyoximato}, \ L^1 = \text{a base})$$

Compounds prepared by insertion reactions are listed in Table 6.

3. Oxidative Addition Reactions

Oxidative addition reactions are most characteristic of iridium(I) and rhodium(I). A square planar iridium(I) complex is converted into an octahedral iridium(III) complex (*217, 218*).

Although this method has proved successful for the preparation of silicon–iridium bonds (*47*), e.g.:

$$IrCl(CO)(PPh_3)_2 + PhSiHCl_2 \longrightarrow IrHCl_2(CO)(PPh_3)_2(SiPhCl_2)$$

analogous products with tin do not appear to have been made. The most closely related reaction appears to be the following (*38*):

$$IrCl(CO)(Ph_3P)_2 + SnCl_2 \xrightarrow{\underset{C_2H_2}{C_2H_4 \text{ or}}} IrCl(CO)(Ph_3P)_2(SnCl_3)L \ (L = C_2H_4, C_2H_2)$$

which may have the structure (**V**) when $L = C_2H_4$.

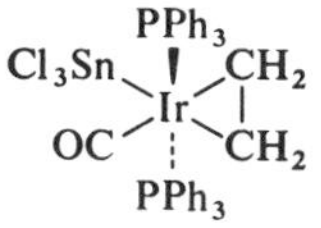

$$
\begin{array}{c}
PPh_3 \\
Cl_3Sn \diagdown \ | \diagup CH_2 \\
\diagup Ir \diagdown \ | \\
OC \diagup \ \vdots \ \diagdown CH_2 \\
PPh_3 \\
\mathbf{V}
\end{array}
$$

The condensation reactions of tin compounds with derivatives of iridium(I), rhodium(I), platinum(O), and platinum(II) reported in the next section could occur via successive oxidative addition and elimination reactions.

Recently Clemmitt and Glockling (*53*) have prepared platinum complexes by reactions which involve oxidative addition at some stage:

$$LLPt(MMe_3)Cl + Me_3SnH(excess) \longrightarrow$$
$$LLPtH(SnMe_3)_3 + H_2 + Me_3MH + Me_3MCl$$

$$LLPtCl_2 + Me_3SnH \longrightarrow LLPt(SnMe_3)_2HCl + Me_3SnCl$$

$$(LL = Ph_2PCH_2CH_2PPh_2, \ M = Si \text{ or } Ge)$$

TABLE 6

COMPOUNDS CONTAINING TIN–TRANSITION METAL BONDS FORMED BY INSERTION REACTIONS

Product	Starting material	mp (bp)	Yield (%)	References
$Cl_3Sn \cdot Mo(CO)_2P(OMe)_3Cp$	$CpMo(CO)_2[P(OMe)_3]Cl$	180°		(166)
$Br_3Sn \cdot Mo(CO)_2P(OMe)_3Cp$	$CpMo(CO)_2[P(OMe)_3]Cl$	198°		(166)
$I_3Sn \cdot Mo(CO)_2P(OMe)_3Cp$	$CpMo(CO)_2[P(OMe)_3]Cl$	215°		(166)
$Cl_3Sn \cdot Mo(CO)_2P(OPh)_3Cp$	$CpMo(CO)_2[P(OPh)_3]Cl$	169°		(166)
$Cl_3Sn \cdot Mo(CO)_2(PPh_3)Cp$	$CpMo(CO)_2(PPh_3)Cl$	240–250°d		(166)
$I_3Sn \cdot Mo(CO)_2(PPh_3)Cp$	$CpMo(CO)_2(PPh_3)Cl$	215–255°d		(166)
$Cl_3Sn \cdot Mo(CO)[P(OMe)_3]_2Cp$	$CpMo(CO)[P(OMe)_3]_2Cl$			(165, 166)
$Cl_2Sn \cdot [Mn(CO)_5]_2$	$Mn_2(CO)_{10}$			(132)
$Cl_3Sn \cdot Fe(CO)_2Cp$	$CpFe(CO)_2Cl$	157°d		(19, 20)
$Cl_2ISn \cdot Fe(CO)_2Cp \cdot MeOH$	$CpFe(CO)_2I$	110°		(164)
$Cl_2Sn[Fe(CO)_2Cp]_2$	$[CpFe(CO)_2]_2$	168°		(20, 77, 126)
$Br_2Sn[Fe(CO)_2Cp]_2$	$[CpFe(CO)_2]_2$	168–71°, 177–9°	70	(22, 190)
$I_2Sn[Fe(CO)_2Cp]_2$	$[CpFe(CO)_2]_2$	180°d		(190)
$Cl_2Sn[Fe(CO)_2Cp][Fe(CO)LCp]$	$Cp_2Fe_2(CO)_3L$			(126)
$Cl_2Sn[Ru(CO)_2Cp]_2$	$[CpRu(CO)_2]_2$			(16)
$Cl_3Sn \cdot Ru(CO)_2Cp$	$CpRu(CO)_2Cl$	112°		(16)
$Cl_2Sn[Co(CO)_4]_2$	$Co_2(CO)_8$	112°		(18, 190)
$Br_2Sn[Co(CO)_4]_2$	$Co_2(CO)_8$	115°		(18, 190)

$I_2Sn[Co(CO)_4]_2$	$Co_2(CO)_8$	105°		(18, 190)
$Cl_2Sn[Co(CO)_3Ph_3P]_2$	$Co_2(CO)_6(Ph_3P)_2$	96–97°		(18, 190)
$Cl_2Sn[Co(CO)_3Bu_3P]_2$	$Co_2(CO)_6(Bu_3P)_2$	128–30°		(18)
$Br_2Sn[Co(CO)_3Bu_3P]_2$	$Co_2(CO)_6(Bu_3P)_2$			(18)
$Cl_2Sn[Co(CO)_3Ph_3As]_2$	$Co_2(CO)_6(Ph_3As)_2$			(18)
$Cl_2Sn[Co(CO)_3Ph_3Sb]_2$	$Co_2(CO)_6(Ph_3Sb)_2$			(18)
$Cl_2Sn[Co(CO)_3(PhO)_3P]_2$	$Co_2(CO)_6[(PhO)_3P]_2$			(18)
$Cl_3SnCo(dimethylglyoxime)L$	$Co(dimethylglyoxime)LCl$	90°d		(198)
$Cl_2Sn[Ni(CO)Cp]_2$	$Cp_2Ni_2(CO)_2$	107–108°	53	(190)
$Br_2Sn[Ni(CO)Cp]_2$	$Cp_2Ni_2(CO)_2$	168–171°	40	(80)
$[(Ph_3P)_2N]_2[Cr_2(CO)_{10}SnI_2]$	$[Cr_2(CO)_{10}]^{2-}$	173–175°	39	(197)
$[(Ph_3P)_2N]_2[W_2(CO)_{10}SnI_2]$	$[W_2(CO)_{10}]^{2-}$			(197)

and Glockling and Hill (*107*) have carried out an oxidative addition with rhodium(I):

$$(Ph_3P)_3RhCl + Bu_3SnH \longrightarrow (Ph_3P)_2RhHCl(SnBu_3)$$

Trimethylstannane, however, reacted extremely vigorously to give rhodium metal, triphenylphosphine, and hexamethylditin.

4. *Condensation Reactions*

Many reactions of an organotin compound with a transition metal derivative to give a metal–metal bonded system with elimination of a small molecule have been reported, and the nature of the small molecule eliminated is very varied. One method which has the potentiality for wide use is the reaction of an N,N-dialkylstannylamine with a transition metal hydride (*39*), e.g.:

$$Me_3SnNMe_2 + CpW(CO)_3H \longrightarrow Me_3SnW(CO)_3Cp + Me_2NH$$

Reaction of a tin hydride with a transition metal amide is also possible (*62*):

$$Ph_3SnH + Ti(NMe_2)_4 \longrightarrow (Ph_3Sn)_4Ti$$

Complicated systems of metal–metal bonds have been constructed in this way (*62*):

$$Zr(NEt_2)_4 + 3Ph_3SnH \longrightarrow (Ph_3Sn)_3ZrNEt_2 + 3Et_2NH$$
$$(Ph_3Sn)_3ZrNEt_2 + HNPhC(O)H \longrightarrow (Ph_3Sn)_3ZrNPhC(O)H$$
$$(Ph_3Sn)_3ZrNPhC(O)H + Ph_2SnH_2 \longrightarrow [(Ph_3Sn)_3Zr]_2SnPh_2$$

A similar reaction is the elimination of hydrazoic acid between trimethyltin azide and a molybdenum hydride (*143*):

$$CpMo(Co)_3H + Me_3SnN_3 \longrightarrow CpMo(CO)_3SnMe_3 + HN_3$$

Direct reaction of tin hydrides with metal carbonyls can occur via loss of hydrogen and carbon monoxide (*57, 58*):

$$R_3SnH + Ru_3(CO)_{12} \longrightarrow (R_3Sn)_2Ru(CO)_4 + R_{10}Sn_4Ru_2(CO)_6$$
$$Me_2SnH_2 + Ru_3(CO)_{12} \longrightarrow (Me_3Sn)_2Ru(CO)_4 + Me_{10}Sn_4Ru_2(CO)_6$$
$$Me_2SnH_2 + Fe_3(CO)_{12} \longrightarrow [Me_2SnFe(CO)_4]_2 + trace\ (Me_3Sn)_2Fe(CO)_4$$

Glockling and Hill (*107*) have used related reactions to prepare derivatives of platinum:

$$LLPtCl_2 + (Me_3M)_2Hg \longrightarrow LLPt(MMe_3)Cl + LLPt(MeMe_3)_2$$
$$(LL = Ph_2PCH_2CH_2PPh_2; M = Si\ or\ Ge)$$

Bonati and his co-workers (*19*) have displaced methyl in a reaction of tin(II)chloride:

$$SnCl_2 + CpMo(CO)_3Me \longrightarrow CpMo(CO)_3SnCl_3$$

and Casey and Manning (*45, 46*) have eliminated mercury(II)chloride between a tin–chloride and an iron–mercury compound, e.g.:

$$SnCl_4 + Hg[Fe(CO)_3NO]_2 \longrightarrow Cl_3SnFe(CO)_3NO$$

They observed the following order of reactivities:

$$SnCl_4 > SnBr_4 > PhSnCl_3 > Ph_2SnCl_2 > Ph_3SnCl$$

and found that $XHgFe(CO)_3NO$ was an intermediate which reacted with more $SnX_4(X = Cl)$. The reaction was also used to prepare the known compounds $Cl_3SnCo(CO)_4$, $Cl_3SnMo(CO)_3Cp$, and $Cl_3SnW(CO)_3Cp$. This method should be particularly useful for transition metals which readily form mercury derivatives.

The direct reaction of tin(IV) halides with carbonyls has also proved useful as a means of making tin–transition metal bonds. For example, Newlands and his co-workers (*75, 77, 215*) have prepared compounds containing tin–iron, tin–nickel, and iron–tin–nickel bonds in this way:

$$[CpFe(CO)_2]_2 + SnX_4 \longrightarrow CpFe(CO)_2SnX_3 + CpFe(CO)_2X$$
$$[CpNi(CO)]_2 + SnX_4 \longrightarrow CpNi(CO)SnX_3 + CpNi(CO)X$$
$$CpFe(CO)_2SnX_3 + [CpNi(CO)]_2 \longrightarrow CpFe(CO)_2SnX_2Ni(CO)Cp + CpNi(CO)X$$

An interesting observation was that diphenyltin dichloride gave a small yield of the monophenyltin–iron product rather than the expected diphenyltin material (*77*):

$$[CpFe(CO)_2]_2 + Ph_2SnCl_2 \longrightarrow CpFe(CO)_2SnPhCl_2 + ?$$

Bonati and Wilkinson (*20*) had previously used tin(IV)chloride to convert *bis*-(dicarbonylcyclopentadienyliron)dichlorotin into the corresponding trichlorotin derivative:

$$[CpFe(CO)_2]_2SnCl_2 + SnCl_4 \longrightarrow 2CpFe(CO)_2SnCl_3$$

and to replace a methyl–tungsten bond by a tin–tungsten bond:

$$CpWMe(CO)_3 + SnCl_4 \longrightarrow CpW(CO)_3SnCl_3 + MeCl$$

Graham and his co-workers (*195*) showed that the products of the reaction between tin(IV)chloride and dodecarbonyltriruthenium depended on the reaction conditions.

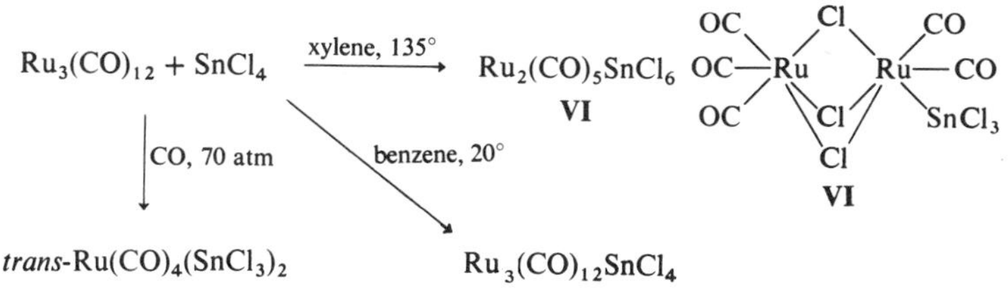

$$Ru_3(CO)_{12} + SnCl_4 \xrightarrow{\text{xylene, 135°}} Ru_2(CO)_5SnCl_6$$

VI

trans-$Ru(CO)_4(SnCl_3)_2$

$$Ru_3(CO)_{12}SnCl_4$$

VII

$$ClRu(CO)_4Ru(CO)_4Ru(CO)_4SnCl_3$$

VIII

Moss and Graham (*168*) have carried out similar reactions with osmium carbonyls and carbonyl hydrides:

$$H_2Os(CO)_4 + SnCl_4 \longrightarrow \textit{cis-}(CO)_4OsH(SnCl_3)$$

$$H_2Os_2(CO)_8 + SnCl_4 \longrightarrow (CO)_8Os_2H(SnCl_3)$$

$$(CO)_8Os_2H(SnCl_3) + CX_4 \longrightarrow (CO)_8Os_2X(SnCl_3)$$

$$Os_3(CO)_{12} + SnCl_4 \longrightarrow Cl_3Sn[Os(CO)_4]_3Cl$$

Stone's group (*60*) has observed similar reactions with tributyltin chloride and iron pentacarbonyl. Their results are summarized in the following reaction scheme:

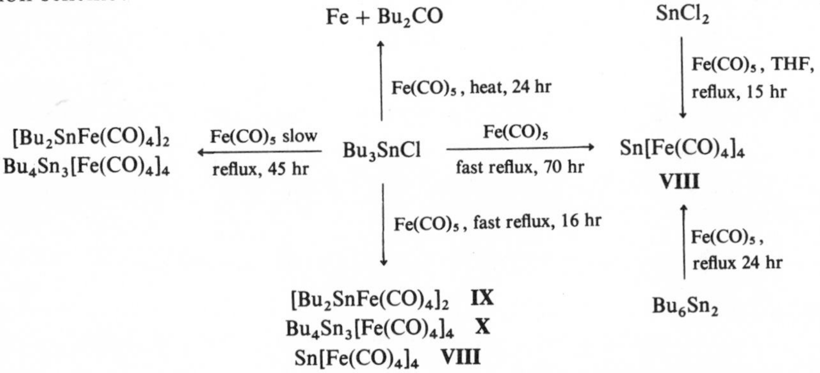

The structures of compounds (**VIII**), (**IX**), and (**X**) are shown below:

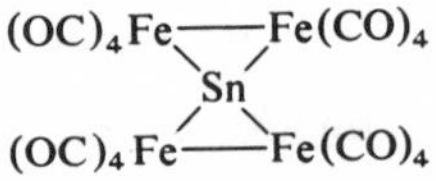

Patmore and Graham (*191, 192*) obtained tris(tetracarbonylcobalt)tin from methyltin trichloride and cobalt carbonyl:

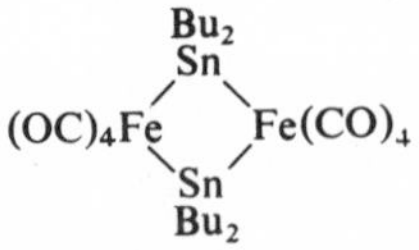

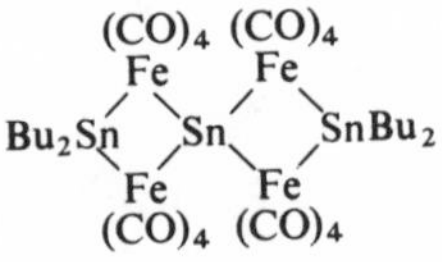

$$MeSnCl_3 + Co_2(CO)_8 \longrightarrow MeSn[Co(CO)_4]_3$$

The reaction of tetravinyltin (*191, 192*) with the same carbonyl gave the same product when the reaction was carried out in tetrahydrofuran and *bis*-(tetracarbonylcobalt)divinyltin in pentane.

The elimination of small organic groups from tin had been previously observed by King and Stone (*147*):

$$R_2Sn(CH:CH_2)_2 + Fe(CO)_5 \longrightarrow [R_2SnFe(CO)_4]_2$$

(R = Et, Bu)

$$Bu_2SnRR' + Fe(CO)_5 \longrightarrow [Bu_2SnFe(CO)_4]_2$$

(R = R' = Ph; R = Bu, R' = Ph)

and by Ibekwe and Newlands (*133, 134*):

$$R_2Sn(C:CR')_2 + Fe_3(CO)_{12} \longrightarrow [R_2SnFe(CO)_4]_2$$

(R = Et, R' = Pr, Bu, Ph; R = Pr, R' = Pr, Bu, Ph; R = Bu, R' = Pr, Bu)

Keppie and Lappert (*143*) have used the lability of the tin–cyclopentadiene bond to prepare systems with tin to chromium, molybdenum, and tungsten bonds:

$$(MeCN)_3M(CO)_3 + Me_3SnCp \longrightarrow CpM(CO)_3SnMe_3$$

Knox and Stone (*148*) prepared ruthenium–tin bonds by displacement of trimethylsilyl groups:

$$[R_3SiRu(CO)_4]_2 + Me_3SnH \longrightarrow (Me_3Sn)_2Ru(CO)_4$$

Similarly, Akhtar and Clark (*1*) have used the lability of the ethylene–platinum bond to prepare compounds containing platinum–tin bonds:

$$(Ph_3P)_2Pt(C_2H_4) + Me_6Sn_2 \longrightarrow (Ph_3P)_2Pt(SnMe_3)_2\text{-}trans$$
$$(Ph_3P)_2Pt(C_2H_4) + Me_3SnH \longrightarrow (Ph_3P)_2Pt(SnMe_3)_2 \ (cis \text{ and } trans)$$
$$(Ph_3P)_2Pt(C_2H_4) + Me_3SnCl \longrightarrow (Ph_3P)_2PtCl(SnMe_3)\text{-}trans$$
$$(Ph_3P)_4Pt + Me_6Sn_2 \longrightarrow (Ph_3P)_2Pt(SnMe_3)_2\text{-}trans$$

Compounds made by these miscellaneous reactions are listed in Table 7.

C. CHEMICAL PROPERTIES

1. *Nucleophilic Displacement at Tin*

Exchange reactions in which halogen attached to tin is replaced by other groups have been reported by a number of groups. Nesmeyanov and his colleagues (*171, 172*) have replaced chlorine by thiocyanate, acetate, ethanethiolate, hydroxide, sulphide, nitrite, and nitrate; e.g.:

$$[CpFe(CO)_2]_2SnCl_2 + M(OAc)_2 \longrightarrow [CpFe(CO)_2]_2Sn(OAc)_2 + 2MCl$$

and they, along with Bonati (*18*), Stone and co-workers (*16*), and many others, have used Grignard reagents to displace chloride by alkyl, e.g.:

$$[(CO)_4Co]_2SnX_2 + 2RMgX \longrightarrow [(CO)_4Co]_2SnR_2 + 2MgX_2 \quad (18)$$
$$[CpRu(CO)_2]_2SnX_2 + 2MeMgI \longrightarrow [CpRu(CO)_2]_2SnR_2 + MgX_2 + MgI_2 \quad (16)$$

TABLE 7

METAL–METAL BONDED SYSTEMS PREPARED BY MISCELLANEOUS REACTIONS

Product	mp (°C)	Yield (%)	Comments	References
$(Ph_3Sn)_4Ti$	130°	30	Ochre	(62)
$[(Ph_3Sn)_2TiO]_2$	>260°	40	White	(62)
$(Ph_3Sn)_2Ti(OMe)_2$	>260°	40	Yellow	(62)
$(Ph_3Sn)_4Zr$	70–73°	—	Yellow, sinters before melting	(62)
$[(Ph_3Sn)_3Zr]_2SnPh_2$	100°	22	Yellow, sinters before melting	(62)
$[(Ph_3Sn)_2ZrSnPh_2]_2$	160°d	49	Orange–yellow, sinters before melting	(62)
$(Ph_3P)_2Rh(SnBu_3)HCl$	110°d	92	Not crystallized, analysis poor	(107)
$(Ph_2PCH_2CH_2PPh_2)PtH(SnMe_3)_3$				(53)
$(Ph_2PCH_2CH_2PPh_2)PtHCl(SnMe_3)_2$				(53)
$CpNi(CO)SnCl_3$	42–3°d	37	Green	(75)
$CpNi(CO)SnBr_3$	56°d	36	Green	(75)
$CpFe(CO)_2SnCl_3$	157	27	Yellow	(77)
$CpFe(CO)_2SnBr_3$	170–171	21	Yellow–orange	(77)
$CpFe(CO)_2SnI_3$	119	29	Red	(77)
$CpFe(CO)_2SnCl_2Ni(CO)Cp$				(215)
$CpFe(CO)_2SnBr_2Ni(CO)Cp$				(215)
$CpFe(CO)_2SnPhCl_2$	108°	107	Pale yellow	(77)
$(CO)_3(NO)FeSnPh_3$	122°		Decomposed without melting	(46)
$(CO)_3(NO)FeSnPh_2Cl$	67°			(46)
$(CO)_3(NO)FeSnPhCl_2$	76°	50–80%		(46)
$(CO)_3(NO)FeSnCl_3$	101°d		Yellow to red	(46)
$(CO)_3(NO)FeSnBr_3$	85°d			(46)
$(Ph_3P)(CO)_2(NO)FeSnPh_3$	179°		Decomposed without melting	(46)
$(Ph_3P)(CO)_2(NO)FeSnCl_3$	145°d			(46)
$(Ph_3P)(CO)_2(NO)FeSnBr_3$	130°d			(46)
$[(PhO)_3P](CO)_2(NO)FeSnCl_3$	102°			(46)

Compound	M.p.	Yield	Color/Notes	References
CpW(CO)₃SnCl₃	187°			(20)
Ru₂(CO)₅SnCl₆			Yellow	(195)
Cl[Ru(CO)₄]₃SnCl₃				(195)
trans-Ru(CO)₄(SnCl₃)₂				(195)
cis-HOs(CO)₄(SnCl₃)				(168)
(CO)₈Os₂H(SnCl₃)				(168)
Cl[Os(CO)₄]₃SnCl₃				(168)
Sn[Fe(CO)₄]₄				(60)
[Bu₂SnFe(CO)₄]₂	112–113°	28–30 (Ref. 155)	Yellow	(60, 133, 134, 147)
Bu₄Sn₃[Fe(CO)₄]₄				(60)
[Et₂SnFe(CO)₄]₂	138°d	12–34 (Ref. 155)	Yellow	(133, 134, 147)
[Pr₂SnFe(CO)₄]₂	128–130°	10–30 (Ref. 155)	Yellow	(133, 134)
CpM(CO)₃SnMe₃			M = Cr, Mo, W	(143)
(Me₃Sn)₂Ru(CO)₄				(148)
trans-(Ph₃P)₂Pt(SnMe₃)₂	180°	40–48	Yellow, decomposed without melting	(1)
trans-(Ph₃P)₂PtCl(SnMe₃)	280°	43%	White, decomposed without melting	(1)

Powell (*196*) reported reactions similar to Nesmeyanov, e.g.:

$$[CpFe(CO)_2]_2SnCl_2 + 2HSR + 2 \text{ base} \longrightarrow [CpFe(CO)_2]_2Sn(SR)_2 + 2 \text{ base HCl}$$

2. Reactions with Halogens and Hydrogen Halides

Reactions with halogens and hydrogen halides were described in 1962 by Gorsich (*119*) working with tin–manganese and tin–iron compounds. In general, he found that hydrogen halides split tin–phenyl bonds without breaking the tin–metal bonds, e.g.:

$$CpFe(CO)_2SnPh_3 + 3HCl \longrightarrow CpFe(CO)_2SnCl_3 + 3C_6H_6$$

but that chlorine tended to break tin–metal bonds as well, e.g.:

$$Ph_2Sn[Mn(CO)_5]_2 \xrightarrow[CH_2Cl_2, 25°]{HCl,} Cl_2Sn[Mn(CO)_5]_2 \xrightarrow{Cl_2}$$

$$Cl_3SnMn(CO)_5 + ClMn(CO)_5$$

Careful control of the conditions made it possible to displace phenyl groups stepwise.

Nesmeyanov and his colleagues (*170, 172*) have reported analogous reactions, including the partial displacement of phenyl groups with tin–molybdenum and tin–tungsten compounds.

Clark's group has studied cleavage reactions of tin–platinum (*1*) and tin–manganese compounds (*23*) with halogens, hydrogen halides, and other electrophiles. They found that chlorine and iodine cleaved the Sn—Mn bond in $Me_3SnMn(CO)_5$ with no evidence for Sn—Me cleavage, whereas hydrogen chloride removed two methyl groups stepwise and did not remove the third. Iodine chloride gave trimethyltin chloride and iodide and manganese carbonyl iodides but no manganese carbonyl chlorides. With iodotrifluoromethane the products were principally trimethyltin iodide, (iododimethyltin)-pentacarbonylmanganese, and manganesepentacarbonyl iodide.

With boron trifluoride (*23*) a methyl group was lost and a cationic product was obtained, perhaps via the reactions:

$$Me_3SnMn(CO)_5 + BF_3 \longrightarrow FMe_2SnMn(CO)_5 + MeBF_2$$

$$BF_3 + FMe_2SnMn(CO)_5 \longrightarrow [Me_2SnMn(CO)_5][BF_4]$$

When the starting material contained a trifluoromethyl group attached to tin, this group was transferred to boron to form part of the anion:

$$CF_3Me_2SnMn(CO)_5 + BF_3 \longrightarrow [Me_2SnMn(CO)_5][BF_3CF_3]$$

Akhtar and Clark (*1*) found that hydrogen caused partial scission of platinum–tin bonds whereas bromine and hydrogen chloride caused complete scission:

$$\textit{trans-}(Ph_3P)_2Pt(SnMe_3)_2 + H_2 \longrightarrow \textit{trans-}(Ph_3P)_2PtH(SnMe_3) + Me_3SnH$$

$$\textit{trans-}(Ph_3P)_2Pt(SnMe_3)_2 + 2Br_2 \longrightarrow \textit{cis-}(Ph_3P)_2PtBr_2 + 2Me_3SnBr$$

$$\textit{trans-}(Ph_3P)_2Pt(SnMe_3)_2 + HCl \longrightarrow \textit{trans-}(Ph_3P)_2PtHCl + Me_6Sn_2$$

It is likely that these reactions occur via octahedral platinum(IV) intermediates, e.g.:

$$
\begin{array}{c}
\text{Me}_3\text{Sn} \diagdown \diagup \text{PPh}_3 \\
\text{Pt} \\
\text{Ph}_3\text{P} \diagup \diagdown \text{SnMe}_3
\end{array}
+ \text{HCl} \longrightarrow
\begin{array}{c}
\text{SnMe}_3 \\
\text{Me}_3\text{Sn} \diagdown | \diagup \text{PPh}_3 \\
\text{Pt} \\
\text{Ph}_3\text{P} | \text{Cl} \\
 \text{H}
\end{array}
$$

$$
\begin{array}{c}
\text{H} \diagdown \diagup \text{PPh}_3 \\
\text{Pt} \\
\text{Ph}_3\text{P} \diagup \diagdown \text{Cl}
\end{array}
+ \text{Me}_6\text{Sn}_2
$$

as originally suggested by Glockling (*27*, *66*, *108*).

3. *Insertion Reactions*

Insertion reactions of compounds containing both tin–carbon and tin–transition metal bonds can, in principle, occur into either or both of these bonds. Most of the published work in this area has been carried out by H. C. Clark's group at the University of Western Ontario, with smaller contributions from Nezmayanov and his co-workers and Newlands and his co-workers.

Clark (*50*, *51*) has shown that fluoro-olefins will react with the tin–manganese bond under ultraviolet irradiation. With tetrafluoroethylene an addition product is produced (i.e., the olefin is inserted into the tin–manganese bond):

$$\text{Me}_3\text{SnMn(CO)}_5 + \text{C}_2\text{F}_4 \xrightarrow{\;h\nu\;} \text{Me}_3\text{SnCF}_2\text{CF}_2\text{Mn(CO)}_5$$

$$+ \text{Me}_3\text{SnF} + \text{CF}_2\text{:CFCOMn(CO)}_5$$

$$+ [\text{CF}_2\text{:CFMn(CO)}_4]_2 \text{ (two isomers)}$$

It is likely that tin fluoride and the three products which do not contain tin arose from decomposition of the addition product, perhaps via a β elimination:

$$
\begin{array}{c}
\text{F}_2\text{C} {-\!\!\!\!-} \text{CF} {-} \text{Mn(CO)}_5 \\
| | \\
\text{Me}_3\text{Sn} \text{F}
\end{array}
\longrightarrow \text{Me}_3\text{SnF} + [\text{CF}_2\text{:CFMn(CO)}_5]
$$

$$
[\text{CF}_2\text{:CFMn(CO)}_5]
\begin{array}{c}
\xrightarrow{+\text{CO}} \text{CF}_2\text{:CFCOMn(CO)}_5 \\
\xrightarrow{-2\text{CO}} [\text{CF}_2\text{:CFMn(CO)}_4]_2
\end{array}
$$

Reactions with trifluoroethylene gave close to 100% of trimethyltin fluoride together with *cis*- and *trans*-(1,2-difluorovinyl)pentacarbonylmanganese. These products are again those expected of a β-elimination from an unstable adduct. With chlorotrifluoroethylene, the products were trimethyltin chloride and fluoride (45% and 9%) (perfluoroacryloyl)pentacarbonylmanganese, and *cis*- and *trans*-(1,2-difluoro-2-chlorovinyl)pentacarbonylmanganese. These products are also readily rationalized via a β-elimination. Finally, reaction with ethylene led to replacement of carbon monoxide from manganese rather than insertion into the metal–metal bond:

$$Me_3SnMn(CO)_5 + C_2H_4 \longrightarrow Me_3SnMn(CO)_4(C_2H_4) + CO$$

In further work Bichler, Booth, and Clark (*9*) have studied the reactions of (trimethyltin)pentacarbonylmanganese and (trimethyltin)cyclopentadienyldi-carbonyliron with other fluoro-olefins and fluoroacetylenes. Their results are summarized in the following equations:

$$Me_3SnMn(CO)_5 + CF_3CF:CF_2 \xrightarrow{\text{uv}} Me_3SnF + \textit{cis-} \text{ and } \textit{trans-}CF_3CF:CF_2Mn(CO)_5$$

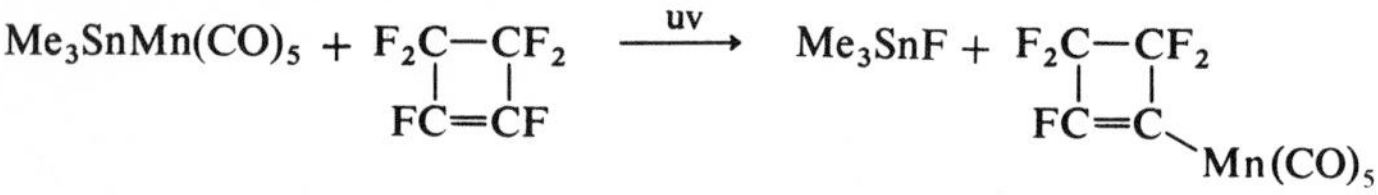

$$Me_3SnMn(CO)_5 + \underset{\underset{FC=CF}{|\quad\ |}}{F_2C-CF_2} \xrightarrow{\text{uv}} Me_3SnF + \underset{\underset{FC=C}{|\quad\ |}}{F_2C-CF_2}\!\!\diagdown_{Mn(CO)_5}$$

(NB: The corresponding iron compound did not react with C_4F_6.)

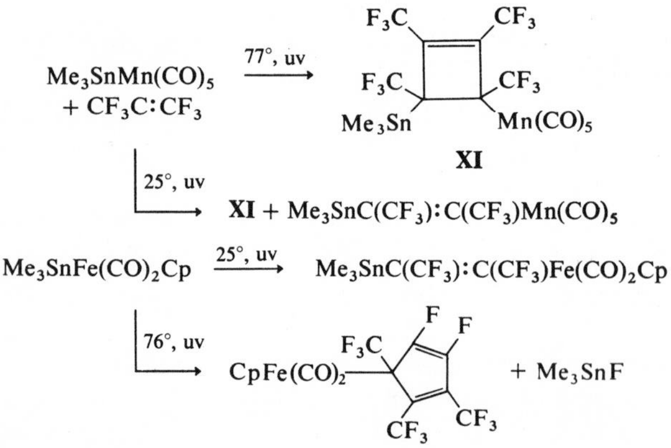

$$\begin{matrix} Me_3SnMn(CO)_5 \\ + CF_3C:CF_3 \end{matrix} \xrightarrow{77°,\ \text{uv}}$$

XI

$$\xrightarrow{25°,\ \text{uv}} \textbf{XI} + Me_3SnC(CF_3):C(CF_3)Mn(CO)_5$$

$$Me_3SnFe(CO)_2Cp \xrightarrow{25°,\ \text{uv}} Me_3SnC(CF_3):C(CF_3)Fe(CO)_2Cp$$

$$\xrightarrow{76°,\ \text{uv}} CpFe(CO)_2\!-\!\cdots + Me_3SnF$$

Neither the manganese nor the iron compound reacted with 3,3,3-tri-fluoropropyne to any extent.

Interestingly, Nesmeyanov and his colleagues (*175*) have studied the reaction of 1 : 3-butadiene with compounds containing tin–iron bonds:

$$2Me_3SnFe(CO)_2Cp + CH_2:CH\cdot CH:CH_2 \longrightarrow [Me_3SnFe(CO)Cp]_2C_4H_6 + 2CO$$

$$Ph_3SnFe(CO)_2Cp + C_4H_6 \longrightarrow Ph_3SnFeCp(C_4H_6) + 2CO$$

but replacement of carbon monoxide occurs in preference to insertion into the tin–iron bond.

Sulfur dioxide also reacts with tin–transition metal compounds. Bichler and Clark (*10*) have reported that the dioxide inserts into the tin–metal bond of $Me_3SnMn(CO)_5$ and $Me_3SnFe(CO)_2Cp$. Evidence for this conclusion is based mainly on infrared evidence. On the other hand, Edmondson and Newlands

(*78*) had earlier shown by unambiguous synthesis that reaction of sulfur dioxide with the compound $Ph_2Sn[Fe(CO)_2Cp]_2$ gave insertion at the tin–phenyl bond:

$$[CpFe(CO)_2]_2SnPh_2 + SO_2 \longrightarrow [CpFe(CO)_2]_2Sn[OS(O)Ph]_2$$
$$[CpFe(CO)_2]_2SnCl_2 + 2NaO_2SPh \longrightarrow [CpFe(CO)_2]_2Sn[OS(O)Ph]_2$$

and this was confirmed by X-ray crystallography (*34*).

More recently Edmondson, Field, and Newlands (*76*) have investigated this type of reaction further:

$$CpFe(CO)_2SnPh_3 + SO_2 \longrightarrow CpFe(CO)_2SnPh[OS(O)Ph]_2$$
$$\textbf{(XII)}$$
$$CpFe(CO)_2SnPh[OS(O)Ph]_2 \xrightarrow{\text{EtOH}} CpFe(CO)_2SnPh[OS(O)Ph](OH)$$
$$\textbf{(XIII)}$$
$$CpFe(CO)_2SnPhCl_2 + NaSO_2Ph \longrightarrow \textbf{(XII)}(18\%) + \textbf{(XIII)}(18\%)$$

Bryan (*35*) has recently shown that (**XIII**) is a hydroxy-bridged dimer in the solid state.

The dimethylanalogue, $Me_2Sn[Fe(CO)_2Cp]_2$, gave a small yield of $CpFe(CO)_2SO_2Me$ with sulfur dioxide but no insertion product, while the dichlorotin compound $Cl_2Sn[Fe(CO)_2Cp]_2$ was recovered unchanged. Kitching and his co-workers have shown in an elegant manner that insertion of sulfur dioxide into tin–carbon bonds is electrophilic (*89*). It would be very interesting to discover what factors determine whether insertion shall be into a tin–metal bond or into a tin–carbon bond.

An interesting reaction was observed when (triphenyltin)-pentacarbonyl-manganese was treated with tetraphenylcyclopentadienone (*119, 120*). In effect the organic ligand is inserted into the tin–manganese bond.

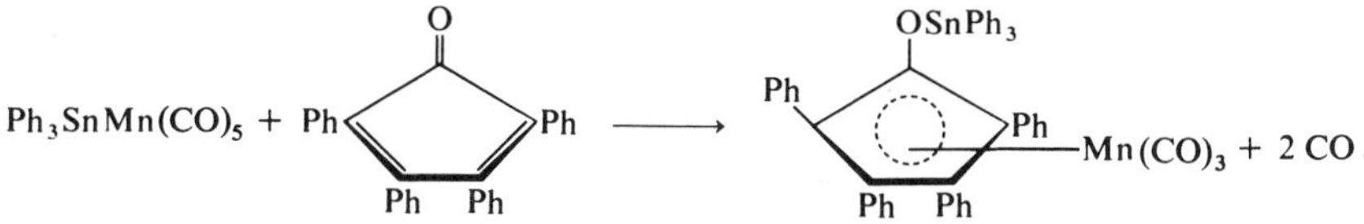

4. Miscellaneous Reactions

In the previous three sections attention has been concentrated on reactions at tin. A very small number of reactions at the transition metal are also covered in the literature. Two of these have already been mentioned—the replacement by ethylene of a carbonyl from $Me_3SnMn(CO)_5$ (*50, 51*) and the replacement by 1,3-butadiene of one or two carbonyls from $R_3SnFe(CO)_2Cp$ (*175*). Replacement of carbonyls by phosphines has also been reported, e.g.:

$$R_2Sn[Co(CO)_4]_2 + 2Bu_3P \longrightarrow R_2Sn[Co(CO)_3Bu_3P]_2 + 2CO \quad (18)$$
$$[Bu_2SnFe(CO)_4]_2 + 2Ph_3P \xrightarrow{\text{uv, 96 hr}} [Bu_2SnFe(CO)_3(Ph_3P)]_2 + 2CO \quad (134)$$

Bonati and Minghetti (21) have made hexacoordinate derivatives of tin containing tin–metal bonds by treatment of suitable starting materials with 2,2′-bipyridyl (bipy) and 8-hydroxyquinoline (HOx), but the reactions were sometimes accompanied by Sn—M bond scission:

$$CpFe(CO)_2SnCl_3 + bipy \longrightarrow CpFe(CO)_2SnCl_3 \cdot bipy$$

$$[CpFe(CO)_2]_2SnCl_2 + 2HOx \longrightarrow CpFe(CO)_2SnClOx_2$$

$$(CO)_3(Bu_3P)CoSnCl_3 + 2HOx \longrightarrow (CO)_3(Bu_3P)CoSnClOx_2 + Cl_2SnOx_2$$

$$CpMo(CO)_3SnCl_3 + 2HOx \longrightarrow CpMo(CO)_3SnClOx_2$$

D. PHYSICAL PROPERTIES

1. Spectra other than Mössbauer

Most papers on compounds containing tin–transition metal bonds contain spectroscopic information. In the following few paragraphs some of the salient points are presented.

A detailed review of spectroscopic studies of metal–metal bonded compounds has been prepared by Walters and Risem (226). Most of the attempts to discuss the tin–transition metal bonds in detail have relied on a combination of infrared and ^1H NMR spectroscopy. Graham's group (121, 136, 186, 188, 190) investigated a large number of Sn—M systems and concluded that the Sn—M bonds had considerable s-character (based particularly on changes in $J_{117SnCH_3}$ and $J_{119SnCH_3}$) and that some form of d_π—p_π interaction might occur between the two metals.

Carey and Clark (42) confirmed these views with series of compounds of the type $(CH_3)_{3-n}Cl_nSnX$, where $X = Mn(CO)_5$ and $Mo(CO)_3Cp$. Interaction between the two metals increases as methyl is replaced by chlorine. Bands in the 170–200 cm^{-1} region are assigned to the Sn—M stretch. Other assignments of Sn—M bands have been made (90, 125).

Stone and his co-workers (68, 87) have studied the compounds $CpFe(CO)_2X$ ($X = SnCl_3$, $SnPh_3$, $SnMe_3$) by infrared spectroscopy and have concluded that π-bonding in the Sn—Fe bond increases in the series $SnMe_3$, $SnPh_3$, and $SnCl_3$. Field and Newlands (86) have reported the variation in v_{CO}, $\delta_{C_5H_5}$, and $\tau_{C_5H_5}$, in the series $CpFe(CO)_2SnPh_{3-n}Cl_n$. The results are in agreement with the views of Graham and Stone.

Bonati and his co-workers (216) have carried out very similar studies with $R_3SnMn(CO)_5$, $R_3SnRe(CO)_5$, $R_3SnFe(CO)_2Cp$, and $R_3SnMo(CO)_3Cp$. They interpret their results in terms of inductive effects with little or no contribution from π-effects.

Casey and Manning (46) have studied the effect of variations in R in $R_3SnFe(CO)_3NO$ on both v_{NO} and v_{CO} and have shown that the effects are analogous to those observed by Graham and Patmore.

Spiess and Sheline (*204*) have used ^{59}Co NMR to investigate the nature of the M—Co bonds in $X_3MCo(CO)_4$ (M = Si, Ge, Sn, Pb; X = Cl, Br, I, and Ph). They found that the paramagnetic shielding decreased in the order I > Br > Cl > Ph. From the nonlinear shift in the paramagnetic shielding with M it was concluded that π-effects in the M—Co bond varied and were greatest in the Sn—Co bond.

Nuclear quadrupole resonance can also provide information about the M—Co bond. Published results are collected in Table 8. The results indicate

TABLE 8

^{59}Co AND ^{35}Cl QUADRUPOLE COUPLING CONSTANTS

Compound	$e^2Qq_{zz}(^{59}Co)$, MHz	$e^2Qq_{zz}(^{35}Cl)$, MHz	References
$Br_3SnCo(CO)_4$	159.88 ± 0.02 (from ^{59}Co NMR)	—	(*204*)
$Ph_3SnCo(CO)_4$	104.11	—	(*30*)
$Ph_3SnCo(CO)_4$	105.38	—	(*174*)
$Ph_2ClSnCo(CO)_4$	119.66	17.42	(*174*)
$PhCl_2SnCo(CO)_4$	143.5	—	(*174*)
$Cl_3SnCo(CO)_4$	163.45	39.76	(*30*)
$Cl_2Sn[Co(CO)_4]_2$	148.9	—	(*174*)
$Cl_2Sn[Co(CO)_4]_2$	146.8	—	(*203*)
$Cl_2Sn[Co(CO)_4]_2$	146.9	30.0	(*122*)
$ClSn[Co(CO)_4]_3$	134.2	—	(*203*)
$ClSn[Co(CO)_4]_3$	136.0	—	(*174*)
$Sn[Co(CO)_4]_4$	129.2	—	(*203*)
$ClPhSn[Co(CO)_4]_2$	127.7	—	(*122*)
$Ph_2Sn[Co(CO)_4]_2$	112.9	—	(*122*)
$Me_3SnCo(CO)_4$	96.66	—	(*174*)
$Me_3SnCo(CO)_4$	96.8	—	(*203*)
$Me_2Sn[Co(CO)_4]_2$	105.7	—	(*203*)
$MeSn[Co(CO)_4]_3$	121.0	—	(*203*)
$Br_2Sn[Co(CO)_4]_2$	146.5	—	(*203*)
$BrSn[Co(CO)_4]_3$	133.0	—	(*203*)
$Ph_3SnCo(CO)_3PPh_3$	144.53	—	(*174*)
$Cl_3SnCo(CO)_3PPh_3$	163.39	—	(*174*)

that the electron density on cobalt is decreased as the electronegativity of the substituents on tin increase, but there is no evidence for an increased electron density at chlorine attached to tin. It appears, therefore, that electron density changes at tin must be small. Brown and his co-workers (*203*) observed that chlorine and bromine had very similar effects in the series $X_nSn[Co(CO)_4]_{4-n}$ and, since chlorine is more electronegative than bromine, it was consequently concluded that two opposing effects must be operating for chlorine, e.g.,

π-donation to tin opposing the inductive effect. These workers have also demonstrated the approximately linear relationship between the ^{59}Co quadrupole coupling constant and the A_1^2 stretching mode of the carbonyl groups.

Kenworthy and Myatt (142) have studied the ESR spectra of the systems $[Cp_2Ti(MPh_3)_2]^-$. The spectra show coupling to ^{47}Ti$(I = 5/2)$, ^{49}Ti$(I = 7/2)$, ^{117}Sn, and ^{119}Sn (both $I = 1/2$) when M = Sn.

Among papers reporting mass spectra of compounds containing M—Sn bonds are one concerned with the series of compounds $CpFe(CO)_2SnPh_nCl_{3-n}$ $(n = 0 - 3)$ (86) and a second by King (145) in which mass spectra of $Me_3SnMo(CO)_3Cp$ and $Me_3SnNCW(CO)_5$ are described.

Lappert and his colleagues (40) have used mass spectrometry to determine M—M bond dissociation energies for the systems $Cp(CO)_3MSnMe_3$ (M = Cr, Mo, W). The M—Sn dissociation energies are 224, 297, and 316 kJ mole^{-1}, respectively. These workers have also reported $\nu_{M-M'}$ for these compounds from Raman and far IR studies.

2. Mössbauer Spectra

The investigation of the structures and bonding of tin compounds via ^{119m}Sn Mössbauer spectroscopy is of increasing importance, as is clear from the number of recent reviews on the subject, e.g., Refs. 111, 201, and 237. The rapidity with which the use of this method is expanding is perhaps best illustrated by the number of compounds with M—Sn bonds tabulated in the 1968 review (153) versus the number in Zuckermann's review of 1970 (98).

Tin Mössbauer spectroscopy was originally used to determine the number of different sites for tin atoms in a molecule or in a lattice and then to determine whether or not a non-zero electric field gradient was present at tin (i.e., presence or absence of quadrupole splitting). This latter point has caused considerable argument between exponents of the school favoring $p_\pi-d_\pi$ bonding [e.g., (92, 124)] and those favoring the point charge approximation [e.g., (183, 184)]. The problem is well discussed in Zuckermann's review (237).

Tin Mössbauer parameters for compounds containing tin–transition metal bonds are collected in Table 9. In general, the changes in isomer shifts parallel the changes observed in, for example, ν_{CO} and $\tau_{C_5H_5}$ in the same series of compounds.

A recent development in Mössbauer spectroscopy is the determination of the sign of the quadrupole coupling constant by application of a large magnetic field to the powdered sample while the spectrum is obtained (55, 91). This method has been applied to organotin compounds (185), including those containing tin–transition metal bonds (11, 112). The results are in accord with the point-charge theory and confirm that the M—Sn bond is predominantly sigma in character.

TABLE 9

TIN MÖSSBAUER DATA

Compound	Isomer Shift[a] (mm sec^{-1})	Quadrupole splitting (mm sec^{-1})	References
Cl$_3$SnMn(CO)$_5$	1.68[b]	1.57	(182)
Cl$_3$SnMn(CO)$_5$	1.63[b]	1.62	(234)
Cl$_3$SnMn(CO)$_5$	1.73	1.56	(141)
Cl$_2$PhSnMn(CO)$_5$	1.68[b]	2.36	(182)
ClPh$_2$SnMn(CO)$_5$	1.57[b]	2.49	(182)
ClPh$_2$SnMn(CO)$_5$	1.62	2.60	(141)
Ph$_3$SnMn(CO)$_5$	1.41[b]	0	(182)
Ph$_3$SnMn(CO)$_5$	1.51[b]	0	(234)
Ph$_3$SnMn(CO)$_5$	1.45	0	(141)
Cl$_2$MeSnMn(CO)$_5$	1.68[b]	2.62	(182)
ClMe$_2$SnMn(CO)$_5$	1.54[b]	2.66	(182)
Me$_3$SnMn(CO)$_5$	1.33[b]	0.61	(182)
Me$_3$SnMn(CO)$_5$	1.46[b]	0.81	(234)
BrMe$_2$SnMn(CO)$_5$	1.54[b]	2.54	(182)
Br$_2$MeSnMn(CO)$_5$	1.69[b]	2.51	(182)
Br$_3$SnMn(CO)$_5$	1.79[b]	1.41	(182)
Br$_3$SnMn(CO)$_5$	1.74[b]	1.77	(234)
Br$_3$SnMn(CO)$_5$	1.84	1.44	(141)
ClSn[Mn(CO)$_5$]$_3$	1.92	1.55	(141)
ClSn[Mn(CO)$_5$][Fe(CO)$_2$Cp]$_2$		2.02	(110)
Cl$_2$Sn[Mn(CO)$_5$][Re(CO)$_5$]	1.96	2.48	(110, 141)
Cl$_2$Sn[Mn(CO)$_5$][Mo(CO)$_3$Cp]	1.98	2.00	(141)
Ph$_2$Sn[Mn(CO)$_5$]$_2$		0.58	(161)
Ph$_2$Sn[Mn(CO)$_5$][Co(CO)$_4$]	1.65	1.15	(141)
Me$_2$Sn[Mn(CO)$_5$]$_2$	1.68[b]	0.92	(234)
MeSn[Mn(CO)$_5$]$_3$	1.83[b]	0.95	(234)
ClSn[Re(CO)$_5$]$_3$	1.82	1.60	(110)
BrSn[Re(CO)$_5$]$_3$	1.82	1.60	(141)
PhSn[Re(CO)$_5$]$_3$	1.75	0	(141)
Ph$_2$Sn[Re(CO)$_5$]$_2$	1.70	0	(141)
Ph$_3$SnRe(CO)$_5$	1.45	0	(141)
Ph$_3$SnRe(CO)$_4$PPh$_3$	1.50	0	(141)
Ph$_3$SnCo(CO)$_4$	1.50	1.00	(141)
ClPh$_2$SnCo(CO)$_4$	1.56	2.22	(141)
Ph$_2$Sn[Co(CO)$_4$]$_2$	1.68	1.15	(141)
Ph$_2$Sn[Co(CO)$_4$]$_2$		1.43	(85)
PhSn[Co(CO)$_4$]$_3$		1.28	(85)
Sn[Co(CO)$_4$]$_4$	1.96	0	(84)
Ph$_3$SnFe(CO)$_2$Cp	1.50	0	(129)
Ph$_3$SnFe(CO)$_2$Cp	1.50	0	(128)
Ph$_2$Sn[Fe(CO)$_2$Cp]$_2$	1.74	0	(110)
Ph$_2$Sn[Fe(CO)$_2$Cp]$_3$	2.00	0	(110)
Et$_2$Sn[Fe(CO)$_2$Cp]$_2$	1.74	0	(128)

Continued

TABLE 9 (*Continued*)

Compound	Isomer Shift[a] (mm sec⁻¹)	Quadrupole splitting (mm sec⁻¹)	References
$Me_2Sn[Fe(CO)_2Cp]_2$	1.68	0	(*128*)
$Cl_3SnFe(CO)_2Cp$	1.74	1.77	(*129*)
$Cl_3SnFe(CO)_2Cp$	1.74	1.82	(*11*)
$Cl_2Sn[Fe(CO)_2Cp]_2$	1.94	2.37	(*128, 129*)
$Cl_2Sn[Fe(CO)_2Cp]_2$	1.97	2.40	(*11*)
$[Me_2SnFe(CO)_4]_2$	1.47	1.22	(*137*)
$[Bu_2SnFe(CO)_4]_2$	1.70	1.26	(*137*)
$Me_4Sn_3Fe_4(CO)_{16}$	2.20	0	(*137*)
	1.45	1.24	
$Bu_3SnFe(CO)_2Cp$	1.47	0.59	(*112*)
$(SCN)_2Sn[Fe(CO)_2Cp]_2$	1.87	2.57	(*112*)
$Cl_2PhSnFe(CO)_2Cp$		2.56	(*161*)
$ClPh_2SnFe(CO)_2Cp$		2.34	(*161*)
$Me_3SnFe(CO)_2Cp$		0.46	(*67*)
$(PhOSO)_2Sn[Fe(CO)_2Cp]_2$		2.54	(*161*)
$(CO)_5MnSnPh(OSOPh)_2$		3.06	(*161*)
$[CpFe(CO)_2]_2SnBr_2$	2.06	2.42	(*11*)
$[CpFe(CO)_2]_2SnI_2$	2.07	2.25	(*11*)
$[CpFe(CO)_2]_2Sn(NCS)_2$	1.90	2.55	(*11*)
$[CpFe(CO)_2]_2Sn(HCO_2)_2$	1.68	2.19	(*11*)
$[CpFe(CO)_2]_2Sn(OAc)_2$	1.70	2.60	(*11*)
$CpFe(CO)_2SnBr_3$	1.82		
$CpFe(CO)_2SnI_3$	1.95		
$CpFe(CO)_2Sn(NCS)_3$	1.72		
$CpFe(CO)_2Sn(HCO_2)_3$	1.16		
$CpFe(CO)_2Sn(OAc)_3$	1.24		

[a] SnO_2 as standard unless otherwise stated.

[b] $BaSnO_3$ as standard.

Bancroft, Mays, and Prater (*6*) have reached the same conclusions as the point-charge theory by use of a simple molecular orbital treatment, while Clark (*32*) has carried out detailed calculations and again reached the same results.

One interesting result of the application of Mössbauer spectroscopy was the demonstration by Herber and Goscinny (*129*) that the compound $[CpFe(CO)_2]_2SnCl_2$ occurred as rotamers in polymethylmethacrylate matrices at 73°K.

It is clear that this spectroscopic method is of considerable value to the organotin chemist, not only as a method of structure determination but also for the study of bonding in these compounds.

TABLE 10

Sn-Transition Metal Bond Lengths

Compound	Sn—M bond length (pm)	Sn—C bond length (pm)	References
[(CO)₄Fe]₄Sn	287		(60)
CpFe(CO)₂SnCl₃	246.6		(32)
CpFe(CO)₂SnBr₃	246.5		(32)
CpFe(CO)₂SnPh₃	253.7	213	(227)
CpFe(CO)₂SnPh₂Cl	250.4		(31)
CpFe(CO)₂SnPhCl₂	246.7	213	(123)
[CpFe(CO)₂]₂SnMe₂	260.5	218	(12)
[CpFe(CO)₂]₂SnCp₂	256, 257	218	(13)
[CpFe(CO)₂]₂Sn[OS(O)Ph]₂	249, 251		(34)
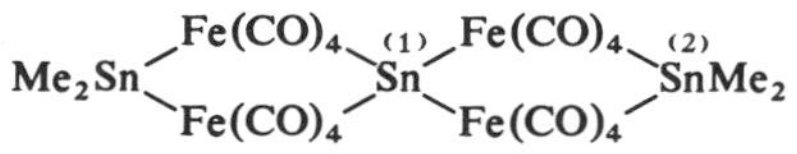 $$\begin{array}{c} \text{Fe(CO)}_4 \quad \overset{(1)}{\diagdown}\;\text{Fe(CO)}_4\;\overset{(2)}{\diagdown}\text{SnMe}_2 \\ \text{Me}_2\text{Sn} \diagup \qquad \text{Sn} \diagdown \qquad \diagup \\ \text{Fe(CO)}_4 \qquad \text{Fe(CO)}_4 \end{array}$$	(1) 275 (2) 262		(208)
[CpFe(CO)₂]₂Sn(ONO)₂	256		(14)
(CO)₄CoSnPh₂Mn(CO)₅	Sn—Mn 273 Sn—Co 266	218	(15)
(CO)₃RuCl₃Ru(CO)₂SnCl₃	256		(81)
trans 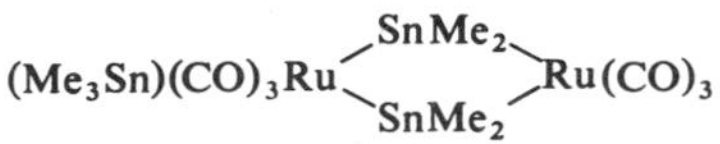 (Me₃Sn)(CO)₃Ru$\overset{\text{SnMe}_2}{\underset{\text{SnMe}_2}{\diagdown\diagup}}$Ru(CO)₃	Ru—Sn *trans* to Sn 269.0 Ru—Sn *trans* to CO 263.8	216	(225)
Me₃SnMn(CO)₅	267.4	205.8, 216.2, 217.0	(33)
Ph₃SnMn(CO)₅	267.4		(227)
Cl₂MeSnMoCl(CO)₃(bipy)(XII)	275		(82)

3. *Crystallographic Structure Determinations*

A number of tin–transition metal compounds have been studied by X-ray crystallography. Some tin–transition metal bond lengths are gathered in Table 10. One of the noteworthy points about the bond lengths is that they are commonly shorter than the sum of the covalent radii for the two metals, a fact which could be due either to predominant s-character of the $Sn-M$ bond or to $p_\pi-d_\pi$ interaction between the two metals. The $Sn-C$ bond lengths appear to be within normal limits. Several of the more unusual structures have been diagramed in the preparative section of the text. The structure of the interesting compound $Cl_2MeSnMoCl(CO)_3bipy$ is shown below (**XII**).

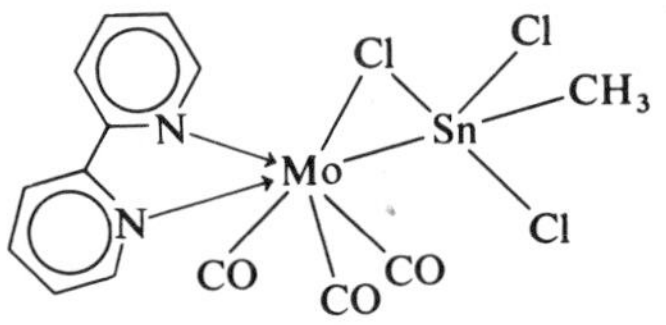

XII

IV. Postscript

It is clear that a great deal of fascinating chemistry has already been uncovered in the realm of the chemistry of compounds containing tin–other metal bonds. Much of the work done so far has been concerned with preparative reactions and physical properties of the compounds produced. Spectroscopic studies and crystallographic structure determinations are leading to a better understanding of the bonding considerations involved, but there is a great lack of both qualitative and quantitative studies of the reactions of these compounds. It is probably in this area that the main advances will come in the next few years.

REFERENCES

1. M. Akhtar and H. C. Clark, *J. Organometal. Chem.*, **22**, 233 (1970).

2. E. Amberger and E. Mülhofer, *J. Organometal. Chem.*, **12**, 55 (1968).

3. E. C. Ashby, *Organometal. Chem. Rev. B.*, **5**, 225 (1969).

4. M. C. Baird, *J. Inorg. Nucl. Chem.*, **29**, 367 (1967).

5. M. C. Baird, *Prog. Inorg. Chem.*, **9**, 1–159 (1968).

6. G. M. Bancroft, M. J. Mays, and B. E. Prater, *J. Chem. Soc. A.*, 956 (1971).

7. U. Belluco, G. Deganello, R. Pietropaola, and P. Uguagliati, *Inorg. Chim. Acta. Rev.*, **4**, 7 (1970).

8. A. D. Beveridge and H. C. Clark, *Inorg. Nucl. Letters*, **3**, 95 (1967).

9. R. E. J. Bichler, M. R. Booth, and H. C. Clark, *J. Organometal. Chem.*, **24**, 145 (1970).

10. R. E. J. Bichler and H. C. Clark, *J. Organometal. Chem.*, **23**, 427 (1970).

11. S. R. A. Bird, J. D. Donaldson, A. F. LeC. Holding, B. J. Senior, and M. J. Tricker, *J. Chem. Soc. A*, 1616 (1971).

12. B. P. Bir'yukov, Yu. T. Struchkov, K. N. Anisimov, N. E. Kolobova, and V. V. Skripkin, *Chem. Comm.*, 159 (1968).

13. B. P. Bir'yukov, Yu. T. Struchkov, K. N. Anisimov, N. E. Kolobova, and V. V. Skripkin, *Chem. Comm.*, 1193 (1968).

14. B. P. Bir'yukov, Yu. T. Struchkov, K. N. Anisimov, N. E. Kolobova, and V. V. Skripkin, *Chem. Comm.*, 750 (1967).

15. B. P. Bir'yukov, Yu. T. Struchkov, K. N. Anisimov, N. E. Kolobova, O. P. Osipova, and M. Ya. Zakharov, *Chem. Comm.*, 749 (1967).

16. T. Blackmore, J. D. Cotton, M. I. Bruce, and F. G. A. Stone, *J. Chem. Soc. A.*, 2931 (1968).

17. D. Blake, G. E. Coates, and J. M. Tate, *J. Chem. Soc.*, 618 (1961).

18. F. Bonati, S. Cenini, D. Morelli, and R. Ugo, *J. Chem. Soc. A.*, 1052 (1966).

19. F. Bonati, S. Cenini, D. Morelli, and R. Ugo, *Inorg. Nucl. Chem. Letters*, 107 (1965).

20. F. Bonati and G. Wilkinson, *J. Chem. Soc.*, 179 (1964).

21. F. Bonati and G. Minghetti, *J. Organometal. Chem.*, **16**, 332 (1969).

22. F. Bonati, S. Cenini, and R. Ugo, *J. Chem. Soc. A.*, 932 (1967).

23. M. R. Booth, D. J. Cardin, N. A. D. Carey, H. C. Clark, and B. R. Sreenathan, *J. Organometal. Chem.*, **21**, 171 (1970).

24. L. M. Bower and M. H. B. Stiddard, *J. Chem. Soc. A.*, 706 (1968).

25. S. Breitschaft and F. Basola, *J. Am. Chem. Soc.*, **88**, 2702 (1966).

26. P. N. Brier, A. A. Chalmers, J. Lewis, and S. B. Wild, *J. Chem. Soc. A.*, 1889 (1967).

27. E. H. Brooks, R. J. Cross, and F. Glockling, *Inorg. Chim. Acta.*, **2**, 17 (1968).

28. E. H. Brooks and R. J. Cross, "Group IVB metal derivatives of the transition elements," *Organometal. Chem. Rev. A*, **6**, 227 (1970).

29. M. P. Brown and G. W. A. Fowles, *J. Chem. Soc.*, 211 (1958).

30. T. L. Brown, P. A. Edwards, C. B. Harris, and J. L. Kirsch, *Inorg. Chem.*, **8**, 763 (1969).

31. R. F. Bryan, *J. Chem. Soc. A*, in press.

32. R. F. Bryan, P. T. Greene, G. A. Melson, P. F. Stokely, and A. R. Manning, *J. Chem. Soc. D*, 22 (1969).

33. R. F. Bryan, *J. Chem. Soc. A*, 696 (1968).

34. R. F. Bryan and A. R. Manning, *Chem. Comm.*, 1220 (1968).

35. R. F. Bryan, unpublished work.

36. H. Bürger and U. Goetz, *Angew. Chem. Int. Ed. Engl.*, **7**, 212 (1968).

37. J. M. Burlitch and S. W. Ulmer, *J. Organometal. Chem.*, **19**, P21 (1969).

38. M. Camia, M. P. Lachi, L. Benzoni, C. Zanzottera, and M. T. Venturii, *Inorg. Chem.*, **9**, 251–4 (1970).

39. D. J. Cardin and M. F. Lappert, *Chem. Comm.*, 506 (1966).

40. D. J. Cardin, S. A. Keppie, M. F. Lappert, M. R. Litzow, and T. R. Spalding, *J. Chem. Soc. A*, 2262 (1971).

41. N. A. D. Carey and H. C. Clark, *Chem. Commun.*, 292 (1967).

42. N. A. D. Carey and H. C. Clark, *Inorg. Chem.*, **7**, 94 (1968).

43. N. A. D. Carey and H. C. Clark, *Chem. Commun.*, 292 (1967).

44. A. Carrick and F. Glockling, *J. Chem. Soc. A*, 623 (1966).

45. M. Casey and A. R. Manning, *J. Chem. Soc. D.*, 674 (1970).

46. M. Casey and A. R. Manning, *J. Chem. Soc. A.*, 256 (1971).

47. A. J. Chalk and J. F. Harrod, *J. Am. Chem. Soc.*, **87**, 16 (1965).

48. D. B. Chambers and F. Glockling, *J. Chem. Soc. A*, 735 (1968).

49. R. F. Chambers and P. C. Scherer, *J. Am. Chem. Soc.*, **48**, 1054 (1926).

50. H. C. Clark and J. H. Tsai, *Inorg. Chem.*, **5**, 1407 (1966).

51. H. C. Clark and J. H. Tsai, *Chem. Commun.*, 111 (1965).

52. M. G. Clark, *Mol. Phys.*, **20**, 257 (1971).
53. A. F. Clemmitt and F. Glockling, *J. Chem. Soc. D.*, 705 (1970).
54. G. E. Coates, M. L. H. Green, and K. Wade, *Organometallic Compounds*, 3rd ed., Methuen, London, 1967.
55. R. L. Collins and J. C. Travis, in *Mössbauer Effect Methodology* (E. I. Gruverman, ed.), vol. 3, Plenum, New York, p. 123.
56. J. P. Collman, F. D. Vastine, and W. R. Roper, *J. Am. Chem. Soc.*, **88**, 5035 (1966).
57. J. D. Cotton, S. A. R. Knox, and F. G. A. Stone, *Chem. Commun.*, 965 (1967).
58. J. D. Cotton, S. A. R. Knox, and F. G. A. Stone, *J. Chem. Soc. A.*, 2758 (1968).
59. J. D. Cotton, S. A. R. Knox, I. Paul, and F. G. A. Stone, *J. Chem. Soc. A.*, 264 (1967).
60. J. D. Cotton, J. Duckworth, S. A. R. Knox, P. F. Lindley, I. Paul, F. G. A. Stone, and P. Woodward, *Chem. Comm.*, 253 (1966).
61. R. S. P. Coutts and P. C. Waites, *Chem. Comm.*, 260 (1968).
62. H. M. J. C. Creemers, F. Verbeek, and J. G. Noltes. *J. Organometal. Chem.*, **15**, 125–30 (1968).
63. H. M. J. C. Creemers, *Hydrostannolysis: A General Method for Establishing Tin–Metal Bonds*, Schotanus and Jens, Utrecht, 1967.
64. H. M. J. C. Creemers and J. G. Noltes, *J. Organometal. Chem.*, 7, 237 (1967).
65. H. M. J. C. Creemers, J. G. Noltes, and G. J. M. van der Kerk, *J. Organometal. Chem.*, **14**, 217 (1968).
66. R. J. Cross and F. Glockling, *J. Chem. Soc.*, 5422 (1965).
67. W. R. Cullen, J. R. Sams, and J. A. J. Thompson, *Inorg. Chem.*, **10**, 843 (1971).
68. J. Dalton, I. Paul, and F. G. A. Stone, *J. Chem. Soc. A.*, 2744 (1969).
69. D. D. Davis and C. E. Gray, "Alkali Metal and magnesium derivatives of Organo-silicon, -germanium, -tin, -lead, -phosphorus, -arsenic, -antimony, and -bismuth compounds," *Organometal. Chem. Rev. A.*, **6**, 283 (1970).
70. R. E. Dessy, P. M. Weissman, and R. L. Pohl, *J. Am. Chem. Soc.*, **88**, 5117 (1966).
71. R. E. Dessy, R. L. Pohl, and R. B. King, *J. Am. Chem. Soc.*, **88**, 5121 (1966).
72. R. E. Dessy and P. M. Weissman, *J. Am. Chem. Soc.*, **88**, 5124 (1966).
73. S. V. Dighe and M. Orchin, *J. Am. Chem. Soc.*, **87**, 1146 (1965).
74. W. Drenth, M. J. Janssen, G. J. M. van der Kerk, and J. A. Vliegenthart, *J. Organometal. Chem.*, **2**, 265 (1964).
75. R. C. Edmondson, E. Eisner, M. J. Newlands, and L. K. Thompson, *J. Organometal. Chem.*, **35**, 119 (1972).
76. R. C. Edmondson, D. S. Field, and M. J. Newlands, *Can. J. Chem.*, **49**, 618 (1971).
77. R. C. Edmondson and M. J. Newlands, *Chem. and Ind.*, 1888 (1966).
78. R. C. Edmondson and M. J. Newlands, *Chem. Comm.*, 1219 (1968).
79. A. N. Egorochkin, S. Ya. Khorshev, N. S. Vyazankin, and E. N. Gladyshev, *Izv. Akad. Nauk SSSR, Ser. Khim.*, 969 (1969).
80. E. Eisner and M. J. Newlands, unpublished work.
81. M. Elder and D. Hall, *J. Chem. Soc. A*, 245 (1970).
82. M. Elder, W. A. G. Graham, D. Hall, and R. Kumner, *J. Am. Chem. Soc.*, **90**, 2189 (1968).
83. J. J. Emeléus and S. F. A. Kettle, *J. Chem. Soc.*, 2444 (1958).
84. D. E. Fenton and J. J Zuckerman, *Inorg. Chem.*, **8**, 1771 (1969).
85. D. E. Fenton and J. J. Zuckerman, *J. Am. Chem. Soc.*, **90**, 6226 (1968).
86. D. S. Field and M. J. Newlands, *J. Organometal. Chem.*, **27**, 213 (1971).
87. N. Flitcroft, D. A. Harbourne, I. Paul, P. M. Tucker, and F. G. A. Stone, *J. Chem. Soc. A.*, 1130 (1966).
88. N. Flitcroft and H. D. Kaesz, *J. Am. Chem. Soc.*, **85**, 1377 (1963).

89. C. W. Fong and W. Kitching, *J. Organometal. Chem.*, **22**, 107 (1970).
90. H. M. Gager, J. Lewis, and M. J. Ware, *Chem. Commun.*, 616 (1966).
91. T. C. Gibb, *J. Chem. Soc. A.*, 2503 (1970).
92. T. C. Gibb and N. N. Greenwood, *J. Chem. Soc. A*, 43 (1966).
93. T. C. Gibb and N. N. Greenwood, *J. Chem. Soc. A*, 43 (1966).
94. H. Gilman and S. D. Rosenberg, *J. Org. Chem.*, **18**, 1554 (1953).
95. H. Gilman, F. K. Cartledge, and S.-Y. Sim., *J. Organometal Chem.*, **4**, 332 (1965).
96. H. Gilman and C. W. Gerow, *J. Am. Chem. Soc.*, **78**, 5823 (1956).
97. H. Gilman and T. C. Wu, *J. Org. Chem.*, **18**, 753 (1953).
98. H. Gilman and C. W. Gerow, *J. Org. Chem.*, **22**, 334 (1957).
99. H. Gilman and C. W. Gerow, *J. Am. Chem. Soc.*, **77**, 4675 (1955).
100. H. Gilman and F. K. Cartledge, *J. Organometal. Chem.*, **5**, 48 (1966).
101. H. Gilman and S. D. Rosenberg, *J. Am. Chem. Soc.*, **75**, 2507 (1953).
102. H. Gilman and S. D. Rosenberg, *J. Am. Chem. Soc.*, **75**, 3592 (1953).
103. H. Gilman and S. D. Rosenberg, *J. Org. Chem.*, **18**, 680 (1953).
104. H. Gilman and S. D. Rosenberg, *J. Am. Chem. Soc.*, **74**, 531 (1952).
105. H. Gilman, O. L. Mars, and S. Y. Sim, *J. Org. Chem.*, **27**, 4232 (1962).
106. E. N. Gladyshev, N. S. Vyazankin, E. A. Arkhangel'skaza, G. A. Razuvaev, and S. P. Korneva, *Dokl. Akad. Nauk. SSSR*, **183**, 338 (1968).
107. F. Glockling and G. C. Hill, *J. Chem. Soc. A.*, 2137 (1971).
108. F. Glockling and K. A. Hooton, *J. Chem. Soc.*, 1060 (1967).
109. F. Glockling and K. A. Hooton, *J. Chem. Soc.*, 3509 (1962).
110. V. I. Gol'danskii, B. V. Borshagovskii, E. F. Makarov, R. A. Stukan, K. A. Anisimov, N. E. Kolobova, and V. V. Skripkin, *Teor. Eksperim. Khim.*, **3**, 478 (1967).
111. V. I. Gol'danskii, V. V. Khrapov, O. Yu. Okhlobystin, and V. Ya. Rochev, "Investigation of the Mössbauer Effect in Organotin Compounds," in *Chemical Applications of Mössbauer Spectroscopy* (V. I. Gol'danskii and R. H. Herber, eds.), Academic, New York, 1968.
112. B. A. Goodman, R. Greatrex, and N. N. Greenwood, *J. Chem. Soc. A*, 1868 (1971).
113. R. D. Gorsich, U.S. Pat. 3,099,666 (1963).
114. R. D. Gorsich, U.S. Pat. 3,069,445 (1962); through *CA*.
115. R. D. Gorsich, U.S. Pat. 3,030,396 (1961).
116. R. D. Gorsich, U.S. Pat. 3,050,537 (1962).
117. R. D. Gorsich, U.S. Pat. 3,088,814 (1963).
118. R. D. Gorsich, U.S. Pat. 3,069,449 (1961); through *CA*.
119. R. D. Gorsich, *J. Am. Chem. Soc.*, **84**, 2486 (1962).
120. R. D. Gorsich, *J. Organometal. Chem.*, **5**, 105 (1966).
121. W. A. G. Graham, *Inorg. Chem.*, **7**, 315 (1968).
122. J. D. Graybeal, S. D. Ing, and M. W. Hsu, *Inorg. Chem.*, **9**, 678 (1970).
123. P. T. Greene and R. F. Bryan, *J. Chem. Soc. A*, 2261 (1970).
124. N. N. Greenwood and J. N. R. Ruddick, *J. Chem. Soc. A.*, 1679 (1966).
125. W. P. Griffith and A. J. Wickham, *J. Chem. Soc. A.*, 834 (1969).
126. R. J. Haines and A. L. DuPreez, *Chem. Commun.*, 1513 (1968).
127. F. Hein and W. Jehn, *Annalen*, **684**, 4 (1965).
128. R. H. Herber, *Prog. Inorg. Chem.*, **8**, 1 (1967).
129. R. H. Herber and Y. Goscinny, *Inorg. Chem.*, **7**, 1293 (1968).
130. W. Hieber and R. Breu, *Chem. Ber.*, **90**, 1270 (1957).
131. W. Hieber and R. Breu, *Angew. Chem.*, **68**, 679 (1956).
132. J. Hoyano, D. J. Patmore, and W. A. G. Graham, *Inorg. Nucl. Chem. Letters*, **4**, 201 (1968).

133. S. D. Ibekwe and M. J. Newlands, *Chem. Comm.*, 114 (1965).
134. S. D. Ibekwe and M. J. Newlands, *J. Chem. Soc. A.*, 1783 (1967).
135. R. K. Ingham, S. D. Rosenberg, and H. Gilman, *Chem. Rev.*, **60**, 459–539 (1960).
136. W. Jetz, P. B. Simons, J. A. J. Thompson, and W. A. G. Graham, *Inorg. Chem.*, **5**, 2217 (1966).
137. M. T. Jones, *Inorg. Chem.*, **6**, 1249 (1967).
138. O. Kahn and M. Bigorgne, *Compt. Rend.*, **261**, 2483 (1965).
139. O. Kahn and M. Bigorgne, *J. Organometal. Chem.*, **10**, 137 (1967).
140. O. Kahn and M. Bigorgne, *Compt. Rend.*, **263**, 973 (1966).
141. A. N. Karasyov, N. E. Kolobova, L. S. Polak, V. S. Shpinel, and K. A. Anisimov, *Teor. Eksperim. Khim.*, **2**, 126 (1966).
142. J. G. Kenworthy and J. Myatt, *J. Chem. Soc. D.*, 447 (1970).
143. S. A. Keppie and M. F. Lappert, *J. Organometal. Chem.*, **19**, 5 (1969).
144. S. F. A. Kettle, *J. Chem. Soc.*, 2936 (1959).
145. R. B. King, *Org. Mass. Spec.*, **2**, 657 (1969).
146. R. B. King and T. F. Korenowski, *J. Organometal. Chem.*, **17**, 95 (1969).
147. R. B. King and F. G. A. Stone, *J. Am. Chem. Soc.*, **82**, 3833 (1960).
148. S. A. R. Knox and F. G. A. Stone, *J. Chem. Soc. A.*, 2559 (1969).
149. K. E. Kolobova, A. B. Antonova, and K. N. Anisimov, *Russ. Chem. Rev.*, **38**, 822 (1969).
150. C. H. Kraus and L. S. Foster, *J. Am. Chem. Soc.*, **49**, 457 (1927).
151. C. H. Kraus and H. Eatough, *J. Am. Chem. Soc.*, **55**, 5008 (1933).
152. C. A. Kraus and W. N. Greer, *J. Am. Chem. Soc.*, **47**, 2568 (1925).
153. C. A. Kraus and W. V. Sessions, *J. Am. Chem. Soc.*, **47**, 2361 (1925).
154. C. A. Kraus and W. H. Kahler, *J. Am. Chem. Soc.*, **55**, 3537 (1933).
155. C. A. Kraus and E. G. Johnson, *J. Am. Chem. Soc.*, **55**, 3542 (1933).
156. E. Krause and R. Pohland, *Ber.*, **57**, 532 (1924).
157. M. R. Kula, J. Lorberth, and E. Amberger, *Chem. Ber.*, **97**, 2087 (1964).
158. J.-C. Lahournère and J. Valade, *J. Organometal. Chem.*, **22**, C3 (1970).
159. M. F. Lappert and J. S. Poland, *J. Chem. Soc. D.*, 1061–2 (1969).
160. A. J. Layton, R. S. Nyholm, G. A. Pneumaticakis, and M. L. Tobe, *Chem. and Ind.*, 465 (1967).
161. B. V. Liengme, M. J. Newlands, and J. R. Sams, *Inorg. Nucl. Chem. Letters*, in press.
162. K. M. Mackay and R. Watt, *Organometal. Chem. Rev. A.*, **4**, 137–224 (1969).
163. A. R. Manning, *J. Chem. Soc. A.*, 651 (1968).
164. A. R. Manning, *Chem. Commun.*, 906 (1966).
165. M. J. Mays and S. M. Pearson, *J. Organometal. Chem.*, **15**, 257 (1968).
166. M. J. Mays and S. M. Pearson, *J. Chem. Soc. A.*, 136 (1969).
167. R. T. Morrison, *Abstr. 137th National Meeting*, A.C.S., 1960.
168. J. R. Moss and W. A. G. Graham, *J. Organometal. Chem.*, **18**, 24 (1969).
169. O. M. Nefedov and M. N. Manakov, *Angew. Chem. Intern. Ed. Engl.*, **5**, 1021 (1966).
170. A. N. Nesmeyanov, K. N. Anisimov, N. E. Kolobova, and M. Ya. Zakharova, *Dokl. Akad. Nauk. SSSR*, **156**, 612 (1964).
171. A. N. Nesmayanov, K. N. Anisimov, N. E. Kolobova, and V. V. Skripkin, *Izvest. Akad. Nauk SSSR, Ser. Khim.*, 1292 (1966).
172. A. N. Nesmeyanov, N. E. Kolobova, M. Ya. Zakharova, B. V. Lokshin, and K. N. Anisimov, *Izv. Akad. Nauk SSSR, Ser. Khim.*, 529 (1969).
173. A. N. Nesmeyanov, K. N. Anisimov, N. E. Kolobova, and V. N. Khandozhko. *Izv. Akad. Nauk SSSR, Ser. Khim.*, 1395 (1967).

174. A. N. Nesmeyanov, G. K. Semin, E. V. Brukhova, K. N. Anisimov, N. E. Kolobova, and V. N. Khandozhko, *Izv. Akad. Nauk SSSR, Ser. Khim.*, 1936 (1969).
175. A. N. Nesmeyanov, N. E. Kolobova, V. V. Skripkin, K. N. Anisimov, and L. A. Fedorov, *Dokl. Akad. Nauk SSSR*, **195**, 368 (1970).
176. A. N. Nesmeyanov, K. N. Anisimov, N. E. Kolobova, and V. N. Khandozhko, *Dokl. Akad. Nauk SSSR*, **156**, 383 (1964).
177. W. P. Neumann, *The Organic Chemistry of Tin*, Wiley, London, 1970, Chaps. 11–13, and 18.
178. W. P. Neumann and U. Blankaut, *Angew. Chem., Intern. Ed. Engl.*, **8**, 611 (1969).
179. W. P. Neumann, B. Schneider, and R. Sommer, *Annalen*, **692**, 1 (1966).
180. H. Nöth and K. H. Hermannsdörfer, *Angew. Chem.*, **76**, 377 (1964).
181. H. Nöth, H. Schaeffer, and G. Schmid, *Angew. Chem., Intern. Ed. Engl.*, **8**, 515 (1969).
182. S. Onaka, Y. Sasaki, and H. Sano, *Bull. Chem. Soc. Japan*, **44**, 726 (1971).
183. R. V. Parish and R. H. Platt, *Chem. Comm.*, 1118 (1968).
184. R. V. Parish and R. H. Platt, *J. Chem. Soc. A.*, 2145 (1969).
185. R. V. Parish and C. E. Johnson, *J. Chem. Soc. A.*, 1906 (1971).
186. H. R. H. Patil and W. A. G. Graham, *Inorg. Chem.*, **5**, 1401 (1966).
187. H. R. H. Patil and W. A. Graham, *J. Am. Chem. Soc.*, **87**, 673 (1965).
188. D. J. Patmore and W. A. G. Graham, *Inorg. Chem.*, **5**, 1587 (1966).
189. D. J. Patmore and W. A. G. Graham, *Inorg. Chem.*, **6**, 981 (1967).
190. D. J. Patmore and W. A. G. Graham, *Inorg. Chem.*, **5**, 1405 (1966).
191. D. J. Patmore and W. A. G. Graham, *Inorg. Nucl. Chem. Letters*, **2**, 179 (1966).
192. D. J. Patmore and W. A. G. Graham, *Inorg. Chem.*, **5**, 2222 (1966).
193. D. J. Patmore and W. A. G. Graham, *Chem. Commun.*, 7 (1967).
194. R. C. Poller, "Compounds Containing Tin–Metal Bonds," in *Chemistry of Organotin Compounds*, Logos, London, 1970, Chap. 9.
195. R. K. Pomeroy, M. Elder, D. Hall, and W. A. G. Graham, *J. Chem. Soc. D.*, 381 (1969).
196. P. Powell, *Inorg. Chem.*, **7**, 2458 (1968).
197. J. K. Ruff, *Inorg. Chem.*, **6**, 2080 (1967).
198. G. N. Schrauzer and G. Kratel, *Chem. Ber.*, **102**, 2392 (1969).
199. H. Schumann and S. Ronecker, *Z. Naturforsch.*, **B22**, 452 (1967).
200. H. Shapiro and F. W. Frey, *Organic Compounds of Lead*, Wiley, New York, 1968.
201. P. J. Smith, *Organometal. Chem. Rev. A*, **5**, 373 (1970).
202. R. Sommer, W. P. Neumann, and B. Schneider, *Tetrahedron Letters*, 3875 (1964).
203. D. D. Spencer, J. L. Kirsch, and T. L. Brown, *Inorg. Chem.*, **9**, 235 (1970).
204. H. W. Spiess and R. K. Sheline, *J. Chem. Phys.*, **53**, 3036 (1970).
205. T. G. Spiro, "Vibrational Spectra and Metal–Metal Bonds," *Prog. Inorg. Chem.*, **11**, 1 (1970).
206. F. G. A. Stone, "Transition Metal Derivatives of Silicon, Germanium, Tin, and Lead," in *New Pathways in Inorganic Chemistry* (E. A. V. Ebsworth, A. G. Maddox, and A. G. Sharpe, eds.), Cambridge University Press, Cambridge, 1968.
207. R. M. Sweet, C. J. Fritchie, Jr., and R. A. Schunn, *Inorg. Chem.*, **6**, 749 (1967).
208. R. M. Sweet, C. J. Fritchie, and R. A. Schunn, *Inorg. Chem.*, **6**, 749 (1967).
209. C. Tamborski and E. J. Sokolski, *J. Am. Chem. Soc.*, **83**, 3734 (1961).
210. C. Tamborski, F. E. Ford, W. L. Lehn, G. J. Moore, and E. J. Sokolski, *J. Org. Chem.*, **27**, 619 (1962).
211. C. Tamborski, F. E. Ford, and E. J. Sokolski, *J. Org. Chem.*, **28**, 181 (1963).
212. C. Tamborski, F. E. Ford, and E. J. Sokolski, *J. Org. Chem.*, **28**, 237 (1963).
213. J. A. J. Thompson and W. A. G. Graham, *Inorg. Chem.*, **6**, 1365 (1967).

214. J. A. J. Thompson and W. A. G. Graham, *Inorg. Chem.*, **6**, 1875 (1967).
215. L. K. Thompson, E. Eisner, and M. J. Newlands, unpublished results.
216. R. Ugo, S. Cenini, and F. Bonati, *Inorg. Chim. Acta.*, **1**, 451 (1967).
217. L. Vaska and J. W. Diluzio, *J. Am. Chem. Soc.*, **83**, 2784 (1961).
218. L. Vaska, *Acc. Chem. Res.*, **1**, 335 (1968).
219. M. E. Volpin, Yu. D. Koreshkov, V. G. Dulova, and D. N. Kursanov, *Tetrahedron*, **18**, 107 (1962).
220. R. L. Voorhees and R. W. Rudolph, *J. Am. Chem. Soc.*, **91**, 2173 (1969).
221. N. S. Vyazankin, E. N. Gladyshev, G. A. Razuvaev, and S. P. Korneva, *Zh. Obshch. Khim.*, **36**, 952 (1966).
222. N. S. Vyazankin, E. N. Gladyshev, and S. P. Korneva, *Zh. Obshch. Khim.*, **37**, 1736 (1967).
223. N. S. Vyazankin, G. A. Razuvaev, E. N. Gladyshev, and S. P. Korneva, *J. Organometal. Chem.*, **7**, 353 (1967).
224. N. S. Vyazankin, G. A. Razuvaev, and O. A. Kruglaya, *Organometal. Chem. Rev. A.*, **3**, 323–423 (1968).
225. K. L. Walters and W. M. Risen, *Inorg. Chim. Acta. Rev.*, **1**, 129 (1969).
226. S. F. Watkins, *J. Chem. Soc. A.*, 1552 (1969).
227. H. P. Weber and R. F. Bryan, *Acta. Cryst.*, **22**, 822 (1967).
228. W. L. Wells and T. L. Brown, *J. Organometal. Chem.*, **11**, 271 (1968).
229. E. Wiberg, O. Stecher, H. J. Andrascheck, L. Kreuzbichler, and E. Staude, *Angew. Chem., Intern. Ed. Engl.*, **2**, 507 (1963).
230. E. Wiberg, E. Amberger, and H. Cambensi, *Z. Anorg. Chem.*, **351**, 164 (1957).
231. L. C. Willemses, Organolead Chemistry International Lead Zinc Research Organization, New York, 1964; *Investigations in the Field of Organolead Chemistry*, International Lead Zinc Research Organization, New York, 1965.
232. G. Wittig, *Angew. Chem.*, **63**, 231 (1959).
233. G. Wittig, F. J. Meyer, and G. Lange, *Annalen*, **571**, 167 (1951).
234. C. Wynter and L. Chandler, *Bull. Chem. Soc. Japan*, **43**, 2115 (1970).
235. J. F. Young, *Adv. Inorg. Chem. Radiochem.*, **11**, 92 (1968).
236. H. Zimmer, I. Hechenbleikner, O. A. Homberg, and M. Danzik, *J. Org. Chem.*, **29**, 2632 (1964).
237. J. J. Zuckerman, *Adv. Organometal. Chem.*, **9**, 22 (1970).

12. APPLICATIONS AND BIOLOGICAL EFFECTS OF ORGANOTIN COMPOUNDS

J. G. A. LUIJTEN

Institute for Organic Chemistry TNO
Utrecht, Netherlands

I. Introduction 931
II. Use of Organotin Compounds as Stabilizers in Polymers 933
    A. Stabilization of Poly(vinyl Chloride) 933
    B. Stabilization of Other Polymers 939
III. Biological Effects of Organotin Compounds 940
    A. Antifungal and Antibacterial Activity 940
    B. Activity against Higher Plants 943
    C. Anthelmintic Activity 943
    D. Molluscicidal Activity 945
    E. Insecticidal Activity 945
    F. Mammalian Toxicity 949
IV. Use of Organotin Compounds as Biocides 953
    A. Agricultural and Veterinary Uses 953
    B. Industrial Uses 954
    C. Medical Use 960
V. Catalytic Uses of Organotin Compounds 961
    A. Polyurethane Formation 961
    B. Silicone Curing 963
    C. Esterification 963
    D. Epoxy Curing 964
    E. Olefin Polymerization 964
VI. Miscellaneous Uses 964
References 966

I. Introduction

Organotin compounds, after their discovery around 1850, long remained of purely scientific interest. The first mention of a practical application was made in a patent filed in 1925. In this and some related patents organotin compounds were claimed as mothproofing agents. They have never been used as such, but shortly afterwards, in 1936, they were again mentioned in a patent, this time as stabilizers for vinyl resins. In this function organotin compounds proved to be outstanding. The stabilization of poly(vinyl chloride) against deterioration by heat and light consequently has become and still is the most important application of organotin compounds.

The biological effects of organotin compounds had not been systematically studied before 1950. In addition to the patents on mothproofing referred to above, there was one on the control of insects other than moths, and one on antifouling. In addition a paper had been published on the removal of intestinal worms from chickens and a few on mammalian toxicity. Since 1950, however, systematic investigations have been carried out on the action of organotin compounds toward fungi and bacteria, marine organisms, parasitic worms, aquatic snails, and insects. These investigations have led to proposals for practical applications, some of which have been successfully realized. The most important of these is undoubtedly the use of organotin compounds as fungicides in agriculture, but organotin compounds have also found ready application in antifouling, the treatment of cooling water, and wood preservation.

Interest in the mammalian toxicity of organotin compounds developed along with their practical applications. It was, of course, much stimulated by the finding of their general biocidal properties, but regrettably enough still more by the occurrence, in 1954 in France, of a number of cases of human poisoning through a faulty pharmaceutical preparation based on organotin. This event, which took the form of a disaster and became widely known, has for many years undeservedly retarded the further development of organotin compounds as practical biocides. It is now realized, however, that of the numerous organotin compounds known today only very few are appreciably toxic.

Minor applications of organotin compounds include their use as catalysts in the manufacture of industrial polymers, and as antiwear and anticorrosive agents. Some potential uses will also be mentioned in this chapter.

It is very difficult to assess a figure for the consumption of organotin in any specific application. However, the total annual world consumption of organotin compounds has been repeatedly estimated. The figures show a strong and sustained growth: 1948—maximally a few tons, 1956—some hundreds of tons, 1962—3,000 tons, 1965—5,000 tons, 1967—10,000 tons. Probably two-thirds to three-quarters of the last-mentioned amounts went into PVC stabilization, the remainder being shared between the several biocidal and catalytic uses of organotin compounds.

A serious difficulty when writing on practical aspects of organotin chemistry is the secrecy which surrounds most applications. Much of the information available is contained in patents, and it is often difficult to trace which of the many compounds claimed are, in fact, being used. Another source of information is found in advertisements, leaflets, technical data sheets, etc. In these, often only trade names are mentioned, together with some vague indication like " organotin compound." The most detailed information of course is given in papers in the professional journals dealing with the results of laboratory or field tests. These are, however, relatively scarce and again they often give no indication as to the actual use of a compound.

In the following an attempt will be made to look at the applications of organotin compounds from the organotin chemist's point of view. This means that the several problems will be regarded only as far as they can be solved by the use of organotin compounds and also that side-problems, like the choice of auxiliary substances in the formulation of an active compound, will be neglected.

A few articles and books in which practical applications of organotin compounds have been dealt with in a general way are mentioned here in chronological order—(*172, 169, 142, 144, 215, 73, 184, 188, 61a, 205b*) as noted.

II. Use of Organotin Compounds as Stabilizers in Polymers

A. STABILIZATION OF POLY(VINYL CHLORIDE)

1. *Types of Stabilizers*

Poly(vinyl chloride) (PVC) for its processing is subjected to temperatures between 150 and 200°C. At these temperatures a decomposition occurs, the nature of which will be discussed below. Its main characteristic is a discoloration: the originally colorless product turns yellow, brown, and finally black. A decomposition also occurs when PVC is exposed to light. In order to protect the polymer during and after processing, stabilizers are added. These fall into three categories: metallic soaps, purely organic compounds, and organotins. The organotin stabilizers are the most powerful but also the most expensive. This restricts their use to those cases in which a perfectly clear and colorless product is required or when extreme temperatures are used in processing. The trend toward higher processing temperatures has, in recent years, strongly promoted the use of organotin stabilizers (*244*).

In the first patent in this field, filed by Yngve (*257*) in 1936, some alkyl-, aryl-, and alkyl-aryltin compounds were mentioned which have never attained commerical importance. The first commercially successful organotin stabilizer, dibutyltin dilaurate, was mentioned in a patent dated a few years later (*258*). Dibutyltin dilaurate is a moderate thermal stabilizer but an excellent light stabilizer. It is still manufactured in quantity. The commercial product is prepared from crude lauric acid containing other acids in addition. This gives the product a melting point below room temperature which facilitates mixing.

During the next twenty years all further developments in the organotin stabilizer field were variations on the dibutyltin theme. Both tri- and mono-butyltin compounds are less efficient stabilizers (*198*). The length of the alkyl groups, however, has little influence on stabilizing efficiency (see below). That butyl has nevertheless emerged as the alkyl group of choice is probably due to a combination of additional factors. The lower alkyltin compounds are more volatile, the higher ones more expensive. Aryltin compounds are poor stabilizers.

A much better thermal stabilizer than dibutyltin dilaurate is dibutyltin maleate, first mentioned in a patent application in 1942 (*206*). The maleate itself has some disadvantages, e.g., its poor solubility in plasticizers. These disadvantages are removed in two types of variation. One is the double salt of dibutyltin oxide with maleic acid and a carboxylic acid, e.g., bis(di-butyltin monolaurate) maleate (*109*):

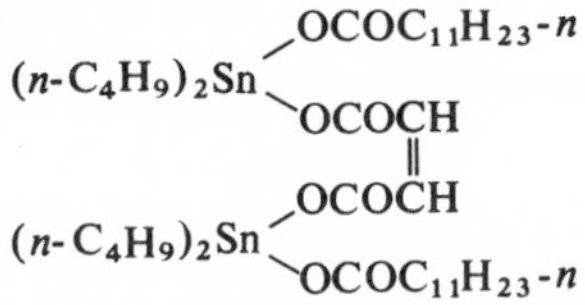

$$(n\text{-}C_4H_9)_2Sn \underset{\diagdown OCOCH}{\overset{\diagup OCOC_{11}H_{23}\text{-}n}{}}$$
$$\|$$
$$(n\text{-}C_4H_9)_2Sn \underset{\diagdown OCOC_{11}H_{23}\text{-}n}{\overset{\diagup OCOCH}{}}$$

The other is the salt of dibutyltin oxide with a half-ester of maleic acid, e.g., dibutyltin bis(mono-2-ethylhexyl maleate) (*193*):

$$(n\text{-}C_4H_9)_2Sn(OCOCH{=}CHCOOC_8H_{17})_2$$

Both types of compounds are liquids, easily miscible with plasticizers.

In addition to the above compounds, many other organotin compounds have been proposed as stabilizers for vinyl resins. Except for the sulfur-containing stabilizers, they generally have been of much less importance. Dibutyltin dialkoxides have been used because they react with hydrogen chloride liberated from the polymer to give alcohols, which are more compatible with vinyls than, e.g., lauric aicd. The hydrolyzability and volatility of these alkoxides is reduced in compounds which may be described as low-molecular weight dialkyltin oxides with alkoxy end groups:

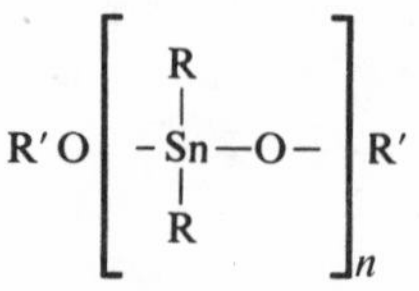

$$R'O\left[\begin{array}{c} R \\ | \\ -Sn-O- \\ | \\ R \end{array}\right]_n R'$$

Other end groups like acyloxy and alkyl have been substituted for the alkoxy groups. More or less polymeric compounds may also result from reactions of dibutyltin oxide with polyhydric alcohols. Still other stabilizers have been prepared from dibutyltin oxide and esters of hydroxy acids. Numerous possibilities finally arise when the various types of alcohol are combined with carboxylic acids or with half-esters of dicarboxylic acids.

Organotin borates, phosphates, sulfonamides, and organotin complex compounds (*243*) are probably of little importance as stabilizers.

The most powerful organotin stabilizers prepared so far are sulfur-containing derivatives. These must be distinguished into compounds with tin-sulfur linkages and those without. The tin-sulfur type is the most active one. Here again many possibilities exist, and indeed many compounds have been mentioned in patents [for a recent compilation, see (*1*)]. The most important are the alkylthio compounds (*39*):

$$(n\text{-}C_4H_9)_2Sn(SR)_2$$

and the mercaptoacetic acid derivatives (*252*):

$$(n\text{-}C_4H_9)_2Sn(SCH_2COOR)_2$$

In these formulas, R is usually a heavy alkyl group like 2-ethylhexyl, 3,5,5-trimethylhexyl, octadecyl, or cyclohexyl. The early tin-sulfur stabilizers tended to smell badly, probably as a result of impurities or of partial hydrolysis (*245*). This problem has evidently been overcome. Some are less efficient light stabilizers than, e.g., maleates (*34*).

A review of the development of organotin stabilizers up to 1959 with ample reference to the patent literature has been given by Verity Smith (*243*). The same author has repeatedly given his opinion on the prevailing situation in the stabilizer field, both from a technical and from an economical standpoint (*240–242, 246*).

Recently, a few organotin stabilizers other than dibutyltin compounds have come into use for special purposes. In 1955, van der Kerk and Luijten (*237*) pointed to the possibility that dialkyltin stabilizers with alkyl groups longer than butyl might possess such a low degree of toxicity that they would be suitable for the stabilization of PVC for foodstuff packaging. This stimulated research on the suitability of dioctyltin compounds, in particular as stabilizers for PVC and on the extractability and oral toxicity of these compounds.

Luijten and Pezarro (*171*) compared the stabilizing activity in plasticized PVC of some dibutyl-, dihexyl-, and dioctyltin compounds. Among the dilaurates the octyl compound was clearly inferior to the others. The three maleates, however, were of the same activity. Excellent results were obtained with some dioctyltin derivatives of mercaptoacetic esters.

Extractability and toxicity tests were carried out by Klimmer and Nebel (*159*). As was to be expected, the extractability of stabilizers from plasticized PVC was higher than from rigid PVC. Extractability also increased with increasing lipophilic character or fat content of the extractant. The oral toxicity of the dioctyltin stabilizers investigated was very low (*30*). Fernley and Horrocks (*98*) showed that the nature of the acid radical in dibutyl- and dioctyltin stabilizers markedly influences the extractability and, moreover, that the direction of change is determined by the solvent. This permits the choice of a minimally extractable stabilizer for each type of foodstuff.

The problem of the toxicity hazard involved in the use of plastics for food-packaging has been very generally considered by van der Heide (*234*). An important aspect is the analysis not only of the stabilizer but also of the stabilized vinyl resin. Methods have been developed for the separation of alkyltin compounds with alkyl chains of various lengths and of mono-, di-, and tri-alkyltin compounds (*125, 235*).

Nontoxic stabilizers alternative to the dioctyltin compounds are the monoalkyltin compounds introduced by Farbwerke Hoechst (*95, 96*). These are polymeric substances of the general formula

$$[RSnY_{1.5}]_n$$

in which R is an alkyl group and Y is oxygen, sulfur, or a combination of both. The compound in actual use is monobutyltin sulfide:

$$[n\text{-}C_4H_9SnS_{1.5}]_n$$

It has a low extractability and no demonstrable oral toxicity, but is stated to be a poor stabilizer and of limited applicability (*215*, pp. 113 and 114).

Dioctyltin stabilizers have been cleared for use in rigid PVC for food-stuffs packaging in Germany, Great Britain, and Italy (*37*) and very recently also in the United States (*15*, cf. *13*) and Canada (*16*). Monobutyltin stabilizers have met approval in Germany (*47*) and the United States (*246*).

To conclude this survey, the synergism may be mentioned which occurs between organotin stabilizers of different types (*159a, 212*) or between organotin stabilizers and purely organic compounds (*241*). In proprietary stabilizers, use is made of this synergism to improve efficiency and reduce costs.

The amount of organotin stabilizer which is added to poly(vinyl chloride) is 0.5–5%, usually about 2%. Roughly 10% of all poly(vinyl chloride) produced is organotin-stabilized which means a world consumption of several thousands of tons of organotin stabilizers per year.

2. *Mechanism of Stabilizing Action*

In order to understand the stabilizing action of organotin compounds in PVC, the degradation of the latter must be understood. The two aspects, degradation and stabilization, are usually considered together.

Early literature on the degradation of PVC has been surveyed (*198*). The following presents a summary to which some, more recent, data have been added.

When PVC is heated in the absence of stabilizers, an evolution of hydrogen chloride occurs. It is commonly assumed that this, on a molecular scale, is accompanied by the formation of a system of conjugated double bonds which would explain the development of color. In an inert atmopshere, an increase in the intrinsic viscosity of the PVC is observed which must be ascribed to the intermolecular cleavage of hydrogen chloride. In an oxidizing atmosphere the degradation is much more severe. This may be due both to a direct attack of oxygen on the PVC and to a secondary attack on the polyene structure. Carbonyl groups are formed which may enhance instability, and chain scission occurs which reduces viscosity. In a later stage viscosity again rises as a result of crosslinking. Irradiation of PVC in the presence of oxygen leads to a similar degradation; in the absence of oxygen only crosslinking occurs.

If PVC were strictly linear and uniform it would be very stable toward heat and light as follows from experiments with model substances. It has been suggested that tertiary chlorine atoms occurring at branch points would be split off first but also it is probable that unsaturated end groups are initial sites of instability. This is borne out by the fact that PVC of a lower molecular weight, containing more end groups, decomposes more rapidly (*80*). For photodegradation, absorption of light is necessary. Here again unsaturation at the chain ends may play a rôle. It is moreover clear that double bonds formed by thermal degradation will promote photodegration (*80*).

The evolution of hydrogen chloride from PVC in a stream of air in the presence and in the absence of stabilizers was measured by Dyson et al. (*89*). They found that organotin stabilizers, for some time, completely inhibited the evolution of hydrogen chloride. The length of the induction period, expressed in minutes, varied considerably among the stabilizers tested. After the induction period the evolution of hydrogen chloride from the stabilized resins was slow as compared with the control, and slower as the stabilizer used was more effective. The authors concluded that the organotin stabilizers do not act by reaction with hydrogen chloride but rather by preventing its formation.

A radically different conclusion was reached by Marks et al. (*177*) who studied the thermal degradation of PVC in a nitrogen atmosphere. These authors likewise found an induction period in the presence of organotin stabilizers during which no hydrogen chloride was evolved. They showed, however, by determining ionic chlorine in the polymer, that during the induction period the formation of hydrogen chloride must have continued undiminished, and also that thereafter the evolution of hydrogen chloride from the stabilized resins was as fast as from the control. The hydrogen chloride formed during the induction period must have reacted with the stabilizer, and this, in a molar ratio of 4 : 1 for a stabilizer of the type R_2SnX_2. The formation of $SnCl_4$ was ruled out for several reasons. Moreover for stabilizers of the types R_3SnX and $RSnX_3$ the ratios were 2 : 1 and 5 : 1, respectively. The authors therefore concluded to the formation of the ions $R_3SnCl_2^-$, $R_2SnCl_4^{2-}$, and $RSnCl_5^{2-}$, which is in accordance with the tendency of tri, di-, and monoalkyltin compounds to form penta- or hexa-coordinated complexes.

Several remarks may be made relative to the above. First, the degradation experiments by Marks et al. were carried out in a stream of nitrogen whereas under practical conditions the polymer is in contact with air. It is known that the evolution of hydrogen chloride from unstabilized PVC is much greater in air than in nitrogen (*86*). This must be due to a primary attack of oxygen on the polymer, creating further sites of instability. Organotin stabilizers, acting as antioxidants, may prevent this attack. Differences in antioxidant power corresponding to differences in stabilizer effectiveness may account for the reduced rates of hydrogen chloride evolution observed by Dyson et al. after the induction period.

Secondly, hydrogen chloride catalyses the evolution of hydrogen chloride, even in the absence of oxygen, as has been clearly demonstrated by Marks et al. (*177*, cf. *86*). Trapping of hydrogen chloride will suppress this catalysis.

Thirdly, it may be doubted whether every chloride ion which is found means that a molecule of hydrogen chloride is lost from the polymer. Experiments with tagged organotin stabilizers by Frye et al. (*105*) have shown that it is probable that during heat treatment, some of the polymer's chlorine atoms are replaced by acid radicals of the stabilizer, with the simultaneous formation of organotin chlorides. A chloride ion is then found without a double bond being formed. Replacement of a chlorine atom on the polymer chain by a less reactive group may, at the same time, mean a stabilization.

The stabilizing action of organotin compounds in PVC is clearly complex. Whereas they, to some extent, prevent the splitting off of hydrogen chloride, this certainly is not the whole of the stabilizing action. It may very well be, however, that the organotin stabilizers reduce the length of the individual polyene structures. This may occur through replacement of chlorine atoms by acid radicals (see above) or through interference with the mechanism of degradation. Marks et al. (*177*), who defend an ionic mechanism for the thermal degradation, suggest ion pair formation between an intermediate carbonium ion and a complex organotin anion like $R_2SnCl_4^{2-}$.

It is a well-known fact that organotin stabilizers not only prevent the development of color but also, if added after some color has developed, restore colorlessness. This of course must be caused by a reaction of the chromophore system. In the case of organotin maleates a Diels-Alder addition to part of the polyene structure has been suggested. Model experiments on this addition have recently been carried out (*185*). Another possibility, put forward by Marks et al. (*177*), is the haloalkylation of a double bond (or system of conjugated double bonds), which in the case of PVC means a crosslinking reaction between one polymer molecule and a partially degraded other one. This type of reaction is promoted by Friedel-Crafts catalysts, and the complex organotin anions formed during degradation may serve as such. Friedel-Crafts catalysts also tend to promote dehydrochlorination. The latter tendency dominates in simple metal chlorides, but it is gradually reduced if the metal is rendered less electronegative by the introduction of electron donating alkyl groups. Indeed, among organotin stabilizers, crosslinking efficiency increases and the tendency to promote dehydrochlorination decreases in the order monobutyl, dibutyl, tributyl (*177*).

A few words remain to be said on the stabilization of PVC against degradation by light. Kenyon (*152*) has found that the addition of carbonyl compounds like acetone or octadecyl lauryl ketone to PVC strongly accelerates the evolution of hydrogen chloride during irradiation. A model substance, *sec*-butyl chloride, did not evolve hydrogen chloride under irradiation unless acetone had been added. Probably also carbonyl groups formed in PVC by oxidation will accelerate photochemical decomposition. This implies that organotin compounds may exert a stabilizing action by serving as antioxidants.

Kenyon has moreover shown that during the irradiation of PVC stabilized with ^{14}C-butyl-labeled dibutyltin diacetate an increasing amount of radioactivity is retained by the polymer. He supposed that butyl groups were abstracted from tin by polymer radicals and saw this as the mechanism of stabilization (*152*). Butylation of the PVC may indeed be of importance in the case of photodegredation but it plays only a very minor role in the stabilization of PVC against deterioration by heat (*105*).

B. STABILIZATION OF OTHER POLYMERS

Many patents on organotin stabilizers refer to "chlorine-containing polymers" rather than "poly(vinyl chloride)". It thus seems that organotin compounds in principle are also useful for the stabilization of other chlorine-containing polymers. To the present author's knowledge, little has been published on this subject. Knowles (*160*) tested dibutyltin maleate and a thiotin compound as stabilizers in plasticized copolymers of vinyl chloride with vinylidene chloride or vinyl acetate. He found a decreased heat stability of the copolymers as compared with PVC. Only with dibutyltin maleate was an improved early color observed. Tetraphenyltin has been mentioned as a thermal stabilizer for poly(trifluorochloroethylene) (*32*). At least one paint manufacturer uses dibutyltin dilaurate or the corresponding maleate to improve the stability of chlorinated rubber enamels (*107*). As little as 0.01 % based on the weight of the chlorinated rubber is sufficient to retard strongly the evolution of hydrogen chloride during aging of the paint film.

In some polymers that are only composed of carbon and hydrogen, organotin compounds may act as antioxidants. The polymers mentioned in the patent literature are polyethylene (*19, 200*), polypropylene (*19, 200, 260*) and natural and synthetic rubbers (*251*). The use of up to 1 % of dibutyltin compounds, most of them containing thio groups, is claimed.

Dibutyltin derivatives and bis(trialkyltin)sulfides have been recommended for the treatment of rayon fibres used in reinforcing rubber. An improved heat resistance is claimed (*259*). Cellulose triacetate may be stabilized by various phenyltin compounds in amounts of 0.5–2% (*103*). Aryltin compounds have also been found to improve the thermal stability of polycarbonates (*195*).

III. Biological Effects of Organotin Compounds

A. ANTIFUNGAL AND ANTIBACTERIAL ACTIVITY

A systematic investigation on the antifungal activity of organotin compounds was started in 1950 at the Institute for Organic Chemistry TNO, Utrecht, the Netherlands. Van der Kerk and Luijten soon found that among organotin compounds of the several possible types

$$R_4Sn \qquad R_3SnX \qquad R_2SnX_2 \qquad RSnX_3$$
(R = hydrocarbon radical; X = anionic group)

some representatives of the type R_3SnX possessed a high fungitoxicity.

The first tests were carried out with the series tetraethyltin, triethyltin chloride, diethyltin dichloride, and ethyltin trichloride. Only triethyltin chloride inhibited the growth of test fungi at concentrations below 10 mg/l. Variation of the acid radical had only a minor influence on the activity of triethyltin salts. Subsequent examination of a series of tri-*n*-alkyltin acetates, on the other hand, showed a considerable influence of the length of the alkyl groups (Table 1). The data given in this table differ somewhat from those given in the original publication. They were obtained in later, careful testing using a prolonged incubation time and a richer culture medium. The most active compounds in the series of tri-*n*-alkyltin acetates were tripropyl- and tributyltin acetate. They inhibited the growth of the test fungi at concentrations of 1 mg/l or lower (*236*).

Experiments with unsymmetrical trialkyltin acetates, i.e., compounds in which the tin atom bore mutually different alkyl groups, revealed that not the

TABLE 1

$R_3SnOCOCH_3$ $R=$	Minimal concentration in mg/l causing complete inhibition of growth of the fungi				
	Botrytis allii	*Penicillium italicum*	*Aspergillus niger*	*Rhizopus nigricans*	Refs.
CH_3	200	500	200	500	(*147*)
C_2H_5	1	10	2	2	(*147*)
n-C_3H_7	0.5	0.5	0.5	0.5	(*147*)
i-C_3H_7	0.1	0.5	1	1	(*147*)
n-C_4H_9	0.5	0.5	1	1	(*147*)
i-C_4H_9	1	1	10	1	(*147*)
n-C_5H_{11}	5	2	5	5	(*147*)
cyclo-C_5H_9	0.5	0.5	5	0.5	(*239*)
n-C_6H_{13}	>500	>500	>500	>500	(*147*)
cyclo-C_6H_{11}	20	20	50	20	(*239*)
C_6H_5	10	1	0.5	5	(*147*)

nature of the individual groups, but the total number of carbon atoms in the three groups was decisive. Dimethyloctyltin acetate, for example, had the same high activity as tripropyltin acetate, whereas both trimethyltin acetate and trioctyltin acetate had a low activity. For a high antifungal activity the total number of carbon atoms in the alkyl groups of a trialkyltin compound should be about 9–12 (*238*).

In addition to the tri-*n*-alkyltin acetates, numerous other triorganotin acetates were tested for antifungal activity. Triisoalkyltin acetates had an activity which was comparable to that of the normal isomers (*147*). Tri-cyclopentyl- and tricyclohexyltin acetate, however, were more active than the *n*-alkyl derivatives (*239*). Triphenyltin acetate had about the same activity as triethyltin acetate. Tri-*m*-tolyl- and tri-*p*-tolyltin acetate differed little from triphenyltin acetate but tribenzyl- and tris(2-phenylethyl)tin acetate were somewhat less active. Tri-α-naphthyltin acetate, probably because of its low solubility, did not show any antifungal activity (*173*).

When, through the addition reactions of organotin hydrides to olefins, functionally substituted organotin compounds became available, a number of them, both of the type R_4Sn and R_3SnX, were tested for antifungal activity. It turned out, however, that in no case did a functionally substituted compound have a higher activity than a comparable unsubstituted compound. On the contrary, in most cases the introduction of a functional group severely reduced antifungal activity. Especially, hydrophilic groups had an adverse effect (*192*).

No active compounds were ever found among the types R_4Sn, R_2SnX_2, and $RSnX_3$ in spite of careful screening. The sole exception is diphenyltin dichloride which inhibits the growth of the fungi mentioned in Table 1 at concentrations of 10–20 mg/l (*146*). In a few cases in which a compound of the type R_4Sn showed some activity, either a compound of the type R_3SnX was present as an impurity or an easy cleavage of one of the R groups probably occurred. An example of the latter is tributyl(cyanomethyl)tin which easily loses the cyanomethyl group under hydrolytic circumstances (*192*).

Several other groups of workers have studied the antifungal properties of organotin compounds. Independent research on simple alkyl- and aryltin compounds with a practical aim has been carried out by Baumann (*35*) and Härtel (*120, 121*) at Farbwerke Hoechst, Frankfort, Germany. This work has led to the development of the first agricultural organotin fungicide *Brestan*, based on triphenyltin acetate (see Sec. IV.A.1). Other workers have extended the above results. In most cases the influence of varying the acid radical in triorganotin salts was studied (*63, 64, 143, 225*). Results at variance with the rules formulated above were only obtained when compounds with highly fungitoxic acid radicals were tested (*65, 100*).

The antifungal organotin compounds appear to have a very broad spectrum of activity. Results of tests on phytopathogenic fungi have been collected (*146*, cf. Sec. IV.A.1). Also wood-destroying fungi have been used as test organisms (*131*, cf. Sec. IV.B.1).

The action of the organotin compounds at the low concentrations employed in the tests is fungistatic rather than fungicidal. The mode of action of the organotin compounds is still not understood, although it has been suggested (*146, 147*) that inhibition of oxidative phosphorylation in the case of the trialkyltin compounds may be the cause of the observed inhibition of fungal growth. The differences in activity among the several trialkyltin compounds might then be attributed both to differences in intrinsic activity on the enzyme system and to differences in permeability into the cells. Permeability in its turn may be dependent on the partition coefficient of the organotin compound between water and lipids.

Antibacterial tests with organotin compounds have been carried out by Kaars Sijpesteijn (*145–147*). Organotin compounds are, in general, much more active toward Gram-positive bacteria like *Bacillus subtilis, Micobacterium phlei* and *Streptococcus lactis* than toward Gram-negative ones like *Escherichia coli* and *Pseudomonas fluorescens*. The most active compounds, inhibiting growth of the Gram-positive species at 0.1–5 mg/l, again belong to the type R_3SnX. Among the trialkyltin acetates maximal activity is associated with the propyl and butyl compounds, although tripentyltin acetate is still highly active against *Mycobacterium phlei*. Triphenyltin acetate is as active as the most active trialkyltin acetates.

It is remarkable that, for the Gram-negative bacteria, triethyl- and tripropyltin acetate are the most active trialkyltin acetates. They inhibit their growth at 20–50 mg/l. Dipropyl-, dibutyl-, and dipentyltin dichloride have no antifungal properties, but they inhibit the growth of Gram-positive bacteria at a concentration of 20–50 mg/l.

Trialkyltin compounds have also been tested against pathogenic bacteria, notably *Staphylococcus aureus* (Gram-positive) and some *Pseudomonas* species (Gram-negative). The results (*117, 264*) confirm the trends signalized above (cf. also Sec. IV.C.1).

As to the mode of action of the organotin compounds against bacteria, the same remarks can be made as in the case of their action against fungi. It is supposed (*146, 147*) that the triorganotin compounds act by their inhibition of oxidative phosphorylation and the diorganotin compounds by their action on enzymes containing thiol groups. Evidence for the latter has recently been presented (*149*).

B. ACTIVITY AGAINST HIGHER PLANTS

The lower trialkyltin acetates are quite toxic to higher plants. For the broad bean (*Vicia faba*) the most toxic members of the series are triethyltin acetate and tripropyltin acetate (*147*). Triphenyltin acetate is much less toxic; however, its phytotoxicity still restricts its use as an agricultural fungicide (*120*). It is notably toxic to rice (*129, 133*). Trivinyltin chloride has been mentioned in a patent (*94*) as a nonselective herbicide. It is claimed to be very toxic to, e.g., charlock (*Sinapis arvensis*) which it kills at 0.2 g/m^2 (0.5% solution).

C. ANTHELMINTIC ACTIVITY

Man and his domestic animals may become infected with several kinds of parasitic worms. Anthelmintics are substances that kill these worms or remove them from the organism. A compound can, in principle, be tested in two ways for anthelmintic activity: *in vitro* and *in vivo*. The *in vitro* test gives the direct toxicity of the compound for the worm. It is of limited value, firstly because some substances are not toxic for the worm but just cause its removal from the host and, secondly because it gives no indication of the toxicity of a substance for the host. In most cases, therefore, the *in vivo* test is used.

In vitro tests against the nematode *Rhabditis macrocerca* by Gras (*114*) have shown that toxicity toward this worm decreases in the series triethyltin hydroxide, diethyltin dichloride, ethyltin trichloride, and tetraethyltin. Di-butyltin dilaurate and dibutyltin maleate in this test were even less toxic than tetraethyltin. The time of survival in a 1 % solution ranged from 2 min to $1\frac{1}{4}$ h among these compounds.

The first *in vivo* tests with organotin compounds were carried out as early as 1941 by Guthrie et al. (*118, 119*). They administered tetraethyltin, tetra-isobutyltin, tetraphenyltin and triphenyltin chloride to chickens artificially infected with the cestode *Railletina cesticillus*, but found no active compound of sufficiently low toxicity. In 1952, Kerr observed that a single dose of 75 mg/kg body weight of dibutyltin dilaurate effectively removed *Railletina cesticillus* from chickens (*153*). This compound has since been used as an anthelmintic for poultry (see Sec. IV.A.2).

During the past fifteen years, the *in vivo* test has been used in several systematic investigations on the anthelmintic properties of organotin com-pounds. Kerr and Walde (*154*) tested a wide variety of dibutyl- and other organotin compounds against two parasitic worms, the cestode *Railletina cesticillus* and the nematode *Ascaridia galli*, in chickens. Gras et al. (*56, 58, 114, 124*) studied the activity of a limited number of organotins, viz. various types of ethyl- and butyltin compounds but also some dioctyl- and diphenyltin derivatives against the cestode *Hymenolepis fraterna* in rats and mice and the nematode *Nippostrongylus muris* in rats. Finally, Graber and Gras (*113*) examined the suitability of dibutyl-, dioctyl-, and diphenyltin compounds as anthelmintics for a heavily infected African type of chicken. The organotin compounds are, in general, much more active toward cestodes than toward nematodes. A high activity is only found in compounds of the types R_3SnX and R_2SnX_2. The applicability of the triorganotin compounds is, however, limited by their toxicity to the host animal which often prohibits the use of an effective dose. The most consistent results were obtained with diorganotin compounds. In the alkyl series a gradual decrease of the anthelmintic activity was noted with increasing length of the alkyl chains. Dioctyltin dilaurate and diphenyltin dilaurate were poor anthelmintics. The corresponding di-chlorides or oxides, however, were fairly active.

As to the mode of action of the organotin compounds on parasitic worms living in the digestive tract, Gras (*114, 124*) supposes that there is, on one hand, a direct toxic action and, on the other hand, an inhibition of the antienzyme system that protects the worm from being digested. The nematodes have a thick cuticle and a digestive tract. They take up substances in much the same way as the host does. The poor effect of organotin compounds in *in vivo* tests with nematodes may therefore be a result of non-selective toxicity. The cestodes, on the contrary, lack a digestive tract and feed through osmosis. Toxic substances in the intestine of the host are very readily taken up. The higher effectivity of the diorganotins as compared with the generally more toxic triorganotins points, however, to a more specific mechanism, e.g., inhibition of the antienzyme system mentioned above.

D. Molluscicidal Activity

Molluscs, in this case several kinds of aquatic snails, are intermediate hosts in the life-cycles of certain parasitic worms which, in man, give rise to a diseased condition known as bilharziasis. Bilharziasis presents a serious problem, especially in the underdeveloped parts of the world where hundreds of millions of people are affected (*101, 187*). The most promising way to break the life-cycles of the parasites seems to be the chemical control of the vector snails. World-wide research on this subject is being coordinated by the World Health Organization.

Recently, a few organotin compounds have been tested as molluscicides. Deschiens and Floch found that triphenyltin chloride and acetate were highly active toward *Biomphalaria glabrata* (*Australorbis glabratus*) and *Bulinus contortus*. The time required to kill the snails depended on the concentration. One mg/l killed in 24 h and 0.25 mg/l in 48 h. The high toxicity of the compounds to other forms of aquatic life presented a disadvantage (*78*). The authors later extended the tests to other snail species. The triphenyltin compounds proved to be very persistent in water (*79*), but it has been found that the acetate is adsorbed onto mud and is thus inactivated (*129*). A high activity is also shown by other triaryltin compounds and by trialkyltin compounds (*129*). Concentrations of a few tenths of a mg/l of tripropyltin oxide and tributyltin acetate killed both embryonic and mature *Biomphalaria glabrata* (*51*, cf. *129*). The most attractive of the organotin compounds tested so far probably is tributyltin oxide. This for certain aquatic snails had an LD$_{50}$ of only 0.01 mg/l when an exposure time of 16 h 40 min was used, followed by an equally long recovery time in clean water (*82*). Field tests have confirmed the high activity of tributyltin oxide, but also its high toxicity to fish (*77*, cf. *2*). The applicability of organotin compounds as molluscicides is moreover restricted by their toxicity to rice (*129, 133*). A safe method for the introduction of the organotin toxicant into the infected water has been developed by Goodrich (*111*). The tin compound is dissolved in an elastomer from which it is slowly released into the water (see also under Antifouling, Sec. IV.B.7).

For the activity of organotin compounds toward marine wood-boring molluscs, see under Wood Preservation (Sec. IV.B.1).

E. Insecticidal Activity

The literature on the insecticidal activity of organotin compounds through 1964 has been reviewed very completely by Ascher and Nissim (*23*). Therefore only the main lines will be discussed here and a few recent publications mentioned.

The first mention of insecticidal properties in organotin compounds was made in a series of patents published around 1929. In addition to compounds of Group V elements, organotin compounds in general were claimed as mothproofing agents (*139*). Twenty years later only trialkyltin chlorides were claimed in a patent (*74*) dealing with the control of insects other than moths. Hueck and Luijten (*137*) in 1958, found mothproofing activity only in some compounds of the type R_3SnX.

Systematic investigations on the insecticidal activity of organotin compounds started with the work of Blum et al. in 1960. Blum and Bower (*41*) had already shown that triethyltin hydroxide and some of its salts were highly toxic when applied topically to house flies (*Musca domestica*). The LD_{50} of the compounds was somewhat higher for DDT-resistant flies than for susceptible flies (e.g., of the hydroxide, 0.40 μg as compared with 0.31 μg per fly). Blum and Pratt (*42*) thereupon investigated a series of forty organotin compounds by the same technique. They found a high activity (LD_{50} 0.1–1 μg per fly) for the trisubstituted compounds, a moderate activity (LD_{50} about 10 μg per fly) for compounds of the types R_4Sn and R_2SnX_2 and a low activity for those of the type $RSnX_3$. In the aliphatic R_3SnX compounds neither the nature of the group X nor the length of the alkyl chains (at least up to butyl), had much influence on the insecticidal activity. A similar result was obtained by Gras et al. (*57, 115*) who tested a series of organotin compounds in aqueous solution against mosquito larvae (*Culex pipiens berbericus*). They extended the series of trialkyl compounds somewhat further, however, and found a sudden fall in activity after hexyl. The concentration of trialkyltin compound killing half of the larvae (LC_{50}) from methyl through hexyl was 0.4–0.5 mg/l. This is still ten times the LC_{50} of DDT, lindane, and malathion in the same test. In the above investigations, triphenyltin compounds had the same activity as the lower trialkyltin compounds.

Kochkin et al. (*161*) likewise investigated a series of organotin compounds, but extended the number of insect species to include flies, bed bugs, cockroaches, mosquitos and fleas. The flies were treated topically; the LD_{50}'s found correspond with those observed by Blum and Pratt (*42*). The Russian authors moreover found trialkyltin compounds active as contact insecticides against all species. Conflicting results were obtained with triphenyltin compounds: triphenyltin acetate was active whereas triphenyltin methacrylate was inactive. Gardiner and Poller (*106*), when testing a series of ten triphenyltin salts as contact insecticides against *Sitophilus oryzae* adults, found none active. One wonders, however, whether in latter investigation the experimental set-up was favorable. Where Kochkin et al. used glass plates, Gardiner and Poller used paper discs, and it is known that organotin compounds are fixed onto cellulose (211). Kubo (164) who investigated the activity of triphenyltin organophosphates as contact insecticides against the adult Azuki-bean weevil (Cellosobruchus chinensis) again used glass (Petri dishes). Many of the compounds, including triphenyltin chloride, were highly active. A strong influence of the nature of the acid radical was noted in this case, and Kubo could demonstrate a correlation between the activity and the solubility of the compounds in organic solvents.

A difference in the mode of action between trialkyl- and triphenyltin compounds is suggested by the results of mothproofing tests by Gardiner and Poller (106). In these tests, treated samples of wool were exposed to attack by larvae of the common clothes moth (Tineola bisselliella). The authors found no attack and 100% kill with 1% of tributyltin oxide in the wool. With triphenyltin salts in the same concentration some wool was always eaten and the percentage kill never attained 100%. The authors conclude that tributyltin oxide acts as a contact insecticide but the triphenyltin salts as stomach poisons. Their observation that the nature of the acid radical in the triphenyltin salts has a distinct influence on the insecticidal activity fits in with Kubo's (164, see above).

A limited series of organotin compounds was tested by Graves et al. (116) against larvae of the bollworm (Heliothis zea) and the tobacco bud worm (Heliothis virescens). On topical application the following LD_{50}'s were found: trimethyltin hydroxide and acetate about 0.2 μg/larva, tributyltin oxide and diethyloctyltin acetate about 5 μg/larva and triphenyltin hydroxide and acetate more than 10 μg/larva. A small but consistent difference in sensitivity was noted between insecticide resistant and susceptible strains. A few investigators examined only one compound, in most cases the commercially available tributyltin oxide. Richardson (211) tested tributyltin oxide in powdered biscuits against the larvae of the drug-store beetle (Stegobium paniceum) a close relative to the common furniture beetle (Anobium punctatum). One tenth of a percent was sufficient in the long run to kill all larvae. The results obtained by Baker and Taylor (27) with tributyltin oxide against wood-boring beetles will be discussed in Sec. IV.B.1.

A compound of the type R_2SnX_2, the commercially available dibutyltin dilaurate (used both as a stabilizer in PVC and as an anthelmintic in poultry), has repeatedly been tested in vivo against endoparasitic insect larvae in cattle. The larvae of the so-called heel flies (Hypoderma lineatum and H. bovis), known as cattle grubs, live under the skin of cattle. After initial success, however, only negative results have been obtained (213). An organotin compound of quite another type, viz. hexamethylditin, has recently been introduced as an agricultural insecticide under the trade-name Pennsalt TD-5032 (199a). It has been tested against several species of noctuidae

(*124a*), and it has been shown to be systemic in cotton (*21a*). The formulated product loses its activity upon standing, but it can be stabilized (*199b*).

Organotin compounds in addition to a toxic effect can exert an "antifeeding" effect on insects. The antifeeding effect, which is probably based on taste, occurs at very low, sublethal concentrations. It has so far only been described for triphenyltin compounds. After its discovery in field tests in which triphenyltin hydroxide and acetate had been used as agricultural fungicides (for a historic survey see *23*) laboratory experiments have confirmed its existence. Ascher et al. (*23, 25*) showed that leaves of sugar beet, sprayed with suspensions of triphenyltin acetate of increasing concentrations, were eaten to a decreasing extent by larvae of two kinds of moths, *Prodenia litura* and *Agrotis ypsilon*. Protection of the leaves was about 90% at the 0.035% concentration. Further experiments against *P. litura* with triphenyltin hydroxide and acetate showed the latter to be superior to the former. The results were capable of quantitative treatment (*23, 24*). The superiority of the acetate over the hydroxide was also borne out in experiments with larvae of the potato tuber moth (*Gnorimoschema operculella*) and the striped maize borer (*Chilo agamemnon*). No complete protection against these insects was obtained, however, even at the highest concentration employed (0.05%) (*180*). In tests with larvae of the Colorado potato beetle (*Leptinotarsa decemlineata*) Byrdy et al. (*49*) compared the antifeeding activity of a series of triphenyltin compounds. From experiments first with potato leaves and then with whole plants the methoxide, benzoate and acetate emerged as the most active. The antifeeding effect of triphenyltins on housefly larvae was again investigated by Ascher et al. Triphenyltin hydroxide and acetate were added to moistened wheat bran in concentrations of 10–40 mg/kg. At these concentrations, parallel to a moderate antifeeding effect, a toxic effect was observe for both compounds (*22*). Also hexamethylditin has been found to possess antifeedant properties (*21a*).

Another effect exerted by organotin compounds at low concentrations and likewise only demonstrated for triphenyltin compounds, is their ability to interfere with insect reproduction. The first report on insect chemosterilant activity of triphenyltins came from Kenaga (*151*). Of the more active compounds in his tests, the fluoride, hydroxide and sulfide caused sterility in house flies well below the lethal concentration. Other insects whose reproduction could be influenced were the German cockroach (*Blatella germanica*) and the confused flour beetle (*Tribolium confusum*). Byrdy et al. (*48*) included the Colorado potato beetle in tests with triphenyltin compounds. Triphenyltin acetate and chloride according to Kissam and Hays were already quite toxic at concentrations required for sterilizing house flies (*155*).

The mode of action of organotin compounds on insects is not known with certainty. Investigations by Pieper and Casida (*204*) on the inhibition of adenosine triphosphatases in the house fly, however, have revealed a correlation between potency for *in vitro* ATPase inhibition and toxicity of triorganotins. The authors suggest that the insecticidal activity of triorganotins may result from interference with ATPase activity or related processes associated with oxidative phosphorylation. A gene has been identified that confers resistance to organotin insecticides and acts as an intensifier of parathion resistance (*134a*). It has been shown that this gene acts by decreasing the rate of absorption (*205a*).

Although mites are not insects, some acaricidal results with organotin compounds may be mentioned here. Reed et al. (*209*) among numerous other experimental compounds tested triphenyltin chloride, hydroxide, and acetate against two rust mites of citrus, *Phyllocoptruta oleivora* and *Aculus pelecassi*. The acetate at 20 mg/l was only active against the last-mentioned species. The other two compounds were highly active against both species even at concentrations as low as 2 mg/l. A miticide based on tricyclohexyltin hydroxide, trade-named *Plictran*, is now being offered in experimental quantities by Dow Chemical Co. (*116a*; cf. *4a, 151a*).

F. MAMMALIAN TOXICITY

Literature on the mammalian toxicity of organotin compounds is immense. The present author has compiled a bibliography of organotin toxicity including well over 100 titles. A copy is available on request. Reviews have repeatedly been given (in chronological order *114, 31, 142, 167, 188, 29*).

A straightforward discussion of organotin toxicity meets with difficulties because the number of variables to be considered is fairly large. There are, first the organotin compound, its formulation and the mode of administration. Then comes the animal species and, finally, the evaluation of the results. In the following, an attempt will be made to sketch the structure-activity relationship using simple oral toxicity data obtained with rats and mice. In addition a few more specific subjects may be treated.

As an introductory remark it may be stated that only very few organotin compounds, e.g., the triethyltin salts, are highly toxic. The economically important tributyl-, dibutyl-, and triphenyltin compounds are of moderate toxicity. Again, many organotin compounds are known which are hardly toxic at all.

Tetraalkyltins, although generally biologically inactive (see preceding sections), are toxic to mammals. Caujolle et al. have investigated the toxicity of a series of tin tetraalkyls administered in several ways to mice and dogs (*59–61, 181*). The methyl compound was allegedly somewhat less toxic than the ethyl compound (the present author's opinion is that this is not borne out by the published data). From tetraethyltin onward, toxicity gradually fell, most markedly after the pentyl compound. An important feature of tetra-alkyltin poisoning is the slow development of toxic symptoms and the long periods after which death may occur. This makes the assessment of lethal doses arbitrary. Just to indicate the order of magnitude: the 24 h LD_{50}'s of tetramethyltin and tetraethyltin upon oral administration to mice were both about 1 mmole (200 mg)/kg. In the long run, one half to one sixth of this amount would kill 50% of the animals. These figures would class the lowest tin tetraalkyls among the moderately toxic compounds. Their high volatility and the absence of a characteristic odor in the pure compounds, however, make them potentially hazardous. A few cases of poisoning of laboratory workers through inhalation have been recorded (265).

The signs of intoxication by tetraalkyltins are similar to those by trialkyltin compounds. This, and the delayed onset of symptoms, suggest a biological conversion in the mammalian organism of one into the other. Experimental proof for one particular case has been given by Cremer (70). She demonstrated the presence of a triethyltin compound in tissue samples of rats and rabbits injected with tetraethyltin. In vitro experiments showed that the main site of conversion is in the liver.

The mammalian toxicity of a series of trialkyltin compounds was first investigated by Stoner et al. (228). The certainly lethal dose on oral administration to rats was lowest for triethyltin sulfate, viz. 10 mg/kg. The corresponding value for trimethyltin sulfate was 30 mg/kg. From triethyltin onward, toxicity again fell with the increasing size of the alkyl groups. Tributyltin acetate had an LD_{100} of 50–100 mg/kg, trihexyltin acetate of over 100 mg/kg (228). In a later paper by Barnes and Stoner (30) LD_{50} values were reported for a series of trialkyltin acetates given orally to rats. For the methyl, ethyl, propyl, butyl, hexyl, and octyl compounds they were 9.1, 4.0, 118.3, 380.2, 1000, and >1000 mg/kg, respectively.

The economically important tributyl- and triphenyltin compounds have about equal toxicity. The actue oral LD_{50} of bis(tributyltin) oxide for rats has been established at 150-200 mg/kg. Also chronic toxicity tests have been carried out with this compound (90). Klimmer (156) found for triphenyltin acetate an LD_{50} of 136 mg/kg (oral, rat), but Stoner (227) reports higher values (430 and 490 mg/kg). The guinea pig is much more sensitive to this compound than the rat (156, 228). Chronic toxicity tests with triphenyltin acetate have been carried out by several groups of workers (156, 227, 247). The acute oral LD_{50} for mice of triphenyltin hydroxide is 500–600 mg/kg (205).

Rats poisoned by the lower trialkyltin compounds first show a characteristic muscular weakness. After a period of apparent recovery, weakness returns and progresses until death occurs. In rabbits, after the recovery period, convulsions are observed. The main site of action of these compounds appears to be in the central nervous system (228). In man, the first symptoms resemble those of concussion of the brain. They are: headache, nausea, and vomiting. More characteristic is a sudden fainting when rising from a horizontal position (265). However, slight cases, both in animals and in man, show complete recovery, owing to the reversible nature of trialkyltin poisoning.

The mechanisms of intoxication by trialkyltin compounds has been extensively investigated. For obvious reasons, attention has been focused on the action on the central nervous sytem. All toxic trialkyltin compounds, except the methyl derivative, produce an edema of the white matter of the brain and spinal cord (176). This edema, most pronounced in the case of triethyltin poisoning, has become the subject of considerable study. A mechanism for its production has recently been proposed (231). The biochemical action of trialkyltin compounds is complex. The best studied is their interference with oxidative phosphorylation (4 and references cited therein). This, and other biochemical aspects, and their relation to the toxic syndrome are still under discussion (for some very recent papers see 3a, 71, 214).

The toxicity pattern of dialkyltin compounds is quite different from that of trialkyltin compounds. Barnes and Stoner studied the toxicity of a series of dialkyltin dichlorides for rats and a few other rodents. At moderate oral doses (40–80 mg/kg) the butyl compound was the most toxic one, at higher doses (160 mg/kg), the methyl, ethyl, and propyl compounds also caused the death of rats. Dioctyltin dichloride, although by the intravenous route as toxic as dibutyltin dichloride, was completely non-toxic by mouth. All compounds through butyl caused damage when applied to the skin (30). Klimmer and Nebel found an LD_{50} of 100 mg/kg (oral, rat) for dibutyltin dichloride. The corresponding figure for dibutyltin dilaurate was 175 mg/kg, while for several other dibutyltin stabilizers it ranged from 500–900 mg/kg. Dioctyltin stabilizers had an oral LD_{50} for rats of 5000–6000 mg/kg or higher (159).

The toxic dialkyltin dichlorides caused a generalized illness in the rat with, as a special feature, an inflammatory lesion of the bile ducts, which was most pronounced in the case of the butyl compound (28). Dimethyltin dichloride did not give this bile duct lesion (30). Biochemically, the dialkyltin compounds act in a manner similar to arsenicals, i.e., they inhibit α-keto acid oxidases, which contain dithiol groups. The inhibition is counteracted by 2,3-dimercaptopropanol (BAL) (3), which consequently can be used as an antidote (228). Bridges (43) has found that diethyltin dichloride is partially dealkylated in the rat. The site of conversion is not in the liver, but in the body tissues and the gut.

Monoalkyltin compounds have been little studied toxicologically, but from the few figures which have been published a low degree of toxicity emerges. Stoner et al. (*228*) for ethyltin trichloride mention a certainly lethal dose of 200 mg/kg intraperitoneally in the rat. The intravenous administration of 150 mg/kg was not fatal to the rabbit. Monobutyltin sulfide, $[C_4H_9 SnS_{1.5}]_n$, used as a stabilizer in rigid PVC for food packaging, has been found to be completely non-toxic (*157*). Remarkably, from the three octyltin chlorides, ocyltin trichloride was slightly more toxic than dioctyltin dichloride and trioctyltin chloride (oral LD_{50} for the rat between 4000 and 5000, > 5000, and > 5000 mg/kg, respectively) (*158*). Ethyltin trichloride is probably not metabolized by the rat (*43*).

There is an indication that the introduction of a hydrophilic group into a tetraorganotin reduces mammalian toxicity. Sodium 3-(tripropylstannyl)-propionate, $(C_3H_7)_3SnCH_2CH_2COONa$, and 4-(triphenylstannyl)butyric acid, $(C_6H_5)_3SnCH_2CH_2CH_2COOH$, have oral LD_{50}'s for mice of 700 and > 10,000 mg/kg, respectively (*239*). For the corresponding unsubstituted compounds, appreciably lower values would be expected. In triorganotin compounds the fourth, ionic, group can influence toxicity. This is borne out by the oral LD_{50}'s for mice of triphenyltin acetate (*227*), hydroxide (*205*), and sulfide (*239*) which are 80, 500–600, and about 700 mg/kg, respectively.

A few words remain to be said about the cases of poisoning by "Stalinon", a pharmaceutical preparation based on organotin. This was sold in France in 1954 as a remedy against boils. It consisted of capsules, each containing 15 mg of diethyltin diiodide in combination with ethyl linoleate and a few other ingredients. More than 200 people became seriously ill after having taken the capsules, and about 100 of them died. In most of the victims who survived, symptoms have persisted (*31, 197*).

During the clinical trial of the preparation a dispensing error seems to have been made, so that the capsules finally used were much stronger than those which had been tested (*197*). However, the toxicity of Stalinon cannot be explained on the basis of its diethyltin diiodide content. There is, in fact, both chemical and toxicological evidence that the capsules must have contained an amount of the highly toxic triethyltin iodide (*31*).

With the advanced knowledge of organotin toxicity it is very unlikely that a case like that of Stalinon will ever occur again. The toxic hazards of organotin compounds in laboratory and industry can be minimized by appropriate safety measures. Special precautions should be taken to prevent inhalation of dusts and vapors, and contact of the chemicals with the skin. Several organotin compounds, especially the halides, and all tributyltin compounds are known to cause skin lesions (*30, 174*). They may also act as percutaneous poisons (*30*). Some triorganotin compounds have been shown to possess sternutatory properties (*178*). The hazard of toxic residues from agricultural sprays will be dealt with in the next section.

IV. Use of Organotin Compounds as Biocides

A. AGRICULTURAL AND VETERINARY USES

1. *Control of Fungal Diseases in Agriculture*

This is probably the second largest application of organotin compounds. It is still mainly restricted to Europe where it originated through research carried out at Farbwerke Hoechst (*35, 36, 121*).

The first compound put into practical use was triphenyltin acetate. Its choice was based on the result of field tests which showed that whereas in the laboratory trialkyltin compounds are better fungicides than triaryltin compounds, the reverse is true in the field. The lower effectivity of the trialkyltin compounds in tests under practical conditions has been ascribed to their lower stability and higher volatility. Triaryltin compounds are moreover less phytotoxic than trialkyltin compounds (*35, 121*). The only other organotin compound in practical use as an agricultural fungicide is triphenyltin hydroxide (*205*).

The triphenyltin compounds are generally formulated as so-called wettable powders containing 20% of the active principle. The preparation of Farbwerke Hoechst, based on the acetate, is trade-named *Brestan*, that of Philips Duphar, based on the hydroxide, *Duter*. These preparations are diluted with water (e.g. to a 0.3% suspension) and sprayed in a quantity of 1.2–2.4 kg/ha (240–480 g of organotin compound/ha). Also a *Brestan* with 60% of triphenyltin acetate is marketed. In *Brestan-Super*, triphenyltin acetate is combined with manganese ethylenebisdithiocarbamate (maneb) (*95a, 130*). A similar preparation of Fisons Pest Control, called *Fennite*, combines triphenyltin hydroxide and maneb (*99*).

The main diseases controlled are late blight (*Phytophthora infestans*) in potatoes, leaf spot (*Cercospora beticola*) in sugar beets, and leaf spot (*Septoria apii*) in celeriac. The early favorable results with these crops (*35, 36, 120, 121*) have been confirmed (*102, 132, 203, 205, 249*). The organotin compounds compare favorably with copper derivatives and dithiocarbamates. When applied as a foliar spray to potatoes, they also lend a high degree of protection to the tubers. Phytotoxicity prevents the use on fruit crops, ornamental, and glass house plants (*120*). On the other hand, onion diseases (*202*) and several tropical plant diseases, e.g., in coffee, ground nuts (*202*), and pecan (*68, 83*) are successfully controlled.

The problem of toxic residues from sprays with organotin compounds has been very thoroughly investigated. An important feature is the relatively short half life of the compounds on plant leaves in the field. For triphenyltin acetate values have been found of 3–4 days (*122*) and about 4 days (*163, 255*). The compounds do not penetrate into the plant (*126, 163*). Accordingly, in potato tubers less than 0.1 mg of tin/kg was found after the foliage had been repeatedly sprayed with triphenyltin acetate (*132*). A special case is presented by sugar beets, the leaves of which, either fresh or after ensilage, are fed to cows. Results of an extensive study (*33*) have shown, among other things, that 90% of the triphenyltin acetate residue on fresh leaves fed to cows is excreted in the feces. The amount taken up is found mainly in the liver and kidneys, but disappears again completely from these organs within 8 weeks after the end of the experiment. Only 0.1% of the triphenyltin acetate ingested is found in the milk. As there is a considerably washing off and degradation of the residues during the growth period of the beets (see half life) the actual amount of triphenyltin acetate in the milk is very small (about $4\mu g/l$). Ensilage causes a complete breakdown of the triphenyltin acetate within 5 weeks. The resulting inorganic tin compounds are not taken up by cattle.

2. *Removal of Intestinal Worms from Chickens*

Following the investigations by Kerr and Walde (*153, 154*), dibutyltin dilaurate has become a much-used anthelmintic for poultry in the United States. The compound has been marketed under the trade name *Butynorate* (*153*). Another preparation of Dr. Salisbury's Laboratories, containing piperazine, phenothiazine, and dibutyltin dilaurate, is called *Wormal* (*254*). The drug is given as a single dose by capsule or mixed with the feed. The recommended dose is 130 mg of dibutyltin dilaurate per bird. As the LD_{50} of dibutyltin dilaurate for healthy chickens is 1,600 mg/kg (*113*), there is a sufficiently wide margin of safety. However, for a weakened, African type of chicken the therapeutic dose is close to the toxic dose (*113*).

After a single dose of 125 mg dibutyltin dilaurate/kg some tin is found in the tissues of the chicken, the highest concentration (2.4–5.8 mg/kg) occurring in the liver. Nine days after the treatment, however, the tin has again been completely eliminated (*113*). The effect of dibutyltin dilaurate on egg production and quality has been recently investigated (*104, 254*).

Among the organotin compounds tested so far (see Sec. III.C) no anthelmintic suited for the treatment of mammals has been found.

B. Industrial Uses

1. *Wood Preservation*

The most common cause of decay of wood is fungal attack. After it had become known that certain organotin compounds are strong fungicides, several groups of workers have examined their suitability as wood preservatives. Hof and Luijten (*131*) first carried out agar tests, the results of which demonstrated the high activity of triethyl- and tributyltin compounds also against wood-destroying fungi. Tests with wood blocks were carried out by the same authors and by Fahlstrom (*92*). Slight differences were found between the activity of triethyl- and tributyltin compounds (Fahlstrom found a low activity for triphenyltin chloride) and also the sensitivity of the fungi varied but sufficient protection from attack was generally achieved when the wood blocks had been impregnated with a 0.1 % solution of the preservatives (retention about 0.5 kg/m^3). Tests with blocks, which after impregnation had been leached with running water, showed a high resistance of the treatment to leaching. This has been ascribed to an affinity for cellulose (*211*).

Although triethyltin compounds are water-soluble, their use must be discouraged because of their disagreeable handling properties and high mammalian toxicity. Tributyltin compounds offer great possibilities. Tributyltin oxide has in fact been used for some time in the United States in formulations trade-named *OZ* (Osmose Wood Preserving Co. of America) (*7, 262*). The use of organotin compounds as wood-preservatives has been announced in Great Britain (*144*) and is being considered in Japan (*189*).

In addition to their low leachability the organotin preservatives have the advantage of being colorless. The treated wood can normally be painted (*7*). They are, moreover, non-corrosive which permits their use in wood which comes into contact with aluminum (*11*).

For the protection of wood from attack by insects, much higher concentrations of organotin compounds are probably required than those which prevent fungal attack. This follows from the results of tests with the powder-post beetle (*Lyctus brunneus*) and the common furniture beetle (*Anobium punctatum*) by Baker and Taylor (*27*), who achieved protection from these insects only by dipping or impregnating wood with 0.5–1 % solutions of tributyltin oxide. In earlier work with termites (*61b, 92*) high concentrations of the organotin compound tested were also required.

Wood immersed in sea-water may be exposed to attack by marine borers. The main organisms involved are shipworms (*Teredo*) (*165*) and gribble (*Limnoria*), i.e., several kinds of molluscs. In early tests under actual conditions by Britton (*45*) it has already been shown that triethyltin hydroxide and tributyltin acetate in concentrations of a few kg/m^3 give wood a better protection from attack by these animals than high loadings of creosote. This has recently been confirmed by Zedler (*263*). A large series of organotin compounds was examined in *in vitro* tests by Vind and Hochman (*248*). They found a high activity for di- and trialkyltin compounds (alkyl = ethyl through pentyl) and triphenyltin compounds. *Teredo* larvae were much more sensitive to the organotin compounds than adult *Limnoria* (the reversed order of sensitivity is found when chlorinated hydrocarbon insecticides are tested against these organisms). The authors also studied the effect of leaching, using impregnated matchsticks and *Limnoria*. The knowledge thus gained has been put into practice in a preparation called *Nautox* (Osmose Wood

Preserving Co. of America) which contains 2% of tributyltin oxide and 2%
of Thiodan (a chlorinated hydrocarbon insecticide) in a petroleum solvent. It
is recommended as an undercoating for wooden hulls (196). A review on
tributyltin wood preservatives has recently been given by Richardson (211a).

2. Textile Preservation

If practiced at all, this is certainly a very minor application of organotin
compounds.

Hueck and Luijten (137) found that tributyltin oxide in 0.1% concentration
makes wool resistant to attack by the clothes-moth (Tineola bisselliella) and
the carpet-beetle (Anthrenus vorax). DDT in the tests had about the same
activity. Both compounds, however, failed completely when fastness to washing was considered. The somewhat less active commercial mothproofing
agent Mitin FF fully retained its activity after washing.

Whereas several "mixed" trialkyltin compounds, viz. diethyloctyltin
acetate and diethyllauryltin acetate, were poor carpet-beetleproofing agents,
these compounds were highly active in rotproofing experiments on cotton
(137). They were not only more active in direct tests than tributyltin oxide,
but, contrary to the latter compound, immune to leaching by water. The
amounts required for complete protection were 0.03% for diethyloctyltin
acetate and 0.3% for diethyllauryltin acetate. Tributyltin chloride and some
experimental formulations based on tributyltin were compared with many
other compounds, most of them copper derivatives, in tests on the rotproofing of jute potato-bags by Hueck et al. (138). The tin compounds were
neither the cheapest nor the best; they were considered "acceptable" by the
authors. Their only advantage, which they shared with the likewise "acceptable" DDM [bis(5-chloro-2-hydroxyphenyl)methane], was their colorlesssness.

A somewhat related investigation is that by Britton on the preservation of
ropes immersed in sea-water (46). In the experiment, carried out under actual
conditions, a 0.5% triethyltin hydroxide or tributyltin acetate solution gave
ropes a better protection during the 18 months' test period than two un-
specified commerical preservatives.

A detailed survey of the above investigations has been given by Salquain
(217).

3. Sanitizing of Textiles

What is meant here is a treatment of textiles, particularly underwear and
socks, which renders them bactericidal. This will prevent the bacterial decomposition of sweat, which is the cause of odor. Tributyltin oxide is used
to this end, but very little information is available on this subject. Zedler
(262) mentions a concentration of 0.025–0.050%, which does not irritate the
skin. The organotin compound may be applied from an aqueous metastable

dispersion as described in a patent by Leatherland (*166*). This method is claimed to result in an impregnation which will stand repeated washing.

4. Slime Control in Paper Mills

Paper making involves the handling of huge quantities of water which by its nutrient content and temperature forms a ready medium for the development of microorganisms. A luxurious growth of microorganisms, in this case mainly bacteria, may lead to the formation of cohering masses, called slime, which may interfere with the paper making process or impair the quality of the paper. Slime formation is being controlled both by hygienic measures and by the addition of chemicals, among which is tributyltin oxide. The two methods of control have been compared by Rathman (*208*).

The amount of tributyltin oxide added to the mill water is very small, according to a patent only a few hundreths of a mg/l. Complete inhibition of growth is not achieved, but the number of bacteria is sufficiently reduced to be of no harm. Almost all of the tributyltin oxide goes into the paper which is claimed to be rendered fungistatic and bacteriostatic (*250*).

This application, one of the first in which use was made of the antimicrobial properties of organotin compounds, is probably not of great importance now, although continued interest is reflected in two recent publications (*150, 199*).

A related problem is the preservation of pulp during storage (cf. *216*). It is not sure whether organotin compounds are applied here; a formulated tributyltin compound has been recommended (*226*). Benzyldiethyltin hydroxide has been tested as a preservative for wet sweet potato starch (*127*).

5. Water Treatment

This application is closely related to the foregoing, only the water, being recirculated cooling water or water for the secondary recovery of oil, is much less rich in nutrients than mill water. The treatment of cooling water to keep it clean from algae, fungi and bacteria presents a major use of tributyltin oxide in the United States. The organotin compound is solubilized and its antimicrobial spectrum is broadened by combining it with quaternary ammonium compounds (*262*). In secondary oil recovery, bacteria may cause directly or indirectly, clogging of the subterranean interstices through which water is pumped to displace the oil. A formulated tributyltin compound is a cheap and effective means to minimize this difficulty (*226*).

6. Paint Preservation

Paint preservation has several aspects. Emulsion paints may be spoiled in the can by bacteria, and molds may grow on painted surfaces. In the latter case it is seldom the paint itself that serves as a substrate (this occurs with nutrient-rich distemper films). In most cases mold growth originates from a source under the paint film, generally a wall. Mold growth on top of a film may occur in a humid atmosphere when the film is covered with a nutrient substrate deposited as a spray or condensate.

Tributyltin oxide alone is not suited for preservation of paint in the can, because it is not active against the Gram-negative bacteria involved. Its combination with, e.g., an organomercurial has been suggested (*38*).

In Great Britain tributyltin oxide has, however, been successfully used as a fungistat in emulsion paints since 1955 (*144*). Results of a comparative laboratory trial, from which tributyltin oxide emerged as a fungistat of very high activity in an emulsion paint based on poly(vinyl acetate), were published in 1956 by Arnold and Clarke. They found a concentration of 0.025% sufficient to prevent the growth of molds from an infected plaster pat through the paint film covering it (*21*). Bennett and Zedler (*38*) made tests on hardboard panels and also on walls and ceilings of breweries. These authors recommend, for interior use in temperate conditions, a paint with 0.05–0.1%, and under more severe conditions of warmth and dampness (as in bottling stores of breweries, or in tropical countries) one with 0.5–1.0% of tributyltin oxide.

Mold growth on oil-based paint films is usually of the type which develops in a condensate on top of the film. In order to suppress this, the film must give off a fungitoxic substance to the condensate. The concentration of tributyltin oxide required here (at least 2%) is stated to retard drying (*38*). Tributyltin acetate has nevertheless been mentioned as an effective fungicide in oil-based paints for use in humid tropical areas (*144*). The rosinate failed, however (*253*).

Organotin compounds have been mentioned, among other biocides, for paints in two German publications (*108, 128*). In an early Swiss patent tri-isopropyl- and tributyltin compounds were claimed as biocides for various types of paint (*186*).

7. *Antifouling*

The term "fouling" refers to the growth of all kinds of organisms, both vegetable and animal, on the hull and other parts of ships and on various other objects immersed in sea-water. This growth may seriously impair the function of the attacked objects. In ships, the increased roughness of the skin has a retarding effect and leads to an increased consumption of fuel. Fouling is generally controlled by the application of an antifouling paint, i.e., a paint which slowly releases a toxic substance in the surrounding sea-water in order to kill or at least to prevent the attachment of the organisms. The toxic substance incorporated in the paint has almost exclusively been cuprous oxide. For full information on this subject the reader is referred to Ref. (*256*).

Organotin compounds, because of their general toxicity, are in principle suited as antifouling agents. In a patent by duPont de Nemours & Co. and W. H. Tisdale, filed in 1943, trialkyltin and -lead compounds, more specifically triethyllead oleate and triethyltin stearate were claimed as ingredients of antifouling paints (87). Research carried out by the Tin Research Institute from 1953 through 1957 has not led to conclusive results, although it was shown that tributyltin compounds give a better performance than triethyltin compounds which are leached from the paint too quickly (170). The same conclusion was reached by Bennett and Zedler (38) who have published the results of extensive tests with tributyltin compounds in various paint systems. Most experiments were carried out with tributyltin oxide, which has the advantage over cuprous oxide of being colorless, easily dispersed in the paint, and non-corrosive. In general, concentrations of 15% tributyltin oxide, based on solids content, are required for good control of fouling. Tributyltin sulfide controlled fouling longer, but it was expected to be also more corrosive than the oxide. Formulation is of decisive importance (38; cf. also 69).

Tributyltin oxide is used in antifouling paints for yachts in the United States. Tributyltin fluoride may be used in Japan, since it has been claimed in a Japanese patent (148). Triphenyltin chloride forms the object of a series of patents by Schering (221). These solid compounds are more difficult to formulate than the liquid tributyltins (38). The development of organotin-based antifouling paints has recently been reviewed by Evans (91a).

A different approach to the antifouling problem has been presented by the *Toxion* (F. A. Hughes & Co.) system (8). Here pipes are fitted to the underside of the ship's hull which carry small nozzles. Air, mixed with a solution of tributyltin oxide in kerosene, is forced through these pipes. The air bubbles leaving the nozzles roll along the hull, depositing there a thin film of kerosene with the toxicant. The system is claimed to be very economic. If effective, it would require only a small amount of material, and this only while the ship is in port, where most of the fouling occurs.

A recent development at B. F. Goodrich concerns antifouling elastomeric coatings. The leading thought behind this development is that such coatings may be made much thicker than coats of antifouling paint. The reservoir of toxicant is thus enlarged, with the result that a much longer fouling-free lifetime is reached. For example, with a 3 mm thick neoprene sheet containing 8% tributyltin oxide the predicted lifetime is in excess of seven years (52). A related application of organotins is in the *CēCAP* (Oceanographic Industries) system of protecting lenses of underwater TV cameras and sensors of underwater instruments from fouling. In this system the lenses etc., are surrounded by a ring of porous material, impregnated with, e.g., tributyltin oxide (182).

8. *Protection of Cables from Rodent Attack*

Gnawing of cables by rodents may damage electrical installations or interrupt telephone connections. Protection of telephone cables in the field is of special and often even vital importance during military operations. One solution of this problem is coating of the cables with a rodent repellent.

In laboratory tests in which small, impregnated, burlap bags containing food were exposed to attack by mice or rats, tributyltin chloride proved to be among the most active of the compounds tested. The R_{50} (amount required to repel 50% of the animals) varied from a few tenths of a mg/cm² for mice to 1.1 mg/cm² for Norway rats. The R_{50} of triphenyltin chloride for mice was 6.8 mg/cm² (*230*). Further research, including field tests, has led to the development of *bioMeT 12*, a rodent repellent cable coating based on organotin (*17*). The exact nature of *bioMeT 12* has not been disclosed, although it has been stated that it contains a mixture of tributyltin salts. It was hoped to be put in production early in 1968 (*14*). Other suggested uses for this rodent repellent are in the protection of hoses, irrigation pipe, plastic tubing and plastic garbage cans, and electrical equipment (*183*).

C. MEDICAL USE

1. *Hospital Disinfection*

A severe problem in hospitals to-day is the occurrence in the hospital environment of antibiotic-resistant strains of infectious bacteria. The most important of these is the "hospital staph" (*Staphylococcus aureus*) which causes wound infection, furunculosis, puerperal sepsis, and neonatal sepsis, sometimes with fatal results (*210*). It has proved impossible to eliminate this organism by normal hygienic measures. The effects of chemical antiseptic agents were only temporary. An agent with lasting bactericidal properties was therefore sought (*136*).

Striking results were obtained in a hospital in the United States with a preparation in which tributyltin oxide was combined with a quaternary ammonium salt (the reason for using this combination has been explained in Sec. IV.B.5). This preparation, developed by the Permachem Corp.*, when applied to the hospital linens, floor, wall and ceiling surfaces, furniture, and air filters, gave a drastic reduction in colony counts of *Staphylococcus aureus*. The treatment had a lasting effect, and because of the very low concentrations employed, was harmless to the patients (*135, 136*). In several other hospitals in the United States and in one in South Africa the above results have been confirmed (*210*).

---

* The activities of Permachem Corp. have since been taken over by Microbiological Laboratories.

In Europe, Desowag-Chemie has marketed a hospital disinfectant under the trade-name *Incidin*†, which contains as active ingredients tributyltin benzoate, formaldehyde, a formaldehyde generator (hexamethylenetetramine) and a small amount of sulfur dioxide (*81*). The formaldehyde and sulfur dioxide not only enlarge the antimicrobial spectrum of the preparation and give a quick killing action, but also protect the organotin compound from oxidation. In experiments with labeled (Sn*) tributyltin benzoate it has, moreover, been demonstrated that this compound passes through the skin when it is alone, but not when it is combined with formaldehyde (*222*). *Incidin* has been found to prevent infections not only by Gram-positive and Gram-negative bacteria, but also by pathogenic fungi (e.g., the causes of thrush and athlete's foot) and in one case by a virus (the cause of Newcastle disease in poultry, see *201*).

The use of the above preparations, and of the comparable formulation *Spectro-San* of Stecker Chemicals (*10*), is not restricted to the hospital, but is indicated wherever there is a risk of infection. An example is the treatment of lockers and training rooms of football players (*12*). In the United States even household sprays are sold based on the combination of a tributyltin compound and a quaternary ammonium compound, but these are probably intended for disinfection in a broader sense, i.e., also for the prevention of mold growth on shoes, tents, etc., during storage (*262*).

The concentration of the organotin compound in the finally used solutions of the above preparations is of the order of a few hundred mg/l.

V. Catalytic Uses of Organotin Compounds

A. Polyurethane Formation

Polyurethanes are polymers of great economic importance. They are best known as foams, both flexible and rigid, the main uses of which are in cushioning of furniture etc., and in insulation, respectively. For detailed information on the chemistry and technology of this class of polymers see Ref. (*220*).

The chemistry of polyurethane formation is complex. The basic reaction is that between an isocyanate group and a hydroxyl group yielding a urethane:

$$R{-}N{=}C{=}O + H{-}O{-}R' \longrightarrow R{-}NH{-}\overset{\displaystyle O}{\overset{\displaystyle \|}{C}}{-}O{-}R'$$

† The Incidin preparations are now being sold by Henkel.

The isocyanate group usually belongs to a toluene diisocyanate, the hydroxyl group being one of the end groups of an already polymeric compound, a polyester, polyether or other. In the preparation of a foam, an important reaction is that between an isocyanate group and water which generates carbon dioxide:

$$R-N=C=O + H-OH \longrightarrow [R-NH-\overset{\overset{\displaystyle O}{\displaystyle \|}}{C}-OH \longrightarrow] \quad R-NH_2 + CO_2$$

Is is clear that the amine formed can further react with isocyanate to give a urea, etc.

Both the urethane-forming and other linking reactions which cause the polymer to gel and the foaming reaction have to be catalyzed. Both types of reaction, moreover, must be carefully balanced against each other. Tertiary amines are highly active in the foaming reaction and are generally sufficiently active in the gelation reaction to allow their sole use either in a two-step process which involves the preparation of a prepolymer which is subsequently foamed and made to gel, or in a so-called one-shot process, if the latter is based on a polyester resin. One-shot polyether foams, however, require a more active catalyst system, and it is here that tin compounds come in.

A table of relative activities of tertiary amines, inorganic tin compounds and organotin compounds in the model reaction between phenyl isocyanate and 1-butanol has been published by Hostettler and Cox (*134*). It was found that both tin(II) and tin(IV) chloride were much more active than even the most active of the amines investigated; the highest activity was, however, shown by the organotin compounds. A larger number of organotin compounds were screened in a gelation test by Britain and Gemeinhardt (*44*). In the series of Bu_nSnCl_{4-n} compounds activity increased with decreasing n, the most active terms being butyltin trichloride and tin(IV) chloride. Also a series of dibutyltin salts was tested which on the whole were very active.

The choice of a tin catalyst for practical purposes is of course directed by activity, but secondary factors like availability and cost, stability (among other things to hydrolysis) and toxicity may be equally important. In polyurethane foam formation two types of tin catalyst are in actual use: tin(II) salts of fatty acids, e.g., the 2-ethylhexoate (stannous octoate) and oleate, and similar dibutyltin salts, e.g., the 2-ethylhexoate and laurate (*6*). Stannous octoate gives thermally stable foams, but it has the disadvantage of being unstable on storage and subject to oxidation when exposed to air. This difficulty has, however, been overcome (*175*). The dibutyltin salts are stable on storage, but it has been found in heat aging tests that they impart thermal instability to polyether foams. This has been ascribed to a promotion of oxidative degradation by the organotin catalysts (*134*). It is, however, known that many of the reactions involved in polyurethane formation are reversible.

It is therefore more likely that the organotin catalysts at higher temperatures promote the reverse reactions, the products of which are liable to oxidation. Improvement of thermal stability by the addition of antioxidants has been suggested (*134*, cf. also *140*). An alternative solution is the use, as catalysts, of dibutyltin salts of aliphatic carboxylic acids substituted at the β-position or beyond by chlorine or bromine (*194*). Stannous octoate has been found to be the best catalyst in the preparation of one-shot urethane and urethane-urea elastomers based on polyether polyols and tolylene diisocyanate (*220*, p. 367 ff.). Dibutyltin dilaurate has been used to catalyze the air cure of a one-can urethane coating based on a castor oil polymer (*14*; *220*, p. 481).

The mechanism of the catalysis of polyurethane formation by organotin compounds is not known with certainty. Several authors have proposed a coordination of the tin atom to the oxygen atoms of the hydroxyl and isocyanate groups in such a way that these are brought into a favorable position to react (*44, 88, 91*). A mechanism involving the intermediate formation of a compound with a tin-nitrogen bond has also been put forward (*40*).

B. Silicone Curing

The main use of organotin compounds in the silicone field is in the cold curing of silicone rubbers (*190*; *191*, p. 147; *215*; *232*, p. 787; for applications see *179*, p. 141). In this process, liquid, linear polysiloxanes are transformed at room temperature into highly elastic materials. The time required for the transformation to take place may vary from minutes to hours, depending on the nature and amount of the catalyst added. Preferable catalysts are organotin compounds, mainly dibutyltin salts of fatty acids like the octoate or laurate.

The curing process involves both polycondensation and crosslinking. An important reaction is that between hydroxyl and alkoxy, both on silicon, leading to the establishment of Si—O—Si bonds. The mechanism of the catalytic action is not clear.

C. Esterification

Organotin compounds are probably not used to any great extent as catalysts in industrial esterification and transesterification processes. They have, however, been mentioned as such in several patents (*50, 93, 110, 123, 261*). In one of these (*110*), even a structure-activity relationship is depicted. Butyl- and phenyltin hydroxides and oxides were compared as catalysts in the reaction between phthalic anhydride and 2-ethylhexanol. The phenyl compounds all had about the same activity which was distinctly below that of the butyl compounds. In the butyl series the best catalyst was butyltin hydroxide oxide, $[n\text{-}C_4H_9SnOOH]_x$.

A mechanism for the catalytic action in a transesterification reaction, involving coordination of tin to carbonyl oxygen, has been proposed (*215*).

D. Epoxy Curing

Here again, it is doubtful whether organotin compounds are really used. It has, however, been reported that the use of organotin catalysts leads to epoxy resins with improved storage properties (*62, 215*).

E. Olefin Polymerization

In 1958, Carrick (*54*) reported on a highly active catalyst system for the low pressure polymerization of ethylene, which in contrast to the usual Ziegler-type catalysts was soluble in hydrocarbons. The original system consisted of a mixture of an aluminum halide and an aluminum trialkyl or triaryl in the molar ratio of 3 : 1 with a trace of a vanadium halide. Later, the organoaluminum compound was replaced by a compound which was able to alkylate or arylate the aluminum halide. The compound most frequently mentioned as such, not only in papers (*55, 229*) but also in patents (*20, 233*), is tetraphenyltin. It has been shown that tetraphenyltin merely acts as a phenylating agent for the aluminum halide and that only two of the four phenyl groups are available for this purpose (*75*). The advantage of using an organotin compound instead of an aluminum alkyl or aryl is obviously in the greater stability and ease of handling of the former. It has been stated that a catalyst system including organotin is actually used in the production of polyethylene (*215*).

Organotin compounds of various types have occasionally been mentioned in papers or patents on other polymerization processes. As the practical importance of the catalysts or catalyst systems concerned is doubtful, no attempt will be made to list them completely here. A few examples may, however, be given; they refer to the polymerization of propylene (*26*), vinyl chloride (*224*), and ε-caprolactam (*218*).

VI. Miscellaneous Uses

One of the oldest uses of organotin compounds is in synthetic liquids, used instead of mineral oils as dielectric, insulating, and cooling agents in electric transformers, capacitors, etc. These liquids, known as Askarels, are composed of chlorinated aromatic hydrocarbons like trichlorobenzene and pentachlorobiphenyl. They are non-flammable and have a high dielectric constant, but upon electric failure (arcing) are decomposed with the formation of hydrogen chloride, which is deleterious, especially to cellulose insulation. An effective means of chasing hydrogen chloride in the Askarel medium is the addition of a small amount of tetraphenyltin (*66, 67*).

Organotin compounds are used as additives in lubricants. Basic work in this field was done by Antler (*18*) who, among other organometallics, tested dibutyltin sulfide. This, under the conditions of high pressure and temperature at the rubbing surfaces, breaks down to a form a layer of inorganic tin compounds (SnO, SnS, SnS_2; on steel surfaces it also forms FeS_2 and an unknown phase) which inhibits wear. An organotin antiwear additive of unstated composition has been used in an experimental lubricating oil for two-stroke engines which was mixed with the fuel in a ratio of only 1 : 100 (*223*).

Dolle (*84, 85*) has recently found that a combination of a diaromatic secondary amine and an aromatic tin compound in a concentration of a few wt. % greatly enhanced the oxidation resistance of aliphatic hydrocarbons and related substances. The amine and tin compounds, when used separately were much less effective. The amine-tin antioxidant system has potential use in oils for various purposes serving at 205–220°C.

Transparent, electrically conductive tin oxide films on glass are usually applied by spraying the glass just below its softening point with a solution of an inorganic tin salt, e.g., tin(IV) chloride in aqueous ethanol (*5, 207*). According to a patent (*219*), however, organotin compounds are also suited to this purpose if they are combined with hydrogen chloride and an ionizable fluorine compound. As an example, dibutyltin oxide is mentioned. In a recent advertisement, the use of dibutyltin dichloride, some dibutyltin carboxylates, and butyltin trichloride is recommended (*53*).

A similar treatment as described above improves the strength of glass containers, probably by increasing their resistance to scratching. One of the compounds used is tin(IV) chloride (*14a*), but in a patent application a treatment with dibutyltin diacetate at 650°C is mentioned, followed by a treatment with a polyethylene emulsion at 100–150°C (*196a*). In Japan, dimethyltin dichloride is used in quantities for making scratch-free glass (*124b*).

The present author has participated in research during which it was found that materials like brick, paper, and textiles can be rendered water-repellent by treatment with a solution of an alkali-metal salt or ester of an alkyl- or aryltin hydroxide oxide (*97*). Examples are the sodium salt of butyltin hydroxide oxide and its ethyl ester, $[n\text{-}C_4H_9SnOONa]_x$ and $[n\text{-}C_4H_9SnOOC_2H_5]_x$, respectively. Further research has, however, shown that the effect is not very strong and it is therefore unlikely that organotin compounds will ever replace silicones in this field.

To conclude this chapter, a few words may be said on organotin polymers. These are polymeric substances containing tin atoms (bound to carbon) in the main chain or in side chains. Numerous representatives of the several possible types have been prepared (for surveys see *141*, pp. 368–387 and *188*, pp. 165–174). Much of the work in the field of organotin polymers has been carried out with the aim of obtaining plastic materials of high thermal stability. This expectation has not been fulfilled (*168*). No commercial use of organotin polymers has, as yet, been developed. Organopolystannoxanes, the tin analogues of silicones, in contrast to the latter tend to be highly coordinated, infusible solids of no applicational value. It has, moreover, been found that replacement of silicon atoms in silicones by heavier group IV metal atoms leads to a decreased thermal stability (*76*). Some suggested uses of organotin polymers are in plastic scintillators (*72*) and in radiation-resistant ion-exchangers (*162*).

REFERENCES

1. E. W. Abel and D. A. Armitage, *Adv. Organometal. Chem.*, **5**, 1 (1967).

2. J. S. Alabaster, *Proc. 4th Brit. Weed Control Conf., Brighton*, p. 84 (1958); through *CA*, **54**, 17776 (1960).

3. W. N. Aldridge and J. E. Cremer, *Biochem. J.*, **61**, 406 (1955).

3a. W. N. Aldridge and M. S. Rose, *FEBS* (*Fed. Eur. Biochem. Soc.*) *Lett.*, **4** (2), 61 (1969); through *CA*, **71**, 87568 (1969).

4. W. N. Aldridge and B. W. Street, *Biochem. J.*, **91**, 287 (1964).

4a. W. E. Allison, A. E. Doty, J. L. Hardy, E. E. Kenaga, and W. K. Whitney, *J. Econ. Entomol.*, **61**, 1254 (1968); through *CA*, **69**, 95401 (1968).

5. Anon., *Tin Its Uses*, **46**, 12 (1959).

6. Anon., *Chem., Eng. News*, **37** (44), 62 (1959).

7. Anon., *Tin Its Uses*, **50**, 9 (1960).

8. Anon., *Tin Its Uses*, **53**, 12 (1961).

9. Anon., *Chem. Process.* (*Chicago*), **26**, (1), 45 (1963).

10. Anon., *Tin Its Uses*, **67**, 13 (1965).

11. Anon., *Tin Its Uses*, **70**, 13 (1966).

12. Anon., *Tin Its Uses*, **71**, 13 (1966).

13. Anon., *Chem. Eng. News.*, **45** (15), 24 (1967).

14. Anon., *Chem. Eng. News*, **45** (52), 24 (1967).

14a. Anon., *Tin Its Uses*, **77**, 3 (1968).

15. Anon., *Tin Its Uses*, **77**, 14 (1968).

16. Anon., *Chem. Age* (June, 1968) p. 9.

17. C. Anthony, Jr. and J. R. Tigner, Paper presented at *16th Int. Wire Cable Symp.* Atlantic City, New Jersey, U.S.A., 29 November–1 December (1967).

18. M. Antler, *Ind. Eng. Chem.*, **51**, 753 (1959); *Tin Its Uses*, **68**, 4 (1965).

19. Argus Chem. Corp., British Pat. 838,502 (1960); through *CA*, **54**, 21864 (1960).

20. R. S. Aries, U.S. Pat. 2,900,374 (1959); through *CA*, **53**, 28099 (1959).

21. M. H. M. Arnold and H. J. Clarke, *J. Oil Colour Chem. Ass.*, **39**, 900 (1956); *Tin Its Uses*, **38**, 12 (1957).

21a. K. R. S. Ascher and J. Moscowitz, *Int. Pest Control*, **11**, 17 (1969); through *CA*, **71**, 12058 (1969).

22. K. R. S. Ascher, J. Moscowitz, and S. Nissim, *Tin Its Uses*, **73**, 8 (1967).

23. K. R. S. Ascher and S. Nissim, *World Rev. Pest Control*, **3**, 188 (1964).

24. K. R. S. Ascher and S. Nissim, *Int. Pest Control*, **7** (4), 21 (1965).

25. K. R. S. Ascher and G. Rones, *Int. Pest Control*, **6** (3), 6 (1964).

26. N. Aschikari and M. Honda, *Bull. Chem. Soc. Jap.*, **34**, 767 (1961); through *CA*, **56**, 4943 (1962).
27. J. M. Baker and J. M. Taylor, *Ann. Appl. Biol.*, **60**, 181 (1967).
28. J. M. Barnes and P. N. Magee, *J. Pathol. Bacteriol.*, **75**, 267 (1958).
29. J. M. Barnes and L. Magos, *Organometal. Chem. Rev.*, **3**, 137 (1968).
30. J. M. Barnes and H. B. Stoner, *Brit. J. Ind. Med.*, **15**, 15 (1958).
31. J. M. Barnes and H. B. Stoner, *Pharmacol. Rev.*, **11**, 211 (1959).
32. W. S. Barnhart and R. H. Wade (to Minnesota Mining & Manufacturing Co.), U.S. Pat., 2,874,143 (1959); through *CA*, **53**, 10848 (1959).
33. K. Barth, J. Brüggemann, H. Götte, J. Herok, O. R. Klimmer and K. H. Niesar, *Zentr. Veterinaermed.*, *A*, **11**, 1 (1964).
34. G. A. Baum, *Mod. Plastics*, **44** (8), 148 (1967).
35. J. Baumann, Ph.D. Thesis, Landwirtschaftliche Hochschule Hohenheim, Germany, 1958.
36. J. Baumann and B. Rademacher, *Pflanzenschutz*, **9**, 44 (1957).
37. F. Belpaire, *Rev. Belge Matières Plastiques*, **6** (3), 201 (1965).
38. R. F. Bennett and R. J. Zedler, *J. Oil Colour Chem. Ass.*, **49**, 928 (1966); through *CA*, **66**, 10134 (1967).
39. C. E. Best, U.S. Pat. 2,731,484 (1956); through *CA*, **50**, 11715 (1956).
40. A. J. Bloodworth and A. G. Davies, *Proc. Chem. Soc.*, 264 (1963).
41. M. S. Blum and F. A. Bower, *J. Econ. Entomol.*, **50**, 84 (1957).
42. M. S. Blum and J. J. Pratt, Jr., *J. Econ. Entomol.*, **53**, 445 (1960).
43. J. W. Bridges, *Biochem. J.*, **105**, 1261 (1967).
44. J. W. Britain and P. G. Gemeinhardt, *J. Appl. Polymer Sci.*, **4** (11), 207 (1960).
45. S. C. Britton, *Tin Its Uses*, **36**, 10 (1956).
46. S. C. Britton, *Tin Its Uses*, **38**, 6 (1957).
47. Bundesgesundheitsamt, 33. Mitteilung: *Bundesgesundheidsblatt*, **9**, 322 (1966).
48. S. Byrdy, Z. Ejmocki and Z. Eckstein, *Bull. Acad. Polon. Sci., Ser. Chim.*, **13**, 683 (1965); *Tin Its Uses*, **71**, 11 (1966).
49. S. Byrdy, Z. Ejmocki, and Z. Eckstein, *Mededel. Rijksfac. Landbouwwetenschap, Gent*, **31**, 876 (1966).
50. J. R. Caldwell (to Eastman Kodak Co.), U.S. Pat. 2,720,507 (1955); through *CA*, **50**, 2205 (1956).
51. T. Camey and E. Paulini, *Rev. Brasil. Malariol. Doencas Trop.*, **16**, 487 (1964); through *CA*, **64**, 20554 (1966).
52. N. F. Cardarelli, *Proc. Symp. Deep Submergence Propulsion and Marine Systems, 1966*, Am. Inst. of Aeronautics and Astronautics, Naval Ordnance Plant, Forest Park, Illinios, U.S.A., p. 391.
53. Carlisle Chemical Works, *Chem. Eng. News*, **45** (21), 35 (1967).
54. W. L. Carrick, *J. Am. Chem. Soc.*, **80**, 6455 (1958).
55. W. L. Carrick, R. W. Kluiber, E. F. Bonner, L. H. Wartman, F. M. Rugg, and J. J. Smith, *J. Am. Chem. Soc.*, **82**, 3883 (1960).
56. P. Castel, G. Gras, and S. Beaulaton, *Rev. Pathol. Gen. Physiol. Clin.*, **715**, 235 (1960).
57. P. Castel, G. Gras, J. A. Rioux, and A. Vidal, *Trav. Soc. Pharm. Montpellier*, **23**, 45 (1963); through *CA*, 61, 4901 (1964).
58. P. Castel, H. Harant, and G. Gras, *Thérapie*, **13**, 865 (1958); through *CA*, **55**, 3841 (1961).
59. F. Caujolle, M. Lesbre, A. Bru, D. Meynier, and Y. Bru, *Compt. Rend.* **240**, 1829, **241**, 1420 (1955).
60. F. Caujolle, M. Lesbre, and D. Meynier, *Compt. Rend.* **239**, 556, 1091 (1954); *Ann. Pharm. Franc.*, **14**, 88 (1956).

61. F. Caujolle, M. Lesbre, D. Meynier, and A. Blaizot, *Compt. Rend.* **240**, 1732 (1955).
61a. L. Chalmers, *Mfg. Chem. Aerosol News*, **38** (6), 37 (1967); through *CA*, **67**, 54182 (1967).
61b. K. Charisius and G. Theden, *Forestry Abstr.*, **20**, 2465 (1959).
62. Chemische Werke Albert, British Pat. 783,764 (1957); through *CA*, **52**, 5883 (1958).
63. P. L. Cheng et al., *Hua Kung Hsueh Pao*, (3), 169 (1965); through *CA*, **65**, 16997 (1966).
64. P. L. Cheng and Y. L. Pai, *Hua Kung Hsueh Pao*, (3), 175 (1965); through *CA*, **65**, 16997 (1966).
65. J. H. Cho, H. S. Hsu, H. Y. Cheng, C. L. Fan, Y. L. Muo and C. F. Yu, *Hua Hsueh Hsueh Pao*, **32**, 196 (1966); *CA*, **65**, 13753 (1966).
66. F. M. Clark, *Chem. Eng. News*, **25**, 2976 (1947).
67. F. M. Clark (to General Electric Co.), U.S. Pat. 2,468,544 (1949); through *CA*, **43**, 5887 (1949).
68. J. R. Cole, *Plant Dis. Rep.*, **49**, 703 (1965); *J. Sci. Food Agr.*, **17**, ii-73 (1966).
69. M. V. Cooksley and D. N. Parham, *Surface Coatings*, **2** (8), 280 (1966); through *CA*, **66**, 76969 (1967).
70. J. E. Cremer, *Biochem. J.*, **67**, 28P (1957), **68**, 685 (1958).
71. J. E. Cremer, *Biochem. J.*, **106**, 8 P (1968).
72. J. Dannin, S. R. Sandler, and B. Baum, *Int. J. Appl. Radiat. Isotopes*, **16**, 589 (1965); *CA*, **64**, 2979 (1966).
73. R. J. Daum, *Ann. N.Y. Acad. Sci.*, **125**, 229 (1965).
74. De Bataafsche Petroleum Maatschappij, Dutch Pat. 130,083 (1950).
75. H. J. de Liefde Meijer, J. W. G. van den Hurk, and G. J. M. van der Kerk, *Rec. trav Chim. Pays-Bas*, **85**, 1018 (1966).
76. A. D. Delman, A. A. Stein, B. B. Simms, and R. J. Katzenstein, *J. Polymer Sci.*, *A-1*, **4**, 2307 (1966); through *CA*, **65**, 13753 (1966).
77. R. Deschiens, H. Brottes, and L. Mvogo, *Bull. Soc. Pathol. Exotique*, **59**, 231, 968 (1966); through *CA*, **66**, 94208 (1967).
78. R. Deschiens and H. Floch, *Compt. Rend.*, **255**, 1236 (1962); through *CA*, **57**, 17136 (1962).
79. R. Deschiens and H. Floch, *Bull. Soc. Pathol. Exotique*, **56**, 22 (1963); through *CA*, **59**, 12103 (1963).
80. Deutsche Advance Produktion, *Advastab-PVC-Stabilisatoren*, Marienberg, 1963.
81. Deutsche Solvay-Werke, German Pat. Appl. 1,269,292 (1968).
82. J. P. De Villiers, *S. African Ind. Chem.*, **19**, 166 (1965); *J. Sci. Food Agr.*, **17**, ii-72 (1966).
83. U. L. Diener and F. E. Garrett, *Plant Dis. Rep.*, **51**, 185 (1967); through *CA*, **66**, 104276 (1967).
84. R. E. Dolle, *Ind. Eng. Chem.*, *Prod. Res. Dev.*, **6**, 177 (1967).
85. R. E. Dolle, Jr., U.S. Pat. 3,322,671 (1967); through *CA*, **67**, 55952 (1967).
86. D. Druesedow and C. F. Gibbs, *Natl. Bur. Standards (U.S.) Circ.*, **525**, 69 (1953).
87. E. I. duPont de Nemours and W. H. Tisdale, British Pat. 578,312 (1946).
88. E. Dyer and R. B. Pinkerton, *J. Appl. Polymer Sci.*, **9**, 1713 (1965).
89. G. M. Dyson, J. A. Horrocks, and A. M. Fernley, *Plastteknik*, Sektion TIF: I (1960).
90. J. R. Elsea and O. E. Paynter, *A.M.A. Arch. Ind. Health*, **18**, 214 (1958); through *CA*, **52**, 20691 (1958).
91. S. G. Entelis, O. V. Nesterov, and R. P. Tiger, *J. Cell. Plast.*, **3** (8), 360 (1967); through *CA*, **67**, 82441 (1967).
91a. C. J. Evans, *Tin Its Uses*, **85**, 3 (1970).
92. G. B. Fahlstrom, *Proc. Am. Wood-Preservers' Assoc.*, **54**, 178 (1958); through *CA*, **53**, 10638 (1959).

93. Farbwerke Hoechst, German Pat. 1,032,240 (1958); through *CA*, **54**, 19490 (1960).

94. Farbwerke Hoechst, German Pat. Appl. 1,061,123 (1959); through *CA*, **55**, 6773 (1961).

95. Farbwerke Hoechst, German Pat. Appl. 1,078,772 (1960).

95a. Farbwerke Hoechst, German Pat. Appl. 1,127,140,/1,143,668; through *CA*, **59**, 9258 (1963).

96. Farbwerke Hoechst, German Pat. Appl. 1,160,177 (1963); H. H. Frey and C. Dörfelt, U.S. Pat. 3,021,302 (1962).

97. C. J. Faulkner, Dutch Pat. 104,156 (1962).

98. A. M. Fernley and J. A. Horrocks, *Plastteknik*, Section TIF: IV (1960).

99. Fisons Pest Control, Pamphlet (1967).

100. I. Földesi and G. Stráner, *Acta Chim. Acad. Sci. Hung.*, **45**, 313 (1965); through *CA*, **64**, 3591 (1966).

101. R. Ford Tredre, *Chem. Ind. London*, 1138 (1962).

102. J. Fraselle, *Rev. Agr. Brussels*, **20**, 1013 (1967).

103. H. Frommelt, E. German Pat. 18,339 (1960); through *CA*, **55**, 3978 (1961).

104. J. L. Fry and H. R. Wilson, *Poultry Sci.*, **46**, 319 (1967).

105. A. H. Frye, R. W. Horst, and M. A. Paliobagis, *Am. Chem. Soc., Div. Polymer Chem., Preprints*, **4** (1), 260 (1963); *J. Polymer Sci.*, A, **2**, 1765, 1785, 1801 (1964).

106. B. G. Gardiner and R. C. Poller, *Bull. Entomol. Res.*, **55**, 17 (1964); through *CA*, **63**, 4888 (1965).

107. J. P. Gay, *Tin Its Uses*, **29**, 6 (1953).

108. M. Giesen, *F.A.T.I.P.E.C. Congr.*, **8**, 185 (1966); through *CA*, **65**, 17625 (1966).

109. C. R. Gloskey, U.S. Pat. 2,826,561 and 2,826,597 (1958); through *CA*, **52**, 7774 (1958).

110. B. F. Goodrich Co., German Pat. 1,005,947 (1957); through *CA*, **54**, 14098 (1960); identical to British Pat. 810,381 (1959); through *CA*, **53**, 15982 (1959).

111. B. F. Goodrich Co., Dutch Pat. Appl. 6702629 (1967).

112. B. F. Goodrich Co., Dutch Pat. Appl. 6704657 (1967).

113. M. Graber and G. Gras, *Rev. Elevage Med. Vét. Pays Trop.*, **15**, 411 (1962), **16**, 427 (1963), **17**, 205 (1964), **18**, 405, 415 (1965), **19**, 7 (1966); through *CA*, **61**, 9986 (1964), **63**, 3372 (1965), **65**, 4327, 4498 (1966).

114. G. C. Gras, Ph.D. Thesis, Univ. of Montpellier, France, 1956.

115. G. Gras and J. A. Rioux, *Arch. Inst. Pasteur Tunis*, **42**, 9 (1965); through *CA*, **65**, 6222 (1966).

116. J. B. Graves, J. R. Bradley, and J. L. Bagent, *J. Econ. Entomol.*, **58**, 583 (1965).

116a. H. E. Gray, *Biokemia* (Dow), **16**, 7 (1968).

117. L. Grün and H. H. Fricker, *Tin Its Uses*, **61**, 8 (1963).

118. J. E. Guthrie and P. D. Harwood, *J. Vet. Res.*, **2**, 108 (1941); through Ref. (*114*).

119. J. E. Guthrie, W. C. Powick and D. Blandel, *North Am. Vet.*, **22**, 22 (1941); through *CA*, **35**, 2614 (1941).

120. K. Hartel, *Tin Its Uses*, **43**, 9 (1958).

121. K. Hartel, *Agr. Vet. Chem.*, **3**, 19 (1962).

122. K. Hartel, *Tin Its Uses*, **61**, 7 (1963).

123. G. Halmi and R. Advani (to Hans J. Zimmer, Verfahrenstechnik), U.S. Pat. 3,297,651 (1967); through *CA*, **66**, 47232 (1967).

124. H. Harant, P. Castel and G. Gras, *Bull. Soc. Pathol. Exotique*, **50**, 427 (1957).

124a. K. Harrendorf and R. E. Klutts, *J. Econ. Entomol.*, **60**, 1471 (1967); *J. Sci. Food Agr.*, **19**, i-57 (1968).

124b. E. S. Hedges, Tin Research Institute, Greenford, England, personal communication (1968).

125. D. Helberg, *Deut. Lebensm. Rundschau*, **62** (6), 178 (1966), **63** (3), 69 (1967).

126. J. Herok and H. Götte, *Int. J. Appl. Radiat. Isotopes*, **14**, 461 (1963); through *CA*, **60**, 2243 (1964).
127. S. Higashi and T. Kanno, *J. Fermentation Technol. Japan*, **39**, 494, 502 (1961).
128. H. Hirschfeld, *Fette Seifen Anstrichmittel*, **61**, 1233 (1959); *Farbenchemiker*, **61** (12), 1 (1959); through *CA*, **54**, 23363 (1960).
129. D. Hocking and P. J. White, *E. African Agr. Forest. J.*, **32**, 380 (1967).
130. Hoechst-Holland, Pamphlet, 1964. cf. German Pat. 1, 127, 140 (1962).
131. T. Hof and J. G. A. Luijten, *Timber Technol.*, **67**, 83 (1959); through *CA*, **54**, 25482 (1960).
132. T. D. Holmes and I. F. Storey, *Plant Pathol.*, **11**, 139 (1962); through *CA*, **58**, 9577 (1963).
133. H. S. Hopf, J. Duncan, J. S. S. Beesley, D. J. Webley, and R. F. Sturrock, *Bull. World Health Organ.*, **36**, 955 (1967).
134. F. Hostettler, and E. F. Cox, *Ind. Eng. Chem.*, **52**, 609 (1960).
134a. R. F. Hoyer and F. W. Plapp, *J. Econ. Entomol.*, **61**, 1269 (1968); through *CA*, **69**, 95403 (1968).
135. P. B. Hudson, G. Sanger and E. E. Sproul, *J. Am. Med. Ass.*, **169**, 89 (1959).
136. P. B. Hudson, G. Sanger, and E. E. Sproul, *Med. Ann. Dis. Columbia*, **28**, 68 (1959).
137. H. J. Hueck and J. G. A. Luijten, *J. Soc. Dyers Colourists*, **74**, 476 (1958).
138. H. J. Hueck, B. G. Ophuis, and J. C. Heusen, *Neth. J. Agr. Sci.*, **8**, 15 (1960); through *CA*, **55**, 12744 (1961).
139. I. G. Farbenindustrie, German Pat. 485,646 (1929), British Pat. 303,092 (1929); through *CZ*, **1929 II**, 2281, U.S. Pat. 1,744,633 (1930), Dutch Pat. 20,570 (1929); through *CZ*, **1930 I**, 146.
140. Imperial Chemical Industries, British Pat. 957,841 (1964); through *CA*, **61**, 9526 (1964).
141. R. K. Ingham and H. Gilman in *Inorganic Polymers* (F. G. A. Stone and W. A. G. Graham eds.), Academic Press, New York, U.S.A., 1962.
142. R. K. Ingham, S. D. Rosenberg and H. Gilman, *Chem. Rev.*, **60**, 459 (1960).
143. H. Iwamoto and M. Kikuchi, *Hakko Kyokaishi*, **17**, 306 (1959); *CA*, **55**, 5846 (1961).
144. W. A. Johnson, *Tin Its Uses*, **54**, 5 (1962).
145. A. Kaars Sijpesteijn, *Mededel. Landbouwhogeschool Opzoekingssta. Staat Gent*, **24**, 850 (1959).
146. A. Kaars Sijpesteijn, J. G. A. Luijten, and G. J. M. van der Kerk, in *Fungicides, An Advanced Treatise* (D. C. Torgeson, ed.), Academic Press, New York, 1969.
147. A. Kaars Sijpesteijn, F. Rijkens, J. G. A. Luijten, and L. C. Willemsens, *Antonie van Leeuwenhoek J. Microbiol. Serol.*, **28**, 346 (1962).
148. I. Kageyama and N. Miyamura (to Osaka Kinzoku Kogyo Co.), British Pat. 917,629 (1963); through *CA*, **58**, 9332 (1963).
149. L. Kahana and A. Kaars Sijpesteijn, *Antonie van Leeuwenhoek J. Microbiol. Serol.*, **33**, 427 (1967).
150. I. Kamitani and N. Hasegawa, *Kami-pa Gikyoshi*, **20**, 55 (1966); through *CA*, **64**, 9941 (1966).
151. E. E. Kenaga, *J. Econ. Entomol.*, **58**, 4 (1965); through *CA*, **62**, 9715 (1965), cf. *Chem. Eng. News*, **42** (30), 37 (1964).
151a. E. E. Kenaga (to Dow Chem. Co.), U.S. Pat. 3,264,177 (1966); through *CA*, **65**, 14364 (1966).
152. A. S. Kenyon, *Natl. Bur. Standards (U.S.) Circ.*, **525**, 81 (1953).
153. K. B. Kerr, *Poultry Sci.*, **31**, 328 (1952); through *CA*, **46**, 11557 (1952).
154. K. B. Kerr and A. W. Walde, *Exp. Parasitol.*, **5**, 560 (1956); through *CA*, **51**, 7566 (1957).

155. J. B. Kissam and S. B. Hays, *J. Econ Entomol.*, **59**, 748 (1966); through *CA*, **65**, 2939 (1966).
156. O. R. Klimmer, *Arzneimittel–Forsch.*, **13**, 432 (1963).
157. O. R. Klimmer, *Tin Its Uses*, **61**, 6 (1963).
158. O. R. Klimmer, personal communication (1965).
159. O. R. Klimmer and I. U. Nebel, *Arzneimittel–Forsch.*, **10**, 44 (1960).
159a. P. Klimsch and P. Kühnert, *Plaste Kaut.*, **16**, 242 (1969); through *CA*, **70**, 107023 (1969).
160. D. G. Knowles, *Plastics Technol.*, **6** (4), 35, 42 (1960).
161. D. A. Kochkin, V. I. Vashkov and V. P. Dremova, *Zh. Obshch. Khim.*, **34**, 325 (1964); through *CA*, **60**, 10706 (1964).
162. L. Kolditz and G. Furcht, *Z. Chem.*, **6**, 381 (1966).
163. E. Kröller, *Deut. Lebensm. Rundschau*, **56** (7), 190 (1960); through *CA*, **55**, 4666 (1961).
164. H. Kubo, *Agr. Biol. Chem. (Tokyo)*, **29**, 43 (1965); through *CA*, **63**, 7032 (1965).
165. C. E. Lane, *Sci. Am.*, **204** (2), 132 (1961).
166. L. C. Leatherland (to Permachem Corp.), U.S. Pat. 2,957,785 (1960); through *CA*, **55**, 5854 (1961).
167. R. le Breton, Ph.D. Thesis, Paris, France, 1962.
168. A. J. Leusink, J. G. Noltes, H. A. Budding and G. J. M. van der Kerk, **AD 629554** (1965); through *CA*, **68**, 13465 (1968).
169. W. R. Lewis and E. S. Hedges, *Adv. Chem. Ser.*, **23**, 190 (1959).
170. J. G. A. Luijten, *T.N.O.-Nieuws*, **10**, 179 (1955).
171. J. G. A. Luijten and S. Pezarro, *Brit. Plastics*, **30** (5), 183 (1957).
172. J. G. A. Luijten and G. J. M. van der Kerk, *A Survey of the Chemistry and Applications of Organotin Compounds*, Tin Research Institute, Greenford, England, 1952.
173. J. G. A. Luijten and G. J. M. van der Kerk, *J. Appl. Chem.*, **11**, 35 (1961).
174. W. H. Lyle, *Brit. J. Ind. Med.*, **15**, 193 (1958).
175. G. P. Mack, *Fibres Plastics*, **21**, 342 (1960).
176. P. N. Magee, H. B. Stoner, and J. M. Barnes, *J. Pathol. Bacteriol.*, **73**, 107 (1957).
177. G. C. Marks, J. L. Benton, and C. M. Thomas, *Soc. Chem. Ind.*, *Monograph*, **26**, 204 (1967).
178. H. McCombie and B. C. Saunders, *Nature*, **159**, 491 (1947).
179. R. N. Meals, *Ann. N.Y. Acad. Sci.*, **125**, 137 (1965).
180. J. Meisner and K. R. S. Ascher, *Z. Pflanzenkrankh.*, **72**, 458 (1965); *Agr. Chem.*, **21** (2), 14 (1966).
181. D. Meynier, Ph.D. Thesis, Toulouse, France, 1955 (publ. 1956).
182. S. M. Miller, *Tin Its Uses*, **65**, 1 (1964).
183. M. & T. Chemicals, Sheet No. 274 (1968).
184. A. S. Mufti and R. C. Poller, *Sci. Ind.*, **4** (3), 157 (1966).
185. A. S. Mufti and R. C. Poller, *Polymer*, **7** (12), 641 (1966); *J. Chem. Soc., C: Org.*, 1767 (1967).
186. A. Muhr, Swiss Pat. 336,923 (1959); through *CA*, **54**, 21785 (1960).
187. R. L. Muller, *World Rev. Pest Control*, **1** (2), 11 (1963).
188. W. P. Neumann, *Die Organische Chemie des Zinns*, F. Enke, Stuttgart, 1967.
189. K. Nishimoto and G. Fuse, *Tin Its Uses*, **70**, 3 (1966).
190. S. Nitzsche and M. Wick, *Kunststoffe*, **47**, 431 (1957).
191. W. Noll, *Chemie und Technologie der Silicone*, Chemie, Weinheim, Bergstr., Germany, 1960.
192. J. G. Noltes, J. G. A. Luijten, and G. J. M. van der Kerk, *J. Appl. Chem.* **11**, 38 (1961).
193. Noury & van der Lande, British Pat. 787,930 (1957); through *CA*, **52**, 7774 (1958).

194. Noury & van der Lande, Dutch Pat. Appl. 6406534 (1965); through *CA*, **64**, 16092 (1966).

195. Onderzoekingsinstituut "Research", Dutch Pat. 98325-98327 (1961); through *CA*, **55**, 27971 (1961).

196. Osmose Wood Preserving Co. of America, Pamphlet, 1963.

196a. Owens-Illinois Glass Company, Dutch Pat. Appl. 6404159 (1964).

197. H.P., *Brit. Med. J.*, **1958**, 515.

198. E. Parker, *Kunststoffe*, **47**, 443 (1957).

199. J. P. Pelissier, *Papeterie*, **86**, 1537 (1964); through *CA*, **66**, 56754 (1967).

199a. Pennsalt Chemicals Corp., U.S. Pat. 3,400,202 (1968); through *CA*, **69**, 105341 (1968).

199b. Pennsalt Chemicals Corp., Ger. Offen, 1,912,335 (1969); through *CA*, **72**, 20878 (1970).

200. Petrochemicals, Brit. Pat. 851,138 (1960); through *CA*, **55**, 9955 (1961).

201. K. Petzoldt and U. Reuss, *Gesundheitswesen und Desinfektion*, **58**, 106 (1966).

202. Philips-Duphar, Pamphlets, 1966.

203. D. Picco, *Notiz. Mal. Piante*, **72–73**, 3 (1965); through *CA*, **65**, 7929 (1966).

204. G. R. Pieper and J. E. Casida. *J. Econ. Entomol.*, **58**, 392 (1965); through *CA*, **63**, 2334 (1965).

205. A. J. Pieters, *Proc. Brit. Insecticide Fungicide Conf. Brighton, 1961*, **2**, 461 (1962).

205a. F. W. Plapp and R. F. Hoyer, *J. Econ. Entomol.*, **61**, 1298 (1968); through *CA*, **69**, 95405 (1968).

205b. R. C. Poller, *The Chemistry of Organotin Compounds*, Logos Press, 1969.

206. W. M. Quattlebaum, Jr. and C. A. Noffsinger, U.S. Pat. 2,307,157 (1943); through *CA*, **37**, 3533 (1943).

207. P. W. Ranby, *Tin Its Uses*, **54**, 9 (1962).

208. H. Rathman, Ph.D. Thesis, Amsterdam, Netherlands, 1962.

209. D. K. Reed, C. R. Crittenden and D. J. Lyon, *J. Econ. Entomol.*, **60**, 668 (1967); through *CA*, **67**, 20977 (1967).

210. G. Rees, *S. African Med. J.*, **36** (9) (1962); reprinted in *Tin Its Uses*, **60**, 1 (1963).

211. B. A. Richardson, *Wood*, June, 57 (1964); *Tin Its Uses*, **64**, 5 (1964).

211a. B. A. Richardson, *British Wood Preservers Association, Annual Convention, 1970.*

212. S. A. Riethmayer, *Kunst.-Rundschau*, **10**, 277, 345 (1963).

213. W. M. Rogoff, P. H. Kohler and R. N. Duxbury, *J. Econ. Entomol.*, **53**, 183 (1960), and publications cited therein.

214. M. S. Rose and W. N. Aldridge, *Biochem. J.*, **106** (1968).

215. A. Ross, *Ann. N.Y. Acad. Sci.*, **125**, 107 (1965).

216. P. Russel, *Chem. Ind. London*, 642 (1961).

217. J. Salquain, *Teintex*, **26**, 615 (1961); through *CA*, **56**, 6413 (1962).

218. Sangyo Ikusei Co., Japanese Pat. 1411 (1960); through *CA*, **54**, 18974 (1960).

219. A. E. Saunders and W. E. Wagner (to Pittsburgh Plate Glass Co.), U.S. Pat. 3,107,177 (1963); through *CA*, **60**, 1221 (1964).

220. J. H. Saunders and K. C. Frisch, *Polyurethanes: Chemistry and Technology.* Part I. *Chemistry* (1962). Part II. *Technology* (1964). Vol. XVI of the series *High Polymers*, Interscience, New York.

221. Schering, German Pat. 1,042,795 (1961); through *CA*, **54**, 23365 (1960). Concordant patents are: Belgian Pat. 569,339 (1958), British Pat. 846,687 (1960), French Pat. 1,197,586 (1959) and Dutch Pat. Appl. 229,992 (1961).

222. H. Schulz-Utermöhl and H. Weissenstein, *Gesundheitswesen und Desinfektion*, **57** (4), (1965).

223. B. L. Sheaffer and F. H. Conaty, Paper presented at S.A.E. National Transportation, Powerplant and Fuels and Lubricants Meeting, Baltimore, Maryland, U.S.A., Md. October 1964; *Tin Its Uses*, **69**, 9 (1965).

224. Società Edison-Settore Chimico, Dutch Pat. Appl. 6503797 (1965); through *CA*, **64**, 8340 (1966).

225. T. N. Srivastava, and S. K. Tandon, *Indian J. Appl. Chem.*, **27** (3-4), 116 (1964); through *CA*, **62**, 4359 (1965).

226. H. Stecker, *Tin Its Uses*, **41**, 13 (1957).

227. H. B. Stoner, *Brit. J. Ind. Med.*, **23**, 222 (1966).

228. H. B. Stoner, J. M. Barnes, and J. I. Duff, *Brit. J. Pharmacol.*, **10**, 16 (1955).

229. L. L. Stotskaya, A. V. Topchiev, and B. A. Krentsel, *Dokl. Akad. Nauk SSSR*, **146**, 372 (1962); through *CA*, **59**, 7652 (1963).

230. J. R. Tigner and J. F. Besser, *J. Agr. Food Chem.*, **10**, 484 (1962).

231. R. M. Torack, *Am. J. Pathol.*, **46**, 245 (1965).

232. *Ullmans Encyklopädie der Technischen Chemie*, Vol. 15, Urban & Schwarzenberg, München, 1964.

233. Union Carbide Corp., Brit. Pat. 873,498 and 873,499 (1961); through *CA*, **56**, 3654, 3655 (1962).

234. R. F. van der Heide, *The Safety for Health of Plastics Food Packaging Materials. Principles and Chemical Methods*, Ph.D. Thesis, Utrecht, Netherlands, 1964.

235. R. F. van der Heide, *Z. Lebensm. Untersuch. u.-Forsch.*, **124**, 348 (1964).

236. G. J. M. van der Kerk and J. G. A. Luijten, *J. Appl. Chem.*, **4**, 314 (1954).

237. G. J. M. van der Kerk and J. G. A. Luijten, *Tin Its Uses*, **32**, 16 (1955).

238. G. J. M. van der Kerk and J. G. A. Luijten, *J. Appl. Chem.*, **6**, 56 (1956).

239. G. J. M. van der Kerk, J. G. A. Luijten, J. C. van Egmond, and J. G. Noltes, *Chimia* (*Aarau*), **16**, 36 (1962).

240. H. Verity Smith, *Plastics (London)*, **17** (9), 264 (1952).

241. H. Verity Smith, *Brit. Plastics*, **25** (9) 304 (1952).

242. H. Verity Smith, *Brit. Plastics*, **27** (5), 176, (6) 213 (8), 307 (1954), **29** (10), 373 (1956), **35** (9), 466 (1962).

243. H. Verity Smith, *The Development of the Organotin Stabilizers*, Tin Research Institute, Greenford, England, 1959.

244. H. Verity Smith, *Rubber J. Intern. Plastics* (June 25, 1960).

245. H. Verity Smith, *Rubber Plastics Weekly*, 21 October (1961).

246. H. Verity Smith, *Brit. Plastics*, **37** (8), 445 (1964).

247. H. G. Verschuren, R. Kroes, H. H. Vink, and G. J. van Esch, *Fd. Cosmet. Toxicol.*, **4**, 35 (1966).

248. H. P. Vind and H. Hochman, *Proc. Amer. Wood-Preservers' Ass.*, **58**, 170 (1962); *Tin Its Uses*, **57**, 10 (1962); through *CA*, 58, 7031 (1963).

249. R. von Hösslin, *Deut. Gartenbauwirtsch.*, **8**, 231 (1960).

250. E. L. Weinberg (to Metal & Thermit Corp.), U.S. Pat. 2,915,428 (1959); through *CA*, **54**, 6128 (1960).

251. E. L. Weinberg et al. (to Metal & Thermit Corp.), U.S. Pat. 2,789,102, 2,789,107, 2,790,785 (1957); through *CA*, **51**, 10930, 10940 (1957).

252. E. L. Weinberg and E. W. Johnson, U.S. Pat. 2,648,650 (1963); through *CA*, **48**, 10056 (1964).

253. P. Whiteley, *J. Oil Colour Chem. Ass.*, **48**, 172 (1965).

254. H. R. Wilson, J. L. Fry and J. E. Jones, *Poultry Sci.*, **46**, 304 (1967); through *CA*, **66**, 92762 (1967).

255. S. L. Wit and K. L. van Lier, *Verslag. Mededel. Betreffende Volksgezondheid,* 180 (1960); through *CA,* **54,** 21534 (1960).
256. Woods Hole Oceanographic Institution, *Marine Fouling and Its Prevention.* U.S. Naval Institute, Annapolis, Maryland, U.S.A., 1952.
257. V. Yngve, U.S. Pat. 2,219,463 (1940); through *CA,* **35,** 1145 (1941).
258. V. Yngve, U.S. Pat. 2,307,092 (1943); through *CA,* **37,** 3532 (1943).
259. Yokohama Rubber Co., U.S. Pat., 3,108,010 (1963).
260. Z. Yoshida and H. Miyoshi, *Kogyo Kagaku Zasshi,* **68,** 580 (1965); through *CA,* **64,** 9890 (1966).
261. D. M. Young, F. Hostettler and C. F. Horn (to Union Carbide Corp.), U.S. Pat. 2,890,208 (1959); through *CA,* **53,** 18546 (1959).
262. R. J. Zedler, *Tin Its Uses,* **53,** 7 (1961).
263. R. J. Zedler, *Trav. Centre Rech. Etud. Oceanogr.,* **6,** 401 (1965); through *CA,* **66,** 105934 (1967).
264. R. J. Zedler and C. B. Beiter, *Soap Chem. Specialities,* **38,** (3), 75, 101 (1962).
265. W. Zeman, E. Gadermann, and K. Hardebeck, *Deut. Arch. Klin. Med.,* **178,** 713 (1951); through *CA,* **46,** 6265 (1952).

13. ORGANOTIN POLYMERS

MALCOLM C. HENRY AND WENZEL E. DAVIDSOHN

US Army Natick Laboratories
Natick, Massachusetts

I.	Introduction	975
II.	Tin Atoms Pendent to Polymer Chain	977
	A. Organotin Polymers	977
	B. Organotin Polyolefins	981
	C. Organotin Aluminoxanes and Titanoxanes	982
III.	Tin Atoms in Polymer Backbone	984
	A. Organotin Polyesters	985
	B. Organotin Polyolefins	985
	C. Polyfunctional Tin-Containing Polymers	987
	D. Organotin Chelate Polymers	989
	E. Miscellaneous Organotin Polymers	990
References		994

I. Introduction

The rapidly developing technology of today has established requirements for new organic materials with combinations of properties presently unknown. The search for new chemical structures and the investigation of their properties are natural challenges to the polymer chemist who is expected to meet these requirements.

Polymers based upon a purely carbon backbone have received the most extensive attention, and, most recently, polymers with elements other than carbon also have begun to be investigated. Thus heteroatomic polymers containing not only carbon but nitrogen, oxygen, and sulfur, for example, have been prepared and characterized.

With the exception of the silicones, polymer structures consisting of regular repeating moieties with group IV atoms contained therein have thus far received relatively minor attention.

There are numerous types of polymers with tin atoms in the repeating moiety. Those containing only tin-carbon bonding can be of two basic types, one in which the tin is present in the polymer backbone and another in which the tin atom is bonded to carbon but is located pendent to the main polymer chain.

Tin-oxygen polymers have also been described where at least one of the bonds of the tin atom is attached to oxygen. In these instances the tin-oxygen bonding constitutes part of the main polymer chain. No cases have been described where tin-carbon bonding constitutes the main chain with the remaining bonding off the main chain being tin-oxygen bonds.

Polymers having multiple tin-tin bonding are known, but these structures will not be dealt with in any great detail. It is not yet possible to create polymers of sufficient size to be useful where only tin-tin bonding constitutes the polymer chain. Polymers with blocks or units of multiple tin-tin bonding alternating with sequences of carbon chains are not known.

The literature dealing with organotin polymers is not extensive. Henry and Davidsohn (27) have described, in a short paper, group IV containing organometallic polymers in general. Neumann (64), Stone and Graham (77), Lappert and Leigh (48), and Andrianov (3) have published texts in which there are sections on organotin polymers. A considerable proportion of the remaining information is found in the patent literature. The literature referred to in this chapter on tin polymers is not intended to be an exhaustive bibliography; rather, an effort has been made to describe representative structures and to cite references which would make it possible to locate additional information if it is so desired.

General considerations that deal with tin polymers as being true analogs of carbon polymers can be useful if not overextended. In cases where the tin atom is far removed from the reaction site, useful analogies can be made in regard to monomer synthesis and polymerization conditions. Specifically, however, the tin-hydrogen bond cannot be considered to be equivalent to the carbon-hydrogen bond; thus there is no stable tin analog of the methyl group. Although methyl acrylate, $CH_2{=}CHCOOCH_3$, might initially seem analogous to trimethyltin acrylate, $CH_2{=}CHCOOSn(CH_3)_3$, from the point of view that they are both $CH_2{=}CHCOOR'$ type molecules, it soon becomes quite clear that the methyl group is not simply an analog of the trimethyltin group. Differences in reactivity of the trimethyltin group attached to oxygen, the stability of the tin-carbon bond, and the relatively large size of the tin atom and methyl groups make these analogies rather tenuous. It is true, however, that both monomers, under certain conditions, can be polymerized if the reaction site is selected to be the vinyl group in each case.

From a synthetic point of view, organotin polymers containing only tin bonded directly to carbon are perhaps the most readily synthesized. Polymers with tin atoms in the chain are prepared by condensation methods. Polymers containing organotin groups, pendent to a carbon backbone are generally obtained by free radical initiated polymerizations.

II. Tin Atoms Pendent to Polymer Chain

A. ORGANOTIN POLYMERS

$$+CH_2-CH+_n$$
$$\mid$$
$$COOSnR_3$$

Commercially available polyacrylates and polymethacrylates are linear polymers with pendent ester groups:

$$+CH_2-C-C(R)+_n$$
$$\mid$$
$$COOR'$$

$$\text{where } R = H, CH_3$$

A number of organotin polyesters of this basic type have been prepared where the R' group contains a tin atom.

1. *Monomer Synthesis*

Three general methods exist for preparing unsaturated organotin ester monomers. The first method (*39, 47*) is the reaction of an unsaturated organic acid salt with an organotin halide as follows:

$$4\text{-}n \text{ } RCH{=}CR'COONa + R''_nSnX_{4-n} \longrightarrow (RCH{=}CR'COO)_{4-n}SnR''_n + 4\text{-}n \text{ } NaX \tag{1}$$

where $n = 0$–3,

R, R' = hydrogen, alkyl, aryl, alkaryl, aralkyl
R'' = alkyl, aryl, alkaryl, aralkyl

The second method involves the reaction of organotin oxides or hydroxides with unsaturated organic acids (*1, 30, 32, 33, 41–43, 45, 46, 54, 75*):

$$(R_3M)_2O + 2 \text{ } R'CH{=}CR''COOH \longrightarrow 2 \text{ } R'CH{=}CR''COOMR_3 + H_2O \tag{2}$$
$$R_3MOH + R'CH{=}CR''COOH \longrightarrow R'CH{=}CR''COOMR_3 + H_2O \tag{3}$$
$$(R_2MO)_x + 2 \text{ } XR'CH{=}CR''COOH \longrightarrow x \text{ } R_2M(OOCCR''{=}CR'H)_2 + x \text{ } H_2O \tag{4}$$

The third general method is the reaction of tetraaryltin with unsaturated organic acids:

$$R_4M + 2 \text{ } R'CH{=}CR''COOH \longrightarrow R_2M(OOCCR''{=}CR'H)_2 + 2 \text{ } RH \tag{5}$$

Alkoxy and acyloxy groups attached to tin are also cleaved by acidic protons. Of the three general methods described, the second method is perhaps the most versatile due to the ready availability of organotin oxides or hydroxides. Methods one and three have also been applied without difficulties, and the starting materials are reasonably accessible. Variations of reactions (1)–(5) have been made that lend further possibilities to the subsequent polymerizations. Functionally substituted acids have been used as follows (*19, 21, 55, 56, 58*):

$$R_2SnO + 2\,XCH_2COOH \longrightarrow R_2Sn(OOCCH_2X)_2$$

$$\text{where}\quad X = \text{-OH, -SH, -NH}_2 \text{ and -COOH}$$

Vinyl benzoic and vinyl naphthoic acids and their salts have been used as shown in reactions (1)–(5) to form vinylbenzoate tin esters starting with organotin oxides and halides of a variety of types (*1, 50*). These salts were in turn polymerized as described in a later section.

2. *Polymerizations*

The general polymerization reaction to form organotin polyesters is illustrated for the case of trimethyltin methacrylate:

$$CH_2 = C(CH_3) \xrightarrow{\text{peroxide}} +CH_2-C(CH_3)+$$
$$\qquad\quad | \qquad\qquad\qquad\qquad\qquad |$$
$$\quad COOSn(CH_3)_3 \qquad\qquad\qquad COOSn(CH_3)_3$$

Polymerizations of organometallic esters containing olefinic linkages may be carried out using heat, peroxides, free radical catalysts or mercaptan-persulfate initiators, and using bulk, solution, or water emulsion techniques. In general, techniques established in the field of polymer chemistry for polymerizing unsaturated systems will be successful in polymerizing olefinic organotin esters. From a chemical point of view, the organotin ester function has little influence on the course of the reaction assuming conditions are utilized that do not cleave the tin-oxygen bond, as for example in a situation favoring transesterification. The properties of the resultant polymers are definitely influenced by the organotin moiety even though the polymerization conditions are not normally influenced by it. However, in a comparison study it was interesting to note that triphenyltin methacrylate polymerizes more rapidly than methyl methacrylate under the same conditions (*44*).

A considerable number of organotin polyesters having the generalized structure

$$+CR_2-CR'+ \qquad \text{where}\quad R \text{ and } R'=H \text{ or alkyl}$$
$$\qquad | \qquad\qquad\qquad\qquad R''=\text{alkyl}$$
$$\quad COOSnR''$$

have been prepared from their respective monomers and polymerized using peroxide, bulk and emulsion polymerizations using potassium persulfate and lauryl mercaptan initiators (*31, 54, 74*). When $x = 3$, linear-type elastomers are obtained. When $x = 2$, nonelastomeric crosslinked plastics result as follows:

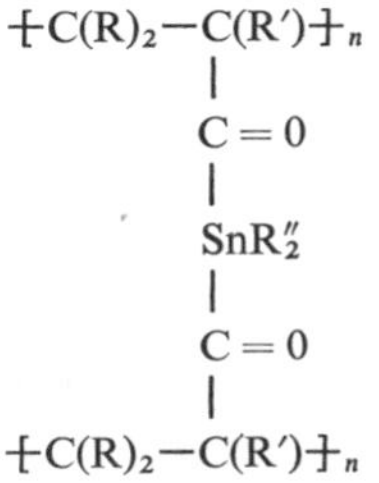

$$
\begin{array}{c}
+C(R)_2-C(R')+_n \\
| \\
C=0 \\
| \\
SnR''_2 \\
| \\
C=0 \\
| \\
+C(R)_2-C(R')+_n
\end{array}
$$

Molecular weights are reported to be in the neighborhood of 162,000. Such polymers may find application as films, foils, coatings, and impregnating agents. Russian (*73*) and Australian (*18*) workers have described polymers of similar types.

Adrova et al. (*1*) have prepared polytributylin-4'-vinyl-4-biphenylcarboxylate and reported it to be a colorless polymer soluble in toluene and stable at 165°C:

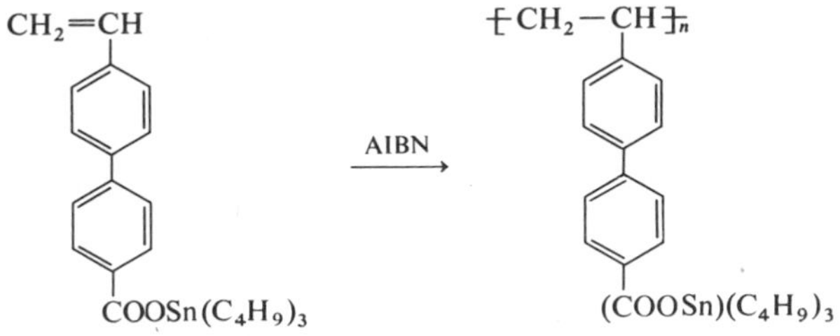

Similarly Leebrick (*50*) prepared an analogous series of polymers based upon vinylbenzoic acid as follows:

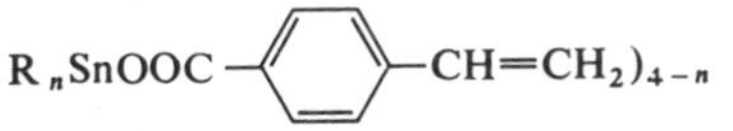

These monomers were homo- and copolymerized with other vinyl-type monomers. The polymers contain at least one tin ester unit in the polymeric structure as illustrated below:

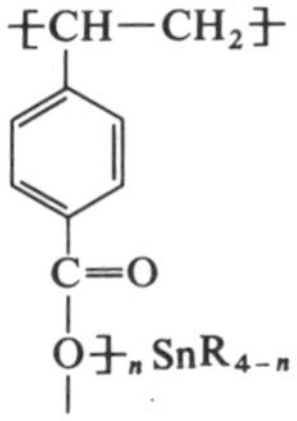

The use of a disubstituted organotin-*p*-vinylbenzoate results in the formation of a polymeric unit designated as follows:

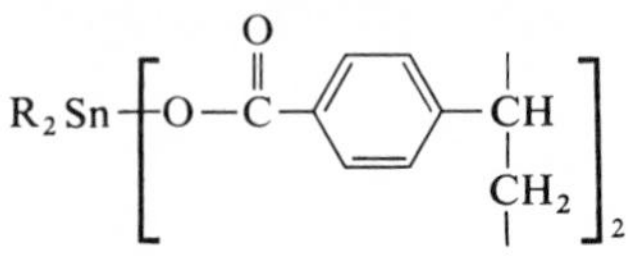

$$R_2Sn\left[O-\overset{\overset{\displaystyle O}{\|}}{C}-\underset{}{\bigcirc}-\overset{\displaystyle CH}{\underset{\displaystyle CH_2}{|}}\right]_2$$

Polytributyltin *p*-vinylbenzoate is reported to a brown rubbery polymer when polymerized with a peroxide and a strong tacky rubber when emulsion polymerized. Copolymerization of tributyltin *p*-vinylbenzoate and *p*-chlorostyrene in an emulsion system and peroxide catalyzed produced a spongy rubber. A similarly prepared copolymer of dibutyltin-*bis*-*p*-vinylbenzoate and styrene formed films out of tetrahydrofuran. These monomers incorporated into polymeric systems impart unleachable fungicidal activity and increased general stability.

Kochkin (*34*) and Rzaev (*70*) have studied a series of organotin co- and terpolymers. These studies resulted from the observation that tributyltin oxide when reacted with maleic anhydride forms a corresponding disubstituted organotin ester as follows:

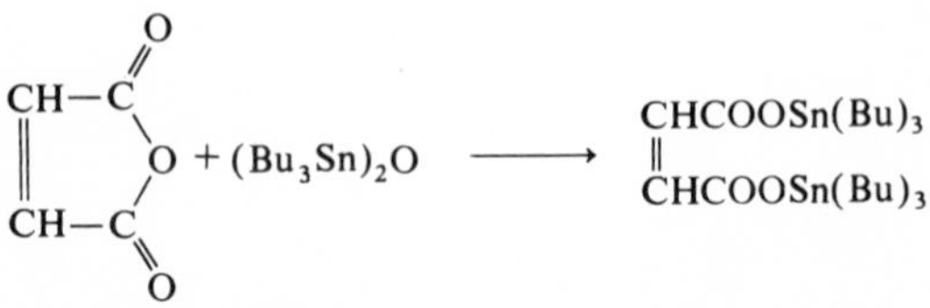

$$\begin{matrix} CH-C \\ \| \qquad \diagdown \\ \qquad O + (Bu_3Sn)_2O \\ CH-C \diagup \\ \| \qquad \diagdown \\ \qquad O \end{matrix} \longrightarrow \begin{matrix} CHCOOSn(Bu)_3 \\ \| \\ CHCOOSn(Bu)_3 \end{matrix}$$

Thus terpolymers of maleic anhydride, styrene, and the organotin diester of maleic anhydride, have been prepared with the following generalized structure:

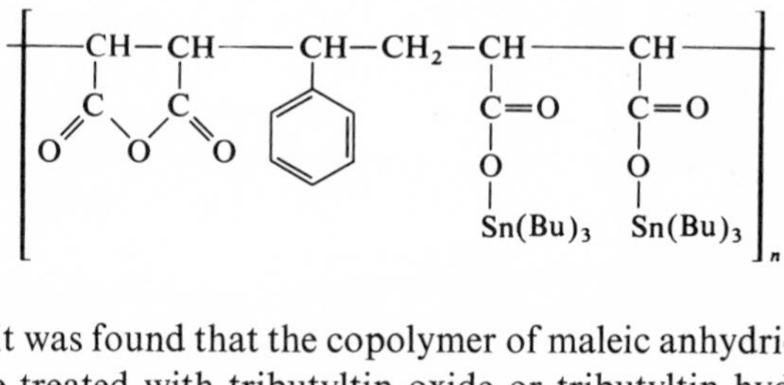

$$\left[\begin{matrix} -CH-CH & CH-CH_2-CH & CH- \\ \diagup C \diagdown C \diagdown & \bigcirc & \underset{\underset{\underset{Sn(Bu)_3}{O}}{|}}{C=O} \quad \underset{\underset{\underset{Sn(Bu)_3}{O}}{|}}{C=O} \\ O \quad O \quad O \end{matrix}\right]_n$$

Alternatively it was found that the copolymer of maleic anhydride and styrene could itself be treated with tributyltin oxide or tributyltin hydroxide with a resultant esterification of the anhydride group in the polymer chain as follows:

$$\left[\begin{array}{c} CH-CH \quad\quad CH-CH_2 \\ | \quad\quad | \\ C \quad\quad C \\ O \diagup \diagdown O \diagdown O \end{array} \right]_n \xrightarrow[\substack{R_3S_nOH \\ \\ (R_3S_n)_2O}]{} \begin{array}{l} \left[\begin{array}{c} CH-CH \quad\quad\quad CH-CH_2 \\ | \quad\quad | \\ C=O \quad C=O \\ | \quad\quad | \\ O \quad\quad OH \\ | \\ SnR_3 \end{array} \right]_n \\ \\ \left[\begin{array}{c} CH-CH \quad\quad\quad CH-CH_2 \\ | \quad\quad | \\ C=O \quad C=O \\ | \quad\quad | \\ O \quad\quad O \\ | \quad\quad | \\ SnR_3 \quad SnR_3 \end{array} \right]_n \end{array}$$

Introduction of Bu_3Sn groups raises the T_g values nearly 100°C. Softening points of the tin esterified maleic anhydride-styrene copolymer are reported to be in the vicinity of 300°C. These polymers are resistant to ultraviolet aging and have bactericidal and general anti-microbial behavior.

B. ORGANOTIN POLYOLEFINS

Organotin polymers containing tin atoms pendent to the main hydrocarbon chain and in addition, containing exclusively tin-carbon bonds, are usually formed from organotin monomers where a vinyl grouping exists not directly adjacent to the tin atom. Normally it can be expected that when the olefinic group is attached directly to a tin atom, back donation of the pi electrons from the olefin to the tin atom will deactivate the vinyl group to the point where polymerization is difficult to accomplish. Thus Korshak (*36*) in studying the polymerization of trialkylvinyltin compounds found that even using pressures of 6000 atm at 120°C for 6 h, only trimers were formed. Minoura (*53*) also has studied the phenomenon of the deactivation of vinyl groups directly attached to a tin atom. Using trimethylvinyltin and tributylvinyltin as model compounds and x-rays, radical or ionic initiation, it was found impossible to successfully carry out polymerizations. This same investigation, however, did result in the synthesis of several new copolymer systems. Even though the triakylvinyltin compounds could not be induced to undergo homopolymerizations, in the presence of styrene or methyl methacrylate and a radical initiator, true copolymers were obtained. Four copolymer types were prepared: (a) styrene-trimethylvinyltin, (b) methylmethacrylate-trimethylvinyltin, (c) styrene-tributylvinyltin, and (d) methylmethacrylate-tribuytlvinyltin. It was concluded that since the rate of copolymerization decreased with increasing molar ratio of the vinyltin compounds/comonomer that the rate of addition of styrene or methylmethacrylate to its own radical is significantly greater than that of the organometallic compound monomer unit. Thus although reactions were carried out in equimolar quantities the resultant polymers are predominantly composed of polystyrene or polymethylmethacrylate block units:

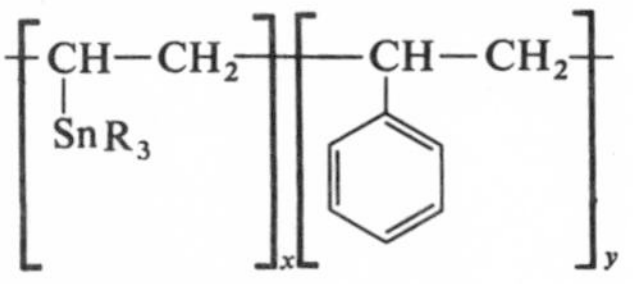

$$
\left[\begin{array}{c} CH-CH_2 \\ | \\ SnR_3 \end{array} \right]_x \left[\begin{array}{c} CH-CH_2 \\ | \\ \bigcirc \end{array} \right]_y \qquad \left[\begin{array}{c} CH-CH_2 \\ | \\ SnR_3 \end{array} \right]_x \left[\begin{array}{c} CH(CH_3)-CH_2 \\ | \\ COOCH_3 \end{array} \right]_y
$$

where y is many times larger than x.

It will be seen in the following sections that when the olefinic group is not directly attached to the tin atom more conventional reactivity of the double bonds toward polymerization reactions may be realized.

1. *Organotin Polybutadiene*

The monomer 2-tributyltin-1,3-butadiene prepared from the Grignard of 2-chloro-1,3-butadiene and tributyltin oxide has been used to form an interesting organotin polymer *(4)*. As indicated above, the polymerization was as to be expected, rather slow. Nevertheless, using a bulk type polymerization and azo *bis*-isobutyronitrile as a catalyst, added incrementally at 2–3 day intervals for 24 days at 60°C, a clear colorless viscous liquid polymer was obtained in yields of 29%. The inherent viscosity (0.1% in benzene at 25°C) was 0.47. Fractionation resulted in a fraction with an inherent viscosity of 0.70. The glass transition temperature was between −80°C and −90°C. The structure was predominantly 1,4 with a *cis*-configuration as shown below:

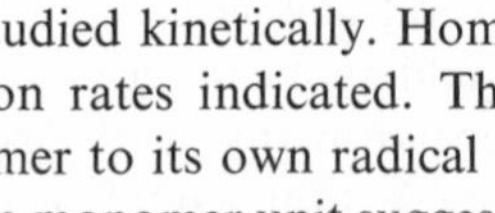

$$
\begin{array}{cc} (C_4H_9)_3Sn & H \\ \diagdown & \diagup \\ C=C \\ \diagup & \diagdown \\ \big(H_2C & CH_2 \big)_n \end{array}
$$

2. *Organotin Polystyrenes*

Copolymers of p-triphenyltin styrene and styrene or vinyl toluene, prepared by Sandler *(71, 72)* were studied kinetically. Homopolymers and copolymers were prepared and reaction rates indicated. The rate of addition of a p-triphenyltin styrene monomer to its own radical is greater than the addition of a styrene or vinyl toluene monomer unit suggesting that small blocks of the tin monomer units should be present in the polymer network. A useful series of polymeric organotin containing ion exchange materials have been prepared by Kolditz *(35)*. p-Styryl organotin compounds $(CH_2=CHC_6H_4)_nSnR_{4-n}$ prepared from organotin halides and the Grignard derivative of p-bromo-styrene were homo- and copolymerized with heat and a radical catalyst to obtain organotin polymers that could in turn be transformed into polyorganotin ion exchangers. Three different cationic ion exchange materials were prepared: (a) sulfonation of polystyryltin resulted in the introduction of sulfonic acid groups into the polymer; a similar material was obtained by copolymerization of tetrastyryltin and *p*-vinylbenzene sulfonic acid; (b) mixed polymerization of tetrastyryltin and maleic acid results in a carboxylic acid type ion exchanger; and (c) phosphorylation of the polystyryltin polymer resulted in a phosphate cationic exchanger. Anionic exchangers were obtained by reactions as follows: (a) bis(*p*-dimethylaminophenyl)-distyryltin and *p*-dimethylaminophenyl-tristyryltin polymerized by AIBN were quarternized with methyl iodide to yield ion exchangers with $-N^+(CH_3)_3$ groups and (b) polytetrastyryltin was chloromethylated and then aminated to yield an ion exchanger based upon available $-CH_2N^+(CH_3)_3$ groups.

3. *Organotin Polyvinyls*

Organotin polymers derived from monomers of the type:

$$
\begin{array}{c}
R \\
| \\
R'-Sn-(CH_2)_nCH=CH_2 \\
| \\
R''
\end{array}
$$

(where $n = 1-4$ and R, R' and R" = aliphatic, aromatic or cycloaliphatic groupings) have been prepared using stereospecific catalysts prepared from a titanium halide reacting with an alkyl aluminum compound (*32*). The crystallinity of these compounds is in general over 40% and they are isotactic in nature. Copolymers of the organotin monomers with other vinyl monomers should be possible to prepare using similar type catalysts; however, no data is available on any specific polymer structures.

Two short Russian patents (*66, 76*) have described the polymerization of organotin substituted vinyl monomers using alkyl lithium and Grignard reagents as initiators for the polymerization. Only very limited information is presented therein. The polymers were derived from vinyl acetylene and the final products contained tin in approximately 40% by weight.

C. ORGANOTIN ALUMINOXANES AND TITANOXANES

Stannoxy-aluminoxane polymers which have organotin side groups and possess outstanding thermal stability have been prepared from monomers of the type $(R_3SnO)_nAl(OR')_{3-n}$ where $n = 1-3$ and R and R' represent alkyl, aryl, aralkyl, alkaryl or mixed alkyl and aryl radicals (*69*). The polymers can be formed using high temperature conditions with or without pressure and an alkali metal alcoholate catalyst. Typical reactions are as follows:

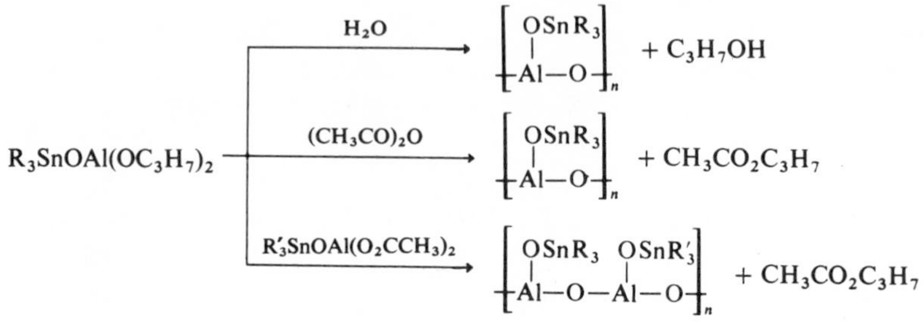

$$R_3SnOAl(OC_3H_7)_2 \begin{cases} \xrightarrow{H_2O} & \left[\begin{matrix} OSnR_3 \\ | \\ Al-O \end{matrix}\right]_n + C_3H_7OH \\[3ex] \xrightarrow{(CH_3CO)_2O} & \left[\begin{matrix} OSnR_3 \\ | \\ Al-O \end{matrix}\right]_n + CH_3CO_2C_3H_7 \\[3ex] \xrightarrow{R_3'SnOAl(O_2CCH_3)_2} & \left[\begin{matrix} OSnR_3 & OSnR_3' \\ | & | \\ Al-O-Al-O \end{matrix}\right]_n + CH_3CO_2C_3H_7 \end{cases}$$

These polymers range from liquids to thermoplastic solids and the cross-linked products derived therefrom may be useful as laminating, molding, varnish, embedding or elastomeric resins.

Similarly organostannoxy titanoxane polymers and copolymers can be prepared from monomers of the type $(R_3SnO)_nTi(OR')_{4-n}$ where $n = 1$–3 and R and R' represent alkyl, aryl, aralkyl, alkaryl or mixed alkyl and aryl radicals (*69*). The methods of preparation of the polymers are similar to those used for the stannoxy-aluminoxanes described above. The uses proposed are also similar.

III. Tin Atoms in Polymer Backbone

The synthesis of polymers containing tin atoms in the polymer backbone are carried out, generally, via condensation type reactions. Thus difunctionally substituted organotin compounds are usually selected to react with organo-monomers which also possess di-functionality.

The nomenclature of such polymers, as regard classification, becomes somewhat unwieldy so that certain arbitrary descriptions become necessary to avoid undue confusion. Thus organotin polyesters will be described where the tin-ester linkage is not only the repeating essential unit of the polymer but also the site where the tin ester linkage is formed from the condensation of the monomers. Polyester tin polymers on the other hand are polymers which have ester linkages as the repeating units of the polymer and as far as the polymerization is concerned the tin atoms are only more or less incidental. Similar differentiation can conveniently be made between other functional classes of polymers such as polyurethanes, polyethers, etc.:

$+Sn(R)_2OOCR'COO+_n$ (a) Organotin polyester R,R' = Hydrocarbon

$+OOCR_{Sn}+_n$ (b) Polyester organotin RSn contains tin atom

A. Organotin Polyesters

Organotin dihalides react with the sodium salt of diacids directly or with diacids converted in situ just prior to the polymerization:

$$R_2SnCl_2 + R'(COONa)_2 \longrightarrow \ \ +Sn(R_2)OOCR'COO+_n + 2\ NaCl$$
(where R and R' are hydrocarbon radicals)

Thus, for example, acid salts derived from adipic, sebacic, terephthalic, fumaric, itaconic, citric, succinic, and acetylene dicarboxylic acids may be cited as typical starting monomers. Reaction conditions are not critical for these polymerizations and a wide range of possibilities exists for varying the structure of the polymer through proper selection of the organic monomer. Thio acids, for example, result in organotin polyesters containing sulphur. Organotin polyesters have biological activity, are stable and in some cases have been made into fibers (20).

Alternatively, organotin diacetates and even dibutyltin oxide can be reacted with organic diacids to form similar products (2). The products are less well characterized and molecular weights reported indicate a lower order of polymerization due in part to cyclization reactions

The condensation products of a bisphenol and a mixture of a diorganotin dihalide and an acyl halide of a dicarboxylic acid are reported to be linear polymers wherein tin is an integral part of and randomly distributed in the main polymer chain (28). The compositions of these polymers are not well understood and can most conveniently be represented as follows:

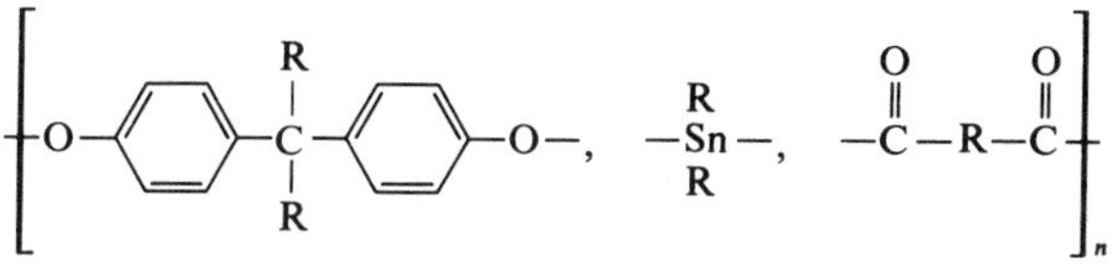

These compositions are described as having good thermal stability and fire retarding properties. They are suitable for stabilizers in polyvinyl chloride, useful as wood preservatives, in the treatment of textiles for imparting insect resistance, and as surface coatings.

Interfacial polymerization techniques are used to prepare these random terpolymers. The relative amounts of the monomers in the final product have not been established except for one case where the resultant polymer contained about 2.5% tin indicating that the predominant reaction is the normal polyester condensation reaction between the bisphenol and the difunctional acid.

B. Organotin Polyolefins

The following type of organotin polymers containing only carbon-tin bonds in the backbone can be prepared:

$$\left[\begin{array}{cc} R'_{4-(x+z)} & R'_{z-(y+x)} \\ | & | \\ (C_nH_{2n})_x-Sn-(C_nH_{2n})_y-Sn- \end{array}\right]_x$$

where R' is an alkyl group having from 2 to 12 atoms, phenyl and hydrogen, each C_nH_{2n} moiety directly bridging two tin atoms, y and z indicating the number of such independent bridges, $n = 2$ and 4, x is an integer having a value of 2–10, y an integer 2–3 and z an integer 1–2, $y + 2$ not being greater than 4 (68). To obtain these polymers, tin halides or organotin halides are treated with olefins, aluminum and hydrogen at elevated pressures.

Poly-addition reactions involving organotin dihydrides and diolefins have been studied by Noltes and van der Kerk (65, 80) and by German workers (6):

$$R_2SnH_2 + CH_2{=}CH{-}R{-}CH{=}CH_2 \longrightarrow \left[\begin{array}{c} R \\ | \\ SnCH_2CH_2RCH_2CH_2 \\ | \\ R \end{array}\right]_n$$

The use of alkyl aluminum catalysts such as di-isobutyl aluminum hydride as a catalyst in these hydrostannations offers more versatility to the reactions (62, 63). Trihydrides of tin and diolefins react as follows:

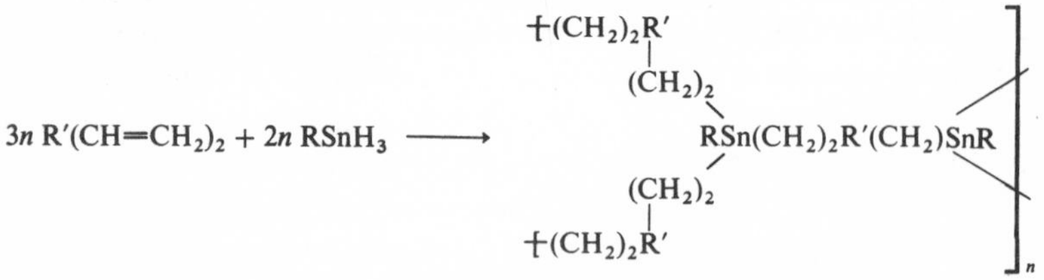

$$3n\ R'(CH{=}CH_2)_2 + 2n\ RSnH_3 \longrightarrow \left[\begin{array}{c} {+}(CH_2)_2R' \\ | \\ (CH_2)_2 \\ \diagdown \\ RSn(CH_2)_2R'(CH_2)SnR \\ \diagup \\ (CH_2)_2 \\ | \\ {+}(CH_2)_2R' \end{array}\right]_n$$

When organoluminum catalysts are employed high molecular weight products are obtained ranging from thick oils to elastomers.

The utilization of the organotin hydride reaction with olefins discovered by Noltes and van der Kerk has been extended to form another series of interesting polymers. Although not fully described, what appear to be block copolymers containing tin may be prepared by the reaction of organotin hydrides such as di-isobutyltin dihydride with butadiene or isoprene followed by a further copolymerization step with olefins such as styrene, acrylonitrile, acrylic acid, acrylic esters, ethylene, vinyl halides, etc. (22, 60). The initial step, a partial polymerization between a diene and an organotin dihydride, is conducted in such a fashion that a product containing at least four butadiene units is obtained which contains 30% tin. This prepolymer is then copolymerized with a wide variety of olefin monomers using standard olefin catalysts as, for example, butyllithium. The products are claimed to be uv light stable, to have shock resistance and good tensile properties.

Stanno-neocarborane polymers can be synthesized by reaction of dilithium-neocarborane and diphenyltin dichloride to yield colorless amorphous substances soluble in THF and chloroform (*8*). Number average molecular weights were between 514 and 9500. The structures of these polymers are represented by the generalized formula shown below:

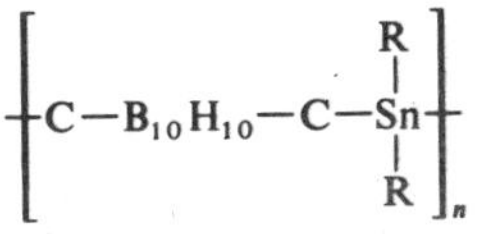

$$\left[C - B_{10}H_{10} - C - \underset{\underset{R}{|}}{\overset{\overset{R}{|}}{Sn}} \right]_n$$

They have softening points ranging from 52 to 260°C.

Similarly the reaction of dilithium salts of diethynyl compounds and organotin dihalides results in polymers reported to have interesting electrophysical properties (*11*):

$$n\ R_2SnCl_2 + n\ R'(C{\equiv}CLi)_2 \longrightarrow \ {+}Sn(R_2)C{\equiv}CR'C{\equiv}C{+}_n + 2nLiCl$$

Modifications of this reaction by Sladkov and co-workers (*79*) resulted in similar type polymers:

$$n\ R_2Sn(OCH_3)_2 + n\ R'(C{\equiv}CH)_2 \longrightarrow \ {+}Sn(R_2){-}C{\equiv}CR'C{\equiv}C{+}_n$$

where $R = -CH_3$, $n\text{-}C_4H_9-$ and $R' = -C_6H_4-$, $-GeR_2-$, and $-SiR_2-$.

Bromine atoms can be added to the triple bonds at elevated temperatures and completely saturated polymers can be obtained by hydrogenation with Raney nickel. Some of the organotin polymers are stable up to 300–350°C (*7, 38, 51*). The use of these polymers for photoconductivity applications has been described (*37, 59*).

The reaction between tin tetrahalides and tetraalkyl tin compounds to yield R_2SnX_2 type compounds is well known. Polster (*67*) has utilized this reaction in an interesting way to prepare linear organotin alkylenes:

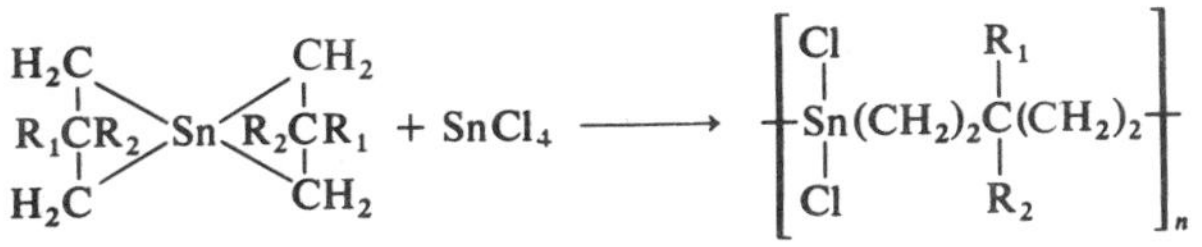

$$\underset{H_2C}{\overset{H_2C}{>}}\underset{R_1CR_2}{\overset{}{}}Sn\underset{R_2CR_1}{\overset{}{}}\underset{CH_2}{\overset{CH_2}{<}} + SnCl_4 \longrightarrow \left[\underset{\underset{Cl}{|}}{\overset{\overset{Cl}{|}}{Sn}}(CH_2)_2\underset{\underset{R_2}{|}}{\overset{\overset{R_1}{|}}{C}}(CH_2)_2 \right]_n$$

The products are useful as stabilizers and catalysts.

C. POLYFUNCTIONAL TIN-CONTAINING POLYMERS

1. *Monomer Synthesis*

Polymers of this general type are formed from organotin monomers with functional groups on the organic radical attached to tin as for example:

$$R_2Sn(O_2CCH_2OH)_2$$

In the case cited, the alcohol function can then react with other organic difunctional molecules to form condensation polymers of the usual type with the resulting polymers having tin in the polymer backbone more or less incidentally as regards the polymerization step.

Organotin compounds of the general type R_nSn $YR'(Z)_{4-n}$ where Y is $-OOC-$, $-O-$, and $-S-$; Z is $-NH_2$, $-OH$, $-SH$, $-CHCH_2O$, and $-COOH$ and $n = 1$ or 2 result in tin monomers capable of being polymerized (*9, 10, 26, 49, 57, 84*).

2. *Polymer Synthesis*

Polyurethanes containing tin can thus be prepared as follows:

$$R(NCO)_2 + R_2'Sn(O_2CCH_2OH)_2 \longrightarrow \left[Sn(R')_2O_2CCH_2OCNRNCOCH_2CO \right]_n \overset{O \quad O}{\underset{}{\overset{\|H \quad H\|}{}}}$$

Where toluene diisocyanate was condensed with a tin compound derived from hydroxyacetic acid, a white powdery polymer was formed softening at 230–240°C (*49, 57*).

Reaction of dialkyltin oxide, R_2SnO, β-mercaptopropionic acid and organotin halides results in polymers of the following type (*26*):

$$Cl_xSn(R)SCH_2CH_2COO[Sn(R)_2SCH_2CH_2COO]_nSn(R)Cl_x$$

reported to be stable to light and therefore useful as stabilizers.

Another route to the synthesis of polyorganotin esters containing tin sulfur bonds has been described by Midgal (*52*). Conversion of tetrabutyl dichlorodistannoxane with adipic acid into the corresponding halotin ester followed by reaction with sodium sulfide resulted in a linear polymer soluble in ethyl acetate, having a melting point of 50–52°C:

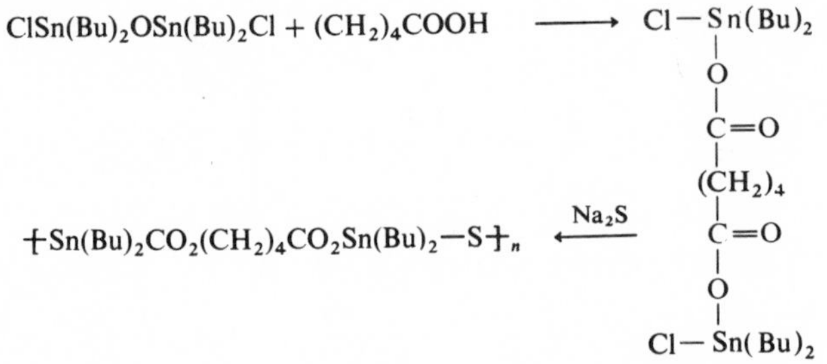

$$ClSn(Bu)_2OSn(Bu)_2Cl + (CH_2)_4COOH \longrightarrow \begin{array}{c} Cl-Sn(Bu)_2 \\ | \\ O \\ | \\ C=O \\ | \\ (CH_2)_4 \\ | \\ C=O \\ | \\ O \\ | \\ Cl-Sn(Bu)_2 \end{array}$$

$$\overset{Na_2S}{\longleftarrow}$$

$$\left[Sn(Bu)_2CO_2(CH_2)_4CO_2Sn(Bu)_2-S \right]_n$$

Polymeric organotin oxides and sulfides of the type,

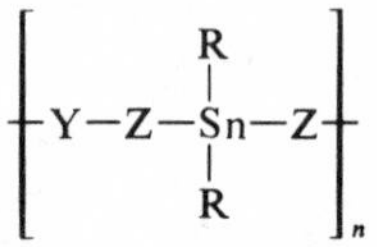

$$\left[Y-Z-\overset{R}{\underset{R}{Sn}}-Z \right]_n$$

where Z is sulfur or oxygen and Y is a hydrocarbon moiety, can be prepared by the reaction of a disubstituted tin halide and a difunctional aromatic hydroxy compound or thiol or an alkali salt thereof (*84*). Mixed polymers may be obtained, for example, by using mercaptophenol. The polymers are stable, well defined compounds ranging from highly viscous fluids to high melting, or waxy, or crystalline solids. They may be useful as functional fluids, plasticizers, sizing materials and for their biological toxicant properties.

A typical polymerization is described as follows:

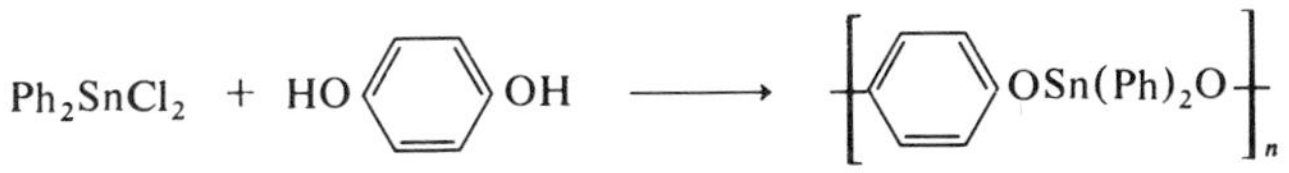

$$Ph_2SnCl_2 \ + \ HO\langle\bigcirc\rangle OH \longrightarrow \left[\langle\bigcirc\rangle OSn(Ph)_2O\right]_n$$

Organotin polyamides, the condensation product of a diamine, an organotin compound and a dicarboxylic acid halide, having the generalized structure shown below have also been reported (*29*).

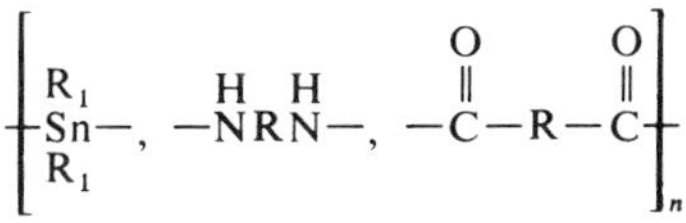

$$\left[\begin{matrix} R_1 & & H \ \ H & & O \ \ \ \ \ \ O \\ -Sn-, & -NRN-, & \overset{\|}{-C}-R-\overset{\|}{C}- \\ R_1 & & & \end{matrix}\right]_n$$

These polymer compositions contain approximately 25 % tin and are claimed to exhibit good thermal stability, fire retarding properties, and to be suitable for use as stabilizers in polyvinyl chloride plastics, as wood preservatives, as surface coatings, and for the treatment of textiles to impart insect resistance.

D. ORGANOTIN CHELATE POLYMERS

Polymers of recurring chelate units have been prepared by reacting tin tetraalkoxides with a N,N,N',N'-tetrakis-hydroxyalkyl-diamine:

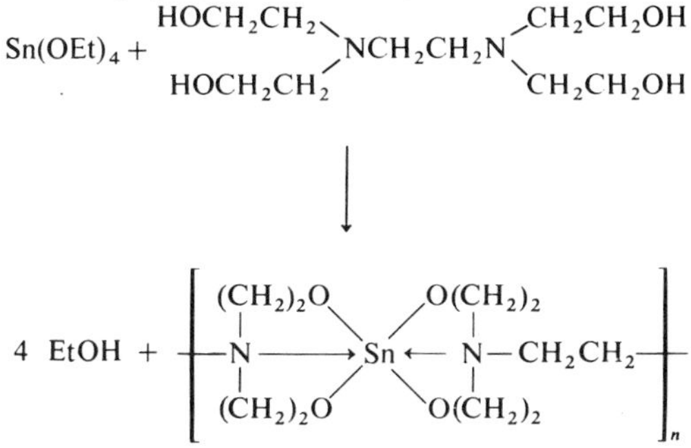

$$Sn(OEt)_4 + \begin{matrix} HOCH_2CH_2 \diagdown & & \diagup CH_2CH_2OH \\ & NCH_2CH_2N & \\ HOCH_2CH_2 \diagup & & \diagdown CH_2CH_2OH \end{matrix}$$

$$\downarrow$$

$$4 \ EtOH + \left[\begin{matrix} (CH_2)_2O \diagdown & & \diagup O(CH_2)_2 \\ -N \longrightarrow & \!\!Sn\!\! & \longleftarrow N-CH_2CH_2- \\ (CH_2)_2O \diagup & & \diagdown O(CH_2)_2 \end{matrix}\right]_n$$

These polymers have utility in coating, molding, and encapsulating applications where high temperature stability is essential (*5, 23*). The polymer prepared from tin tetraethoxide and N,N,N',N'-tetrakis (2-hydroxy ethyl)-*para*-phenylene diamine, for example, is reported to melt at about 300°C and was not completely melted at 360°C.

E. Miscellaneous Organotin Polymers

1. *Stannylimidophosphines, -arsines, and -stibines*

These classes of polymers (*81–83*) are derived from the known reaction of organometallic azides with trisubstituted phosphines, arsines and stibines:

$$R_3SnN_3 + Ar_3P \longrightarrow R_3SnN{=}PAr_3 + N_2$$

From this basic reaction, polymeric products can be found useful as hydraulic fuels, transformer oils, lubricating oils, and greases. They also impart thermal, oxidative, and ultraviolet light stability to existing materials. The products may be drawn into fibers, fabricated into films and sheet laminates or incorporated into varnishes for use as surface coatings. Thus for example:

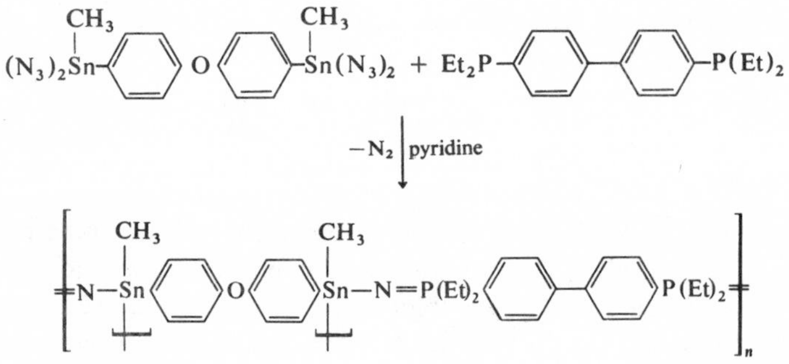

Two classes of polymers are possible, either linear or cross-linked. Generalized types are as follows:

Class I

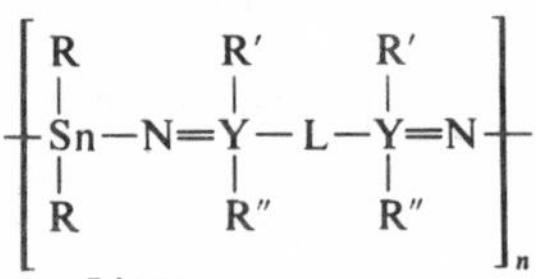

Linear 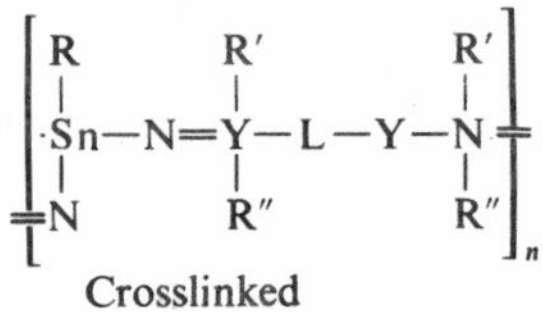 · · · · · · · · · Crosslinked

Class II

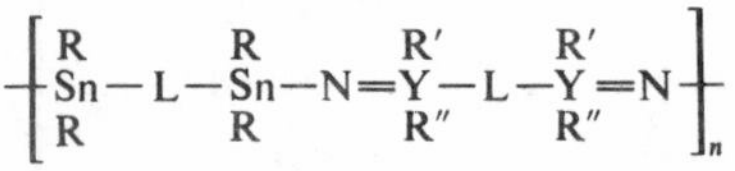

Linear

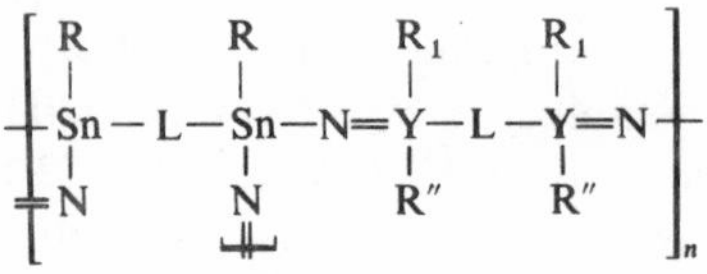

Crosslinked

2. *Polystannanes*

Organotin hydrides when reacted with organotin oxides under certain conditions can result in the formation of structures as follows:

$$R_2SnH_2 + R_2SnO \longrightarrow 2/n + R_2Sn +_n + H_2O$$

Such materials would appear not to offer anything of more than academic interest since the chance of obtaining any useful polymer containing multiple organotin moieties is highly improbable. Polystannanes are discussed in Chap. 10.

3. *Polyorganotin Acetates*

The condensation of sodio sodium acetate and dialkyltin dihalides results in the formation of polymers of the structure $+(R_2)SnCH_2COO+_n$. The reactions must be conducted under anhydrous conditions. The products are useful as PVC stabilizers, plasticizer-stabilizers, or as fungicide additives in paint (*17*).

4. *Polymeric Organotin Arsonates*

Polymers may be derived from the reaction of dialkyltin dihalides with the disodium salts of organoarsonic acids:

$$x\,(CH_3)_2SnCl_2 + x\,RAs(O)(ONa)_2 \longrightarrow 2\,NaCl + +Sn(R_2)OAs(R)(O)O+_n$$

or by reaction of dialkyltin dihalides with silver arsenate (*12*):

$$3x(CH_3)_2SnCl_2 + 2x\,Ag_3AsO_4$$
$$\longrightarrow 6x\,AgCl + +OAsO\langle[OSn(CH_3)_2O]_2\rangle\,As\,(O)OSn(CH_3)_2+_x$$

These polymers have been synthesized and characterized, but little is known of their chemical and physical properties. No known use has been cited.

5. *Stannoxy-Titanoxane Polymers*

Polymers containing alternating titanium-oxygen-tin atoms in the polymer chain have been prepared by the following reaction (*69*):

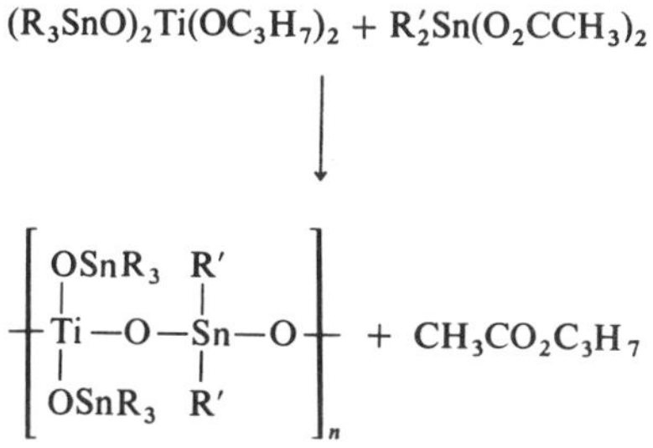

$$(R_3SnO)_2Ti(OC_3H_7)_2 + R_2'Sn(O_2CCH_3)_2$$

$$\downarrow$$

$$\begin{bmatrix} & OSnR_3 & R' & \\ & | & | & \\ +Ti & -O-Sn-O & + \\ & | & | & \\ & OSnR_3 & R' & \end{bmatrix}_n + CH_3CO_2C_3H_7$$

Such polymers are reported to be useful as fillers and reinforcing agents. They also may be treated with chelating agents to form organotin-chelated titanium oxide copolymers (*78*):

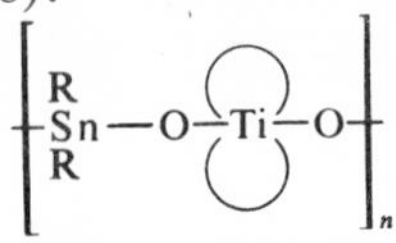

$$\left[\begin{array}{c} R \\ \mathrm{Sn-O-Ti-O} \\ R \end{array}\right]_n$$

where ⌒ is a α,β-diketone or a β-keto ester, β-hydroxy or β-amino ketone or ester. Alternatively one may start with the titanium chelated monomer as follows:

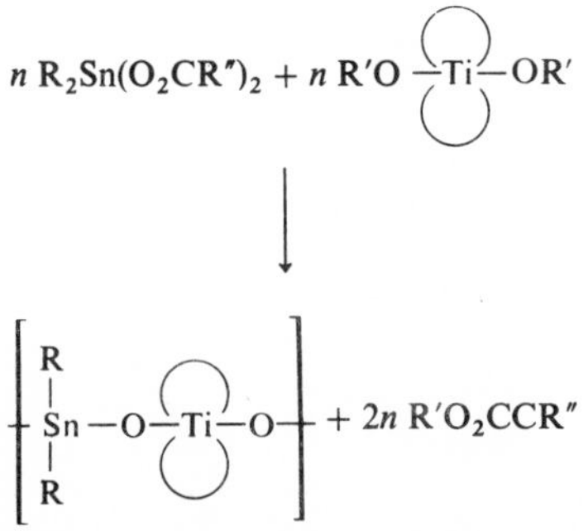

$$n\ R_2Sn(O_2CR'')_2 + n\ R'O-Ti-OR'$$

$$\downarrow$$

$$\left[\begin{array}{c} R \\ | \\ \mathrm{Sn-O-Ti-O} \\ | \\ R \end{array}\right] + 2n\ R'O_2CCR''$$

Copolymers can also be prepared by proper selection of initial monomers. This class of compounds is claimed to be useful in preparing modifications of a variety of resinous materials of enhanced thermal properties, mechanical strength at elevated temperatures, weathering resistance, etc.

6. Stannoxy-Siloxane Polymers

Polymers containing tin-oxygen-silicon repeating units in the molecular backbone may be prepared by reaction of organotin halides and Grignard derivatives of siloxanes (*25*), by the reaction of the partial hydrolysis product of alkyl chlorosilanes and the alkali metal salt of selected organotin silanols (*24*), or by the reaction of silanols and triphenyltin hydroxide in the presence of aluminum chloride to give products tentatively described as follows (*16*):

$$\mathrm{Ph_3SnOH + Ph_3SiOH} \xrightarrow[\substack{225-250°C \\ 1\ hr}]{AlCl_3} \mathrm{Ph\text{-}[Sn(Ph)_2O]\text{-}Si(Ph)_2OH}$$
$$2\text{--}5$$

$$\mathrm{Ph_3SnOH + Ph_2Si(OH)_2} \xrightarrow{AlCl_3} \begin{array}{c} \mathrm{HOSn(Ph)_2OSi(Ph)O\ \ Si(Ph)OSn(Ph)_2OH} \\ | \qquad\qquad | \\ O \qquad\qquad O \\ | \qquad\qquad | \\ \mathrm{Si(Ph)_2OSi(Ph)_2} \end{array}$$

The conclusions from these studies encompassed all of the group IV elements. The thermal stability of the products obtained in these reactions could be related to three factors: (a) the dissociation energy of the metal-oxygen bond, (b) the number of organic groups connected directly to the metal atom. and (c) the structure of the molecule as a whole. The substitution of Sn—O bonds for a portion of the Si—O linkages in conventional siloxane structures produced products which had lower heat stabilities. These tin-containing polymers apparently are useful for improving the lubricating properties of polyorganosiloxanes.

7. Polymeric Stannoxanes

Utilizing displacement type reactions, polymers containing multiple tin-oxygen bonds in the macromolecule may be obtained.

Thus dialkyltin diacetates in the presence of alkoxytin compounds react to form polymeric stannoxanes (*40*):

$$Bu_2Sn(O_2CCH_3)_2 + (EtO)_4Sn \longrightarrow CH_3CO_2 \{Sn(Bu)_2OSn(OEt)_2\}_4 \, OEt$$

Alternatively dibutyltin diacetate and dibutyltin dibutoxide react to form polymeric stannoxanes with molecular weights up to 4200 (*86*):

$$Bu_2Sn(O_2CCH_3)_2 + Bu_2Sn(OBu)_2 \longrightarrow CH_3CO_2 \{Sn(Bu)_2{-}O\}_n \, OBu$$

Extensions of these reactions by Zemlyanskii (*85*) making use of a final acid hydrolysis step to cleave terminal alkoxy groups has resulted in even higher molecular weight compounds:

$$Bu_2Sn(O_2CCH_3)_2 + Bu_2Sn(OCH_3)_2 \longrightarrow CH_3CO_2 \{Sn(Bu)_2{-}O\}_4 CH_3$$

$$\downarrow \text{hydrolysis}$$

$$2\,CH_3OH + CH_3CO_2 \{Sn(Bu)_2O\}_8(O)CCH_3$$

Davies (*14, 15*), in addition to studying hydrolysis reactions whereby alkyl tin dihalides were connected with poorly defined polystannoxanes, $(R_2SnO)_n$, investigated telomerizations where the reaction was an insertion reaction of a dialkyltin oxide moiety (*13*). Thus from the reaction of dibutyltin dichloride and dibutyltin oxide in toluene a number of fractions were isolated and their melting points recorded:

$$Bu_2SnCl_2 + \{Bu_2Sn\}_nO \longrightarrow Cl(Bu)_2Sn\{OSn(Bu)_2\}_zCl$$

z	m.p.°C
1	109
2	89–90
3	94–95
4	90–92
5	100–102
6	178–180
9	~140
12	~178

REFERENCES

1. N. A. Adrova, M. M. Koton, and E. M. Moskvina, *Izv. Akad. Nauk. SSSR Otdel. Khim. Nauk*; 1804 (1962).
2. T. M. Andrews et al., *J. Am. Chem. Soc.*, **80**, 4102 (1958).
3. K. A. Andrianov, *Metalorganic Polymers*, Interscience, New York, 1965.
4. C. A. Aufdermarsh, Jr. and R. Pariser, *J. Polymer Sci. A*, **2**, 4727 (1964).
5. J. T. Baker Chem. Co., British Pat. 1,038,186 (1966).
6. BASF, Dutch Pat. 6,514,261 (1966).
7. A. A. Berlin, *Usp. Khim.*, **29**, 1189 (1960).
8. S. Bresadola, F. Rossetto, and G. Tagliavini, *Chem. Commun.*, **17**, 623 (1966); *European Polymer J.*, **4**, 75 (1968).
9. A. Bende and R. Bekker, Russian Pat. 181,100 (1966).
10. A. Bende and R. Bekker, Russian Pat. 181,098 (1966).
11. British Patent 1,027,021 (1966).
12. B. L. Chamberlain and A. G. MacDiarmid, *J. Chem. Soc.*, 445 (1961).
13. A. G. Davies, et al., *J. Organometal. Chem.*, **7**, 13 (1967).
14. A. G. Davies, et al., *J. Organometal. Chem.*, **10**, 33 (1967).
15. A. G. Davies, et al., *J. Chem. Soc.*, 5439 (1963); 5744 (1964).
16. A. D. Delman et al., *J. Polymer Sci. A1*, **4**, 2307 (1966).
17. D. O. DePree and R. Cordova, U.S. Pat. 3,161,664 (1964).
18. P. Dunn, *36th Congr. ANZAAS*, Sidney, Australia (1962).
19. M. Frankel, et al., *J. Appl. Polymer Sci.*, **9**, 3383 (1965).
20. M. Frankel, et al., French Pat. 1,484,693 (1966).
21. M. Frankel, et al., *J. Organometal, Chem.*, **9**, 83 (1967).
22. J. G. Frielink and G. F. van der Beek, Dutch Pat. 6,514,261 (1966).
23. E. J. Friihauf and J. P. Bonsack, U.S. Pat. 3,245,921 (1966).
24. M. L. Galashina et al., Russian Pat. 166,834 (1964).
25. M. L. Galashina et al., *Plastich. Massy*, **26** (1966); *Organometal. Compounds*, **8**, 182 (1966).
26. C. R. Glosky, French Pat. 1,386,988 (1964).
27. M. C. Henry and W. E. Davidsohn, *Ann. N.Y. Acad. Sci.*, **125**, 172 (1965).
28. E. F. Jason and E. K. Fields, U.S. Pat. 3,262,915 (1966).
29. E. F. Jason and E. K. Fields, U.S. Pat. 3,247,167 (1966).
30. R. M. Kiseleva, M. M. Koton, and G. M. Chetyrkima, *Izv. Akad. Nauk. SSSR Otdel. Khim. Nauk.*, 1798 (1962).
31. D. A. Kochkin et al., *Vysokomolekul, Soedin.*, **1**, 482, 1507 (1959).
32. D. A. Kochkin, *Dokl. Akad. Nauk. SSSR.*, **135**, 857 (1960).
33. D. A. Kochkin, Y. D. Novichenko, G. I. Kuznetsova, and L. V. Laine, Russian Pat. 133,224; through *CA*, **55**, 11923*i* (1960).
34. D. A. Kochkin et al., *Vysokomolekyl. Soedin.*, **9** (10), 2208 (1967).
35. L. Kolditz, and G. Furcht, *Z. Chem.*, **6**, 381 (1966).
36. V. V. Korshak et al., *Izv. Akad. Nauk. SSSR Otdel. Khim. Nauk.*, 174 (1959).
37. V. V. Korshak et al., Russian Pat. Appl. 948609/26-25 (20 March 1965; granted 31 August 1965).
38. I. L. Kotlyarenskii et al., *Izv. Akad. Nauk. SSSR Otdel. Khim. Nauk.*, 956 (1960).
39. M. M. Koton, T. M. Kiseleva, and R. M. Paribok, *Dokl. Akad. Nauk. SSSR*, **125**, 1263 (1959).
40. M. M. Koton and T. M. Kiseleva, *Dokl. Akad. Nauk. SSSR*, **130**, 86 (1960).
41. M. M. Koton, *Vysokomolekul. Soedin.*, **2**, 1639 (1960).

42. M. M. Koton, T. M. Kiseleva, and F. S. Florinski, *Vysomolekul, Soedin.*, **2**, 1639 (1960); *J. Polymer Sci.*, **52**, 237 (1961).
43. M. M. Koton and T. M. Kiseleva, *Izv. Akad. Nauk. SSSR, Otdel. Khim. Nauk.*, 1783 (1961).
44. M. M. Koton, *J. Polymer Sci.*, **52**, 237 (1961).
45. M. M. Koton and F. S. Florinski, *Zhur. Obschchei Khim.*, **32**, 3057 (1962).
46. E. S. Lane, British Pat. 907,775 (1962).
47. C. M. Langkammerer, U.S. Pat. 2,253,128 (1941).
48. M. F. Lappert and G. J. Leigh, *Developments in Inorganic Polymer Chemistry*, Chap. 8, Sec. 4, Elsevier, Amsterdam, 1962.
49. J. Leebrick, French Pat. 1,400,617 (1965).
50. J. Leebrick, U.S. Pat. 3,167,532 (1965).
51. L. K. Luneva, A. M. Sladkov, and V. V. Korshak, *Vysokomolekul. Soedin.*, **7**, 427 (1967); *A*9, 910 (1967).
52. S. Midgal, D. Gertner, and A. Zilkha, *Can. J. Chem.*, **45** (23), 2987 (1967).
53. Y. Minoura et al., *J. Polymer. Sci.* *A*1, **4**, 2757 (1966).
54. J. Montermoso, L. P. Marinelli, and T. M. Andrews, U.S. Pat. 3,016,369 (1962); *J. Polymer Sci.*, **32**, 523 (1958).
55. M. & T. Chemicals, Inc., French Pat. 1,386,988 (1964).
56. M. & T. Chemicals, Inc., Dutch Pat. 6405136 (1964).
57. M. & T. Chemicals, Dutch Pat. 6405137 (1964).
58. M. & T. Chemicals Inc., French Pat. 1,400,617 (1965).
59. V. S. Mylnikov et al., *Dokl. Akad. Nauk. SSSR*, **144**, 840 (1962).
60. H. Naarmann and E. Kastning, French Pat. 1,455,503 (1966).
61. G. Natta et al. Swiss Pat. 392,889 (1965).
62. W. P. Neumann, H. Nierman, and B. Schneider, *Ann.*, **707**, 15 (1967).
63. W. P. Neumann and B. Schneider, *Ann.*, **707**, 20 (1967).
64. W. P. Neumann, *Die Organishe Chemie des Zinns*, Ferdinand Enke Verlag, Stuttgart (1967).
65. J. G. Noltes and G. J. M. van der Kerk, *Rec. trav. Chim.*, **80**, 623 (1961); **81**, 41 (1962); *Chimia*, **16**, 122 (1962).
66. N. A. Plate et al., Russian Pat. 176,408 (1965).
67. R. Polster, Swiss Pat. 413,372 (1966).
68. B. Rudner and M. S. Moores, U.S. Pat. 3,314,980 (1967).
69. J. Rust and G. C. Denault, U.S. Pat. 3,178,375 (1965).
70. Z. M. Rzaev and D. A. Kochkin, *Dokl. Akad. Nauk. SSSR* (English Transl.), Consultants Bureau Vol. 172, No. 103, January (1967).
71. S. R. Sandler and K. C. Tsou, *J. Phys. Chem.*, **68**, 300 (1964).
72. S. R. Sandler, J. Dannin, and K. C. Tsou, *J. Polymer Sci. A*, **3**, 3199 (1965).
73. M. F. Shostakovskii et al., *Angnew Chem.*, **72**, 1711 (1960).
74. M. F. Shostakovskii et al., *Vysokomolekul. Soedin.*, **3**, 1131 (1961).
75. M. F. Shostakovskii et al., *J. Polymer Sci.*, **52**, 223 (1961).
76. M. F. Shostakovskii et al., Russian Pat. 172,777 (1965).
77. F. G. A. Stone and W. A. G. Graham, *Inorganic Polymers*, Chap. VI, Part III, Academic Press, New York, 1962.
78. H. H. Takimoto and J. B. Rust, U.S. Pat. 3,244,645 (1966).
79. Tezisy Dokladov XV Konferentsii po Vysokomolekulyarnym Soedineniyam Posvyashchennym Polucheniyu Khimicheskikh Novykh Veshchestv, Moska, Yanvar, 1965, Summaries of papers presented at the XV*th Conf. High Mol. Wt. Compounds*, Devoted to the Production of Chemically New Substances, Moscow, January 1965, Izd. Nauka, Moscow, 1965.

80. G. J. M. Van der Kerk and J. G. Noltes, *Ann. N.Y. Acad. Sci.*, **125**, 25 (1965) and references therein.

81. R. M. Washburn and R. A. Baldwin, U.S. Pat. 3,112,331 (1963).

82. R. M. Washburn and R. A. Baldwin, U.S. Pat. 3,311,646 (1963).

83. R. M. Washburn and R. A. Baldwin, U.S. Pat. 3,341,477 (1967).

84. G. R. Wilson, U.S. Pat. 3,184,430 (1965).

85. N. N. Zemlyanskii et al., *Zhur. Obshchei Khim.*, **35**, 1029 (1965).

86. S. M. Zhivukhin et al., *Zhur. Obshchei Khim.*, **32**, 3059 (1962).

14. ANALYSIS OF ORGANOTIN COMPOUNDS

C. R. DILLARD

Department of Chemistry
Brooklyn College of the City University of New York

I.	Introduction	997
II.	Wet Analyses	997
III.	Instrumental Methods	998
	A. Analysis for Specific Compounds by Spectrophotometry	998
	B. Chromatography	948
IV.	Infrared Spectroscopy	999
V.	Nuclear Magnetic Resonance Spectroscopy	1001
VI.	Mössbauer Spectroscopy	1004
	References	1004

I. Introduction

The chemical analysis of organotin compounds presents no problems of great magnitude. The compounds are decomposed to inorganic tin in a suitable manner, and tin is determined either gravimetrically or by a colorimetric procedure. Detailed procedures and references to original papers have been given in earlier reviews and books (*32, 53, 54*). Therefore in this chapter it is only necessary to comment generally on the methods and to point out some recently reported methods which may be more suitable in particular cases.

Numerous descriptions of infrared and nuclear magnetic resonance studies of organotin compounds have been given in the previous chapters of this book. In this chapter spectroscopic data are summarized, and correlations are made which should be of diagnostic use in both the analysis of organotin compounds and in the determination of their structures.

II. Wet Analyses

Tin in organotin compounds is usually determined as tin(IV) oxide. Most compounds can be completely decomposed in a platinum or a Vycor crucible by heating with concentrated sulfuric acid to which a few drops of nitric acid are added during the latter stages of the digestion (26, 57). After digestion, the sample is ignited to SnO_2. Some workers prefer a considerable excess of nitric acid in addition to the concentrated sulfuric acid. In this case the digestions are run in Erlenmeyer flasks and are usually followed by reduction of the inorganic tin and subsequent titration of the tin(II) ion (22, 25). For routine analyses of large numbers of samples, the titration method is preferred (25). Oxidations of the organotin compounds may be carried out in a Paar bomb (23) or, for micro samples, by the Schöniger method (68).

After wet oxidation of the organotin compounds, tin may be determined photometrically, using the reagent cacotheline (23) or the reagent dithiol (12, 13, 21, 39, 61); also polarography has been employed in cases where the quantity of tin present has been small (5, 28, 50, 84).

Wet analyses for elements other than tin are carried out according to conventional procedures and no significant modifications are mentioned here. A high frequency titration method for the quantitative analysis of halogens in alkyltin halides have been reported to give errors of less than 3 % for halide content ranging from 10 to 75 % (47). Another useful technique is the determination and differentiation between trialkyl (or triaryl) organotin hydroxides and the corresponding oxides by the difference in magnitude of the values of "apparent" water content determined by a Karl Fischer titration (40).

III. Instrumental Methods

A. ANALYSIS FOR SPECIFIC COMPOUNDS BY SPECTROPHOTOMETRY

Diethyltin and triethyltin moieties may be separated by aqueous extraction of chloroform solutions in the presence of a borate-EDTA buffer (pH = 8.4). Then the trialkyltin and dialkyltin moieties are determined photometrically as dithizone complexes at 510 mμ and 610 mμ, respectively (2, 11).

Dibutyltin dichloride has been determined spectrophotometrically in the presence of a 100-fold excess of mono-, tri- and tetrabutylin compounds using diphenylcarbazone (73).

Catechol violet (1, 7) and 4-(2 pyridylazo)-resorcinol (62) have been used as complexing agents for the photometric determination of dialkyltin and diaryltin moieties.

Hexaorganoditin compounds have been determined in the presence of tetraorganotin compounds by coulometric-amperometric procedures (75, 76).

Tin in organotin compounds may be determined by direct spectrographic analysis of frozen cumene solutions (80).

B. CHROMATOGRAPHY

Thin layer chromatography has been employed to identify various organotin compounds used as polyvinyl chloride stabilizers. The absorbent was activated silica gel on Whatman No. 4 paper. Mobile phases included butanol-acetic acid (*80, 83*), isopropyl alcohol and $(NH_4)_2CO_3$ solution (*6*), isopropyl ether (*51*), and trimethylpentane-isopropyl ether-acetic acid (*29*). Developing reagents included dithizone, diphenylcarbazone, catechol violet, and bromine vapor followed by Rhodamine B. R_f values of numerous individual compounds have been determined.

Gas chromatography is being used for an increasing number of separations of organotin compounds. However, column parameters must be carefully chosen in order to avoid disproportionation reactions or decomposition at elevated temperatures. Some typical separations and retention times for a variety of compounds have been reported: (*24, 31, 65, 71, 72, 74*). The elution of alkyltin compounds from various stationary phases supported on celite have been studied, and correlations have been made between the retention indexes and boiling points (*63, 66*).

IV. Infrared Spectroscopy

Infrared spectroscopy has been the most widely used tool for the elucidation of the structures of organotin compounds. As has been amply illustrated in the previous chapters, the observed spectra are influenced by such factors as the sampling technique, i.e., solid vs solution or vapor, temperature effects, and the tendency of tin to assume various coordination numbers in different environments. Therefore much information about the detailed structures of organotin compounds is obtained by observing the infrared spectra under a variety of conditions.

Because of the comparatively large mass of the tin atom, the internal vibrations of two or more organic groups attached to the same tin atom are not coupled to each other, hence the vibrational spectra are rather simple. Characteristic "group frequencies" are readily identified (*17, 20, 41*). On the other hand the frequencies of skeletal vibrations, involving atoms attached directly to tin are sensitive to the environment about the tin atom. It is these vibrations which provide clues to the structures of organotin compounds. Okawara (*58*) has pointed out that in the case of compounds containing R_3Sn-moieties and R_2Sn-moieties, the observation of only one tin-carbon stretching vibration is an indication that the configuration of carbon about the tin atom is planar or linear, respectively. This criterion can be applied as well to ethyltin compounds and phenyltin compounds, but for propyl and higher alkyl groups there are additional tin-carbon vibrations due to the existence of more than one torsional configuration of the alkyl group.

Tin-carbon stretching frequencies depend upon the organic group attached to tin and, most importantly, upon the coordination number of the tin atom. Compounds in which the tin atom has a coordination number of four include

TABLE 1

TIN-CARBON STRETCHING FREQUENCIES

Derivative	ν_{sym}	ν_{asym}	References
Methyl	506–516	528–536	(17–20, 58, 77)
Ethyl	479–490	501–518	(42, 77)
Phenyl	226–263	265–270	(64)

tin tetraalkyls and tin tetraaryls, organotin hydrides, organotin halides in the liquid state or dissolved in non-polar solvents, and organotin alkoxides. Some ranges of tin-carbon stretching frequencies for this class of compound are given in Table 1.

Compounds in which tin exhibits a coordination number of five include solid trialkyltin carboxylates (53, 58); polymeric distannoxanes (59), trialkyltin nitrates (87), adducts of triorganotin halides with donor molecules (16, 48), dialkyltin halide carboxylates (86), and perhaps solid trialkyltin halides. The methyltin derivatives of these compounds have been studied extensively, and only one tin-carbon stretching frequency is observed in the range 540–565 cm^{-1}.

Organotin compounds in which tin has a coordination number of six include diorganotin *bis* chelates (49), diorganotin diacylates (44, 45) and various monoorganotin salts. For most of the dimethyltin derivatives, only one tin-carbon stretching frequency is observed which occurs in the range 560–590 cm^{-1}. The Sn—C stretching vibration of six coordinate monomethyltin derivatives occurs at 570–580 cm^{-1}. Other tin-carbon skeletal modes include the C—Sn—C bending, and for higher alkyls, the Sn—C—C bending. These occur below 250 cm^{-1} and are beyond the range of most commercial instruments (77).

Due possibly to the lack of coupling between the hydrogen atoms attached to the massive tin atom, only one Sn—H stretching frequency is observed corresponding to both the symmetric and asymmetric modes.

TABLE 2

TIN-HYDROGEN VIBRATIONS

Type	Stretch.	Deform.	Wag.	Rock.	Twist.
$RSnH_3$	1869–1890	701–731	—	415	
R_2SnH_2	1832–1858	726	712	571	492
R_3SnH	1840	—	—	671	—

The observed frequency ranges for tin-hydrogen vibrations are shown in Table 2 (*18, 35*).

If electronegative groups as well as hydrogen are attached to the tin atom, the Sn—H stretching vibration is observed at a somewhat higher frequency than those listed in Table 2 (*35, 69, 70*).

Frequencies of tin-halogen stretching vibrations in organotin compounds are listed in Table 3. The observed frequencies are sensitive to the environ-

TABLE 3

TIN-HALOGEN STRETCHING FREQUENCIES
(R = ALKYL OR ARYL GROUP)

	F	Cl	Br	I
RSnX$_3$	—	364–385	225–256	~230
R$_2$SnX$_2$	559(345)[a]	338–345[b]	238–242[b]	182[b]
		349–361[c]	252–254[c]	200[c]
R$_3$SnX	325–372	325	257	170

[a] Sn—F—Sn bridging.
[b] Asymmetric stretch.
[c] Symmetric stretch.

ment about the tin atom and also vary with the physical state of the sample (*77*). Details of the assignments and descriptions of tin-halogen modes other than stretching are given in the original papers (*3, 9, 42, 64, 77*).

Infrared bands attributed to tin-oxygen vibrations are found in the frequency range 300–800 cm^{-1}. Some typical examples are listed in Table 4. It has been suggested that the higher the frequency, the greater the amount of covalent character in the tin-oxygen bond (*34*).

V. Nuclear Magnetic Resonance Spectroscopy

Three of the ten stable isotopes of tin, ^{115}Sn, ^{117}Sn and ^{119}Sn, have non-zero magnetic moments and nuclear spins of $\frac{1}{2}$. Of these ^{115}Sn has too small a natural abundance to be important. On the other hand ^{117}Sn and ^{119}Sn give nuclear magnetic resonance spectra in which chemical shifts of as much as 1800 ppm have been observed and in which direct spin-spin coupling constants to protons are of the order of 2000 cps while indirect spin-spin coupling constants with protons in alkyl groups are of the order of 50–100 cps (*8, 35*).

Proton magnetic resonance is a very versatile tool in the determination of structure of organotin compounds, providing information on bonding and

TABLE 4

INFRARED BANDS ATTRIBUTED TO TIN-OXYGEN VIBRATIONS

Frequency range	Vibration mode	Compound type	References
300 (broad)	Sn—O	$(CH_3)_3Sn-O-\overset{\overset{\displaystyle C}{\Vert}}{}\overset{\overset{\displaystyle O}{\Vert}}{}CH$	(56)
310–390	Sn—O	Pyridine *N*-oxide complexes $(CH_3)_3X_2OC_5H_4N$	(34)
370	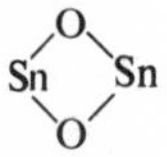 Sn⟨O,O⟩Sn	$[(CH_3)_3SnOH]_x$	(59)
400–460	Sn—O	$XX'Sn(acac)_2$	(37)
481–530	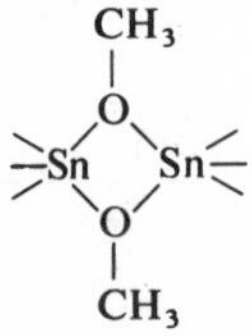 ⟩Sn⟨O(CH₃),O(CH₃)⟩Sn⟨	$[(C_5H_7O_2)_2Sn(OCH_3)X]_2$	(36)
500–580	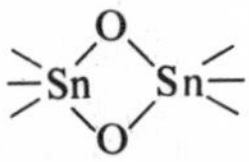 ⟩Sn⟨O,O⟩Sn⟨	$[(CH_3)_3SnOH]_2$	(59)
510–540	Sn—O	$XY\,Sn(Ox)_2$	(78)
532–645	$\nu_{sym}(Sn-O)$	$R_2Sn(OR')_2$	(10)
552–580	Sn—O	$XY\,Sn\,(Kj)_2$ and $R_2Sn(Kj)_2$	(40)
580–600	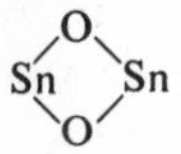 Sn⟨O,O⟩Sn	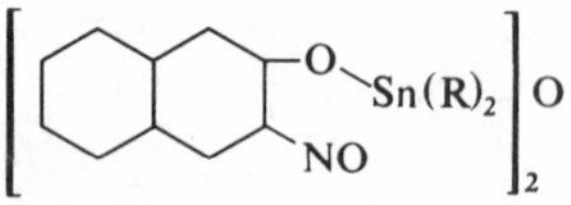 $\left[\,\text{(decalin)}O\text{-}Sn(R)_2,\,NO\,\right]_2 O$	(79)
600–630	$\nu_{asym}(Sn-O)$	$R_2Sn(OR')_2$	(10)
740–780	Sn—O	$(R_3Sn)_2O$	(85)

X and Y = halogen; R and R' = alkyl or aryl;
Ox = 8 hydroxyquinoline; acac = acetylacetone;
Kj = Kojic acid anion.

geometry as well as information on the relative numbers of protons of various types in a given molecule.

Theoretical studies (67) indicate that the Fermi contact term chiefly determines the magnitudes of the tin to proton spin-spin coupling constants, therefore the coupling constants provide information about the effective

nuclear charge of the tin atom and the fraction of s-character in its bonding orbitals. Factors not necessarily peculiar to the tin atom, such as hyperconjugation, neighbor anisotropy, and inductive effects, contribute to the observed proton chemical shifts (*14, 81, 82*). A study of solvent effects on the proton magnetic spectra of dimethyltin dichloride and trimethyltin chloride (*46*) classifies solvents into four groups as follows:
(1) Non-interacting solvents in which chemical shifts and coupling constants remain invariant from solvent to solvent. (2) Donor solvents in which the chemical shifts for the respective protons is unchanged upon changing solvents but in which certain of the coupling constants vary over a wide range. (3) Coordinating solvents in which the coupling constants increase while the chemical shifts relative to an internal standard decrease as the solvents are varied. (4) Solvents exerting a diamagnetic effect, in which chemical shifts vary widely but tin-proton coupling constants remain unchanged as different solvents are used. Also for this group, for a given solvent, the chemical shifts have a pronounced temperature dependence.

For protons directly bonded to tin, such as the alkyltin hydrides (but not the aryltin hydrides), the frequencies of the tin-hydrogen stretching vibrations ν_{Sn-H} are linearly related to the tin hydrogen spin-spin coupling constants, $J(^{119}Sn-H)$:

$$\nu(SnH) = 946.2 - 707.1\sigma^* + (0.4947 + 0.3691\sigma^*)J(^{119}SnH)$$

where the parameter σ^* is the Taft function expressing the electronegativities of the groups attached to tin (*35, 43*).

In the case of methyltin compounds, indirect tin-proton coupling constants can be used to infer the bond hybridization of the tin atom (*30, 38*). The percentage of s character in the bond hybrid is plotted against the indirect coupling constant, $J(^{119}Sn-CH)$. A straight line is drawn from the origin through the value of the observed tin-proton coupling constant for tetramethyltin in which the tin-carbon bonds are sp^3 hybrids having 25% s character. On such a plot, the observed tin-proton coupling constant for the case of the $(CH_3)_3Sn^+$ ion, in which there is sp^2 hybridization about the tin atom, corresponds to 33% s character while the ion, Me_2Sn^{2+}, having sp hybrid bonds on the tin atom has 50% s character. As a further example, the coupling constant, $J(^{119}Sn-CH)$ observed for the adduct between dimethylsulfoxide and trimethyltin chloride, corresponds to 33% s character which suggests a trigonal bipyramidal configuration for the adduct with the methyl groups occupying equatorial positions about the tin atom (*48*).

However, it must be noted that the use of the above device for determining bond hybridization is limited to those cases in which d-orbitals are not involved (*4*). Also compounds containing tin-tin bonds are anomalous (*15*).

VI. Mössbauer Spectroscopy

Inasmuch as the isotope ^{119}Sn has a nuclear excited state of appropriate lifetime, it is possible to observe the Mössbauer effect in organotin compounds. Some results of Mössbauer effect studies have been described in earlier chapters by Gielen and Nasielski and by Van der Kelen et al. To date, no simple correlations exist between the Mössbauer parameters and structural information obtained by means of other techniques. However, it is possible to distinguish between the formal oxidation states Sn(II) and Sn(IV) by means of Mössbauer spectroscopy. Compounds of Sn(II) have isomer shifts δ, which are positive relative to β-tin, while compounds of Sn(IV) have δ-values which are negative relative to β-tin. For example, it has been shown that the so-called diorganotins, R_2Sn, are in fact Sn(IV) species *(27)*. This is corroborated by chemical *(52)* and x-ray *(55)* studies.

REFERENCES

1. J. H. Adamson, *Analyst*, **87**, 597 (1962).
2. W. N. Aldridge and T. E. Cremer, *Analyst*, **82**, 37 (1957).
3. I. R. Beattie and G. P. McQuillan, *J. Chem. Soc.*, **1963**, 1519.
4. E. V. Van den Berghe and G. P. van der Kelen, *J. Organometal. Chem.*, **11**, 479 (1968).
5. V. D. Bezuglyi, E. A. Preobrazhenskaya, and V. N. Dmitrieva, *Zhur. Anal. Chim.*, **19**, 1033 (1964).
6. K. Burger, *Z. Anal. Chem.*, **192**, 280 (1962).
7. K. Burger, *Z. Lebensm. Untersuch. Forsch.*, **114**, 1 (1961).
8. J. C. Burke and P. C. Lauterbur, *J. Am. Chem. Soc.*, **83**, 326 (1961).
9. F. K. Butcher, W. Gerrard, E. F. Mooney, R. G. Rees, and H. A. Willis, *J. Organometal. Chem.*, **1**, 431 (1964).
10. F. K. Butcher, W. Gerrard, E. F. Mooney, R. G. Rees, and H. A. Willis, *Spectrochim. Acta*, **20**, 51 (1964).
11. A. H. Chapman, M. W. Duckworth, and J. W. Price, *Brit. Plastics*, **32**, 78 (1958).
12. R. E. D. Clark, *Analyst*, **61**, 242 (1936).
13. R. E. D. Clark, *Analyst*, **82**, 182 (1957).
14. H. C. Clark, N. Cyr, and J. H. Tsai, *Can. J. Chem.*, **45**, 1073 (1967).
15. H. C. Clark, J. T. Kwan, and E. J. Wells, *Inorg. Chem.*, **3**, 907 (1964).
16. H. C. Clark, R. J. O'Brien, and J. Trotter, *J. Chem. Soc.*, 2332 (1964).
17. C. R. Dillard and J. R. Lawson, *J. Opt. Soc. Am.*, **50**, 1270 (1960).
18. C. R. Dillard and L. May, *J. Mol. Spectry*, **14**, 250 (1964).
19. W. F. Edgell and C. H. Ward, *J. Am. Chem. Soc.*, **77**, 6486 (1955).
20. W. F. Edgell and C. H. Ward, *J. Mol. Spectry*, **8**, 343 (1962).
21. M. Farnsworth and J. Pekola, *Anal. Chem.*, **26**, 735 (1954).
22. M. Farnsworth and J. Pekola, *Anal. Chem.*, **31**, 410 (1959).
23. G. Fritz and H. Scheer, *Z. anorg. allgem. Chem.*, **331**, 151 (1964).
24. H. Geissler and H. Kriegsmann, *Z. Chem. Leipzig*, **4**, 354 (1964).
25. R. Geyer and H. J. Seidlitz, *Z. Chem. Leipzig*, **4**, 468 (1964).

26. H. Gilman and S. D. Rosenberg, *J. Am. Chem. Soc.*, **75**, 3592 (1953).

27. V. I. Goldanskii, V. Ya. Rochev, and V. V. Khrapov, *Dokl. Akad. Nauk SSSR*, **156**, 909 (1964).

28. S. Gorbach and R. Bock, *Z. Anal. Chem.*, **163**, 429 (1958).

29. D. Helberg, *Deut. Lebensm. Rundschau*, **62**, 178 (1966).

30. J. R. Holmes and H. D. Kaesz, *J. Am. Chem. Soc.*, **83**, 3903 (1961).

31. K. Hoppner, U. Prosch, and H. Wiegleb, *Z. Chem.*, **4**, 31 (1964).

32. R. K. Ingham, S. D. Rosenberg, and H. Gilman, *Chem. Rev.*, **60**, 459 (1960).

33. M. J. Janssen, J. G. A. Luijten, and G. J. M. Van der Kerk, *Rec. trav. Chim.*, **82**, 90 (1963).

34. Y. Kawasaki, M. Hori, and K. Uenaka, *Bull. Chem. Soc. Japan*, **40**, 2463 (1967).

35. Y. Kawasaki, K. Kawakami, and T. Tanaka, *Bull. Chem. Soc. Japan*, **38**, 1102 (1965); K. Kawakami, T. Saito, and R. Okawara, *J. Organometal. Chem.*, **8**, 377 (1965).

36. Y. Kawasaki, T. Tanaka, and R. Okawara, *J. Organometal. Chem.*, **6**, 95 (1965).

37. Y. Kawasaki, T. Tanaka, and R. Okawara, *Spectrochim. Acta*, **22**, 1571 (1966).

38. G. P. van der Kelen, *Nature*, **193**, 1069 (1962).

39. L. K. van Kien and T. Tuong, *C.A.*, **51**, 11435 (1957).

40. B. G. Kuschlefsky and A. Ross, *Anal. Chem.*, **34**, 1666 (1962).

41. E. R. Lippincott, P. Mercier, and M. C. Tobin, *J. Phys. Chem.*, **57**, 939 (1953).

42. D. H. Lohmann, *J. Organometal. Chem.*, **4**, 382 (1965).

43. M. L. Maddox, N. Flitcroft, and H. D. Kaesz, *J. Organometal. Chem.*, **4**, 50 (1965).

44. Y. Maeda, C. Dillard, and R. Okawara, *Inorg. Nucl. Chem. Letters*, **2**, 197 (1966).

45. Y. Maeda and R. Okawara, *J. Organometal. Chem.*, **10**, 247 (1967).

46. G. Matsubayashi, Y. Kawasaki, T. Tanaka, and R. Okawara, *Bull. Chem. Soc. Japan*, **40**, 1566 (1967).

47. H. Matsuda and S. Matsuda, *J. Chem. Soc. Japan Ind. Chem. Sect.*, **64**, 539 (1961).

48. N. A. Matwiyoff and R. S. Drago, *Inorg. Chem.*, **3**, 337 (1964).

49. M. M. McGrady and R. S. Tobias, *Inorg. Chem.*, **3**, 1157 (1964).

50. P. Naugniot and P. H. Martens, *Anal. Chem. Acta.* **24**, 276 (1961).

51. G. Neubert, *Z. Anal. Chem.*, **203**, 265 (1964).

52. W. P. Neumann, *Angew. Chem.*, **75**, 225 (1963).

53. W. P. Neumann, *Angew. Chem. Int. Ed.*, **2**, 165 (1963).

54. W. P. Neumann, *Die Organische Chemie des Zinns*, Ferdinand Enke Verlag, Stuttgart (1967).

55. D. H. Olsen and R. E. Rundle, *Inorg. Chem.*, **2**, 310 (1963).

56. R. Okawara and M. Ohara, *J. Organometal. Chem.*, **1**, 360 (1964).

57. R. Okawara and E. G. Rochow, *J. Am. Chem. Soc.*, **82**, 3285 (1960).

58. R. Okawara, D. E. Webster, and E. G. Rochow, *J. Am. Chem. Soc.*, **82**, 3287 (1960).

59. R. Okawara, and K. Yasuda *J. Organometal Chem.*, **1**, 356 (1964).

60. J. Otera, Y. Kawasaki, and T. Tanaka, *Inorg. Chim. Acta*, **1**, 294 (1967).

61. T. C. J. Ovenstone and C. Kenyon, *Analyst*, **80**, 566 (1955).

62. G. Pilloni and G. Plazzogna, *Anal. Chim. Acta*, **35**, 325 (1966).

63. F. H. Pollard, G. Nickless, and D. J. Cooke, *J. Chromatography*, **13**, 48 (1964).

64. R. C. Poller, *Spectrochim. Acta*, **22**, 935 (1965).

65. U. Prosch and H. J. Zopfl, *Z. Chem.*, **3**, 97 (1963).

66. R. C. Putnam and H. Pu, *J. Gas Chromatography*, **3**, 160 (1965).

67. N. F. Ramsey, *Phys. Rev.*, **91**, 303 (1953); M. Karplus and D. H. Anderson, *J. Chem. Phys.*, **30**, 6 (1959).

68. R. Reverchon, *Chim. Analyt.*, **42**, 70 (1965).

69. A. K. Sawyer, J. E. Brown, and E. L. Hanson, *J. Organometal. Chem.*, **3**, 464 (1965).

70. A. K. Sawyer and H. G. Kuivila, *J. Org. Chem.*, **27**, 837 (1962).
71. K. Sisido and S. Kozima, *J. Organometal. Chem.*, **11**, 503 (1968).
72. K. Sisido, T. Miganisi, K. Nabika, and S. Kozima, *J. Organometal. Chem.*, **11**, 281 (1968).
73. R. T. Skeel and C. E. Bricker, *Anal. Chem.*, **33**, 428 (1961).
74. R. Steinmeyer, A. Fentiman, and E. Kahler, *Anal. Chem.*, **37**, 520 (1965).
75. G. Tagliavini, *Anal. Chim. Acta*, **34**, 24 (1966).
76. G. Tagliavini and G. Plazzogna, *Richerche Sci.*, *R. C. H.*, **2**, 356 (1962).
77. P. Taimsalu and J. L. Wood, *Spectrochim. Acta*, **20**, 1043 (1964); *ibid.*, **20**, 1357 (1964); *Trans. Faraday Soc.*, **59**, 1754 (1963).
78. T. Tanaka, M. Komura, Y. Kawasaki, and R. Okawara, *J. Organometal. Chem.*, **1**, 484 (1964).
79. T. Tanaka, R. Ueda, M. Wada, and R. Okawara, *Bull. Chem. Soc. Japan*, **37**, 1554 (1964).
80. M. Turler and O. Hogl, *Mitt. Lebensm. Hyg.*, **52**, 123 (1961).
81. L. Verdonck and G. P. Van der Kelen, *J. Organometal. Chem.*, **11**, 491 (1968).
82. L. Verdonck, G. P. Van der Kelen, and Z. Eeckhart, *J. Organometal. Chem.*, **11**, 487 (1968).
83. B. Visitin, A. Pepe, and S. A. Guiseppe, *Ann. Ist. Super Sanita*, **1**, 767 (1964).
84. J. Vogel and J. Deskusses, *Helv. Chim. acta*, **47**, 181 (1964).
85. N. V. Vyshinskii and N. K. Rudnevskii, *Opt. Spectr.*, **10**, 421 (1961); H. Kriegsman, H. Hoffman, and S. Pischtochan, *Z. anorg. allgem. Chem.*, **315**, 283 (1962).
86. M. Wada, M. Shindo, and R. Okawara, *J. Organometal. Chem.*, **1**, 95 (1963).
87. K. Yasuda and R. Okawara, *J. Organometal. Chem.*, **3**, 75 (1965).

CUMULATIVE AUTHOR INDEX

Numbers in parentheses are reference numbers and indicate that an author's work is referred to although his name is not cited in the text. Numbers in italics show the page on which the complete reference is listed.

A

Abe, T., *503*

Abel, E. W., 118(1), *137*, 298(1, 13), 303(3, 7), 304(3, 14), 306-309(2, 3, 5, 6, 9, 10, 11, 14, 17, 17a, 232), 314(7), 316-318(2, 7), 320(5, 8), 324(7), 327-330(4, 7, 9, 18, 19), 340(3, 16), 343(15, 16), 344(8), 347(2, 5), 350(2, 3, 7, 8, 9, 10, 12, 17b), 351(7), 354(12), 359(7), 365(7, 9, 10, 11, 12, 14), 366(7, 9), 368(8), 374-376(4, 7, 8, 14), 402(232), 424(2, 3, 5, 7, 9), 436(4, 7, 9), 438-440 (18), 454(4, 7), 491(3, 8, 15), *495, 504*, 513(2), 514(2), 530(1), 532(3), 536(1), 541(3), 542(1, 2), 553(1), *575*, 582(1b), 589(1b), 595(1a), 597(1b), 602(1a, 1b, 1c), 608-613(1, 1a, 1b, 1c, 1d, 1e), *620*, 875(5a), *876*, 935(1), *966*

Abraham, M. H., 629(1, 2), 630(2), 652(2), 653(2), 664(2), 665(2), *809*

Abramova, A. N., 27(17), 63(16), *72*, 277 (13), *292*, 95(370), *146*

Abramova, L. V., 83(2, 3, 4, 280), 92(280), 132(2), *137, 144*

Adamiya, S. V., 176(111), 177(111), 179 (111), *246*, 725(159), 732(159), *813*

Adamson, J. H., 998(1), *1004*

Addison, C. C., 270(1), 273(1), *292*

Adrova, N. A., 39(1), *72*, 977(1), 978(1), 979(1), *994*

Advani, R., 963(123), *969*

Akhtar, M., 23(2), 38(2, 3), *72*, 875(5b), *876*, 911(1), 913(1), 914(1), *924*

Alabaster, J. S., 945(2), *966*

Albert, H. J., 43(141), *76*, 681(289), *817*

Alcais, C., 659(2a), 697(2a), 698(2a), *809*

Aldridge, W. N., 951(3, 4, 214), *966, 972*, 998(2), *1004*

Aleksandrov, A. Yu., 109(5, 6), 111(7), *137, 138*, 172(4), 192(8, 9, 11), 193(2, 10), 209(259), 210(3), 217(2), 220(1, 7, 8), 221(5, 6), *243, 244, 250*, 257(2), 277(2), 278(2), *292*, 325(20, 21), 430 (20), *495*, 626(4, 6, 7), 689(4, 7), *809*, 855(2), 863(1, 2, 3), *876*

Alester, G., 304(138a), 351(138a), *500*

Alexander, R. P., *818*

Allan, R. B., 118(8), *138*, 848(6), *876*

Alleston, D. L., 25(215), 65(4), *72, 78*, 93(9), 97(11a), 99(9), 121(10), 122(10, 11), 125(9), 130(9), 137(10, 11), *138*, 155(13), 173(14), 179(13), 183(13), 190(14), 193(14), 194(14), 200(16, 17), 201(12, 16), 203(15, 17), 204(17) 205(17), 206(17), 207(16, 17), 208(16), 216(285), 217(285), 218(285), *244, 251*, 262-264(3, 4), *292*, 539(4), 572(4), *575*, 850(7), *876*

Allison, W. E., 949(4a), *966*

Allred, A. L., 646(81), 648(81, 82), 699 (81, 82), *811*

Allsopp, C. B., 106(12), *138*

Altman, L. J., 20(4a), *72*

Amberger, E., 9(105), 10(5, 6, 7, 105), 14(104), 18(257), 70(104), 71(104), *72, 75, 79*, 162(18, 19), 174(18, 19), 183(18), 184(18), *244*, 523(5), 528(87), 542(8), 543(5), 548(87), *575, 577*, 614(2, 3), 616(2, 3), *620*, 646(445), 649(8, 212), 697(212), 698(212), 699 (212), 758(212), 766(212), 793(212), 795(212), *809, 814, 822*, 886(2), 887 (157), 890(2), 891(2), 892(2), 893(230), 894(230), 895(230), *924, 928, 930*

Anderson, A., 100(74), 102(74), *139*

Anderson, D. G., 661(10, 12), 700(10, 12), *809*

Anderson, D. H., 13(83), *74*, 1002(67), *1005*
Anderson, H. H., 86(13), 89(13), 93(14), 121(15), 130(14, 15), *138*, 160(20), *244*, 254(7, 8, 8a), 262(8), 265(8), 277(6), 278(6), *292*, 303(24), 306(22), 315(23), 317(22, 24), 350(22, 23), 424(22, 23, 24), *495*, 512(6), 539(7, 8), 570(8), 571(7, 8), *575*, 771(9), *809*
Ando, T., 26(8), *72*
Andrascheck, H. J., 885(229), 890(229), *930*
Andrews, T. M., 161(41), 187(41), *244*, 261(9), *292*, 977(54), 979(54), *994, 995*
Andrianov, K. A., 216(21), 271(22), *244*, 976(3), *994*
Anisimov, K. N., 304(24a), 305(135, 136a), 374(24a, 135), 376(136a), 433 (135), *495, 500*, 887(110), 896-902 (149, 170, 171, 173, 176), 911(171, 172), 914(170, 172), 916(175), 917(175), 918(174), 921(110, 141), 923(12-15), *925, 927, 928*
Ankel, T., 107(60), *139*
Anthony, C., Jr., 960(17), *966*
Antler, M., 965(18), *966*
Antona, A. B., 896(149), *928*
Apsitis, A., 311(24b), 416(24b), *495*
Arbenz, U., 584(46, 46a), 589(46a), 595 (46, 46a), 596(46a), 597(46), 602(46a), 605(46a), 606(46a), *622*
Arbuzow, B. A., 120(16), 130(16), 132(16), *138*, 581(4, 5, 6, 7), *620, 621*
Aries, R. S., 964(20), *966*
Arkhangel'skaza, E. A., 886(106), *927*
Armbrecht, F. M., Jr., 258(103), *294*, 638(362), 640(362), 675(360, 362, 365), 677(362), *819*, 872(100), *879*
Armenskaya, L. V., 84(17, 18), 89(17), 120(18), *138*
Armitage, D. A., 298(1), 303(3), 304(3), 306(3), 308(2, 5), 318(2), 320(5), 327(4), 328(4), 340(3), 347(2, 5), 350(2, 3), 365(3), 374(4), 424(2, 5), 436(4), 454(4), 491(3), *495*, 530(1), 536(1), 542(1), 553(1), *575*, 935(1), *966*
Armour, A. G., 11(101), *74*, 520(85), *577*, 833(54), 843(54), 847(54), 853(54), 866(54), *877*

Arnold, M. H. M., 958(22), *966*
Arntzen, C. E., 130(168), 131(168), 133(168), *141*
Aronheim, B., 85(20), 94(20), 112(20), 131(19, 20), 133(20), *138*, 189(23), 200(23), 201(23), *244*
Ascher, K. R. S., 945(23), 948(21a, 22, 24, 25, 180), *966, 971*
Aschikari, N., 964(26), *967*
Ashby, E. C., 884(3), 886(3), *924*
Ashley, J. N., 133(176), *142*
Atavin, A. S., 175(24), *244*, 721(391), *820*
Atkins, A. M., 307(6), *495*
Atwell, W. H., 824(8, 32, 33), 826(32), 831(33), 834(36a), 840(33), 846(34), 854(32), 858-860(32), 863(36a), 868(35), 869(32, 36), *876, 877*
Aue, W. A., 220(67), *245*
Aufdermarsh, C. A., Jr., 744(13, 14), *809*, 982(4), *994*
Austin, J. A., 329(41), 462(41), *496*, 665(14a), 734-736(14a), 770(14a), *809, 810*
Aynsley, E. E., 539(9), 573(9), *575*
Azerbaev, I. N., 298(104a), *499*

B

Bachman, G. B., 130(21), *138*
Backer, H. J., 297(27), 303(28, 29, 30, 99), 308(28, 29, 30, 99), 329(25, 29), 330(25), 339(26, 27), 343(27), 359(28, 29), 373(29), 376-378(25, 27-30, 99), 454(25), 462(29), 491(26, 27), *495, 498*
Backer, H. S., 133(22), *138*
Baekelmans, P., 633(17), 649(17), 652(16), 657(17), 658(17), 669(17), 678(17a), 680(16, 17a), 689(17a), 691(17), 705(17a), 713(17), 730(17a), 737(17a), *809*
Bagent, J. L., 947(116), *969*
Bähr, G., 86(24), 93(24, 25), 131(23), *138*, 197(25), *244*, 625(21), 628(19), 629(18, 19), 673(18, 19), 674(18, 19), *809*, 835(9), 864(9), *876*
Bai, L. I., 693(22), *809*
Bailie, J. C., 88(26), *138*
Baird, M. C., 882(5), 896(4, 5), 901(4), 904(5), *924*

Baird, S. R., 920(11), 922(11), *924*
Bajer, F. J., 646(23), 796(23, 24), *809*
Baker, H. R., 86(46), *139*
Baker, J. M., 947(27), 955(27), *967*
Balashova, L. D., 304(43), 351(43), *496*,
    514(26), *575*, 584(8, 9, 10), 598(8, 9,
    10), *621*
Baldwin, J. C., 524(11), 536(10, 11), *575*
Baldwin, R. A., 537(186), 572(186),
    579, 990(81, 82, 83), *996*
Ballczo, H., 130(27), 131(27), *138*
Bamberg, P., 303(30*a*), 354(30*a*), *495*
Bancroft, G. M., 922(6), *924*
Baney, R. H., 195(327, 328), 196(327, 328),
    197(327, 328), *252*
Bankovskii, J., 303(214*e*), *503*
Banks, C. K., 161(261), *250*, 298(90), *498*
    665(25), *809*
Bannist
Bannister, E., 513(12, 13), *575*
Baranovskii, V. I., 625(26), *809*
Barbieri, R., 119(83), 122(86, 87), 123
    (83, 86, 87), 130(28), 131(28), 132(28),
    133(28), *138*, *139*, 183(275), 189(275),
    190(96), *246*, 279(10, 92, 93), 281(29),
    286(92), 287(10), *292*, *294*, 539(35),
    572(35),
Barbour, R. V., 22(40), *73*
Barnes, J. M., 936(30), 949-952(28, 30,
    31, 176, 228), *967*, *971*, *973*
Barnetson, C., 42(9), *72*
Barnett, W. E., 26(9*a*), *72*
Barnhart, W. S., 939(32), *967*
Baron, G., 706(144), *812*
Barth, K., 954(33), *967*
Basola, F., 900(25), 901(25), *925*
Bass, K. C., 629(27, 28), *809*
Bassileiados, K., 82(237), 132(237),
    133(237), *143*
Baukov, J. I., 317(139*a*), *500*
Baukov, Yu. I., 64(9*b*), *72*, 163(250),
    185(250), 239(250), *250*, 538(40),
    570(40), *576*, 640(249), 703(249), *816*
Baum, B., 966(72), *968*
Baum, G. A., 9(10), *72*, 200(26), 201(26),
    204(56), 205(56), 207(56), 210(56),
    244, *245*, 322(31), 430(31), *495*,
    513(14), 514(14), *575*, 855(10), 858(10),
    868(10), *876*, 935(34), *967*
Baumann, J., 942(35), 953(35), *967*

Beattie, I. R., 113(30, 32), 119(39), 123(31),
    125(31), 129(30), *138*, 254(11), *292*,
    1001(3), *1004*
Beaulaton, S., 944(56), *967*
Beaumel, O. F., 338(112), 480(112), *499*
Beck, W., 539(15), 573(15), *575*
Becker, E. I., 9(132, 225), 11(224), 25(130),
    27(132, 191, 192), 28(132, 181),
    37(225), 50(256), 54(131), 57(216,
    256), 65(181), 66(181), *75*, *77*, *78*, *79*,
    206(98), *246*, 268(30), 269(30, 104),
    271-273(30, 104), *292*, *294*, 304(145),
    315(123, 145), 324(123), 357(145),
    425(123, 145), *499*, *501*, 846(117),
    848(117), *879*
Becker, E. J., *148*
Becker, R., 86(293), 91(293), 93(293),
    131(293), 133(293), *145*, 834(50),
    859(50), 864(50), *877*
Becker-Palossy, K., 684(268), *816*
Beesley, J. S. S., 943(133), 945(133), *970*
Beg, M. A. A., 871(11), *876*
Behringer, H., 254(126), 266(126), *295*,
    855(118), 870(118), *879*
Beiter, C. B., 943(264), *974*
Bekker, R., 988(9, 10), *994*
Belavin, I. Yu., 64(9*b*), *72*
Belkina, M. A., 676(191), 702(191),
    735(191), *814*
Bellegarde, B., 10(10*a*), *72*, 157(238),
    158(237), 180(237), 181(237, 238),
    182(237, 238), 216(27), 217(27),
    227(27), *244*, *249*, 643(305), 738(305),
    740(305), 741(305), 742(305), *817*
Belluco, U., 867(105), 870(105), *879*,
    882(7), *924*
Belpaire, F., 936(37), *967*
Belyaev, V. A., 191(28), *244*
Benda, H., 585(47, 48, 48*a*, 48*b*), 593(48*c*),
    594(48*c*), 596(47, 48, 48*a*, 48*b*),
    598(48), 600(47, 48, 48*a*, 48*b*),
    601(47, 48), 605(48*a*, 48*b*), *622*
Bende, A., 988(9, 10), *994*
Benkeser, R. A., 660(28*a*), *809*
Bennett, R. F., 958(38), 959(38), *967*
Bent, H. A., 13, *72*
Benton, J. L., 937(177), 938(177), 939(177),
    971
Benzoni, L., 905(38), *925*
Berlin, A. A., 987(7), *994*

Bertz, T., 190(269), 193(269, 270), *250*
Besser, J. F., 960(230), *973*
Best, C. E., 935(39), *967*
Beumel, O. F., Jr., 12(94), 49(95, 96),
    50(96), 51(95, 96), *74*, 164(174),
    197(173, 174), *248*, 679(207*a*),
    795(207*a*), 802(207*a*), *814*, 832(52),
    864(52), *877*
Beveridge, A. D., 37(13), 39(13), *72*,
    643(30, 31), 677(30, 31), 689(29),
    773(29), *809*, *810*, 900(8), 901(8), *924*
Bevillard, P., 339(218), 493(218), *503*
Beyerly, W., 834(63), 856(63), *877*
Bezuglyi, V. D., 998(5), *1004*
Bhattacharya, S. N., 314(213*b*), 425(213*b*),
    503, 537(169), 538(170), 569(169),
    571(170), *579*
Bichler, R. E. J., 644(32), 685(32), 691(32),
    810, 916(9, 10), *824*
Bigorgne, M., 899-901(138, 139, 140), *928*
Bigotto, A., 101(156), *141*
Biller, D., 513(143, 144), 514(143, 144),
    556(143, 144), *578*
Birnbaum, E. R., 10(14, 15), *72*
Bir'yokov, B. P., 923(12-15), *925*
Blackmore, T., 887(16), 904(16), 906(16),
    911(16), *925*
Blaizot, A., 949(61), *968*
Blake, D., 125(41), *138*, 187(29), 189(29),
    244, 279(12), 286(12), *292*, 303(32),
    304(32), 357(32), 373(32), *495*, 883(17),
    887(17), 888(17), *925*
Blanchard, E. J., 513(81), *577*
Blandel, D., 944(119), *969*
Blank, D. R., 693(363, 370), *819*
Blankaut, U., 886(178), *929*
Blazso, M., 665(119), 679(119), *812*
Blears, D. J., 664(35), 668(35), 678(35),
    810
Blitzer, S. M., 84(550), 118(550), 130(550),
    131(550), 132(550), *151*, 212(341), *252*
Bliznyuk, N. K., 337(118*a*), 475(118*a*),
    477(118*a*), *499*
Blohm, C., 265(101), *294*
Bloodworth, A. J., 160(33, 39), 161(38),
    167(32, 33), 169(31, 36), 170(36),
    174(31), 181(33), 183(31), 190-193(38),
    202(38), 204(38), 205(38), 217(36),
    224(28), 228(33, 39), 231(31, 33, 39),
    232(33, 39), 233(34, 37, 40), 234(37),

235(30), 237(39), 240(33), 241(30, 39),
    242(35), 243(36, 40), *244*, 517-519
    (16-25), 521(19, 20, 22, 24),
    523(19, 20, 21, 22, 24), 524(21, 25),
    528(21, 22), 531(25), 534(21, 25),
    538(25), 540(191, 192), 560-563(16-25),
    565(16, 17), 573(17, 25), *575*, *579*,
    963(40), *967*
Blum, M. S., 946(41), *967*
Blut, A. H., 124(313), 126(313), *145*,
    288(63), 290(63), 291(63), *293*
Bobrashinskaya, T. S., 88(42), 133(42),
    138
Bochkarev, M. N., 63(15*a*, 247),
    64(15*a*, 246*a*, 246*c*, 247), 65(246*b*),
    72, *79*, 314(64*c*), 315(225, 226, 227,
    227*a*, 227*c*, 227*d*), 316(36*b*, 225, 227,
    227*b*), 320(36*b*, 65), 336(227),
    341-346(36*b*, 64*a*, 64*c*, 65, 225-227,
    227*a*, 227*b*, 227*c*, 227*g*), 424(36*b*, 64*c*,
    225, 227, 227*a*, 227*b*), 426(65),
    429(65, 226, 227*b*, 227*d*), 474(227),
    491(36*b*, 64*c*, 65, 225, 227, 227*a*, 227*b*),
    492(226, 227), 494(36*b*, 64*a*, 64*c*, 65,
    225, 227, 227*a*, 227*b*, 227*c*, 227*g*),
    496, *497*, *503*, *504*, 616-619(17, 73),
    621, *623*, 864(113), *879*
Bochkareva, G. P., 133(383), *147*
Bock, R., 998(28), *1005*
Boescken, J., 131(43), *138*
Böeseken, J., 824(12), 831(12), 840(12),
    846(12), 859(12), *876*
Bogdanova, I. V., 704(294), 736(294), *817*
Bolles, T. F., 108(46), 120(46), 124(44, 45,
    46), *138*, *139*
Bonati, F., 311(39, 39*a*), 313(39),
    337(37, 38), 338(38), 418-421(39, 39*a*),
    475(37, 38), 476(37, 38), *496*, 776(36),
    810, 887(19), 901(18), 906-909(18, 19,
    20, 22), 913(20), 917(18, 216), 918(21),
    925, *930*
Bond, A. C., Jr., 8(53), *73*
Bondjouk, P. R., 628(214), 633(214),
    646(214), 661(214), 672(214), 794(214),
    801(214), *814*
Bonner, E. F., 964(55), *967*
Bonsack, J. P., *994*
Booth, M. R., 644(32), 685(32), 691(32),
    810, 916(9), 914(23), *924*, *925*
Borbely-Kuszmann, A., 684(268), *816*

Borgstrom, P., 85(48), 90(48), *139*, 321(40), *496*
Borisenko, V. V., 175(289), 178(156), *247, 251*
Borisov, A. E., 27(17), 49(137*b*, 137*c*, 137*d*, 137*e*), 63(16), *72, 76*, 89(47), 95(370, 374, 376), 131(375), 132(372, 373, 374, 375), 133(374, 375, 376), *139, 146*, 215(213), *249*, 277(13), *292*, 614(34), 616(34), *621*, 644(280), 657(275), 668(67), 689(280), 723(279), 730(281), 744(278, 279), 787(279), *810, 816, 817*
Bork, V. A., *496*
Bornstein, J., 161(41), 187(41), *244*
Borodavko, I. A., 633(328), *818*
Borror, A. L., 304(178), 353(178), *502*
Borshagovskii, B. V., 887(110), 921(110), *927*
Bost, R. W., 85(48), 86(49), 90(49), *139*, 321(40), *496*
Bott, R. A., 87(50), *139*
Bott, R. W., 637(39), 646(38), 653(37), 655(37), 659(36*a*, 38), 660(36*a*), 671(36*a*), 676(39), 684(37, 38), 685(39), 686(39), 698(36*a*, 38), 699(38), 712(37), 726(36*a*), 756(36*a*), 757(36*a*), 767(36*a*), *810*
Boué, S., 87(52), 92(51), *139*, 629(40, 41, 42), 630(42), 632(42, 45), 634(45), 648-653(40, 42, 43, 45), 655(41), 656(41, 42), 664-666(14*a*, 40, 41, 43, 44), 677-680(40-44), 683-686(43, 44, 45), 697-699(43), 701(40-44), 706(40, 41, 42), 734-737(14*a*, 349*a*), 741(349*a*), 770(14*a*), 804(45, 349*a*), 805(349*a*), 807(45, 349*a*), *809, 810, 818*, 861(12*a*), 862(12*a*), *876*
Bowden, S. T., 90(232), 93(232), 130-134 (232), *143*
Bower, F. A., 261(9), *292*, 946(41, 42), *967*
Bower, L. M., 898(24), 899(24), 901(24), *925*
Brack, O., 203(241), 205(241), *250*
Bradley, D. C., 310(40*a*), 311(40*a*), 313(40*a*), 421(40*a*), *496*
Bradley, J. R., 947(116), *969*
Bradney, M. A. M., 661(10), 700(10), *809*

Brady, D. B., 303(3, 7), 304(3, 14), 306(3, 7, 9), 307(14), 308(2, 7, 8), 314(7), 316-318(2, 7, 9), 320(5, 8), 324(7), 329(7, 9), 330(7), 340(3), 344(8), 347(2), 350(2, 3, 7, 8, 9), 351(7), 359(7), 365(3, 7, 8, 9, 14), 366(7, 9), 374(7, 8, 14), 375(7), 376(8), 424(2, 7, 9), 436(7, 9), 454(7), 491(3, 8), *495*, 511(2), 513(2), 514(2), 530(1), 536(1), 542(1, 2), 553(1), *575*, 610-612(1), *620*
Brago, I. N., 664(46), *810*
Brainina, E. M., 134(53), *139*
Brändle, K. A., 37(210), 60(210), *78*, 163(286), 179(286), 203(286), 204(286), *251*
Braum, W., 627(47*a*), 665(47*a*, 215), *810, 815*
Braun, J., 36(17*a*), *72*, 641(47), 705(47), *810*
Braye, E. H., 646(48), 798(48), *810*
Breau, R., 900-902(130, 131), *927*
Bregadze, V. I., 647(450), 661(49), 797(49), *809, 810, 822*
Breitschaft, S., 900(25), 901(25), *925*
Bren, R., 215(130), *247*
Brennan, T., 646(374), 698(374), *819*
Breslow, R., 27(18, 19), *72*
Brevnova, T. N., 172(320, 321), *252*, 633(438), 664(437, 438), 665(438), *821*
Bricker, C. E., 998(73), *1006*
Bridges, J. W., 951(43), 952(43), *967*
Brier, P. N., *925*
Brighton, C. A., 310(40*b*), *496*
Brilkina, T. C., *876*
Brilkina, T. G., 173(42, 296), 176(43), 183(43), 203(296), 221(44), *245*, *251*, 626(50), *810*, 863(1), *876*
Britain, J. W., 962(44), 963(44), *967*
Britton, D., 112(458), *148*, 537(150*a*), *578*, 649(340), 695(340), *818*
Britton, S. C., 955(45), 956(46), *967*
Brockway, L. O., 113(54), *139*
Brodskaya, E. I., 720(387), 722(387), 777(387), *820*
Brooks, E. H., 882(28), 915(27), *925*
Brottes, H., 945(77), *968*
Brown, D. H., 102(55), *139*
Brown, H. P., 329(41), 462(41), *496*

Brown, J. E., 11(98), 15(196, 197), 16(197, 17(19198), 7, 198), 57(197), 61(196, 197, 198), 63(196), 69(198), 70(196, 197, 198), 71(196, 198), *77*, 107(454, 455, 456), 137(455), *148*, 846(92), 849(92), *878*, 1001(69), *1005*
Brown, J. H., 220(300), *251*
Brown, M. P., 107(59), *139*, 204(45), 208(45), 214(45), *245*, 324(42), 430(32), *496*, 834-836(14), 867(14), *876*, 883(29), *925*
Brown, T. L., 105(56), 107(56, 57), 108(58), 117(58), *139*, 648(51), 664(51), *810*, 833(15), 838(117*a*), 842(15), *876*, *879*, 887(228), 919(30, 203), *925*, *929*, *930*
Bru, A., 949(59), *967*
Bru, Y., 949(59), *967*
Brügel, W., 107(60), *139*
Bruggemann, J., 954(33), *967*
Bruikmann, F. E., 646(310), 660(310), 671(310), 696(310), 747(310), 766(310), 769(310), 793(310), 796(310), 798(310), *817*
Bruker, A. B., 304(43), 351(43), *496*, 514(26), *575*, 584(8, 9, 10), 598(8, 9, 10), *621*
Brukhova, E. V., 918(174), *929*
Brüning, R., 513(158), 515(158), 535(158), 555(158), 556(158), *598*
Bryan, R. F., 917(34, 35), 922(32), 923(31-34, 123, 227), *925*, *927*, *930*
Bryce-Smith, D., 137(61), *139*
Brykhanov, V. A., 257(14), *292*
Bryuchova, E. V., 109(62, 461), *139*, *148*
Bryukhanov, V. A., 109(63), *139*
Buchev, F. K., 284(15), *292*
Buchman, O., 87(64, 65, 366), 88(66), *139*, *146*, 646(52, 53), 659-661(53, 54, 55, 56, 270, 271, 271*a*), 698(52, 53, 55, 56, 271), 699(52, 53, 55, 271), 733(271), 734(54, 270, 271), 747(52, 54), *810*, *816*
Buchwald, H., 582(30), 597(30), *621*
Buckton, G. B., 130(67), *139*
Budding, H. A., 39(128, 129), 46(119, 123, 124), 47(114, 115, 116, 119, 123, 124), 48(114, 115, 116, 118, 120), 49(128, 129), 52(117), 53(118), 54(120),

55(120), *75*, 422(121), *499*, 518(102), *577*, 644(234, 235), 645(235), 647(231, 237), 649(228), 678(227, 231), 689-693(227, 228, 231, 232, 234, 235), 704(227, 231), 714-719(227, 228, 231, 232, 237), 719(231, 234, 235, 236), 721(227, 231), 728(227, 231), 730(227, 231), 744(228, 231, 232), 745(228, 231), 763(231), 773(226), 776(226), 777(226), *815*, 872(15*a*), *876*, 966(168), *971*
Buisset, M. B., 98(119*a*), *140*
Buisson, R., 136(318), *145*
Bullard, R. H., 8(20), *72*, 86(70, 71, 283), 88(69), 131(70), 132(69), 133(70), 135(71), 136(69), *139*, *144*, 194(162), 196(47, 162), 197(163), 198(163), 212(46, 162), *245*, *248*, 520(27), 553(27), *575*, 824(46), 863(46), *877*
Bulten, E. J., 872(15*a*), *876*
Burdon, I., 94(72), *139*
Burg, A. B., 869(16), *876*
Bürger, H., 606(30), *621*, 890(36), 891(36), 892(36), 895(36), *925*
Burger, K., 998(7), 999(6), *1004*
Bürgerland, H., 535(28), 547(28), *575*
Burke, J. C., 1001(8), *1004*
Burke, J. J., 98(73), 107(73), *139*, 435(144), 430(44), *496*
Burkhardt, G., 90(386), 91(386), *147*
Burlachenko, G. S., 64(9*b*), *72*
Burlitch, J. M., 25(207), *77*, 675(356, 367), *819*, 898(37), 904(37), *925*
Burnashova, T. D., 175(288), 176(288), 178(288), 180(288), 181(288), *251*, 695(385), 721(385), 724(385), 725(385), 732(385), 746(385), *820*
Bush, R. P., 118(1), *137*, 309(10), 327(4), 328(4), 350(10), 365(10), 374(4), 436(4), 454(4), *495*
Bush, S. F., 102(135), *141*
Butcher, F. K., 100(74), 102(74), *139*, 156(48), 184-186(48), 189(48), *245*, 1001(9), 1002(10), *1004*
Buttgenbach, H., 112(75), *139*
Bychkov, V. T., 65(248), *79*, 92(522), *150*, 314(64*b*), 341(64*b*), 345(64*b*), *497*, 848(114), 865(115), 870(115), *879*
Byrdy, S., 948(48, 49), *967*

C

Cadiot, P., 658(321), 670(224), 678(223, 225), 689(223, 224, 225*b*, 225*c*), 695(57, 223), 696(223, 224), *810*, *815*, *818*

Cahours, A., 82(76, 81), 84(76), 93(76), 130(76, 77, 79, 80), 131(78, 80), 132(76, 80), 133(76), *139*, 196(49), 212(50), *245*, 572(29), *575*

Calabretta, P. J., 311(116, 117), 312(116, 117), 313(117), 315(116), 321(117), 418(116, 117), 419(117), 420(117), 425(116), 431(117), *499*, 513(88, 89), 520(90), *577*

Calas, R., 52(21), *72*, 163(315), 164(51), 181(51), 182(51), *245*, *252*

Caldwell, J. R., 963(50), *967*

Callis, C. C., 130(284), *144*

Cambensi, H., 18(257), *79*, 646(445), *822*, 893(230), 894(230), 895(230), *930*

Camey, T., 945(51), *967*

Camia, M., 905(38), *925*

Campbell, I. G. M., 276(16), *292*, 583(11), 590(11), 592(11), 596(11), 597(11), 598(11), 605-609(11, 12), 612(12), 614-616(12), *621*

Caplier, I., 646(48), 798(48), *810*

Cardarelli, N. F., 959(52), *967*

Cardin, D. J., 522(31, 31*a*, 33), 527(30, 31*a*, 32), 528(32, 33, 34), 530(33, 34), 541(31, 31*a*, 32), 573(34), *575*, 908(39), 914(23), 920(40), *925*

Carey, F. A., 48(21*a*), *72*

Carey, N. A. D., 338(44*b*), *496*, 872(17), *876*, 886(43), 890(43), 900(8, 41, 42), 914(23), 918(42), *925*

Carlson, A. A., 50(77*a*), *74*

Carlson, G. L., 130(21), *138*

Carlsson, D. J., 24(22, 23), *72*

Carr, H. G., *496*

Carrick, A., 884(44), 895(44), *925*

Carrick, W. L., 964(54, 55), *967*

Cartledge, F. K., 824(32, 33), 826(32), 831(33), 840(33), 854(32), 858-860(32), 869(32), *876*, *877*, 889(95), *927*

Casey, M., 908(45, 46), 912(46), 918(46), *925*

Casida, J. E., 948(204), *972*

Cassan, J., 104(333), 105(344), 131(333), *145*

Cassol, A., 119(83), 122(84, 85, 86, 87), 123(82, 83, 86, 87, 88, 89), *139*, *140*, 539(35), 572(35), *575*

Castel, P., 944(56, 58, 124), *967*, *969*

Cattanach, C. J., 102(90), *140*

Caujolle, F., 949(59, 60, 61), *967*

Cawley, S., 664(35), 668(35), 678(35), *810*

Cenini, S., 311(39*a*), 337(37, 38), 338(38), 420(39*a*), 421(39*a*), 475(37, 38), 476(37, 38), *496*, 887(19), 901(18), 906-908(18, 22), 911(18, 216), 917(18), *925*, *930*

Chalk, A. J., 905(47), *925*

Challenger, F., 133(91), *140*

Chalmers, A. A., *925*

Chalmers, L., 933(61*a*), *968*

Chamberlain, B. L., 991(12), *994*

Chamberland, B. L., 278(17), 279(17), *292*

Chambers, D. B., 664(59, 60), *810*, 890(48), *925*

Chambers, R. D., 88(92), 94(92), 100(94), 107(93), 131(94), *140*, *810*, 873(17*a*), *876*

Chambers, R. F., 8(24), *72*, 200(52), 201(52), *245*, 887(49), *925*

Chan, L. H., 574(35*a*), *575*

Chan, S. S., 675(61), *810*

Chandler, L., 921(234), *930*

Chandra, G., 522(37), 523(38), 526(39). 528(37, 38, 38*a*), 529(37, 38), 531(37, 39), 532(38*a*), 533(38*a*), 541(37, 38), 542(38*a*), *575*, *576*, 680(62), 692(62), 694(62), 705(62), 706(62), 711(62), *810*

Chapman, A. C., 206(53), *245*

Chapman, A. H., 998(11), *1004*

Charisius, K., 955(61*b*), *968*

Chatt, J., 130(94*a*), *140*, 661(63), 698(63), 726(63), *810*

Chauzov, V. A., 538(40), 570(40), *576*

Cheng, H. Y., 942(65), *968*

Cheng, P. L., 942(63, 64), *968*

Cheng, X. Y., 418(235), *504*

Chernick, C. L., 91(407), 117(407), *147*

Chernyshev, E. A., 684(407), *820*

Chetyrkima, G. M., 977(30), *994*

Chipperfield, J. R., 661(12), 700(12), *809*

Chirgadze, Y. N., 217(154), *247*

Chiu, K. K., 115(217), 116(217), *143*, 648(175), *813*

Chivers, T., 88(92), 94(92), 118(120), *140*, 344(63), 491-493(63), *497*, 511(42), 525(41, 42), 531(41, 42), 541(42), *576*, 646(65, 66), 648(66), 649(66), 661(65), 665(66), 675(65, 66), 689(65, 66), 698(65, 66), *810*, 848(25), 857(25), *876*

Cho, J. H., 65(233), *78*, 636(425), 642(425), 701(425), 735(425), 737(425), *820*, 942(65), *968*

Chodkiewicz, W., 658(321), *818*

Chow, Y. M., 540(193), *579*

Chromy, V., 308(44*a*), *496*

Chubarova, M. A., 781(152), 787(151), *813*

Chumaevskii, N. A., 668(67), *810*

Churamani, L. K., 646(183), 733(183), 747(183), *813*

Claesson, M. P., 302(45), *496*

Clark, F. M., 964(66, 67), *968*

Clark, H. C., 23(2), 37(13), 38(2, 3, 25, 26, 27, 28), 42(9, 25, 26), 69(25), *72*, 97(101), 100(97), 101(95, 101), 106(96), 107(93), 112(101, 102), 113(98, 99), 124(100), 125(103, 104), 126(95), 127(103), 128(97, 98, 99, 101, 102), 129(95), *140*, 268(21, 22), 269(19), 273(21), 275(19, 21), 276(22), 277(19, 21), 278(18, 19), 279(18), 291(20), *292*, 338(44*b*), *496*, 642(68), 643(30, 31, 69), 644(32), 677(30, 31, 68, 69), 679(68), 682(68), 685(32), 689(29, 68), 691(32), 773(29), *809*, *810*, *811*, 871-873(11, 17, 17*a*, 19, 19*a*), 875(5*b*, 19*a*), *876*, 886(43), 890(43), 898(50, 51), 900(8, 41, 42), 901(8), 911(1), 913(1), 914(1, 23), 915(50, 51), 916(9, 10), 917(50, 51), 918(42), *924*, *925*, 1000(16), 1003(14, 15),

Clark, J. P., 284(23), 288(23, 24), 289(23), 290(24), 291(23, 24), *292*

Clark, M. G., *926*

Clark, R. E. D., 998(12, 13), *1004*

Clarke, H. J., 958(21), *966*

Clemmit, A. F., 905(53), 912(53), *926*

Cleverdon, D., 180(60), 183(60), *245*

Coates, G. E., 82(105), 125(41), *138*, *140*, 187(29), 189(29), *244*, 279(12), 286(12), *292*, 298(46), 303(32), 304(32), 357(32), 373(32), *495*, *496*, 510(43),

576, 883(17), 887(17), 888(17), 895(54), *925*, *926*

Coc, P. L., 94(72), *139*

Cochran, J. C., 655(211), 692(211), 694(211), 719(70, 211), *811*, *814*

Cohen, G., 131(106), *140*

Cohen, H. J., 219(54), 220(54), *245*

Cohen, M. M., 89(467), 91(467), 131(467), 132(467), 133(467), *149*

Cohen, S. C., 629(72), 646(71), 671(72), 672(71, 72), 793(71), 800(71), *811*

Colaitis, D., 131(107), 133(107), *140*

Cole, J. R., 953(68), *968*

Colemann, D. J., 665(73), 678(73), 680(73), *811*

Colin, G., 52(182*a*, 182*b*), *77*, 654(302), 736(302), 740(302), 741(302), *817*

Collier, M. R., 523(43*a*), 574(43*a*), *576*

Collins, R. L., 920(55), *926*

Collman, J. P., 901(56), *926*

Combarieu, J., 94(108), *140*

Conaty, F. H., 965(223), *973*

Connolly, R. E., 520(90), *577*

Considine, W. J., 8(190*c*), 9(10), 35(190*b*), *72*, *77*, 87(440), *148*, 161(55, 58), 186(57), 187(55), 188(55), 196(59, 268), 200-202(26, 58), 204-207(56, 58, 268), 210(26), *244*, *245*, *250*, 265(90), 275(90), *294*, 303(47), 309(166), 315(47), 317(54*a*), 320(166), 322(31, 54*a*), 326(54*a*), 369(47), 404(166), 430(31), 433(166), *495*, *496*, *501*, 627(332), 647(331), 664(332), 665(331*a*), 759(331), *818*, 855(10), 858(10), 868(10), *876*

Cooke, D. J., 304(151), 309(151), *501*, 640(311), 681(311), 683(311), 693(311), *817*, 999(63), *1005*

Cooksley, M. V., 959(69), *968*

Cooley, J. H., 25(252), *79*

Cordey-Hayes, M., 110(109), *140*, 664(74), *811*

Costa, G., 118(110), 130(110, 111), 131(110), *140*

Cotton, J. D., 642(68), 677(68), 678(68), 679(68), 682(68), 689(68), *810*, 871(18), *876*, 887(16), 899(59), 900(57, 58, 59), 904(16), 906(16), 908(57, 58), 910(60), 911(16), 913(60), 923(60), *925*, *926*

Coutts, R. S. P., 896(61), 897(61), *926*

Cox, E. F., 960(134), 962(134), *970*

Craeybeal, J. D., 108(185), 109(185), *142*

Crain, R. D., *248*

Creemers, H. M. J. C., 8(30), 18(30, 33),
54(35, 38), 60(30-36, 38), 61(32, 35, 38),
62(38), 63(31, 32), 64(37, 39, 230),
72, 73, 78, 171(225), 175-178(61, 225),
180(225), 182(225), 185(62), 197(62),
212(62), 223(61, 225), *245, 249,*
298(222*b*), 304-306(48, 49, 50),
311(48), 312(48), 315(48), 316(48),
350(48), 351(48), 354(48), 357(48),
422(48), 424(48), 425(48), 431(48),
496, 503, 526(44-47), 527(47), 543(47),
552(47), 559(46, 47), *576,* 582(70*b*),
593(13, 14), 597(13), 612(13), 614(13),
617(13), 618(13), *621, 623,* 637(292),
654(292), 703(292), 704(292), *817,*
824(20), 827-831(20), 834-840(20, 21,
22, 23,) 846(20, 21), 850(21),
852(20, 21), 864-867(20), 869(20), *876,*
884(63, 65), 886(63, 64), 888(65),
890(63, 64), 893(64), 895(62), 908(62),
912(62), *926*

Cremer, J. E., 950(70), 951(3), *966, 968*

Cremer, T. E., 998(2), *1004*

Cresswell, W. T., 117(521), 130(521),
131(521), 134(521), 135(521), 136(521),
150, 811

Cristol, S. J., 22(40, 40a), 26(41), *73*

Crittenden, C. R., 949(209), *972*

Croon, H., 177(129), 178(129), 185(129),
247

Cross, R. J., 258(103), *294,* 675(360), *819,*
882(28), 915(27, 66), *925, 926*

Crosse, B. C., 298(13), 304(14), 306(9, 11,
322), 307(6, 11, 12, 14, 17, 232),
317(9), 329(9), 340(16), 343(15, 16),
350(9, 12), 354(12), 365(9, 11, 12, 14),
366(9), 374(14), 402(232), 424(9),
436(9), 491(15), *495, 504*

Crow, J. P., 307(17*a*), *495,* 532(3), 541(3),
575, 589(1*b*), 595(1*a*), 597(1*b*),
602(1*b*, 1*c*), 609(1*c*), 610(1*a*, 1*b*)
612(1*a*, 1*b*), 613(1*b*), *620*

Cullen, W. R., 23(44), 37(44), 46(43),
52(42), *73,* 165(63), 166(63), 174(63),
184(63), 186(63), *245,* 636(77),
678(76), 689(76), 690(76, 77), 691(76),

692(75), 695(77), 718(76), 745(76),
773(77), 774(77), 787(75, 76), *811,*
871(24), *876,* 904(67), *926*

Culter, A., 269(116), 271(116), 273(116),
294

Cummins, R. A., 102(112, 113), *140,*
186(65), 210(65), *245,* 254(25),
257(26), *292,* 308(52), 313(52),
318(51, 52), 324(51, 52), 413(52),
424(51, 52), 430(51, 52), *496,* 520(48),
537(48), 538(48), 539(48), 564(48),
571(48), *576,* 664(78), *811*

Cumper, C. W. N., 320(53, 54),
348(53, 54), 424(53), *496,* 665(79), *811*

Curran, C., 110(363), 125(363), 128(363),
146, 309(145*c*), 482(145*c*), 483(145*c*),
501

Curtis, M. D., 646(81), 647(80),
648(81, 82), 699(81, 82), *811*

Cutler, A., 57(232), *78*

Cuvigny, T., 540(194, 195), *579*

Cyr, N., 1003(14), *1004*

D

Dahl, L. F., 306(232), 307(232), 402(232),
504

Dahlman, J., 190(273), 191(273), 193(273),
194(273), 220(271, 272, 273), 221(273),
250

Dalton, J., 918(68), *926*

Dalton, R. F., 515(50), 522(49), 535(51),
539(49), 540(224), 541(50, 51),
542(51), 543(51), 547(49, 51), 552(50),
553(49, 51), 570(49), 571(49), *576*

Damle, S. B., 317(54*a*), 322(54*a*), 326(54*a*)
496

Danek, O., 83(114), *140,* 196(66), *245,*
303(55), 314(55), 320(55), 356(55),
372(55), 425(55), 431(55), *496*

Dannin, J., 966(72), *968,* 982(72), *995*

Dannley R. L., 220(67), *245*

Dangiz, M., 834(124), *879,* 884(236), *930*

D'Ans, J., 131(115), 133(115), 134(115),
140, 183(68), *245*

Danyluk, S. S., 664(35), 668(35), 678(35),
810

Danzik, M., 78(551), 91(551), 131(551),
133(551), 135(551), 136(551), *161,*

197(342), *252*, 666(83, 461), 708(461), 750(461), 776(461), 784(461), *811*, *822*

Dao-Huy-Giao, M., 629(84), 665(84), *811*

Darragh, K. V., 675(368), *819*, 872(101), *879*

Dasgupta, J., 314(213*b*), 425(213*b*), *503*

Das Kumar, V. G., 290(61), 291(61), *293*

Daum, R. J., *968*

David, B., 511(42), 525(41, 42), 531(42), 541(42), *576*, 646(65, 66), 648(66), 649(66), 661(65), 665(66), 675(65, 66), 689(65, 66), 698(65, 66), *810*

Davidson, W. E., 39(111), 65(111), *75*, 160(179), 186(179), *248*, 303(56, 118), 304(56), 311(56), 315(88), 317(168*a*), 323(168*a*), 327(56), 335-337(56, 88, 168*a*), 357(56), 366(118), 373(56), 414(56), 425(56), 429(88), 437(56), 467(56), 474(88), *496*, *498*, *499*, *501*, 628(85), 635(85), 639(85), 670(85), 695(85, 113), 696(85), 720-725(85), 744(85), 751(85), 754(85), 756(85), 777(85), 779(85), 787(85), *811*, *812*, 976(27), *994*

Davies, A. G., 65(4), *72*, 93(9), 97(11*a*), 99(9), 121(10), 122(10, 11), 125(10), 130(9), 137(10, 11, 117), *138*, *140*, 155(13), 156(70, 72), 159(85), 160(33, 39, 84, 85, 90), 161(38), 162(85, 90), 167-170(32, 33, 36, 71, 82, 84, 85, 88, 89, 90), 173(14, 69), 175(80), 179-194(14, 33, 38, 72, 73, 76, 80, 82, 84, 85, 89, 90), 199-211(14, 16, 17, 36, 38, 53, 72, 75, 77, 84), 216-220(36, 57, 77, 78, 81), 222-226(38, 72, 74, 75, 77, 83, 85, 90), 228(33, 39, 79, 80), 231-243(33, 34, 35, 36, 37, 39, 40, 73, 79, 80, 83, 84, 85 89, 90), *244*, *245*, *246*, 262-264(3, 4, 27), *292*, 298(57*a*), 304(58), 306(58), 311(34-36*a* 57, 59, 60*a*), 313(35, 36, 57, 60*a*), 315(33, 35, 36, 57, 59, 60*b*), 316(60), 317(61, 62), 320-321(60, 60*b*), 325(60*a*), 362(58), 417-419(34-36, 57, 60*a*, 60*b*), 422(35, 36, 59), 424(35, 36, 36*a*, 57), 426(60, 60*a*), 430(60, 60*a*, 62), 433(60*a*), 433(60*a*), *495*, *496*, 511(54), 517-521 (16-25, 52, 53, 55), 523-525(19, 20, 21, 22, 24, 25, 52, 54), 528(21, 22), 531(25), 533(52), 534(21, 25), 538(25, 55),

539(4), 540(192, 196, 197), 541(52), 543(52, 54), 544(54), 552(55), 559-564(16-25, 53, 55), 565(16, 17), 570(55), 571(54), 572(4), 573(17, 25), *575*, *576*, *579*, 582(15), *621*, 642(86), 643(87), 645(86), 671(86), 675(87, 88), 735(87), 736(86), 737(86), *811*, 850(7), *876*, 963(40), *967*, *993*(13, 14, 15), *994*

Davies, H., 132(118), *140*

Davies, W. C., 90(232), 93(232), 130-134(232), *143*

Davis, D. D., 882(69), *926*

Davis, V. E., 90(232), 93(232), 130-134(234) *143*

Dawson, D. S., 692(75), 787(75), 871(24), *876*, *811*

De Aguirre, I., 87(235), *143*, 630(186), 665(186), *814*

De Alti, G., 101(156), *141*

Deblandre, C., 629(89), *811*

Debreezeni, E., 86(445), 87(445), 136(445), *148*

Debye, N. W. G., 110(119), 112(119), 128(119), *140*

Dec, S. M., 628(419), 661(419), 671(419), *821*

De Clercg, M., 648(89*a*), 649(89*a*), 683(89*a*), 687(89*a*), *811*

De Croocg, D., 87(235), *143*, 630(186), 665(186), *814*

Deganello, G., 882(7), *924*

Del Franco, G. J., 12(45), 42(45), *73*, 647(90), 760(90), 761(90), 762(90), *811*

Delhaye, A., 697(91), *811*

Delhaye, M., 98(119*a*), *140*

De Liefde Meijer, H. J., 634(92), *811*, 964(75), *968*

Delinskaya, E. D., 119(182), *142*, 648(150), *813*

Delman, A. D., 217(91), *246*, 966(76), *968*, 992(16), *994*

Delmas, M. A., 45(45*a*), *73*, 320(63*c*), 425(63*c*), 492(63*c*), *497*

Delwaulle, M. L., 98(119*a*), *140*

Delyagin, N. N., 109(5, 6, 63), *137*, *138*, *139*, 257(2, 14), 277(2), 278(2), *292*, 325(20, 21), 430(20), *495*

Demarcey, E., 82(81), 130(81), 131(81), 132(81), *139*, 196(49), 212(50), *245*

Denault, G. C., 983(69), 984(69), 991(69), 995
Denney, D. B., 21(46), 73
DePree, D. O. 991(17), 994
DePuy, C. H., 26(41), 73
Dergunov, Y. I., 90(437, 438), 148, 629(329), 633(329), 818, 832(83, 84), 858(83), 867(83), 878
De Ridder, J. J., 850(87a), 860(87a), 878
de Roche, I. S., 102(347), 130(347), 131(347), 132(347), 146
Dersin, H. J., 303(191), 304(191), 305(191), 307(191), 321(191), 341(191), 357(191), 373(191), 430(191), 431(191), 502, 634(342), 659(342), 818
Dertouzos, H., 25(207), 27(208), 77, 78, 636(366, 369), 642(369), 651(366), 675(366), 678(369), 380(366), 681(366), 682(366), 705(366), 739(369), 819
Derwish, G. A. W., 102(187, 189), 103(187), 105(186), 106(188), 142, 176(110), 246, 648(157), 813
Deschiens, R., 945(77, 78, 79), 968
Deskusses, J., 998(84), 1006
Dessy, R. E., 58(47), 73, 118(120), 119(121), 140, 344(63), 491(63), 492(63), 493(63), 297, 848(25), 857(25), 876, 895(70, 71), 898(72), 903(70, 71), 926
Des Tombe, F. J. A., 64(230), 78
Devaud, M., 117(122, 123), 118(124), 140, 325(63b), 434(63b), 407
De Villiers, J. P., 945(82), 968
Devooght, J., 110(125, 367), 112(367), 121(367), 124(367), 128(367), 140, 146
Dianov, E. M., 116(224), 143
Dibeler, V. H., 117(126), 140
Diener, U. L., 958(83), 968
Dietzsch, W. 329(92), 330(92), 336(92), 460(92), 464(92), 470(92), 498
Dighe, S. V., 902(73), 926
Digiovanni, S., 744(447), 786(447), 822
Dijkstra, G., 664(93), 811
Dillard, C. R., 12(45), 14(83), 42(45), 73, 74, 130(127), 132(127), 134(127), 140, 204(197), 248, 259(66), 263(68), 293, 647(90), 760-762(90), 811, 999(17), 1000(44), 1001(18), 1004, 1005

Diluzio, J. W., 905(217), 930
Ditmar, M., 132(210), 134(210), 142
Dmitrieva, V. N., 998(5), 1004
Doi, H., 744(261), 816
Dolan, D. N., 640(313), 678(313), 727(313), 770(313), 804(313), 818
Dolle, R. E., 965(84, 85), 968
Domange, L., 102(128), 130(128), 132(128), 140
Donadille, M., 320(63c), 425(63c), 492(63c), 497
Donadio, R. E., 646(310), 660(310), 671(310), 696(310), 747(310), 766(310), 767(310), 769(310), 793(310), 796(310), 798(310), 817
Donaldson, J. D., 920(11), 922(11), 924
Doretti, L., 857(26, 27), 876
Dörfelt, C., 325(63a), 434(63a), 497
Doty, A. E., 949(4a), 966
Dorfman, Y. G., 111(7), 137, 678(94), 679(94), 689(94), 811
Dorn, K. H., 589(18), 595(18), 596(18), 597(18), 603-605(18), 621
Drago, R. S., 61(48), 73, 108(46, 355), 120(46, 355), 123(355), 124(44, 45, 46, 355), 138, 139, 146, 157(203), 161(203), 187(203), 188(203), 196(203), 249, 648(96), 664(95, 96), 811, 1000(48), 1003(48), 1005
Dreeskamp, H., 14(48a), 73, 597(18b), 606(18b), 621, 648(97), 664(97, 98), 811
Dremova, V. P., 197(157), 247, 946(161), 971
Drenth, W., 47(115, 116), 48(115, 116, 118, 121), 52(117), 53(118), 75, 329(25), 330(25), 376(25), 454(25), 495, 637(333), 644(235), 645(235), 647(237), 651(333), 669(233), 690(232), 691(235), 703(233), 704(333), 706(333), 715(232, 237), 717(232), 719(235), 744(232), 815, 818, 892(74), 926
Druce, J. G. F., 93(130), 132(131), 134(129, 130, 131, 132), 140, 212(93), 215(92, 93), 246
Druesedow, D., 938(86), 968
Dub, M., 298(64), 497, 582(16), 621, 824(28), 876
Dubb, M., 82(133), 141

Dubois, J. E., 87(166), *141*, 664(133), *812*
Dubova, R. I., 175(24), *244*
Duckworth, J., 910(60), 913(60), 923(60), *926*
Duckworth, M. W., 998(11), *1004*
Dudikovz, E. D., 186(340), 209(339, 340), 210(340), *252*, 261(134), 264(134), *295*, 847(123), 852(123), *879*
Dufermont, J., 13(49), *73*
Duff, J. I., 950(228), 951(228), 952(228), *973*
Dulova, V. G., 904(219), *930*
Dumler, V. A., 102(314), 105(314), *145*
Duncan, J., 943(133), 945(133), *970*
Dunn, P., 254(25), 273(28), 274(28), 277(28), *292*, 308(52), 313(52), *496*, 520(48), 537(48), 538(48), 539(48), 564(48), 571(48), *576*, 979(18), *994*
DuPreez, A. L., 904(126), 906(126), *927*
Dupuis, T., 131(134), *141*
Durgaryan, S. G., 678(94), 679(94), 689(94), *811*
Durig, I. R., 102(135), *141*
Duval, C., 131(134), *141*
Duxbury, R. N., 947(213) 972
Dworkin, R. D., 317(214c), *503*
D'yachkovskaya, O. S., 90(438), *148*, 172(263), 173(322), 224(324), *250*, *252*, 264(121), *294*, 317(161b), *501*, 832(84), *878*
Dyer, E., 963(88), *968*
Dyson, G. M., 937(89), *968*
Dzevitskii, B. E., 625(26), *809*

E

Earborn, C., 64(50), *73*, 87(50), *139*, 637(39), 638(102), 646(38, 99, 102, 103), 653(37), 655(37), 659(36a, 38, 103a), 660(36a, 98a), 661(100, 103), 671(36a), 676(39), 684(37, 38), 685(39), 686(39), 697-699(36a, 38, 99, 100, 102, 103, 103a), 712(37), 726(36a, 99), 734(99), 756(36a, 103a), 757(36a, 103a), 767(36a), 768(99). 769(99), *810, 811*
Eatough, H., 895(151), *928*
Ebsworth, E. A. V., 512(56), *576*
Eckstein, Z., 665(104), *811*, 948(48, 49), *967*

Edgar, S. A., 132(136), *141*
Edgell, W. F., 100(137), *141*, 999(19, 20), *1004*
Edmondson, 906(77), 908(75, 76), 909(77), 912(75, 77, 78), *926*
Edwards, C., 90(232), 93(232), 130-134 (232), *143*
Edwards, P. A., 919(30), *925*
Eeckhart, Z., 1003(82), *1006*
Eeckhaut, Z., 99(38), 107(518), 108(38), *138, 150*
Egmont, J. C., 94(138), *141*
Egorochkin, A. N., 314(64b, 64c), 343(64c), 344(65), 345(64a, 64b, 64c), 346(64a, 64c, 65), 424(64c), 426(65), 429(65, 227d), 491(64c, 65), 494(64a, 64c, 65), *497, 505*, 616-619(17), *621*, 890(79), *926*
Egorov, Y. P., 104(139, 140, 317), 106(317), 107(139), 128(140), *141*, 145, 664(106), 678(105), 679(105), *811*
Einstein, F. W., 113(141), *141*
Eints, J., 606(41a), *622*
Eisch, J., 8(64), *73*, 846(34), *877*
Eisendrath, G., 706(144), *812*
Eisner, E., 907(80), 908(75), 909(215), 912(75, 215), *926, 930*
Ejmocki, Z., 665(104), *811*, 948(48, 49), *967*
Ekstroem, B., 303(30a), 354(30a), *495*
el Assam, M. K., 648(162), 670(162), *813*
Elder, M., 909(195), 913(195), 923(81, 82), *926, 929*
El Kaissi, F., 710(334), 742(334), *818*
Ellermann, J., 589(18), 595(18), 596(18), 597(18), 603-605(18), *621*
Ellner, J. J., 534(164), 542(164), *578*
Elsakiv, N. V., 695(307), 703(307), 716(307), 720(307), 722(307), *817*
Elsea, J. R., 950(90), *968*
Elsner, H., 597(18b), 606(18b), *621*
Emakova, M. N., 217(22), *244*
Emeleús, H. J., 161(94), 184(94), 188(94), *246*, 883(83), 885(83), 900(83), *926*
Emerson, M. T., 26(178a), *77*
Endrulat, E., *140*
Engelhardt, G., 596(19), 598(19), 605(19), 606(19), *621*
Engelhardt, V. V., 38(90), *74*

Engelmann, H., 539(15), 573(15), *575*
Entelis, S. G., 963(91), *968*
Epstein, L. M., 334(67), 348(66), 436(67), 437(67), 441(67), 454(67), 455(67), 457(67), 462(67), 463(67), *497*
Eskin, I. T., 133(142), *141*, 189(95), 212(95), *246*, 320(68), 431(68), 433(68), *497*
Evans, C. J., 959(91*a*), *968*
Evans, D. P., 117(233), 131(233), 132(233), 135(233), *143*, 197(144), *247*
Evans, F. W., 23(51, 57), *73*
Evans, J. V., *245*
Evans, R. B., 133(176), *142*
Evans, R. L., 97(231), 132(321), 177(231), *143*, 201(143), 203(143), 206(143), *247*, 850(44), *877*
Evnin, A. B., 639(364), 659(364), 685(364), 686(364), 693(108, 363, 364, 370), 694(364), 697(364), 698(108), 699(108), 797(364), *811, 819*

F

Faddei, F., 664(245), *815*
Fahlstrom, G. B., 955(92), *968*
Fairbrother, F., 134(142), *141*
Faizi, N. A., 261(108), *294*
Faizi, N. K., 127(181), *142*
Fajnberg, V. S., 317(139*a*), *500*
Faleschini, S., 761(109), 734(109), 746(109), *812*, 857(106), 861(106*a*), *879*
Fan, C. L., 418(235), *504*, 942(65), *968*
Fantazier, R. M., 20(52), *73*
Faraglia, G., 183(275), 189(275), 190(96), *246, 250*, 279(10, 92, 93), 281(29), 286(92), 287(29), *292, 294*
Farbenindustrie, I. G., 946(139), *970*
Farnsworth, M., 998(21, 22), *1004*
Farrar, W. V., 833(29), 839(29), 852(29), 860(29), *876*
Farrer, H. N., 105(145), 108(145), 123(145), *141*
Faulkner, C. J., 84(146), 130(146), *141*, 965(97), *969*
Faulkner, D., 180(60), 183(60), *245*
Fedorov, L. A., 916(175), 917(175), *929*
Fedotova, E. I., 850(82*d*), *878*
Fedotova, E. S., 141(434), *148*

Fekete, J., 665(119), 679(119), *812*
Fenster, A. N., 206(98), *246*, 268(30), 269(30), 271(30), 272(30), 273(30), *292*
Fentiman, A. F., 83(147, 148), *141*, 628(111), 664(413), 679(412), 771(412), *812, 821*, 999(74), *1006*
Fenton, D. E., 649(112), 799(112), *812*, 921(85), *926*
Fergusson, J. E., 128(149), *141*
Fernley, A. M., 936(98), 937(89), *968, 969*
Fetyukova, V., 131(435), *148*
Field, D. S., 908(76), 918(86), 920(86), *926*
Fields, E. K., 985(28), 989(29), *994*
Figgis, B. N., 121(10), 122(10), 137(10), *138*
Finch, A., 102(50), *141*, 330(69), 437(69), 442(69), 454(69), 457(69), *497*
Finck, F. H., 329(70), 330(70), 463(70), *497*
Findeiss, W., 695(113), *812*
Finholt, A. F., 8(53), *73*
Finkelshtein, E. S., 678(94), 679(94), 689(94), *811*
Fionov, V. I., 317(161*b*), *501*
Fish, R. H., 39(54), 40(54), 41(100), 42(54), 43(54, 100), 44(100), *73, 74*, 644(208), 678(208), 679(114), 680(208), 681(114), 683(114), 685(114), 686(114), 687(114), 689(208), 691(208), 692(208), *812, 814*
Fitzsimmons, B. W., 110(151), 112(151), 126(151), *141*, 314(70*a*), 419(70*a*), 420(70*a*), *497*
Flagg, E. E., 67(55, 190*d*), *73, 77*
Flitcroft, N., 10(56), 13(56), 14(134), 69(134), 70(134), 71(134), *73, 75*, 887(88), 900(87), 918(87), *926*, 1003(43), *1005*
Floch, H., 945(78, 79), *968*
Flood, E. A., 130(152), 132(152), *141*
Florinski, F. S., 977(42, 45), *995*
Fluck, E., 110(153), *141*, 606(20, *41a*), *621, 622*
Foldesi, I., 174(99), 182(99), 183(99), 189(99), 190(99), *246*, 287(31), *292*, 678(115), *812*, 942(100), *969*
Fong, C. W., 917(89), *927*

Ford, F. E., 9(228, 229), *78*, 94(501), *149*, 868(107), *879*, 882(210, 211, 212), 883(210, 211), 889(210, 211, 212), *929*

Forder, R. A., 540(198, 199, 200), 573(199), *579*

Forstner, J. A., 325(71), 434(71), *497*

Foster, L. S., 894(150), 895(150), *928*

Fowles, G. W. A., 276(16), *292*, 513(12, 13), *575*, 583(11), 590(11), 592(11), 596(11), 597(11), 598(11), 605-609(11, 12), 612(12), 614-616(12), *621*, 834-836(14), 867(14), *876*, 883(29), *925*

Fox, R. J., 23(51, 57), *73*

Frankel, M., 65(58), 67(57a), *73*, 202(100), 204(100), 206(100), *246*, 259(32), *292*, 978(19, 21), 985(20), 994

Frankland, E., 82(154), 132(154), *141*

Fraselle, J., 953(102), *969*

Freeman, J. P., 254(33), *292*

Freidlina, B. K., 95(271), 132(271, 272), 133(271), 134(53), *139*, *144*

Frema, F., 707(143), *812*

Fresnel, P., 87(166), *141*

Fresnet, M., 664(133), *812*

Frey, F. W., 886(200), *929*

Fricker, H. H., 943(117), *969*

Frieber, E., 195(101), 196(101), 197(101), 212(101), *246*

Frielink, J. G., 986(22), *994*

Friihauf, E. J., *994*

Frisch, K. C., 960(220), 963(220), *972*

Fritchie, C. J., Jr., 900(207), 902(207), 923(207), *929*

Fritz, G., 16(59, 60), *73*, 998(23), *1004*

Fritz, H. E., 97(230, 231), 132(230, 231), 137(230, 231), *143*, 201(142, 143), 203(142, 143), 206(143), *247*, 850(43, 44), 855(43), *877*

Fritz, H. P., 10(5), *72*, 649(8), 666(117, 118), *908*, *812*, 834(30), 853(30), *876*

Frommelt, H., 940(103), *969*

Frommer, U., 65(158b), *76*

Fry, J. L., 954(104, 254), *969*, *973*

Frye, A. H., 310(72, 73, 74, 75, 76), 335(72, 73, 74, 75, 76), 391(72, 74, 76), 444(72, 74, 76), *497*, 938(105), 939(105), *969*

Fuchs, O., 86(155), *141*, 197(102), 212(102), *246*

Fuchs, R., 35(61), *13*

Fueno, T., 129(504), *149*, 176(304), 178(304), *251*

Fujita, K., 83(203), *142*

Fujitani, K., 202(234), 204(234), 205(234), 216(234), 217(234), *249*

Fukui, M., 540(201) *579*

Fukumoto, Y., 315(93a) 424(93a), *498*, 533(67), 539(67), 540(206), 553(67), *596*, *580*

Fulton, M., 94(72), *139*

Fulton, R. F., 45(62), *73*

Funasaka, W., 26(8), *72*

Furcht, G., 966(162), *971*, 982(35), *994*

Furnival, S. G., 38(25), 42(25), 69(25), *72*

Fürth, K., 8(180), *77*

Furukawa, J., 129(504), *149*, 176(304), 178(304), *251*

Fuse, G., 955(189), *971*

G

Gadermann, E., 950(245), 951(265), *974*

Galashina, M. L., 992(25, 26), *994*

Galasso, V., 101(165), *141*

Galitskova, N. P., 704(294), 736(294), *817*

Galiulina, R. F., 64(250), *79*

Garber, J. D., 646(442), 801(442), *821*

Gardiner, B. G., 946(106), 947(106), *969*

Garilov, G. S., 131(539), 132(539), 134(539), *150*

Garrett, F. E., 958(83), *968*

Garzo, G., 665(119), 679(119), *812*

Garzuly, R., 298(77), *497*

Gastilovich, E. A., *812*

Gavrilov, G. I., 94(541), 131(541), 132(541), 134(541), 150, 212(331), *252*

Gay, J. P., 940(107), *969*

Gay, R. S., 308(90a), 357(90a), *498*

Gebbie, H. A., 100(74), *139*

Geissler, H., 102(157, 301), 103(301), *141*, *145*, 195(169), 196(169, 171), 197(169, 171), *248*, 314(109), 318(78, 109), 319(109), 323(109), 324(78, 109a), 325(109a), 343(109, 109a), 347(109), 424(109, 109a), 425(109), 430(109, 491(109a), 492(109a), *497*, *499*, 665(121, 122, 123), *112*, 999(24), *1004*

Gelius, R., 86(24), 93(24), *138*, 625(21), 628(19), 629(18, 19), 646(124, 125), 661(125), 671(125), 673(18, 91), 674(18, 19), 677(125), 795(125), 797(125), 799(125), 802(125), 803(125), *809*, *812*, 835(9), 864(9), *876*

Gemeinhardt, P. G., 962(44), 963(44), *967*

Genero, E., 857(106), *879*

George, M. V., 515(57), *576*

George, T. A., 304(79*b*), 311(79, 79*a*), 315(79), 350(79b), 418(79), 423(79*a*), *497*, 511(58), 512(58), 514(59), 517(59, 61), 522(37, 59, 61), 523(38), 524(58), 528(37, 38, 59, 60), 529(37, 38, 59, 60, 61), 531(73, 58, 61), 532(58, 61), 534(58, 61), 541(37, 38, 58-61), 543(58), 56(58), 565(58), 573(58), *575*, *576*, 593(21*a*), 595(21, 21*a*), *621*, 680(62), 692(62), 694(62), 705(62), 706(62), 711(62), *810*, *812*

Gerow, C. W., 889(96), 890(98, 99), 895(98), 920(98), *927*

Gerrard, W., 100(74), 102(74), 107(158), *139*, *141*, 155(104), 156(48), 184(48, 103, 104), 185-187(48, 103, 104), 189(48, 103, 104), *245*, *246*, 279(34), 286(34), *292*, 1001(9), 1002(10), *1004*

Gertner, D., 65(58), 67(57a), *73*, 202(100) 204(100), 206(100), *246*, 259(32), *292*, 314(129), 316(129), 317(129), 320(129), 331(129), 335(129), 424(129), 426(129), 428-431(129), 467(129), 468(129), *500*, 988(52), *995*

Geyer, R., 310(80), *497*, 998(25), *1004*

Giamundo, L., 308(227*k*), *504*

Gibb, T. C., 14(63), *73*, 982(93), 920(91, 92), *927*

Gibbons, A. J., 86(446), 87(446), 90(446), 134(446), 135(446, 447), 136(447), 137(158b), *141*, *148*, 161(58), 196(276), 200(58, 105), 201(105), 202(58, 105), 205(58), 206(58), 212(276), *245*, *246*, *250*, 303(47), 315(47), 369(47), *496*, 846(31), 847(31), 850(31), 870(31), *876*

Gibbs, C. F., 938(86), *968*

Gick, W., 304(181*b*), 318(181*b*), 429(181*b*), *502*

Gielen, M., 87(52, 160–166), 92(51), 108(160, 161), 110(125), 117(159), 118(160, 161), 120(160, 161), 122(161, 167, 190), *139–142*, 298(81), *297*, 629(40, 41, 42, 89, 131), 630(42), 632–634(17, 42, 45, 129, 130, 131, 135, 136, 144a), 648–653(16, 17, 40, 42, 43, 45, 89*a*, 137, 138, 141), 655(130, 136), 657(17), 658(17), 659(144*a*), 664–666(14*a*, 40, 41, 43, 44, 129, 130, 131, 132, 133, 135, 136), 669(17), 677–680(16, 17*a*, 40–44, 141, 409*a*), 683–689(17*a*, 43, 44, 45, 89*a*, 139, 225*c*, 427), 691(17), 697–699(43, 137), 701(40–44), 705(17*a*), 706(40, 41, 42, 44), 707(143), 708(142), 713(17), 726(137), 733–737 (14*a*, 17*a*, 137, 349*a*), 747(137), 770(14*a*), 804(45, 349*a*, 409*a*), 805(349*a*), 807(45, 349*a*, 409*a*), 808(144*a*) 808(144*a*), *809–812*, *814*, *815*, *818*, *820*, *821*, 861(12*a*), 862(12*a*), *876*

Giesen, M., 958(108), *969*

Gilman, H., 8(64), 35(61), *73*, 82(221), 83(172), 87(169), 91(221), 92(221), 93(221), 130(168), 131(168, 170, 171, 173, 174), 132(221), 133(168, 170), 134(170), *141*, *142*, *143*, 154(137), 174(137), 176(137), 179(137), 195(137), 197(137), 212(137), 215(137), *247*, 253(42), *293*, 298(93), *498*, 515(57), *576*, 581(23), 598(23), *621*, 626(181), 628(181), 629(181), 633(181), 641(181), 646(145, 145*a*, 374), 664–672(145, 145*a*, 181), 675–679 (181), 681(181), 684(181), 685(181), 687–689(181), 698(374), 701–704(181), 706–709(181), 711–713(181), 725(181), 727–731(181), 734–737(181), 739–744 (181), 746(181), 748–755(181), 767(145), 770–773(181), 775(181), 776(181), 778(181), 780–786(181), 789(181), 791(181), 799(145), 801 (145*a*), 804(181), 805(181), *812*, *813*, *819*, 824(8, 41), 826(32, 41), 833(41) 854(32), 858–860(32, 41), 862(41), 864(41), 865(41), 869(32), *876*, *877*, 881–883(101, 102, 103, 104, 105, 135), 886(104), 889(94, 95, 96, 101, 102), 890(97, 99, 99), 895(98), 920(98), *927*, 933(142), 949(142), 965(141), *970*, 997(32), 998(26), *1005*

Gilson, T., 113(30), 129(30), *138*, 254(11), *292*

Gingold, K., 132(175), *142*, 320(82), 430(82), *497*

Ginsburg, V. A., 94(540, 541), 131(541), 132(540, 541), 134(541), *150*, 203(332), *252*

Gipp, N. A., 94(381), 132(381), *147*

Gist, L. A., Jr., 87(169), 131(170), 133(170), 134(170), *141*

Gitlitz, M. H., 310(40*a*), 311(40*a*), 313 (40*a*), 421(40*a*), *496*

Gl'adyshev, E. N., 90(437), *148*, 314(64*b*), 341(64*b*), 345(64*b*), *497*, 629(329), 633(328, 329), *818*, 886(106), 890(70, 221, 222, 223), *926, 927, 930*

Gliniecki, F., 311(83, 196*a*), 313(83, 196*a*), 416(83, 196*a*), 417(83, 196*a*), *497, 502*

Glocking, F., 664(59, 60), *810*, 884(44, 109), 890(48), 895(44), 905(53), 908(107), 912(53, 107), 915(27, 66, 108), *925–927*

Glosky, C. R., 934(109), *969*, 988(26), *994*

Glotz, G., 215(182), *248*

Glushakova, V. N., 209(259), *250*

Goddard, A. E., 89(177), 133(176), *142*

Goddard, D., 89(177), *142*

Goel, R. G., 101(95), 126(95), 129(95), *140*, 269(19), 275(19), 277(19), 278(19), 291(20), *292*

Goetz, U., 606(20), *621*, 890(36), 891(36), 892(36), 895(36), *925*

Gold, H., 183(68), *245, 822*

Goldanskii, V. I., 107(259), 109(62, 63), 110(178, 180), 112(179), 120(179), *139, 142, 144*, 210(206), *246*, 257(14), *292*, 308(83*c*, 135*a*), 314(83*c*), 320(83*c*, 83*d*), 325(83*c*), 351(135*a*), *498, 500*, 649(149), 664(147, 149, 193), 665(149), 675(193), 676(193), 701–704(146, 149, *809, 812, 814*, 887(110), 920(111), 921(110), *927*, 1004(27), *1005*

Goldstein, I. P., 119(182, 183), 122(183), 127(181), *142*, 155(107), 157(107), 188(107), *246*, 263(133), 264(133), 295, 308(83*a*, 83*b*), 309(83*a*, 83*b*), 324(83*a*, 83*b*), 354(83*a*, 83*b*), 362(83*a*, 83*b*), 366(83*a*, 83*b*), 430(83*a*, 83*b*), *497*, 648(150), *813*

Golovanova, N. I., 720(387), 721(373), 722(387), 724(373), 725(387), 746(373), 777(387), *819, 820*

Golubeva, E. S., 95(376), 133(376), *146*

Goodman, B. A., 920(112), 922(112), *927*

Goodrich, R. A., 89(512*a*), *150*, 629(424), *821*

Gorbach, S., 998(28), *1005*

Gordon, M. E., 675(356), *819*

Gordy, W., 12(76*a*), *74*

Goreau, T. N., 131(71), *141*

Gormley, J. J., 270(35), 271(35), 273(35), *292*

Gorshkova, G. N., 781(152), 787(151), *813*

Gorsich, R. D., 183(108, 109), *246*, 751(153), 755(153), 771(154), 772(153), 791(153), *813*, 896-900(113-119), 914(119), 917(119, 120), *927*

Goscinny, Y., 921(129), 922(129), *927*

Götte, H., 953(126), 954(33), *967, 970*

Götze, H., 540(222), *580*

Götze, H. J., 540(212, 222), *580*

Gould, R., 308(83*e*), *498*

Graber, M., 944(113), 954(113), *969*

Grady, G. L., 10(64*a*), *73*

Graham, I. F., 161(38), 169(71), 190(38), 191(38), 192(38), 193(38), 204(38), 205(38), 224(38), 228(71), 238(71), *244, 245*

Graham, W. A. G., 104(403), *147*, 256(105), 257(106), *294*, 303(144*c*), 308(90*a*, 144*b*), 320(217), 330(217), 350(144*b*), 357(90*a*, 144*b*), 437(217), *498, 500, 503*, 535(65), 542(65), *576*, 896-901(136, 186, 187, 189, 191, 192, 193, 213, 214), 903(191, 192, 913), 94(132, 190), 906(132, 190), 907(190), 909(195), 910(168, 191), 913(168, 195), 918(121, 136, 186, 188, 190), 923(82), *927–930*, 978(77), *995*

Granenkina, L. S., 337(118*a*), 475(118*a*), 477(118*a*), *499*

Grant, D., 90(184), 91(184), 108(184), *142*, 307(227*i*), 353(227*i*), 354(227*i*), 327(227*i*), *504*, 631(155), 651(155), 664(155), *813*

Gras, G., 944(56, 58, 114), 946(115), 954(113), *967, 969*

Graves, J. B., 947(116), *969*

Gravilenko, V. V., 645(156), 724(156), 725(156), *813*
Gray, C. E., 882(69), *926*
Gray, H. E., 949(116*a*), *969*
Graybeal, J. D., 108(498), 109(498), *149*, 919(133), *927*
Greatrex, R., 920(112), 922(112), *927*
Grechkin, N. P., 581(4, 5, 6), *620*
Greeard, W., 284(15), *292*
Green, B. S., 572(62), *576*
Green, M. L. H., 895(54), *926*
Green, P. J., 108(185), 109(185), *142*
Greene, F. D., 23(65), 27(65), *73*
Greene, M. L. H., 298(46), *496*
Greene, P. T., 922(32), 923(32, 123), *925*, *927*
Greenwood, N. N., 14(63), *73*, 539(9), 573(9), *575*, 892(93), 920(92, 124), 922(112), *927*
Greer, W. N., 8(89), 56(89), *74*, 85(286) 130(285), 132(287), *144*, 824(47), 827(47), 830(47), 837(47), 839(47), 845(47), 955(47), 868(47), *877*, 882(152), 883(152), *928*
Grewe, F., 303(180), 327(180), 344(180), 350(180), 352(180), 353(180), 355-357, 355-357(180), 442(180), *502*
Griffiths, D. C., 117(233), 131(233), 132(233), 135(233), *143*, 197(144), *247*
Griffiths, V. S., 102(187, 189), 103(187), 105(186), 106(188), *142*, 176(110), *246*, 648(157), *813*
Griffith, W. P., 918(125), *927*
Grim, S. O., 119(468), 125(468), 127(468), 131(472), *149*
Grimm, A., 336(167, 168), *501*
Grimme, W., 26(246), *79*
Grosjean, M., 87(64, 65, 366), 88(66), 122(190), *139*, *142*, *146*, 646(52, 53), 659(53, 54, 55, 56, 270, 271, 271*a*), 660(53, 55, 270), 661(56), 697-699(52, 53, 55, 56, 270, 271), 733(271), 734(54, 270, 271), 747(52, 54), *810*, *816*
Groves, J. T., 27(18), *72*
Grün, L., 943(117), *969*
Grüttner, G., 82(193), 86(192, 193), 130(192), 131(191, 192), 135(192, 193), 136(192), *142*, 775(158), *813*, 834(37), 835(37), *877*

Guerchais, J. E., 540(216), *580*
Guiseppe, S. A., 999(83), *1006*
Guistiniani, M., 279(10), *292*
Gulwell, T., 117(233), 131(233), 132(233), 135(233), *143*, 197(144), *247*
Gupta, V. D., 157(204), 176(204), 180(205), 186(205), 223(303), *249*, *251*, 298(128*a*), 303(128, 128b, 215), 304(128, 215), 306(215), 354(128*b*), 359(215), 366-369(128*b*, 215), 377(128), 449(215*a*), 450(215*a*), 451(215*a*), 457(215*a*), *500*, *503*
Guryanova, E. N., 119(182, 183), 122(183), 127(181), *142*, 155(107), 157(107), 188(107), *246*, 263(133), 264(133), *295*, 308(83*a*, 83*b*), 309(83*a*, 83*b*), 324(83*a*, 83*b*), 354(83*a*, 83*b*), 362(83*a*, 83*b*), 366(83*a*, 83*b*), 430(83*a*, 83*b*), *497*, 648(150), *813*
Guseva, I. S., 175(288), 176(288), 178(288), 180(288), 181(288), *251*, 695(197, 385), 720(197, 195, 376), 721(385), 722(197, 200, 376), 724(385), 725(385), 732(200, 376, 385), 746(376, 385), *814*, *819*, *820*
Guthrie, J. E., 944(118, 119), *969*
Gutman, V., *142*
Guy, J., 102(128), 130(128), 132(128), *140*
Gverdtsiteli, I. M., 176(111), 177(111), 179(111), *246*, (725(159), 732(159), *813*

H

Hädge, P., 26(251), *79*
Haendler, H. M., 100(534), 101(534), 127(534), 129(534), *150*, 284(127), *295*
Haertig, M., 310(211*a*), 402(211*a*), *503*
Hague, D. N., 856(38), *877*
Haines, R. J., 904(126), 906(126), *927*
Hall, D., 909(195), 913(195), 923(81, 82), *926*, *929*
Hall, J. R., 512(56), *576*
Halmi, G., 963(123), *969*
Halvorson, D. O., 97(231), 132(231), 137(231), *143*, 201(143), 203(143), 206(143), *247*, 850(44), *877*
Hamilton, W. C., 112(459), 129(449, 459), *148*

Hammer, D., 583(44), 597(44), 600(44), *622*

Hammond, G. S., 67(66), *73*

Hancock, M., 122(11), 137(11), *138*, 200(16), 201(16, 17), 203(17), 204(16, 17), 205(17), 206(17), *244*, 264(4), *292*

Hanson, E. L., 16(197), 17(197), 59(197), 61(197), 70(197), *77*, 107(455), 137(455), *148*, 842(93), 846(92), 849(92), 850(93), 875(93), *878*, *1001*(69), *1005*

Hannecart, E., 87(366), *146*, 659(270), 660(270), 697(270), 734(270), *816*

Hanson, E. M., 638(362), 640(362), 642(362), 675(362), 677(362), *819*

Harada, T., 84(195, 196, 199), 85(196), 130(195, 196, 198, 199), 132(196, 198, 199), *142*, 196(119), 197(112, 115, 117, 119, 120, 121, 164), 198(112, 115, 116, 118, 120, 164,) 203(112–126), 204(121), 207(115, 116, 120, 125), 208(127), 210(125, 126), 212(115, 126), 224(119), *246*, *247*, *248*, 264(36), *292*, 314(84, 86), 317(84), 320(85, 86, 87), 322(87), 424(84, 86), 430(86, 87), 431(85), *498*, 834(39), 845(40), 868(40), *877*

Harant, H., 944(58, 124), *967*, *969*

Harbourne, D. A., 900(87), 918(87), *926*

Hardebeck, K., 950(265), 951(265), *974*

Hardy, J. L., 949(4*a*), *966*

Harrah, L. A., 104(200), *142*

Harrendorf, K., 948(124*a*), 965(124*a*), *969*

Harris, C. B., 919(30), *925*

Harrison, J. B., 190(199), 191(199), 193(199), 194(199), 204(199), 205(199), *248*

Harrison, P. G., 127(117), *140*, 156(72), 184–189(72, 73, 76), 199(74, 75), 203(72), 204(72), 209–211(77), 216(78), 217(18), 218(75), 219(75, 78), 220(75, 78), 225(72), 226(74, 75, 77), 239(73), *245*, 262–264(27), *292*, 298(87*a*), 304(58), 306(58), 311(59), 313(59, 60*a*), 315(59), 316(60), 322(60), 325(60*a*), 362(58), 418(60*a*), 419(60*a*), 422(59), 426(60, 60*a*), 427(60), 430(60, 60*a*), 433(60*a*), *496*, *498*, 518(53), 521(53), 540(202), 562(53), *576*, 582(21*b*, 21*c*), *621*

Harrod, J. F., 905(47), *925*

Hartel, K., 942(120, 121), 943(120), 953(120, 121, 122), *970*

Hartmann, H., 658(160, 161, 162), 670(161, 162), 695(160), 751(160), 753(160), 754(150), *813*

Harwood, P. D., 944(118), *969*

Hasegana, N., 957(150), *970*

Hashimoto, H., 659(163), 660(163), 726(163), *813*

Hathaway, B. J., 113(201, 395), *142*, *147*, 268(78), 277(78), *293*

Hayakawa, Y., 129(504), *149*, 176(304), 178(304), *251*

Hayashi, K., 10(67), 15(67), *74*, 216(128), 217(128), 227(128), *247*, 629(164), 677(164), *813*

Hayashi, J., 83(353), *146*

Hayashi, T., 35(67*a*), *74*, 83(202, 203), *142*

Hayes, M. C., 110(204, 205), *142*

Hays, S. B., *971*

Heap, R., 132(206), *142*

Heaton, L., 191(326), *252*

Hechenbleikner, I., 87(551), 91(551), 131(551), 133(551), 135(551), 136(551), *151*, 197(342), *252*, 666(461), 708(461), 750(461), 776(461), 784(461), *822*, 834(124), *879*, 884(236), *930*

Hedges, E. S., 933(169), *969*, *971*

Hein, F., 114(491), *149*, 899(127), 900(127), 901(127), *927*

Helberg, D., 936(125), *969*, 999(29), *1005*

Heldt, E., 664(165), 701(165), 770(165), *813*

Heller, I., 95(412), 130(412), 134(412), *147*

Hemberg, O. A., 834(124), *879*

Hemmert, F., 107(334), *145*

Henderson, A., 254(37), 265(37), *292*, 669(166), *813*

Henry, M. C., 37(69), 39(68, 111), 65(111), *74*, *75*, 169(179), 186(179), *248*, 303(56, 118), 304(56, 118), 311(56), 315(88), 317(168*a*), 323(168*a*), 327(56), 335(56), 336(168*a*) 337(88), 357(56), 366(118), 373(56), 413(56), 425(56), 429(88), 437(56), 467(56), 474(88), *496*, *498*, *499*, *501*, 628(85), 635(85), 639(85), 670(85), 695(85, 113), 696(85), 720–725(85),

744(85), 751(85), 754(85), 756(85), 777(85), 779(85), 787(85), *811*, *812*, 976(27), *994*

Henzen, J. C., 956(138), *970*

Herber, R. H., 14(70, 71, 72), 17(71), 70(71), *74*, 110(207, 208, 209, 446), 111(209), 112(496), 121(208, 209), 128(208, 209), *142*, *149*, 269(38), 275(38), *292*, 317(214*d*), 320(89), 348(89), 424(214*d*), 425(89), *498*, *503*, 535(63), 537(63), 568(63), *576*, 664(169, 414), 666(167, 168), 668(167), *813*, *821*, 921(128, 129), 922(128, 129), *927*

Hermannsdörfer, K. H., 9(176), *77*, 885(180), 886(180), 889(180), *929*

Herok, J., 953(126), 954(33), *967*, *970*

Hertel, H., 298(110*a*), *499*

Hess, G. G., 680(170), *813*

Hester, R. E., 512(64), 524(64), 534(64), 535(64), 541(64), 547(64), 553(64), *576*, 596(22), 605(22), 611(22), 612(22), 615(22), *621*

Heying, T. L., *818*

Heymann, E., 52(142, 143), 55(144), 56(144), *76*, 165(218), 166(218), 175(217, 218), 176(217, 218), 177(217, 218), 180(218), 182(218), 183(218), *249*, 341(138), 342(138), 491(318), *500*, 518(118, 119, 120), 523(118), 544(118, 120), 561(119), 573(120), *578*

Heymons, A., 117(129), 178(129), 185(129), *247*

Hickner, R. A., 660(28*a*), *809*

Hieber, T., 58(47), *73*

Hieber, W., 215(130), *247*, 900–902(130, 131), *927*

Higashi, S., 957(127), *970*

Highsmith, R. E., 540(203, 204), *579*, *580*

Hill, D. T., 514(188), 520(188), 528(188), 530(188), 534(188), 567(188), *579*

Hill, G. C., 908(107), 912(107), *927*

Hill, J. A., 629(1), *809*

Hills, K., 303(56), 304(56), 311(56), 327(56), 335(56), 357(56), 373(56), 413(56), 425(56), 437(56), 467(56), *496*

Hilpert, S., 132(210), 134(210), *142*

Hiramatsu, Y., 298(175*c*), 303(175*c*), *502*

Hirotoshi, S., *498*

Hirschfeld, H., 958(128), *970*

Hirschland, H. E., 298(90), *498*

Hjortdahl, M., 112(211), *142*

Hobroek, B. G., 117(217), *142*

Hochman, H., 955(248), *973*

Hocking, D., 943(129), 945(129), *970*

Hof, T., 942(131), 954(131), *970*

Hoffmann, H., 100(302), *145*, 195(172), 196(171, 172), 197(171, 172), 198(170), *248*, 284(59), *293*, 314(108, 109), 318(108, 109), 319(109), 323(109, 324(108, 109*a*), 325(108, 109*a*), 343(108, 109, 109*a*), 347(109), 424(108, 109, 109*a*), 425(109), 430(108, 109), 434(108), 491–493(108, 109*a*), *499*, 1002(85), *1006*

Hogben, M. G., 308(90*a*), 357(90*a*), *498*, 535(65), 542(65), *576*

Hogl, O., 998(80), 999(80), *1006*

Hoke, D. I., 660(28*a*), *809*

Holden, F. R., 88(69), 132(69), 136(69), *139*, 212(46), *245*

Holland, G. W., 22(192*a*), *77*

Holiday, A. K., 254(37), 265(37), *292*, 669(166), *813*

Holloway, J. H., 540(205), *580*

Holmes, J. M., 91(214), 94(215), 131(214), 133(215), *142*, 196(132), 197(132), *247*, 279(40), 286(40), *293*, 628(171), 633(171), *813*

Holmes, J. R., 14(73), *74*, 106(213), 115(213), *142*, 194(131), *247*, 280(38), *293*, 1003(30), *1005*

Holmes, T. D., 953(132), 954(132), *970*

Homberg, O. A., 257(135), *295*, 666(461, 462), 667(462), 668(462), 708(461), 750(461), 776(461), 784(461), 789(461), *822*, 884(236), *930*

Homrowski, S., 308(90*b*), 350(90*b*), *498*

Honberg, O. A., 197(342), *252*

Honda, M., 313(90*c*, 91), 418–420(90*c*, 91), *498*, 964(26), *967*

Honigschmidt-Grossich, R., 608(1*d*), 609(1*d*), 610(1*d*), 612(1*d*), *620*

Hooton, K. A., 298(91*a*), *498*, 884(109), 915(108), *927*

Hopf, H. S., 943(133), 945(133), *970*

Höppner, K., 664(165, 172, 173),
677(173), 701(165), 770(165, 173),
813, 999(31), *1005*
Horder, J. R., 170(133), 174(133), *247*,
531(66), 541(66), *576*
Hori, M., 284(49), 288(49), 290(49),
291(49), *293*, 1001(34), 1002(34), *1005*
Horn, C. F., 963(261), *974*
Hornberg, O., 87(551), 91(551), 131(551),
133(551), 135(551), 136(551), *151*
Hornfeld, H. L., 646(99), 661(100),
697(99, 100), 698(99, 100),
699(99, 100), 726(99), 734(99),
768(99), 769(99), *811*
Hornig, P., 513(145), 514(145), 523(145),
535(145), 540(220), 555(145), 556(145),
558(145), *578, 580*
Horrocks, J. A., 936(98), 937(89), *968*
Horst, R. W., 310(72, 73, 74, 75, 76),
335(72, 73, 74, 75, 76), 391(72, 74, 76),
444(72, 74, 76), *497*, 938(105),
939(105), *969*
Horvitz, L., 130(152), 132(152), *141*
Hosaka, H., 298(175c), 303(175c), *502*
Hostettler, F., 960(134), 962(134), 963(261),
970, 974
Hoyano, J., 904(132), 906(132), *927*
Hoyer, E., 329(92), 330(92), 336(92),
460(92), 464(92), 470(92), *498*
Hoyer, R. F., 949(134a, 205a), *970, 972*
Hoyte, R. M., 21(46), *73*
Hsu, H. S., 942(65), *968*
Hsu, M. W., 919(122), *927*
Huang, H. H., 115(217), 116(217), *143*,
648(174, 175), 697(174), 698(174),
813
Hubel, W., 646(48), 798(48), *810*
Huber, F., 184(134), 185(134), 189(134),
247, 280(41), 286(41), 287(41), *293*
Huber, H., 311(92a), *498*
Hübner, H., 26(251), *79*
Hudson, J. A., 525(174), *579*
Hudson, P. B., 960(135, 136), *970*
Hueck, H. J., 946(137), 956(137, 138),
970
Hügel, G., 132(218), *143*
Huggins, D. K., 675(177), 677(176),
701(178), *813*
Hui, K. M., 115(217), 116(217), *143*,
648(174, 175), 697(174), 698(174), *813*

Hulme, R., 113(32, 219), 124(219), *138,
143*
Hulse, R., 161(135, 136), 188(136),
215(135), *247*
Hunter, B. K., 107(220), 108(220),
120(220), *143*, 314(92b), 320(92b),
325(92b), 415(92b), 418(92b), 425(92b),
430(92b), 431(92b), *498*
Hunter, G., 539(9), 573(9), *575*
Hurenkamp, J. B. G., 339(26), 491(26), *495*
Husseh, H., 216(282, 283), 217(282, 283),
218(283), 219(282), 220(282), *251*
Hutchinson, J. M., 216(159), 217(159), *248*
Hutson, G. V., 307(6), 340(16), 343(15,
16), 491(15), *495*
Hutton, R. E., 83(391, 392), *147*

I

Ibekwe, S. D., 730(180), 779(180), 787(180),
813, 911(133, 134), 913(133, 134),
917(134), *928*
Iida, M., 665(448), 742(448), 776(448),
822
Illingworth, S. M., 350(17b), *495*, 582(1f),
589(1b), 595(1a), 597(1b), 602(1b, 1c),
608(1d, 1e), 609(1c, 1d, 1e), 610(1a,
1b, 1d), 612(1a, 1b, 1d, 1e), 613(1b),
620
Ing, S. D., 919(122), *927*
Ingham, R. K., 8(74), *74*, 82(221),
91(221), 93(221), 132(221), *143*,
154(137), 174(137), 176(137), 179(137),
195(137), 197(137), 212(137), 215(137),
247, 253(42), *293*, 298(93), *498*,
581(23), 598(23) *621*, 626(181),
628(181), 629(181), 633(181), 641(181),
664–670(181), 675–679(181), 681(181),
684(181), 685(181), 687–689(181),
701–704(181), 706–709(181),
711–713(181), 725(181), 727–731(181),
734–737(181), 739–744(181), 746(181),
748–755(181), 770–773(181), 775(181),
776(181), 778(181), 780–786(181),
789(181), 791(181), 804(181), 805(181),
813, 824(41), 826(41), 833(41), 860(41),
862(41), 864(41), 865(41), *877*,
881(135), *928*, 933(142), 949(142),
965(141), *970*, 997(32), *1005*

Ingold, C. K., 103(222), *143*
Ingold, K. U., 24(22, 23), *72*
Ionin, B. I., 638(455), 658(455), 720(455), *822*
Ireland, J., 130(223), 132(223), *143*
Irisova, N. A., 116(224), *143*
Irmscher, R., 83(225), *143*
Isaeve, L. S., 133(383), *147*
Ishii, Y., 169(138), 174(138), 176(138), 224(138), *247*, 298(95), 303(175*a*), 306(93*b*), 307(92*c*, 94*a*), 311(92*c*, 94*c*, 175*a*), 315(93*a*, 94, 94*b*), 424(93*a*, 94, 94*b*), 482(94*c*), *498*, *501*, 533(67, 68, 69), 539(67, 68), 540(201, 206, 207, 208), 543(69), 553(67, 68,) *576*, *579*, *580*, 582(25), *621*
Isibasi, F., 728(399), 776(399), 778(399), *820*
Isibasi, T., 92(478), *149*, 859(101*a*), 873(101*a*), 874(101*a*), *879*
Issleib, K., 11(75), *74*, 276(43), *293*, 585(24), 591(24), 597(24), 598(24), *621*
Ito, Y., 65(193), *77*
Itoh, K., 8(75*a*), *74*, 169(138), 174(138), 176(138), 224(138), *247*, 298(95), 306(93*b*), 307(92*c*, 94*a*), 311(92*c*, 94*c*), 315(93*a*, 94, 94*b*), 424(93*a*, 94, 94*b*), 482(94*c*), *498*, 533(67, 68, 69), 539(67, 68), 540(201, 206, 207, 208), 543(69), 553(67, 68), *576*, *579*, *580*, 582(25), *621*
Itoi, K., 10(76), *74*
Ivavov, L. L., 645(156), 724(156), 725(156), *813*
Iwamoto, H., *970*
Iyoda, J., 10(67), 15(67), *74*, 216(128), 217(128), 227(128), *247*, 629(164), 677(164), *813*

J

Jackel, G. S., 12(76*a*), *74*
Jacobi, E., 181(139), *247*
Jaffri, B. J., 314(213*b*), 425(213*b*), *503*
Jaggard, J. F., 311(196*a*), 312(191*a*), 313(196*a*), 416(191*a*, 196*a*), 417(191*a*, 196*a*), *502*

Jakusik, E. R., 304(113), 321(113), 372(113), 431(113), *499*, 859(53), 861(53), 864(53), 865(53), 867(53), 874(53), *877*
Jander, G., 265(101), *294*
Janeck, A., 325(63*a*), 434(63*a*), *497*
Jansons, E., 311(24*b*), 416(24*b*) *495*
Janssen, M. J., 54(170, 171), *76*, 94(138), *141*, 194(140), *247*, 254(44), *293*, 312(141, 142), 315(142), 422(141, 142), 424(142), *500*, 514(78, 109), 518(130, 131), 520(70, 78, 109), 523(109), 529(70), 533(78, 109), 534(131), 537(109), 548–550(78, 109), 559(130, 131), 560(131), 565(130, 131), 568(109), *576*, *577*, 637(333), 651(333), 703(333), 704(333), 706(333), *818*, 892(74), *926*, *1005*
Jarvis, B. B., 22(76*b*, 76*c*), *74*
Jasching, W., 336(96), *498*
Jason, E. F., 985(28), 989(29), *994*
Jauquet, M., 659(271*a*), *816*
Jaura, K. L., 646(183), 733(183), 747(183), *813*
Javora, P. H., 10(14, 15), *72*
Jayawant, M., 257(135), *295*, 666–668(462), 789(462), *822*
Jeanmaire, A., 513(159), *579*
Jefferson, M., 832(95), 864(95), *878*
Jeffrey, D. A., 83(147), *141*
Jehn, W., 899–901(127), *927*
Jehring, H., 118(226), *143*
Jenker, H., 94(227), *143*
Jenkins, A. D., 311(96*b*), *498*, 524(70*a*), 525(70*a*), 528(38*a*), 532(38*a*), 533(38*a*), 542(38*a*, 70*a*), *576*
Jenkins, C. R., 118(1), *137*, 307(96*a*), 309(10), 327(18), 329(18, 19), 350(10), 365(10), 438(18), 439(18), 440(18), *495*, *498*
Jenkins, H. O., 113(54), *139*
Jensen, F. R., 27(77), *74*
Jetz, W., 898(136), 899(136), 918(136), *928*
Johnson, C. E., 920(185), *929*
Johnson, E. G., 883(155), 887(155), *928*
Johnson, E. W., 935(252), *973*
Johnson, F., 50(77*a*), *74*, 669(219, 221), 774(219, 221), 792(219), 798(219), *815*

Johnson, O. H., 97(230, 231, 231*a*), 132(230, 231), 137(230, 231), *143*, 201(141, 142, 143), 203(141, 142, 143), 206(143), *247*, 850(42, 43, 44), 855(43), *877*
Johnson, W. A., 933(144), 955(144), 958(144), *970*
Johnson, W. K., 130(228), 131(228), *143*
Johnson, W. T., 94(229), *143*
Jolley, K. W., 649(112), 799(112), *812*
Jolly, W. L., 18(78, 79), *74*
Jones, J. E., 954(254), *973*
Jones, K., 162(145), *247*, 298(98), 311(79, 97), 312(79), 313(79), 315(79), 418(79, 97), *497, 498*, 510–513(58, 64, 72–76), 515(50, 71, 72, 74), 516(72, 74), 521–525(49, 58, 64, 72, 73, 74, 75), 531(58, 73), 532(58, 72), 534(58, 64, 72), 535(51, 64), 539–548(49, 50, 51, 58, 64, 72–75, 224), 552(50), 553(49, 51, 64, 72, 74), 554(72), 563(58, 72), 565(58, 73), 570(49), 571(49), 573(58, 73), *576, 580*, 581(26), 582(28), 584(26, 27), 596(22), 597(26, 27), 665(22), 607(26, 27), 611(22), 612(22, 26, 27), 615(22), *621*, 682(184), 686–688(184), 695(184), 696(184), 702(184), 712(184), 725(184), 735(184), 740(184), *812, 814*
Jones, M. T., 922(137), *928*
Jones, R. C., 204(56), 205(56), 207(56), *245*, 646(442), 801(443), *821*
Jones, W. J., 90(232), 93(232), 117(233), 130–135(232, 233), *143*, 197(144), *247*
Joshi, K. K., 122(234), 125(234), *143*
Jouve, P., 664(185), *814*
Judat, A., 337(111), 338(111), 475(111), *499*
Jula, T. F., 27(208), *78*
Jula, T. T., 636(369, 371), 642(369), 678(369), 679(361, 369), 681(369), 739(369), *819*
Jungers, J. C., 87(235), *143*, 630(186), 665(186), *814*
Jutzi-Mebert, B., 513(157), 515(157), 535(157), 555(157), *578*
Jutzi, P., 304(199, 201), 311–313(199, 201), 316(200), 336(200), 338(200), 358(199, 201), 421(199, 201), 425(200), 476(200), *502*, 517(155), 566(155), *578*, 590–595(49, 50, 51, 52), 598(50, 51), 605(50), *622*

K

Kaabak, L. V., 86(236), *143*, 265(45), *293*, 628(187), 664(46, 187), 665(187), *810, 814*
Kabitzke, K., 12(205), *77*, 857(99), *879*
Kadowaki, T., 315(144*c*), 425(144*c*), *500*, 864(82), 866(82), *878*
Kaesz, H. D., 10(56), 13(56), 14(73, 134), 69(134), 70(134), 71(134), *73, 74, 75*, 106(213), 115(213), *142*, 194(131), *241*, 280(39), *293*, 675(177), 677(176), 701(178), *813*, 872(44*a*), *827*, 887(88), *926*, 1003(30, 43), *1005*
Kagan, G. I., 721(387*a*), 722(387*a*), *820*
Kagayama, I., 959(148), *970*
Kahana, L., 943(149), *970*
Kahlen, N., 131(472), *149*, 521(161), 539(160), 571(160), 573(161), *579*
Kahler, E., 999(74), *1006*
Kahler, E. J., 83(538), *150*, 664(412), 679(412), 771(412), *821*
Kahler, W. H., 883(154), 887(154), *928*
Kahn, O., 899–901(138, 139, 140), *928*
Kaiser, R., 184(134), 185(134), 189(134), *247*, 280(41), 286(41), 287(41), *293*
Kaiser, W., 43(141), *76*, 681(289), *819*
Kalina, S. P., 84(312), *145*
Kalinina, G. S., 64(248*a*, 248*b*), *79*, 341(227*g*), 342(227*g*), 345(227*g*), 346(227*g*), 494(227*g*), *504*, 582(70*c*), 615(70*c*, 73), *623*
Kalinina, S. P., 175(289), 178(156), *247*, *251*
Kalk, W., 513(158), 515(158), 535(158), 555(158), 556(158), *579*
Kaltwasser, H., 627(47*a*), 665(47*a*, 215), *810, 815*
Kamitani, I., 957(150), *970*
Kamitani, T., 126(506), *149*, 284(112), 288(112), 291(112), *294*, 341(98*a*), 493(98*a*), *498*
Kanno, T., 957(127), *970*
Kanzawa, T., 264(130), *295*

Kaplan, L., 24(81), 52(82*a*), 33(80, 82), *74*
Karakin, N. V., 826(82*b*, 82*c*), *878*
Karantassis, T., 82(237), 132(237), 133(237), *143*
Karasev, A. N., 664(189, 190), *814*
Karasyov, A. N., 921(141), *928*
Karbstein, B., 658(160), 695(160), 751(160), 753(160), 754(160), *813*
Karplus, M., 13(83), *74*, 1002(67), *1005*
Kartsev, G. N., 114(238), 130(238), 132(238), *143*
Karvchenko, A. L., 114(238), 130(238), 132(238), *143*
Kasai, N., 100(542), 101(542), 128(542), *150*
Kasatochkin, V. I., 781(152), 787(151), *813*
Kashireninov, O. E., 117(399), 128(399), 129(399), *147*
Kastning, E., 986(60), *995*
Kato, Y., 306(93*b*), *498*
Katomtzeff, J., 118(239), 130(239), *143*
Katsumura, T., 157(146), 186(146), 187(146), *247*
Katsuura, T., 311(94*c*), 482(94*c*), *498*, 540(208), *580*
Katzenstein, R. J., 217(91), *246*, 966(76), *968*
Kawakami, K., 12(85), 16(84), 17(84), 61(84), 69(85), 70(85), 71(85), *74*, 104(241), 107(241), 119(240), 129(240, 526), *143*, 150, 174(147), 177(147), 182(147), 183(147), 184(148), 185(147), 186(147), 190(147), *247*, 279(47, 123), 280(47), 281(46, 47), 286(49), 287(46, 47, 123), *293, 295*, 539(184), *579*, 1001(35), 1003(35), *1005*
Kawasaki, Y., 12(85), 69(85), 70(85), 71(85), *74*, 100(542), 101(542), 108(242, 243, 244, 245, 247, 248, 349), 119(348), 120(349), 125(107), 126(281, 348), 128(542), 129(242, 244, 245, 246, 247, 248, 400), 130(243), 132(247), *143, 144, 146, 147, 150*, 184(306, 313), 185(306, 313), 187(306), 189(313), 190(313), *251, 252*, 279(113), 281–284(46, 48–53, 85, 113, 117), 286–288(46, 49, 85, 113, 117),

290(49), 291(49), *293, 294*, 313(90*c*, 91), 418–420(90*c*, 91), *498*, 1001(34, 35), 1002(34, 36, 37, 78), 1003(35, 46), *1005, 1006*
Kazankova, M. A., 49(85*a*), *74*, 676(191), 702(191), 735(191), *814*
Kelker, H., 795(101), 196(101), 197(101), 212(101), 246
Kemann, L. P., 646(326), 647(326), 798(326), *818*
Kenaga, E. E., 753(192), *814*, 948(151, 151*a*), 949(4*a*), *966, 970*
Kennedy, J. D., 180(80), 183(80), 228(79, 80), 235(79), 236(80), 238(80), *245*, 311(60*b*), 313(60*a*), 315(60*b*), 320(60*b*), 321(60*b*), 325(60*a*), 418(60*a*, 60*b*), 419(60*a*, 60*b*), 426(60*a*), 430(60*a*), 433(60*a*), *496*, 540(196), *579*
Kenworthy, J. G., 897(142), 902(142), 920(142), *928*
Kenyon, A. S., 939(152), *970*
Kenyon, C., 998(61), *1005*
Keppie, S. A., 522(31, 31*a*), 527(30, 31*a*, 76*a*), 541(31, 31*a*, 76), *575, 576*, 908(143), 911(143), 913(143), 920(40), *925, 928*
Kerr, K. B., 944(153, 154), 948(154), 954(153, 154), *970*
Kettle, S. F. A., 520(80), 545(80), *577*, 834(45), 845(45), *877*, 883(83, 144), 885(83), 900(83), *926, 928*
Khandozhko, V. N., 878(173), 899(173, 176), 901(173), *928, 929*
Khasapov, B. N., 640(249), 703(249), *816*
Khukhlov, P. S., 337(118*a*), 475(118*a*), 477(118*a*), *499*
Khoo, L. E., 59(86), *74*
Khorshev, S. Y., 314(64*b*, 64*c*), 315(227*d*), 341(64*b*, 64*c*), 343(64*c*), 345(64*a*, 64*b*, 64*c*), 346(64*a*, 64*c*), 424(64*c*), 429(227*d*), 491(64*c*), 494(64*a*, 64*c*), *497, 504*, 890(79), *926*
Khranovskii, V. A., 104(140), 128(140), *141*, 664(106), *811*
Khrapov, V. V., 107(259), 109(62), 110(180), 112(179), 120(179), *139, 142, 144*, 210(106), *246*, 308(83*c*, 135*a*), 314(83*c*), 320(83*c*, 83*d*), 325(83*c*), 351(135*a*), *498, 500*,

649(149), 664(149, 193), 665(149),
675(193), 676(193), 701–704(146, 149,
193), 720(149), 770(149), 777(149),
809, *912*, *814*, 887(111), 920(111),
927, 1004(27), *1005*
Kidooka, S., 665(448) 742(448), 776(448),
822
Kiesel, R. J., 20(106, 107), 22(107),
28(108, 109), 31(108, 109), 32(109),
36(107), 57(109), 58(109), *75*, 846(55),
848(55), 874(55), *877*
Kikhawa, S., 35(67a, 179a), *74*, *77*,
83(202, 203), *142*, 298(127), 434(127),
500, 739(296), *817*
Kikuchi, M., *970*
Kimmel, H., 14(83), *74*
King, R. Bruce., 8(209), 68(209), *77*,
298(185, 186, 187), 307(170a), *501*,
502, 582(39, 40, 41), *622*, 895(71),
899(146), 903(7), 911(147), 913(147),
920(145), *926*, 928
Kingston, B. M., 527(30), *575*
Kinsinger, J. B., 205(309), 215(309),
216(309), 217(309), *251*
Kinugawa, Z., 83(479), *149*
Kipping, F. B., 86(261), 88(261), 93(261),
131(261), 133(261), 136(261), *144*,
196(149), 200(149), 201(149), *247*
Kipping, F. S., 86(486), 90(486), 132(118),
136(486), *140*, *149*, *251*
Kircher, J. F., 83(147, 148, 538), *141*,
150, 628(111), *812*
Kireev, V. V., 209(339), *252*
Kirei, G. G., 678(105), 678(105), *811*
Kirsch, J. L., 919(30, 203), *925*, *929*
Kiseleva, R. M., 977(30), *994*
Kiseleva, T. M., 131(282), *144*, 977(39, 42,
43), 993(40), *994*, *995*
Kiser, R. W., 117(217), *142*
Kissam, J. B., *971*
Kitching, W., 108(262, 263), 118(120),
127(263), *140*, *144*, 184(150), 185(150),
247, 279(54), 290(61), 291(61),
293, 344(63), 491–493(63), *497*,
848(25), 857(25), *876*, 917(89), *927*
Klages, V. A., 39(1), *72*
Klasens, H. A., 297(27), 303(99), 308(99),
339(27), 343(27), 377(27, 99), 491(27),
495, *498*
Kleiner, F. G., 722(283), *817*

Kleinschmidt, D. C. K., 225(81), *246*
Klimmer, O. R., 278(114), *294*, 298(99a),
499, 936(159), 950–952(156, 157, 158),
954(33), *967*, *971*
Klimsch, P., 308(99b), *499*, 936(159a), *971*
Klimova, V. A., 94(381), 132(381), *147*
Klimova, W. A., 94(278), *144*
Kloetzer, D., 627(47a), 665(47a), *810*
Klose, G., 648(194), 664(194), *814*
Kluiber, R. W., 964(55), *967*
Klutts, R. E., 948(124a), 965(124a), *969*
Knöpke, W., 83(225), *143*
Knowles, D. G., 939(160), *971*
Knox, S. A. R., *876*, 899(59), 900(57, 58,
59, 148), 903(148), 908(57, 58),
910(60), 911(148), 913(60, 148),
923(60), *926*, 928
Kobayashi, S., 65(193), *77*, 169(138),
174(138), 176(138), 224(138), *247*
Kobayashi, Y., 303(175a), 311(175a),
315(175a), *501*
Kobelt, D., 325(63a), 434(63a), *497*
Kochkin, D. A., 175(289), 178(156),
194(155), 197(157), 217(154), 218(155),
247, *251*, 298(104a), *499*, 946(161),
971, 977(32, 33), 979(31), 980(34, 70),
983(32), *994*, *995*
Kochsehkov, K. A., 83(2, 3, 4, 280),
88(42), 89(277, 279, 379), 90(266,
268, 269, 270, 273, 274, 482), 91(268),
92(279, 280), 93(276, 378, 408),
94(276, 278, 377, 381), 95(271),
119(182, 183), 122(183), 127(181),
130(266, 268, 269, 270, 275, 377),
131(274, 365), 132(2, 268–272, 275,
279, 377, 381, 482), 133(42, 142,
266, 267, 271, 275, 377, 408, 482),
134(264–268, 408), *137*, *138*, *141*,
142, *144*, *146*, *147*, *149*, 155(107),
157(107), 189(95, 107), 208–210(337),
212(95, 151, 243, 305), 215(151, 152,
214, 243), *246*, *247*, 249–252, 254(131),
261(108), 263(133), 264(55, 132, 133),
293, *294*, *295*, 298(100a), 308(83a,
83b), 309(83a, 83b), 314(134),
320(68, 100, 101, 104, 136, 149, 216),
324(83a, 83b), 325(102, 103, 104,
136, 149), 354(83a, 83b), 362(83a,
83b), 366(83a, 83b, 426(134),
430–434(68, 83a, 83b, 100, 101, 102,

103, 104, 136, 149, 216), *497, 499,*
500, 501, 503, 582(28*a*), *621,* 648(50),
813, 834(63*a*), 849(122), 869(45*b*),
877, 879
Kockeskhov, K. A., 582(28*a*), *621*
Koebel, R. F., 26(9*a*), *72*
Koenig, P. E., 216(159), 217(159), *248,*
513(81), *577*
Köhler, H., 510(82), 539(82), 573(82),
574(82), *577*
Kohler, P. H., 947(213), *972*
Kokurina, S. N., 192(11), 193(10), *244*
Kolbanovskii, Y. A., 664(190), *814*
Kolditz, L., 966(162), *971,* 982(35), *994*
Kolesnikov, S. P., 664(375), *819*
Kolobova, N. E., 304(24*a*), 305(135,
135*a*), 374(24*a*, 135), 376(136*a*),
433(135), *495, 500,* 887(110),
896–902(149, 170, 171, 176),
914(170, 172), 916(175), 917(175),
918(174), 921(110, 141), 923(12–15),
925, 927, 928, 929
Komarev, N. V., 175(288), 176(288),
178(288), 180(288), 181(288), *251,*
635(198), 640(390), 664(384, 390), 666
(199), 670(199), 695(197, 385), 706(390),
720–722(195, 196, 197, 200, 376, 378,
385, 387, 392, 393, 394), 724(385),
725(385, 387, 388, 389*a*, 390),
732(198, 200, 376, 385, 388, 389*a*,
393), 746(376, 385, 393, 394),768 (199),
777(385, 387), 779(384), 787 (384),
812, 814, 819, 820
Komura, M., 125(507), 126(281), *144,*
150, 184(306), 185(306), 187(306),
251, 279(113), 281(56), 283(58),
284(58, 113), 285(57), 287(56, 57),
293, 294, 313(90*c*), 314(105), 325(105),
418–420(90*c*), 428(105), 434(105),
498, 499, 1002(78), *1006*
König, K., 11(145, 147, 148), 12(146), *76,*
171(160), 178(160), *248,* 654(201),
658(201), 703(201), 704(201), 725(201),
814, 824(72), 829(72), 833(68, 70, 71),
836(70, 72), 840–844(68, 69, 70, 71),
847(68, 70), 853(68, 70), 860(68), *878*
Köpf, H., 583(53, 57), 584(53, 56, 57),
587(53, 54, 55), 590(55, 56, 57),
592(55, 56, 57), 597–602(53, 54, 55,
56, 57), *622*

Korenowski, T. F., 899(146), *928*
Koreshkov, Yu, D., 904(219), *930*
Korneva, S. P., 64(249, 250), *79,* 859(116),
865(116), *879,* 886(106), 890(221, 222,
223), *927, 930*
Korotaeva, I. M., 223(294), *251,*
725(386), *820*
Korotevskii, K. N., 84(17, 18), 89(17),
120(18), *138*
Korshak, V. V., 635(246*a*), 773(246*a*),
774(245*a*, 246*a*), 787(246*a*), *815,*
981(36), 987(37, 51), *994*
Korte, S., 26(246), *79*
Korytko, L. A., 109(63), *139,* 257(14), *292*
Köster, R., 128(387), *147*
Kostiner, E., 304(105*b*), 378(105*a*), *499*
Kostyanovskii, R. G., 107(259), *144,*
515(83), 535(83), 542(83), 548(83),
577, 637(203), 639(203), 649(205),
664(193, 205), 675(193, 203, 204),
676(193, 203, 204), 701–703(193,
203), 731(202), *814*
Kotkhekar, V., 325(105*b*), 430(105*b*), *499*
Kotlyarenskii, I. L., 987(38), *994*
Koton, M. M., 39(1), *72,* 131(282), *144,*
977(1, 30, 39, 41, 42, 43, 45),
978(1, 44), 979(1), 993(40), *994, 995*
Kotov, A. N., 847(123), 852(123), *879*
Kotrelev, V. N., 84(312), *145,* 175(289),
178(156), *247, 251*
Kozima, S., 20(218), *78,* 83(476), 92(478),
102(477), *149,* 511(164), 513(165),
514(164, 165), 522(164), 523(164, 165),
534(165), 542(165), 543(164), 544(164),
553(165), *579,* 628(401, 402),
640(401), 647(400), 649(400),
652(398), 658(398), 664(401), 665(402),
677(400), 679(400), 684(400),
688(400), 697(400), 701(400), 726(400),
728(399), 735(400), 754(400), 758(400),
770–772(400), 776(399, 401),
778(399), 793(400), 795(400), 806(400),
820, 859(101*a*), 873(101*a*, 101*b*),
874(101*a*, 101*b*), *879,* 999(71, 72), *1006*
Kozlova, T. V., 102(524), *150*
Kramer, J., 132(22), *138,* 303(28, 29),
308(28, 29), 359(28, 29), 373(29),
376–378(28, 29), 462(29), *495*
Kramer, K. A. W., 65(88), *74,* 648(206),
814

Krapf, H., 521(106), 522(106), 523(106), 528(106), 537(106), 566(106), 568(106), 569(106), *577*

Kratel, G., 905(198), 907(198), *929*

Kraus, C. A., 8(89), 56(89), *74*, 85(286, 290), 86(283), 130(284, 285, 288, 290), 132(287), 133(289), *144*, 174(165), 194(162), 196(162), 197(163, 164), 198(163, 164), 212(162), *248*, 316(106), 424(106), *499*, 520(84), 535(84), *577*, 824(46–49), 827(47), 829(48), 830(47), 834(48*a*), 837(47, 48), 839(47), 845(47, 48), 855(47), 856(49), 863(46, 49), 864(49), 867–870(47, 48*a*, 49), *877*, 882(152, 153), 883(152, 154, 155), 887(153, 154, 155), 888(153), *928*

Kraus, C. H., 894(150), 895(150, 151), *928*

Krause, E., 82(193, 294), 85(291), 86(192, 193, 293, 295, 296, 299, 300), 87(298), 91(293), 93(296, 298, 299, 300), 130(192, 292), 131(192, 291, 292, 293, 296, 299, 300), 132(292), 133(293, 294, 296, 300), 135(192, 193, 292), 136(192), *142*, *144*, 195(168), 196(167, 168), 197(166), 200(168), 201(166, 168), *248*, 298(107), 491(107), *499*, 775(158), *813*, 823(51), 834(50), 859(50), 864(50), 873(51*a*), *877* 883(156), *928*

Kravchenko, A. L., 629(262), *816*

Kravtsov, D. N., 303(107*a*), 308(135*a*), 351(107*a*, 135*a*), 357(107*a*), *499*, *500*

Krebs, K. H., 664(165), 701(165), 770(165), *813*

Kreiter, C. G., 10(5), *72*, 535(86), 542(86), 544–547(86), *577*, 649(8), 666(117, 118), *809*, *812*

Krentsel, B. A., 964(229), *973*

Krespan, C. G., 38(90), *74*

Kreuzbichler, L., 885(229), 890(229), *930*

Kriegsmann, H., 14(90*a*), 25(90*a*), *74*, 100–103(157, 301, 302, 303, 304), 105(303, 304), 123(303, 304), 128(304), *141*, *145*, 195(169, 172), 196(169, 171, 172), 197(169, 171, 172), 198(170), *248*, 284(59), *293*, 314(108, 109), 318(78, 108, 109), 319(109), 323(109), 324(78, 108, 109*a*),

325(108, 109*a*), 343(108, 109, 109*a*), 347(109), 424(108, 109, 109*a*), 425(109), 430(108, 109, 109*a*), 434(108), 491–493(108, 109a), *497*, *499*, 665(121, 122, 123), *812*, 999(24), 1002(85), *1004*, *1006*

Krizhanskii, L. M., 625(26), *809*

Kroes, R., 950(247), *973*

Kroller, E., 953(163), *971*

Krückeberg, F., 107(60), *139*

Kruglaya, O. A., 64(248*a*, 248*b*, 250, 250*a*), *79*, 172(323), *252*, 224(324), *252*, 298(227*e*, 227*f*), 314(64*b*), 320(65), 341(64*b*), 344(65), 345(64*a*, 64*b*), 346(64*a*, 65), 426(65), 429(65), 491(65), 494(64*a*, 65), *497*, *504*, 582(70*c*, 70*d*), 616–619(17, 29, 29*a*, 70*c*, 71, 72), *621*, *623*, 881(224), 882(224), 885(224), 889(224), 896(224), *930*

Kubo, H., 273(60), *293*, 337(110), 477(110), 478(110), *499*, 947(164), *971*

Kuchen, W., 298(110*a*), 337(111), 338(111), 475(111), *499*, 582(30), 597(30), *621*

Kuchkarev, A. B., 195(200), *249*

Kuehnert, P., 308(99*b*), *499*

Kühlein, K., 110(90*b*), *74*

Kuhnert, P., 936(159*a*), *971*

Kuivila, H. G., 8(92, 93), 10(64*a*), 11(101), 12(92, 94), 15(199, 201, 203), 16(201), 17(200), 19(98, 99), 20(99, 137), 21(137, 255), 23(137), 24(98, 137), 25(98, 137), 28(103, 253), 29(103, 253), 30(103), 31(91, 253, 253*a*), 32(91), 33(103), 36(92, 102, 103, 137, 219, 255), 38(92), 39(54), 40(54), 41(100), 42(54, 92), 43(54, 100, 102, 219), 44(100), 49(95, 96), 50(92, 96), 51(95, 96), 52(92), 57(97), 58(199, 202, 203), 61(199, 201, 203), *73–79*, 97(456*a*), 118(305), 137(456*a*), *145*, *148*, 164(174), 197(173, 174), *248*, 262–264(96, 97, 98, 99), 267(96, 98, 99), *294*, 304(113), 321(113), 338(112), 372(113), 431(113), 480(112), *499*, 520(85), *577*, 642(409), 644(208), 655(207, 211), 679–685(114, 207, 207*a*, 208, 209, 210, 409), 687(409), 691(208), 692(208, 211),

694(211), 719(211), 795(207*a*),
802(207*a*), *812, 814, 821,* 832(52),
833(54), 843(54), 846–850(54, 95–98),
853(54), 854(95), 859(53, 97),
860(97), 861(53), 864(52, 53, 96, 97),
865(53), 866(54), 867(53), 868(96),
870(96, 98), 874(53), *877–879,*
1001(70), *1005*
Kula, M.-R., 9(105), 10(5, 6, 105),
14(104), 70(104), 71(104), *72, 75,*
107(323), *145,* 162(18, 19), 174(18, 19),
183(18), 184(18), *244,* 518(108),
523(5, 107), 528(87), 535(86, 107, 108),
541–544(5, 86, 87, 107, 108),
555–557(108), *575, 577,* 649(8, 212),
697(212), 698(212), 699(212), 758(212),
766(212), 793(212), 795(212), *809,*
814, 887(157), *928*
Kulheim, K., 860(51*b*), *877*
Kulmitz, P., 130(306), *145,* 297(115),
314(114, 115), 424(115), 425(115),
499
Kumano, S., 10(76), *74*
Kumner, R., 923(82), *926*
Kunze, H., 83(225), *143*
Kupchik, E. J., 20(106, 107), 22(107),
28(108, 109), 31(108, 109), 32(109),
36(107), 57(109), 58(109), 63(110),
75, 303(117*a*), 311(116, 117, 117*a*),
312(116, 117), 313(117), 315(116),
321(117), 358(117*a*), 359(117*a*),
418(116, 117, 117*a*), 419(117),
420(117, 117*a*), 425(116), 431(117),
499, 512(92), 513(88, 89, 92),
520(90, 91, 92), 551(92), *577,*
628(214), 633(214), 646(213, 214),
661(213, 214), 672(213), 793(213),
794(213, 214), 800(213), 801(214), *814,*
846(55), 848(55), 874(55), *877*
Kursanov, D. N., 904(219), *930*
Kuschlesky, B. G., 998(40), 1002(40),
1005
Kuschuk, R., 665(215), *815*
Kushlefsky, B. G., 195(175, 176),
196(59), 197(175), *245, 248*
Kuszmann–Borbely, A., 648(267),
697(267), *816*
Kuznetsova, C. I., 175(289), 178(156),
247, 251
Kuznetsova, G. I., 977(33), *994*

Kwon, J. T., 37(13), 38(25, 26, 27, 28),
39(13), 42(9, 25, 26), 69(25), *72,*
106(96), *140,* 689(29), 773(29), *809,*
1003(15), *1004*

L

Lachi, M. P., 905(38), *925*
Ladenburg, A., 84(311), 86(310), 91(307),
92(309), 130(307, 308, 310, 311),
132(307, 309, 310), 136(310), *145,*
174(178), 212(177), *248,* 856(56),
870(56), *877*
Lahournére, J. C., 10(110*a*), *75,* 884(158),
928
Laine, L. V., 84(312), *145,* 977(33), *994*
Laliberte, B. R., 39(111), 65(111), *75,*
160(179), 161(41), 186(179), 187(41),
244, 248, 261(9), *292,* 303(118),
304(118), 317(168*a*), 323(168*a*),
336(168*a*), 366(118), *499, 501*
Lambourne, H., 215(180), *248*
Lampe, F. W., 117(544), *150,* 649(216,
449), 664(449), 677(449), 680(170,
216), 684(449), *813, 815, 822*
Lane, C. E., 955(165), *971*
Lane, E. S., 977(46), *995*
Lange, G., 8(259), *79,* 131(536), 137(536),
150, 883(233), *930*
Langer, H. G., 124(313), 126(313), *145,*
288(62, 63), 290(62, 63), 291(63), *293,*
666(217), *815*
Langford, V. M., 284(23), 288(23),
290(23), 291(23), *292*
Langkammerer, C. M., 977(47), *995*
Lanigan, T., 63(110), *75,* 520(91), *577*
Lapitskii, G. A., 337(118*a*), 475(118*a*),
477(118*a*), *499*
Lapkin, I. I., 102(314), 105(314), *145*
Lappert, M. F., 64(111*a*), *75,* 162(145),
170(133), 174(133), *247,* 298(98, 119),
304(79*b*), 311(79, 79*a* 96*b*), 97),
312(79), 313(79, 79*a*), 315(79),
350(79*b*), 418(79, 97), 423(79*a*),
497, 498, 499, 510–517(58, 59, 61,
72–76, 96, 97, 99), 521–534(11,
31–34, 37, 38, 38*a*, 39, 43*a*, 58, 59, 60,
61, 66, 70*a*, 72–75, 92*a*, 93, 93*a*, 94,
95, 95*a*, 95*b*, 96, 98, 99), 536(10, 11),

537(92*b*, 95*a*, 97), 538(97),
541–548(31, 31*a*, 32, 37, 38, 48,
58–61, 66, 70*a*, 72, 73, 74, 75, 76*a*,
93, 93*a*, 98), 553(74), 554(72),
563(58, 72), 565(58, 73), 568(95*a*),
573(34, 58, 73), 574(43*a*, 95, 98),
575, 576, 577, 581(26), 582(28, 30),
584(27, 27), 593(21*a*), 595(21, 21*a*),
597(26, 27, 30), 607(26, 27), 612(26,
27), *621*, 635(218), 675(218), 677(218),
680(62), 682(184), 686–688(184),
692(62), 694(62), 695(184), 696(184),
702(184), 705(62), 706(62), 711(62),
712(184), 725(184), 735(184), 740(184),
812, 810, 814, 815, 908(39, 143),
911(143), 913(143), 920(40), *925,
928*, 976(48), *995*
Lauer, G. G., 94(402), 132(402), *147*
Lauterbur, P. C., 98(73), 107(73), *139*,
325(44), 430(44), *496*, 1001(8), *1004*
Law, K. K., 834(57*a*), *877*
Lawson, J. R., 999(17), *1004*
Layer, A., 10(7), *72*
Layton, A. J., 896(160), 901(160), *928*
Leane, J. B., 107(158), *141*
Leatherland, L. C., 957(166), *971*
Leavitt, F. C., 49(111*b*), *75*, 669(219, 221),
774(219, 221), 792(219), 798(219), *815*
Lebedev, V. B., 695(307), 703(307),
716(307), 720(307), *817*
le Breton, R., 949(167), *971*
Lecoq, R., 132(315), *145*
Lee, H. H., 59(86), *74*
Lee, I. K., 315(94), 424(94), *498*, 533(68),
539(68), 553(68), *576*
Lee, R. L., 648(82), 699(82), *811*
Leebrick, J., 978(50), 979(50), 988(49), *995*
Leedham, T. J., 307(17), *495*
Leeper, R. W., 83(172), 95(316), *141, 145*
Leermakers, P., 67(66), *73*
Lefort, M., 701(222), 735(222), 775(222),
781(222), *815*
Lehman, D. S., 669(219), 774(219),
792(219), 798(219), *815*
Lehmkuhl, H., 628(458), 664(458), *822*
Lehn, W. L., 57(232), 65(232*a*), *78*,
91(513), 92(513), 94(501), *149, 150*,
269(116), 271(116), 273(116), *294*,
513(14, 100, 182), 514(14), 533(182),
535(100), 537(101), 539(182), 553(100,

182), 564(100), 568(101), 571(182),
580(225), *575, 577, 579, 580*, 863(112),
865(112), 870(112), *879*, 882(210),
883(210), 889(210), *929*
Lehnhardt, R., 93(413), 132(413, 414),
134(413, 414), *147*, 320(148), 325(148,
148), 337(146), 430(148), 434(147),
474(147), *501*
Le Holding, A. F., 920(11), 922(11), *924*
Leicester, J., 117(521), 130(521), 131(521),
134(521), 135(521), 136(521), *150, 821*
Leigh, G. J., 976(48), *995*
Leites, L. A., 104(317), 106(317), *145*
Lejeune, S., 110(125, 367), 112(367),
121(367), 124(367), 128(367), *140, 146*
Lemmon, P. H., 670(339), *818*
Lepedina, O. L., 111(7), *137*, 678(94),
679(94), 689(94), *811*
Leprêtre, B., 104(333), 131(333), *145*
Le Quan, M., 633(225*a*), 634(225*a*),
658(321), 659(225*a*), 670(224),
678(223, 225), 689(223, 224, 225*b*,
225*c*), 695(57, 223), 696(223, 224),
806(225*a*), *810, 815, 818*
Lerwill, B. R., 511(2), 513(2), 514(2),
542(2), *575*
Lesbre, M., 65(112), *75*, 90(319), 95(508),
102(347), 130(347), 131(107, 347),
132(347), 133(107), 134(508), 136(318),
140, 145, 146 150, 215(182), *248*,
949(59, 60, 61), *967*
Leung, K. L., 317(214*d*), 424(214*d*), *503*
Leusink, A. J., 8(113), 35(126), 39(128,
129), 43(126), 45(127*a*), 46(119, 123,
124), 47(114, 115, 116, 119, 120, 123,
124), 48(114, 115, 116, 118, 120, 121,
122, 125), 49(128, 129), 51(127),
52(117), 53(118), 54(120, 125, 127),
55(120), 63(31), *72, 75*, 165(183),
166(183), 167(183), 168(183), 174(183),
175(183), 177(183), 179(183), *248*,
312(120), 422(120), *499*, 518(102, 103),
527(103), *577*, 644(229, 234, 235),
647(230, 231, 237), 649(228), 669(233),
678(227, 229, 231), 679(229),
689–693(227, 228, 231, 232, 234, 235),
703–705(227, 229, 231), 714–717(227,
228, 231, 232, 237), 719(231, 234, 235,
236), 721(227), 728(227, 231), 730(227),
734(229), 736(229), 737(229), 744(228,

231, 232), 745(228, 231, 232), 763(231, 232), 773(226), 776(226), 777(226), *815*, 966(168), *971*
Levins, P. L., 57(97), *74*
Levitt, T. E., 530(92*a*), *577*
Lewinsohn, M., 95(508), 134(508), *150*
Lewis, J., 918(90), *925, 927*
Lewis, W. R., 933(169), *971*
Liengme, B. V., 921(161), 922(161), *928*
Lievin, P., 685(139), 812
Light, J. R. C., 664(59), *810*
Limbourg, M., *810*
Lind, H., 67(149, 149*a*, 166), *76*, 193(219), *249*, 304(138*a*), 351(138*a*), *500*, 513(126), 515(126), 519(121, 126), 552(121), 573(126), *578*, 702(284), 709(284), 720(284), 723(284), *817*
Lindley, P. F., 910(60), 913(60), 923(60), *926*
Lippincott, E. R., 100(320), 117(321), 130(320), 132(320), *145*, 999(41), *1005*
Lisina, Z. M., 163(251), *250*, 645(320), 677(320), 703(320), 720(320), *818*
Litvinova, O. V., 538(40), 570(40), *576*
Liu, J. S., 26(136), *75*
Litzow, M. R., 920(40), *925*
Loginova, I. E., 721(379), 722(379), 724(379), *819*
Lohmann, D. H., 102(322), *145*, 256(64), 277(64), *293*, 318(122), 319(122), 325(122), 424(122), 430(122), *499*, *815*, 1000(42), 1001(42), *1005*
Lokshin, B. V., 304(24*a*), 305(136*a*), 374(24*a*, 136*a*), *495, 500*, 911(172), 914(172), *928*
Longi, P., 664(239), *815*
Lorberth, J., 9(105), 10(105), *75*, 107(323, 325), 114(324), 116(324), *145*, 156(185), 162(19), 163(185), 174(19, 185), 179(185), 183–186(185), 189(185), 190(185), *244, 248*, 515(108), 521–523(5, 104, 105, 105*a*, 106, 107), 525(93, 93*a*, 104), 528(87, 106), 533(93, 93*a*), 535(86, 93, 93*a*, 107, 108), 537(106), 541–547(5, 86, 87, 93, 93*a*, 104, 105, 107, 108, 209–212), 555–557(108), 566(106), 568(93), 569(106), *575, 577, 580*, 635(218), 648(240, 242), 664(242), 675(218), 677(218), 695(241), 720(241), 746(241),

774(241), 777(241), 787(241), *815*, 887(157), *928*
Lorenz, D. H., 9(132), 25(130), 27(132), 28(132), 54(131) *75*, 315(123), 324(123), 425(123), *499*
Loveland, B. A., 661(10), 700(10), *809*
Löwig, C., 82(326), 84(326), 91(326), 130(326) 132(326), *145*, 824(58), 833(58), *877*
Löwig, G., 200(186), 204(186), *248*
Lowry, N. C., 23(65), 27(65), *73*
Lübke, K., 131(552), *140, 151*
Lucas, C. R., 303(123*a*), 357(123*a*), 369(123*a*), *500*
Lucenko, I. F., 317(139*a*), *500*
Luftensteiner, H., 132(415), *147*, 320(148), 325(148), 430(148), *501*
Luijten, J. G. A., 8(236), 9(241, 242), 11(243), 34(237, 240), 35(240), 37(240, 243), *78, 79*, 82(328), 84(251), 86(254, 328), 87(254, 255), 90(329), 91(250), 93(328), 94(138), 104(254, 255), 130(251, 255, 328), 131(250, 255, 328), 132(250, 251, 253, 328), 133(328), 134(252, 328), 135(253, 254, 255, 328), 136(255, 328), *141, 143, 144, 145*, 176(316), 194–197(140, 188, 189, 316, 317), 212–215(187, 318), *247, 248, 252*, 254(44), 257(118), 258(65), *293, 294*, 298(125, 126*a*, 222*a*, 222*b*), 309(222), 314(126), 402(124), 424(126), *500, 503*, 510(113), 514(77, 78, 109, 110), 520(70, 77, 78, 109, 110, 111), 521(112), 523(109), 528(110), 529(70), 533(78, 109), 537(112), 542–551(78, 109, 110, 111, 112), 564(77), 567(77, 110), 568(109, 112), *576, 577, 578*, 582(31*a*, 70*b*), *621, 623*, 631(244), 643(243), 645(243), 695(243), 720(243), 732(243), 746(243), *815*, 834(45*a*), 862(45*a*), *877*, 933(172), 935(171, 237), 940(236, 192), 941(147, 173, 238, 239), 942(131, 146, 147, 192), 943(146, 147), 946(137), 952(239), 954(131), 959(170), *970, 971, 973, 1005*
Lukevits, E. Y., 8(133), *75*
Luk'yanova, L. V., 194(155), 218(155), *247*
Lunazzi, L., 664(245), *815*

Luneva, L. K., 628(246), 633(246), 635(246, 246a), 645(246), 658(246), 770(404), 773(246, 246a), 774(245a, 246, 246a), 781(152), 787(151, 246, 246a), *813, 815, 820*, 987(51), *995*

Lust, S., 181(139), *247*

Lutsenko, I. F., 64(9b), 49(85a), *72, 74*, 158(216, 254), 163(250, 251, 252), 170(253), 174–176(190, 216, 253, 254), 178(190, 216, 252, 253, 254), 179(253, 255), 185(250), 224(191), 228(190, 191), 238(190), 239(191, 250), *248, 249, 250*, 316(160), 424(160), *501*, 640(249), 643(277), 645(320), 676(191), 677(320), 702–704(191, 249, 294, 319, 320), 716(248), 720(320), 722(248), 735(191), 736(247, 276, 277, 294), *814, 816, 817, 818*

Lutz, H., *145*

Lvova, F. P., 695(197), 720(197), 722(197), *814*

Lyle, W. H., 952(174), *971*

Lyon, D. J., 949(209), *972*

Lysenko, E. N., 84(17, 18), 89(17), 120(18), *138*

M

Ma, S. C., 65(233), *78*, 636(425), 642(425), 701(425), 735(425), 737(425), *820*

MacDiarmid, A. G., 278(17), 279(17), *292*, 824(59), *877*, 991(12), *994*

Maciel, G. E., 669(250), *816*

Mack, G. P., 130(331), 131(331), 132(330, 331), *145*, 180(194), 181(194), 182(194), 185(195, 196), 186(195), 187(196), 189(195), *248*, 514(114, 115), 565(114, 115), *578*, 737(251), *816*, 962(175), *971*

Mack, J., 540(213), *580*

Mackay, K. M., 824(60), *877*, 882(162), 889(162), 890(162), *928*

Mackillop, M. J., 512(56), *576*

Maddox, M. L., 14(134), 69(134), 70(134), 71(134), *75*, 1003(43), *1005*

Maeda, Y., 203(198), 204(197, 198), 208(198), *248*, 259(66, 67), 263(68), 264(67), *293*, 1000(44, 45), *1005*

Magee, P. N., 951(28, 176), *967, 971*

Mageli, O. L., 190(199), 191(199), 193(199), 194(199), 204(199), 205(199), 205(199), *248*

Magon, L., 122(84, 85, 86, 87), 123(86, 87, 89), *139, 140*

Magos, L., 949(29), *967*

Mahr, C., 597(32), 598(32), 600(32), 612(32), *621*

Maire, J. C., 13(49), 45(45a), *73*, 104(333), 105(344), 107(334), 131(333), *145*, 257(120), *294*, 320(63c), 425(63c), 492(63c), *497*, 628(252), 634(252), 649(252), 671(252), *816*

Makarov, E. F., 109(63), *139*, 210(106), *246*, 257(14), *292*, 320(83d), *498*, 704(146), *812*, 887(110), 921(110), *927*

Makarov, S. P., 94(540, 541), 131(539, 541), 132(539, 540, 541), 134(539, 541), *150*, 203(332), 212(331), *252*

Makarova, L. G., 95(382), *147*, 215(213, 215), *249*

Malatesta, L., 132(335), *145*, 581(33), 598(33), *621*

Malfroid, P., 633(17), 649(17), 657(17), 658(17), 691(17), 713(17), *809*

Malinowski, E. R., 14(245), *79*, 106(520), *150*, 664(434), *821*

Mal'tseva, E. N., 45(135, 135a), *75*

Manakov, M. N., 904(169), *928*

Mangravite, J., 678(253), *816*

Manning, A. R., 898(163), 905(164), 906(164), 908(45, 46), 912(46), 917(34), 918(46), 922(32), 923(32, 34), *925, 928*

Mans, O. L., 868(35), *877*

Manuel, T. A., 669(219), 774(219), 792(219), 798(219), *815*

Manulkin, Z. M., 85(336, 339), 86(337, 448), 88(340), 89(340–343), 114(339), 130(336, 338, 340, 342, 368), 131(337, 339, 341), 132(336, 340, 341, 342), 135(337, 338, 340, 368), 136(342, 368, 368a), *145, 146, 148*, 195(200), 196(258), 201(258), *249, 250*, 646(337), 748(423), 751(423), 752(337), 754(423), 756(337), 778(336), 780(336), 785(336), 788(336, 423), 790(336, 338), *818, 821*

Marchand, A., 179(205), 181(205), 182(205), 186(205), *249*, 665(258), *816*

Mares, F., 525(174), *579*
Maretina, I. A., 45(135), *75*
Marimoto, Y., 659(163), 660(163), 726(163), *813*
Marinelli, L. P., 977(54), 979(54), *995*
Markau, K., 12(205), *77*
Marks, G. C., 937(177), 938(177), 939(177), *971*
Marrot, J., 104(333), 105(334), 131(333), *145*
Mars, O. L., 882(105), 883(105), *927*
Marshall, C. J., Jr., 65(232*a*), *78*, 540(227), *580*
Marsman, J. W., 46(119, 123, 124), 47(119, 122, 123, 124), 48(122), *75*, 647(231), 649(228), 678(227, 231), 689–693(227, 228, 231), 704(227, 231), 714–717(227, 228, 231), 719(231), 721(227), 728(227, 231), 730(227, 231), 744(228, 231), 745(228, 231), 763(231), *815*
Martens, P. H., 998(50), *1005*
Martin, D. F., 108(533), 118(345, 346), 129(533), *146*, *150*, 155(211), 164(212, 260), 182(329), 184(329), 189(211, 329), *249*, *250*, *252*, 279(75, 125), 285(125), 286(125), 287(75, 125), *293*, *295*, 661(254, 255, 272, 273), 723(273), *816*
Mason, P. S., 513(81), *577*
Massey, A. G., 304(105*a*), 378(105*a*), *499*, 629(72), 646(71), 649(112), 671(72), 672(71, 72), 793(71), 799(112), 800(71), *811*, *812*
Mathis, R., 102(347), 130(347), 131(347), 132(347), *146*
Matsubayashi, G., 108(349), 119(348), 120(349), 126(348), *146*, 284(69), 289(69), 291(69), *293*, 1003(46), *1005*
Matsuda, H., 83(350, 351, 352, 353, 354), *146*, 159(202), 176(202), 195(202), 197(202), 212(202), *248*, 998(47), *1005*
Matsuda, I., 311(94*c*), 315(94, 94*b*), 424(94, 94*b*), 482(94*c*), *498*, 533(68), 539(68), 540(207, 208), 553(68), *576*, *580*
Matsuda, S., 35(67*a*, 179*a*, 179*b*), *74*, *77*, 83(202, 203, 351, 352, 353, 354), *142*, *146*, 159(202), 176(202), 195(702), 197(202), 212(202), *249*, 298(127),

434(127), *500*, 738(297), 739(296), 240(297), *817*, 998(47), *1005*
Matsumoto, H., 104(543), *150*, 200(333), 201(333), 204(333), 205(333), 208(333), *252*, 270–273(129), *295*
Matsumura, Y., 315(212), 321(212), 324(212), 325(212), 336(212), 338(212), 425(212), 430(212), 480(212), *503*
Matsuzaki, K., 307(94*a*), *498*
Matternas, L. U., 49(111*b*), *75*, 669(219), 774(219), 792(219), 798(219), *815*
Matwiyoff, N. A., 108(335), 120(355), 123(355), 124(355), *146*, 157(203), 161(203), 187(203), 188(203), 196(203), *249*, 664(95) *811*, 1000(48), 1003(48), *1005*
Maxfield, P. L., 656(256), 681(256), 687(256), *816*
May, G. S., 11(198), 16(198), 17(198), 61(198, 204), 69(198), 70(198), 71(198), *77*, 107(456), *148*
May, L., 15(135*b*), *75*, 1001(18), *1004*
Maybury, P. C., 118(345), *146*, 661(254), *816*
Mayence, G., 117(159), *141*, 649(138), *812*
Mayer, K. K., 649(212), 697(212), 698(212), 699(212), 758(212), 766(212), 793(212), 795(212), *814*
Mays, M. J., 904(166), 906(165), 922(6), *924*, *928*
Mazzocchi, R., 664(239), *815*
McCombie, H., 952(178), *971*
McFarlane, W., 106(144), *141*, 156(192), *248*, 648(256*a*), 664(256*a*), *816*
McFarling, J. C., 628(111), *812*
McFarling, J. L., 83(148, 538), *141*, *150*
McGrady, M. M., 105(145, 356), 108(145, 356), 123(145), *141*, *146*, 184(193), 189(193), *248*, 270(70, 71), 280(71), 282(71), 287(71), *293*, 1000(49), *1005*
MacGregor, P. T., 21(46), *73*
McInerney, E. F., 303(117*a*), 311(117*a*), 358(117*a*), 359(117*a*), 418(117*a*), 420(117*a*), *499*, 512(92), 513(92), 520(92), 551(92), *577*
McKean, D. C., 512(56), *576*
McNeill, E. H., 130(127), 132(127), 134(127), *140*
McQuillan, G. P., 113(32), 123(31), 125(31), *138*, 540(205), *580*

McWhinnie, W. R., 634(257), *816*, 875(61), *877*
Meals, R. N., 93(357), *146*, 963(179), *971*
Mehner, H., 118(226), *143*
Mehrotra, R. C., 157(204), 176(204), 180(205), 186(205), 223(303), *249, 251*, 298(128a), 303(128, 128b, 215), 304(128, 215), 306(215), 354(128b), 359(215), 366–369(128b, 215), 377(128), 449–451(215a), 457(215a), *500, 503*
Meinwald, J., 26(136), *75*
Meisner, J., 948(180), *971*
Melnikoff, A., 320(53, 54), 348(53, 54), 424(53), *496*, 665(79), *811*
Melson, G. A., 922(32), 923(32), *925*
Melvin, H. W., 131(173), *141*
Menapace, L. W., 19(98, 99), 20(99, 137), 24(99, 137), 25(99, 137), 36(137), *74, 76*
Mendelsohn, J., 102(358), *146*, 157(206), 158(237), 179(205), 180(237), 181(202, 237), 182(205, 237), 186(205, 206), *249*, 643(305), 665(258), 738(305), 740(305), 741(305), 742(305), *816, 817*
Mercier, P., 100(320), 130(320), 132(320), *145*, 999(41), *1005*
Merku, K., 857(99), *878*
Merkulova, E. N., 94(541), 131(541), 132(541), 134(541), *150*
Metten, J., 337(111), 338(111), 475(111), *499*
Meyer, F. J., 8(259), *79*, 131(536), 137(536), 137(536), *150*, 883(233), *930*
Meyer, H., 647(259), *816*
Meyer, K., 658(161), 670(161), *813*
Meynier, D., 949(59, 60, 61, 181), *967, 971*
Michelet, J., 659(260), 660(260), 699(260), *816*
Michigan, E. V., 170(253), 175(253), 276(253), 178(253), 179(253), *250*, 704(319), *818*
Miganisi, T., 999(72), *1006*
Migdal, S., 314(129), 316(129), 317(129), 320(129), 321(129), 335(129), 424(129), 426(129), 428–431(129), 467(129), 468(129), *500*, 988(52), *995*
Miller, F. A., 670(339), *818*

Miller, S. M., 959(182), *971*
Milne, J. N., 180(60), 183(60), *245*
Minghetti, G., 311(39a), 420(39a), 421(39a), *496*, 918(21), *925*
Minoura, Y., 744(261), *816*, 981(53), *995*
Mironov, V. F., 114(238), 130(238), 132(238), *143*, 629(262), 678(94, 308), 679(94), 689(94, 308), *811, 816, 817*
Mirskov, R. G., 49(245), *79*, 155(291), 157(292), 159(295), 168(290), 170(208), 175(290, 292, 295, 319), 176(291, 292, 295), 178(208), 223(293, 294), 225(207, 290), *249, 251, 252*, 317(213a), 321(213a), *503*, 637(389), 644(435), 658(435), 714(380a, 435), 716(380a), 435), 719(435), 721(263, 373, 377, 379, 382, 383, 387a, 389), 722(263, 377, 379, 387a, 389, 435), 724(373, 379, 383, 389), 725(264, 383, 386), 746(373), *816, 819, 820, 821*
Miscowiec, J., 309(130), 391(130), *500*
Misyunas, V. K., 175(288), 176(288), 178(288), 180(288), 181(288), *251*, 635(198), 664(384), 695(385), 720–722(195, 376, 378, 385, 387), 724(385), 725(385, 387, 389a), 732(198, 385, 389a), 736(376), 746(376, 385), 777(384, 387), 779(384), 787(384), *814, 819, 820*
Mitchell, T. N., 170(82), 175(82), 180(82), 222(83), 232(83), *246*, 313(60a), 317(61), 325(60a), 418(60a), 419(60a), 426(60a), 430(60a), 433(60a), *496*, 511(54), 520(55), 525(54), 538(55), 540(197, 214), 543(54), 544(54), 552(55), 559(55), 560(55), 561(55), 563(55), 564(55), 571(55), 571(54), *576, 579, 580*, 675(88), *811*
Mitrofanov, K. P., 109(5, 6), 111(7), *137, 138*, 210(3), *243*, 257(2), 277(2), 278(2), *292*, 325(20, 21), 430(20), *495*
Miyamura, N., 959(48), *970*
Miyanisi, T., 107(477), *149*, 647(400), 649(400), 677(400), 679(400), 684(400), 697(400), 701(400), 726(400), 735(400), 754(400), 770(400), 771(400), 772(400), 793(400), 795(400), 806(400), *820*, 873(101b), 103(101b), *879*
Miyoshi, H., 940(260), *974*
Mo, Y. L., 418(235), *504*

Moedritzer, K., 108(360), *146*, 298(131), 323(132), 325(132), 336(132), 430(132), *500*

Mohammed, A., 102(55), 127(361), *139*, *146*, 290(72), *293*

Mohring, H., 110(90b), *74*

Monastyrskii, L. M., 84(17, 18), 89(17), 120(18), *138*

Montermoso, J. C., 161(41), 187(41), *244*, 261(9), *292*, 977(54), 979(54), *995*

Mooney, E. F., 100(74), 102(74, 90), 107(158), *139*, *140*, *141*, 155(104), 156(48), 184(48, 103, 104), 185(48, 103, 104), 186(48, 103, 104), 187(103, 104), 189(48, 103, 104), *245*, *246*, 279(34), 284(15), 286(34), *292*, 1001(9), 1002(10), *1004*

Moore, G. J., 94(501) *149*, 882(210), 883(210), 889(210), *929*

Moore, M. S., 986(68), *995*

Moore, P. W., 100(362), *146*

Moore, R. C., 660(98a), *811*

Moorhouse, S., 876(5a), *876*

Moormeier, L., 94(388), *147*

Morelli, D., 887(19), 901(18), 906–908(18, 22), 911(18), 917(18), *925*

Morgan, G. L., 105(56), 107(56), *139*, 833(15), 842(15), *876*

Morris, H., 834(63), 856(62, 63), 868(62), *877*

Morris, J. M., 513(81), *597*

Morrison, R. T., 884(167), *928*

Moscowitz, J., 948(21a, 22), *966*

Moskvina, E. M., 977–979(1), *994*

Moss, J. R., 910(168), 913(168), *928*

Motoyoshi, M., 298(175c), 303(175c), *502*

Mücke, H., 308(133), *500*, 336(167, 168), *501*

Muetterties, E. L., 283(74), 287(74), *293*, 325(71), 434(71), *497*, 513(189), 542(189), *579*

Mufti, A. S., 200(209), 205(209), 206(209, 210), 208(209, 210), *249*, 261(73), 263(73), *293*, 538(116), 553(116), 570(116), *578*, 933(184), *971*

Mühlstädt, M., 26(251), *79*

Muhr, A., 958(186), *971*

Mui, J. Y-P., 636(366), 651(366), 675(356, 366, 367), 380(366), 382(366), 705(366), *819*

Mukai, T., 285(57), 287(57), *293*

Mülhofer, E., 886(2), 890(2), 891(2), 892(2), *924*

Müller, E., 39(137a, 167), 41(137a), 52(167), *76*, 167(223), *249*, 518(127), 537(127), 540(215, 225), 573(127), *578*, *580*

Müller, H., 329(92), 330(92), 336(92), 460(92), 464(92), 470(92), *498*

Muller, L. I., 693(22), *809*

Muller, R. L., 945(187), *971*

Mullins, F. P., 309(145c), 482(145c), 483(145c), *501*

Mullins, M. A., 110(363), 125(363), 128(363), *146*

Muo, Y. L., 942(65), *968*

Muratova, A. A., 288(86), 291(86), *294*, 586(37), *622*

Murin, A. N., 131(364), *146*

Murphy, C. M., 131(106), *140*

Mvogo, L., 945(77), *968*

Myatt, J., 897(142), 902(142), 920(142), *928*

Mylnikov, V. S., 987(59), *995*

N

Naarmann, H., 986(60), *995*

Nabika, K., 107(477), *149*, 647(400), 649(400), 677(400), 679(400), 679(400), 684(400), 697(400), 701(400), 726(400), 735(400), 754(400), 770–772(400), 793(400), 795(400), 806(400), *820*, 873(101b), 874(101b), *879*, 999(72), *1006*

Nad, M. M., 90(273, 274), 131(274, 365), *144*, *146*, 212(151), 215(151), 152), *247*, 314(134), 320(101), 325(102, 103), 426(314), 432(101), 434(102, 103), *499*, *500*, 834(63a), *877*

Nagy, J., 648(267), 684(268), 697(267), *816*

Nakamara, M., 83(354), *146*

Nakamura, Y., 204(227), *249*, 264(77), *283*, 327(144), 440(144), *500*

Nakatani, M., 303(134a), 481(134a), *500*

Namigata, F., 26(8), *72*

Nash, G. A., 57(223), *78*, 664(269), 665(269), 669(269), *816*

Nasielski, J., 87(52, 64, 65, 160–166, 366), 88(66), 92(51), 108(160, 161), 110(367), 112(367), 118(160, 161), 120(160), 121(367), 122(161, 167, 190), 124(367), 128(367), *139, 141, 142, 146,* 629(40, 41, 42, 89, 131, 132), 630(42), 632–634(17, 42, 45, 129, 130, 131, 135, 144*a*), 646(52, 53), 648–653(16, 17, 40, 42, 43, 45 89*a*, 132, 137, 141), 655(130), 657–661(2*a*, 17, 53, 54, 55, 56, 144*a*, 270, 271, 271*a*), 664–666(14*a*, 40, 41, 43, 44, 129, 130, 131, 132, 133, 135), 669(17), 677–680(16, 17*a*, 40–44, 141, 409*a*), 683–687(43, 44, 45, 89*a*, 139, 427), 689(17*a*), 691(17), 697–699(2*a*, 43, 52, 53, 55, 56, 91, 137, 270, 271), 701(40–44), 705(17*a*), 706(40, 41, 42), 713(17), 726(137), 730(17*a*), 733–737(14*a*, 17*a*, 54, 137, 270, 271, 349*a*), 747(52, 54, 137), 770(14*a*), 804(45, 349*a*, 409*a*), 805(349*a*), 807(45, 349*a*, 409*a*), 808(144*a*), *809–812, 816, 818, 820, 821,* 861(12*a*), 862(12*a*), *876, 879*

Natta, G., *995*

Naugniot, P., 998(50), *1005*

Naumov, S. N., 130(368), 135(368), 136(368, 368*a*), *146*

Neal, A. M., 130(288), 133(289), *144,* 174(165), *248,* 520(84), *535*(84), *577,* 824(48, 48*a*), 829(48), 834(48, 48*a*), 837(48), 845(48), 869(48*a*), *877*

Nefedov, O. M., 664(375), *819,* 904(169), *928*

Nefedov, V. D., 131(364), *146*

Neimann, M. B., 132(369), *146*

Nelson, B. W., 20(4*a*), *72*

Nelson, W. H., 155(211), 164(212), 189(211), *249,* 279(75), 287(75), *293,* 661(272, 273), 723(273), *816*

Nemtsov, M. S., 191(28), *244*

Nesmeyanov, A. N., 49(137*b*, 137*c*, 137*d*, 137*e*), *76,* 89(277, 279, 379), 92(279), 93(276, 378), 94(276, 278, 377, 381), 95(370, 374, 376, 382), 130(275, 377), 131(375), 132(275, 279, 372–375, 377, 381), 133(142, 275, 374–377, 383), *141, 144, 146, 147,* 158(216), 174(216), 178(216), 189(95), 212(95), 215(213, 214, 215), *246, 247,*
249, 303(107*a*), 305(135, 136*a*), 308(135*a*), 320(68, 104, 136), 325(104, 136), 351(107*a*, 135*a*), 357(107*a*), 374(135), 376(136*a*), 431–434(68, 104, 135, 136,) *497, 499, 500,* 582(28*a*), 614(34), 616(34), *621,* 643(277), 644(280), 657(275), 689(280), 723(279), 730(281), 736(276, 277), 744(278, 279), 787(279), *816, 817,* 869(45*b*), *877,* 897–902(170, 171, 173), 911(171, 172), 914(170), 916(175), 917(175), 918(174), *928, 929*

Nesterov, O. V., 963(91), *968*

Neubert, G., 999(51), *1005*

Neumann, W. P., 8(138, 139, 140), 9(150, 162), 10(90*b*), 11(145, 147, 148, 150, 155), 12(140, 146, 205), 15(156), 16(156), 18(157, 222), 35(153, 154, 156), 36(151, 152, 154, 206), 39(137*a*, 160, 163, 165, 167), 41(137*a*, 220), 42(164), 43(141), 52(142, 143, 153, 167), 55(144), 56(144), 60(157, 159, 161, 221, 222), 61(156, 161, 162), 65(158, 158*a*, 158*b*), 67(149, 149*a*, 166), 71(140, 150, 154, 157), *74, 76, 77,* 90(386), 91(386), 94(385, 549), 97(387*a*, 489*a*), 128(384, 387), 137(387*a*, 489*a*), *147, 149, 151,* 165(218), 166(218), 167(223), 171(160), 175–178(160, 217, 218), 180(218, 222), 182(218), 183(218), 185(220), 189(218, 220), 193(219), 197(222), 223(221, 222), *248, 249,* 298(137), 304(138*a*), 315(139), 317(139), 340–342(138, 139), 351(138*a*), 424(139), 491(138, 139), *500,* 510(117), 513(126), 515(126), 518(118–120, 122, 127), 519(121, 126), 523(118, 166), 526(123, 124, 125, 167, 168), 527(125, 167, 168), 529(166), 537(127), 540(214, 215, 225), 543–547(118, 120, 122–125, 167, 168, 214, 215, 225), 552(121), 553(125), 561(119), 573(120, 126, 127, 166), *578, 579, 580,* 582(35, 36), 593(36), 597(36), *622,* 631(282), 634(286), 635(290), 638(286), 640(290), 642(286), 648(290), 454(201), 458(201), 664(290), 665(285, 290), 667(290), 681(289), 703(201), 704(201, 287),

706–710(284, 285, 286, 287, 288, 345),
711(286), 722–725(201, 283, 284, 290),
728(345), 729(290), 737(345), 741(286),
742(287, 345), 743(287), 748(286, 345),
749(345), 752(286), 754(287), 781(288),
783–785(286, 287, 288, 345),
788(287, 288), *814, 817, 818,*
824(64, 66, 67, 72), 825(76),
827–829(64, 72, 78, 103, 104),
832–847(65–76, 78, 79, 103, 104),
849(74, 104), 850(74, 104), 852(73),
853(68, 70, 75), 855–875(76, 99, 104),
860(51*b*, 60, 68, 73), 861(73),
865(77), 868(104), *877–879,* 882(177),
886(178), 890(179, 202), *929,* 933(188),
949(188), 965(188), *971,* 978(64),
986(62, 63), *995,* 997(53, 54),
1000(53), 1004(52), *1005*

Nevett, B. A., 275(115), *294*

Newlands, M. J., 730(180), 779(181),
787(181), *813,* 906–909(75, 76, 77, 80,
215), 911–913(75, 77, 178, 133, 134,
215), 918(86), 920(86), 921(161),
922(161), *926, 928, 930*

Newson, H. C., 63(168), *76*

Nguen, D. C., 317(139*a*), *500*

Nickless, G., 304(151), 309(151), *501,*
640(311, 312, 313), 664(312),
665(312), 677(312), 678(312, 313),
679(312), 681(311), 683(311), 693(311),
694(311), 703(312), 727(312, 313),
728(312), 735(312), 736(312),
770(312, 313), 771(312), 775(312),
778(312), 804(313), *817, 818,* 999(63),
1005

Niederreuther, U., 589(69*a*, 69*b*, 69*c*),
595(69*a*, 69*b*, 69*c*), 596(69*a*, 69*b*),
602(69*a*, 69*b*, 69*c*), 605(69*a*, 69*b*,
69*c*), 606(69*a*, 69*b*, 69*c*), *623*

Niermann, H., 9(150), 11(150), 35(153,
154), 36(151, 152, 154), 38(154),
52(153), 71(150, 154), *76,* 518(122),
544(122), *578,* 986(62), *995*

Niesar, K. H., 954(33), *967*

Nile, T., 537(92*b*), *577*

Nimetz, A. A., 26(136), *75*

Nishimoto, K., 955(189), *971*

Nishino, M., 204(325), 205(325), 208(325),
252, 539(185), 591(185), 572(185), *579*

Nissim, S., 945(23), 948(22, 23, 24), *966*

Nitzsche, S., 963(190), *971*

Nixon, L. A., 583(11), 590(11), 592(11),
596(11), 597(11), 598(11), 605–609(11),
612(12), 614–616(12), *621*

Nixon, L. V., 276(16), *292*

Nobis, J. F., 94(388), *147*

Noffsinger, C. A., 934(206), *972*

Noll, W., 963(191), *971*

Noltes, H. G., 829–831(21), 836(21),
839(21), 840(21), 846(21), 850(21),
852(21), *876*

Noltes, J. G., 8(236, 238), 9(241, 242),
11(243), 18(33), 19(172), 27(172),
34(174, 237, 239, 240), 35(126, 240),
36(172), 37(69, 172, 239, 240, 243),
38(174, 239), 39(69, 128, 129, 173,
174, 175), 43(126, 169), 45(127*a*, 239),
46(124), 47(124), 48(120, 121, 125),
49(128, 129, 175), 50(172), 51(127, 239),
52(239), 54(35, 38, 120, 125, 127, 170,
171), 55(120), 56(169), 60(33, 34, 35,
36, 38, 169), 61(35, 38), 62(38),
63(31, 32), 64(37, 39, 230), *72, 74–79,*
87(257), 88(257), 130(389, 390),
131(256, 389, 390), 132(389, 390),
134(389, 390), *143, 144, 147,* 171(225),
174–178(61, 224, 225), 180(225),
182(225), 185(62), 197(62), 212(62),
222(224), 223(61, 225), 237(224),
245, 248, 249, 265(119),
295, 298(222a), 306(49, 50), 311(140),
312(140, 141, 142), 315(140, 142, 143),
422(121, 140, 141, 142), 424(142),
425(143), *496, 499, 500, 503,*
518(102, 103), 128, 129, 130, 131),
520(129), 526(44–47, 128), 527(47,
103), 534(128, 131), 543(47),
552(47, 128), 559(46, 47, 128–131),
561(129), 564(129), 565(130, 131),
576, 577, 578, 582(70*b*), 593(14),
621, 623, 637(292), 654(292), 644(229),
647(230), 669(233), 678(227, 229),
679(229), 689–691(227), 703–705(227,
229, 292), 714–716(227), 721(227),
728–730(227, 428), 734(229), 736(229),
737(229), 773(226), 776(226), 777(226),
815, 817, 821, 835–838(23), 831(23),
850(87*a*), 854(110), 855(80), 860(87*a*),
872(15*a*), *876, 878,* 886(64, 65),
888(65), 890(64), 893(64), 895(60),

913(60), 923(60), *926*, 941(192), 942(192), 966(168), *971*, 986(65, 80), *995, 996*

Noreen, A. L., 22(40*a*), *73*

Normant, H., 540(194, 195), *579*

Norris, T., 273(28), 274(28), 277(28), *292*

Nosek, J., 196(226), *249*

Nöth, H., 9(176), *77*, 114(324), 116(324), *145*, 521–523(106), 528(106), 537(106), 540(212), 566(106), 568(106), 569(106), *577, 580*, 629(293), 648(240), *815, 817*, 885(180, 181), 886(181), 889(180, 181), 892(181), *929*

Novichenko, Y. D., 977(33), *994*

Novikova, N. V., 49(137*d*), *76*, 89(47), 95(374), 131(375), 132(372–375), 133(374, 375), *139, 147*, 614(34), 616(34), *621*, 644(280), 689(280), *817*

Novikova, Z. S., 179(255), *250*, 704(294), 736(294), *817*

Nyholm, R. S., 896(160), 901(160), *928*

O

Oakes, V., 83(391, 392), *147, 817*

O'Brien, R. J., 97(101), 100(97), 101(101), 112(101, 102), 113(98, 99), 124(100), 128(97, 98, 99, 101, 102), *140*, 268(21, 22), 273(21), 275(21), 276(22), 277(21), 278(18), 279(18), *292*, 1000(16), *1004*

Occolowitz, J. L., 117(393), *147*

Oesper, P. F., 114(394), *147*

Ogura, J., 264(130), *295*

Ohara, M., 10(177), *77*, 204(227), *249*, 255(79, 80), 258(76), 264(77), 284(80), *293*, 328(144), 440(144), *500*, 1002(56), *1005*

Ohnishi, S., 35(179*b*), *77*, 738(297), 740(297), *817*

Okawara, R., 10(177), 16(84), 17(84), 61(84), *74, 77*, 100(398),104(241, 543), 107(241), 108(245, 247, 348), 113(395), 119(240, 348), 120(349), 122(398), 125(507), 126(281, 348), 129(240, 245, 246, 247, 526), 130(396, 525), 132(247), 137(397), *143, 144, 146, 147, 150*, 174(147), 177(147), 182–187(147, 148, 232, 306, 313),

189(313), 190(147, 313), 195(235), 200–205(45, 197, 198, 227, 229, 231, 233, 234, 325, 333, 334), 207(228, 230, 233), 208(45, 198, 233, 307, 325, 333), 212(307), 214(231), 216(232, 234), 217(232, 234), 218(232), *245, 247, 249, 251, 252*, 254–256(79, 80, 83, 84, 95), 258(76), 259(66, 67, 95), 262–264(67, 68, 77, 81, 124), 268(78, 128), 270–275(128, 129), 277(78, 82), 279–285(46, 47, 51–56, 58, 69, 80, 113, 117, 123), 287(46, 47, 56, 57, 117, 123), 289(69), 291(69), *293, 294, 295*, 298(227*h*), 313(90*c*), 314(105), 315(144*c*, 212), 321(212), 323(234), 324(42, 212), 325(105, 212), 327(144), 336(212), 338(212, 213), 418–420(90*c*), 425(144*c*, 212), 428(105), 430(42, 212, 213), 434(105), 440(144), 480(212, 213), *496, 498, 499, 500, 503, 504*, 539(184, 185), 571(185), 572(185), *579*, 864(82), 866(82), *878*, 998–1003(35, 36, 37, 44, 45, 46, 56, 57, 58, 59, 78, 79, 86, 87), *1005, 1006*

Okhlobystin, O. Yu., 112(179), 120(179), *142, 151*, 197(335, 336), 210(3), *243, 252*, 626(4), 647(450), 661(49), 689(4), 797(49), *809, 810, 822*, 887(111), 920(111), *927*

Oki, Y., 298(144*a*), *500*

Okubo, T., 320(87), 322(87), 430(87), *498*

Oliver, A. J., 303(144*b*), 308(90*a*, 144*b*), 350(144*b*), 357(90*a*, 144*b*), *498, 500*, 535(65), 542(65), *576*

Oliver, J. P., 26(178, 178*a*), *77*

Olsen, D. H., 11(179), *77*, 833(81), 841(81), 843(81), *878*, 1004(55), *1005*

Omae, I., 35(179*a*, 179*b*), *77*, 738(297), 739(296), 740(297), *817*

Onaka, S., 921(182), *929*

Ophius, B. G., 956(138), *970*

Orchin, M., 902(73), *926*

O'Rear, J. G., 131(106), *140*

Orgins, I., 275(115), *294*

Ormerzano, L., 132(335), *145*

Osipov, O. A., 117(399), 128(399), 129(399), *147*

Osipova, M. A., 131(375), 132(375), 133(375), *146*

Osipova, O. P., 923(15), *925*

Österman, Th., 607(58), 608(58), 612–616(58, 59), *622*
Otera, J., 129(400), *147*, 284(85), 287(85), *294*, 315(144c), 425(144c), *500*, 864(82), 866(82), *878*
Ouchi, A., 303(134a), 481(134a), *500*
Ovenstone, T. C. J., 998(61), *1005*

P

Pachavskaya, V. M., 308(135a), 351(135a), *500*
Pai, Y. L., 942(64), *968*
Palan, P. R., 159(85), 160(84, 85), 162(85), 168(84, 85), 169(84), 179–183(84, 85), 186(84), 187(84), 202(84), 205(84), 223(85), 232(85), 234(84), 243(84), *246*
Paliobagis, M. A., 310(73, 74, 75, 76), 335(73, 74, 75, 76), 391(74, 76), 444(74, 76), *497*, 938(105), 939(105), *969*
Palossy–Becker, K., 648(276), 697(267), *816*
Pande, K. C., 538(132), 571(132), 572(132), *587, 811*
Paneth, F., 8(180), *77*
Pang, M., 28(181), 65(181), 66(181), *77*, 304(145), 315(145), 357(145), 425(145), *501*
Pannell, K. H., 537(92b), *577*
Panov, E. M., 119(183), 122(183), *142*, 155(107), 157(107), 188(107), 208(337), 209(337, 338), 210(337), *246, 252*, 254(131), 261(108), 263(133), 264(55, 132, 133), *293, 294, 295*, 308(83a, 83b), 309(83a, 83b), 324(83a, 83b), 354(83a, 83b), 362(83a, 83b), 366(83a, 83b), 430(83a, 83b), *497*, 582(28a), *621*, 849(122), *879*
Papetti, S., 130(401), 131(407), 132(401), 133(401), *147*, 215(236), 216(236), *249, 818*
Parham, D. N., 959(69), *968*
Paribok, R. M., 977(39), *994*
Pariser, R., 744(14), *809*, 982(4), *994*
Parish, R. V., 14(182), *77*, 320(144d), 325(144d), 425(144d), 431(144d), *500*, 920(183, 184, 185), *929*

Parisi, G. I., 14(71), 17(71), 70(71), *74*, 664(169), 666(169), *813*
Parisi, H. I., 110(207), *142*
Parker, E., 130(331), 131(331), 132(330, 331), *145*, 185(195, 196), 186(915), 187(196), 189(195), *248*, 514(114, 115), 565(114, 115), *578*, 934(198), 937(198), *972*
Parker, Z., 737(251), *816*
Parnes, Z. N., 27(17), *72*
Parnev, Z. N., 277(13), *292*
Passino, H. J., 94(402), 132(402), *147*
Patil, H. R. H., 896–898(186, 187), 900(187), 918(186), *929*
Patmore, D. J., 104(403), *147*, 901(189, 191, 192, 193), 903(191, 192, 193), 904(132, 190), 906(132, 190), 907(190), 910(190, 191), 918(188, 190), *927, 929*
Patterson, D. B., 27(77), *74*
Paul, I., 899(59), 900(59, 87), 910(60), 913(60), 918(68, 87), 923(60), *926*
Paulik, F., 58(47), *73*, 119(121), *140*
Pauling, H., 114(491), *149*
Pauling, L., 113(404), *147*
Paulini, E., 945(51), *967*
Paulus, E. F., 325(63a), 434(63a), *497*
Pauly, S., 100(303), 105(303), 123(303), *145*
Pavlova, I. D., 104(317), 106(317), *145*
Payne, D. A., 329(70), 330(70), 463(70), *497*
Paynter, O. E., 950(90), *968*
Peach, M. E., 303(123a, 145a, 145b), 306(145a), 308(145a, 145b), 354(145a), 357(123a, 145a), 366–369(123a, 145a), 378(145a), *500, 501*
Peachy, S. J., 86(426), 93(423), 134(424, 425), 135(422), 136(421, 422), *148*
Peacock, R. D., 91(214), 94(215), 110(109), 131(214), 133(213), *140, 142*, 196(132), 197(132), *247*, 279(40), 286(40), *293*, 628(171), 633(171), 664(74), *811, 813*
Pearson, S. M., 904(166), 906(165), *928*
Pedain, J. A., 11(155), 15(156), 16(156), 18(157), 35(156), 60(157), 61(156), 71(157), *76*, 97(387a), 137(387a), *147*, 185(220), 189(220), *249*, 833(73, 74, 75), 835(75), 836(75), 840–843(73, 74, 75), 845(73), 849(74), 850(74), 852(73), 853(73), 860(73), 861(73), *878*

Peddle, G. J. D., 107(405), *147*, 317(62), 430(62), *496*
Pedinoff, M. E., 665(298), *817*
Pedley, J. B., 91(407), 117(406, 407), *147*, 524(11), 524, 536 (10, 11, 94), *575, 577*
Pelczar, F. A., 685(209), *814*
Pelissier, J. P., 957(199), *972*
Pellegrini, J. P., 647(299), 747(299), *817*
Pekola, J., 998(21, 22), *1004*
Penfold, B. R., 113(141), *141*
Pepe, A., 999(83), *1006*
Pereyre, M., 10(10*a*), 27(208), 51(183, 185), 52(182*a*, 182*b*, 184), 53(184), *72, 77, 78*, 157(238), 158(237, 314), 163(315), 167(239, 240), 180(237, 314), 181(237, 238, 240, 314), 182(237, 238, 239), 216(27), 217(27), 227(27, 247), *244, 249, 250, 252*, 636(369), 640(303), 642(300, 369), 643(305), 647(304), 654(302), 678(369), 679(369), 681(369), 736(302, 303), 737(303), 739(369), 740(301, 302, 304, 305), 741(300, 302, 305), 742(305), *817, 819*
Pericante, V. A., 646(213), 661(213), 672(213), 673(213), 793(213), 794(213), 800(213), *814*
Perkins, N. A., 137(61), *139*
Person, M., 118(124), *140*
Peruzzo, V., 861(81*a*), *878*
Peterson, E., 526(123), 543(123), *578*, 825(76), 835(76), 856(76), 858(76), 865(76), *878*
Peterson, W. G., 184(103), 185(103), 186(103), 187(103), 189(103), *246*
Petillon, F., 540(216), *580*
Petridis, D., 309(145*c*), 482(145*c*), 483(145*c*), *501*
Petrii, O. P., 224(191), 228(191), 239(191), *248*, 716(248), 722(248), *816*
Petrov, A. A., 45(135, 135*a*, 260), *75, 79*, 637(454), 638(455, 456), 658(455), 695(307, 452, 453, 454, 456), 703(307), 716(307, 453), 719–724(306, 307, 372, 451, 453, 454, 455, 456), 732(453, 456), 744(456), *817, 819, 822*, 868(121), *879*
Petrova, V. N., 49(245a), *79*, 159(295), 175(295, 319), 176(295), *251, 252*, 644(435), 658(435), 714(380*a*, 435), 716(380*a*, 435), 719(435), 721(382,

383), 722(435), 724(383), 725(383), *819, 820, 821*
Petrovskaya, L. I., 704(294), 736(294), *817*
Petukhov, V. A., 664(375), 678(308), 689(308), *817, 819*
Petzoldt, K., 960(201), *972*
Pezarro, S., 402(124), *500*, 935(171), *971*
Pfeiffer, P., 92(411), 93(413, 416), 95(410, 412), 125(531), 130(412, 531), 132(409, 410, 411, 413, 414, 415, 531), 134(412, 413, 414), *147, 150*, 203(241), 205(241), *250*, 320(148), 325(147, 148), 333(146), 430(148), 434(147), 474(147), *501*, 873(82*a*), *878*
Phillips, J. R., 872(44*a*), *877*
Picco, D., 948(203), *972*
Pickard, A. L., 124(100), *140*, 268(22), 276(22), *292*
Picko's, R., 155(242), *250*
Pieper, G. R., 948(204), *972*
Pieters, A. J., 950(205), 952(205), 953(203), *972*
Pietropaola, R., 882(7), *924*
Pikina, E. I., 212(243), 215(243), *250*, 320(149), 325(149), 431(149), *501*
Pikina, E. J., 93(408), 133(408), 134(408), *147*
Pilloni, G., 629(417), *821*, 861(106*a*), 867(105), 870(105), *879*, 998(62), *1005*
Pinkerton, R. B., 963(88), *968*
Pinzelli, R., 45(45*a*), *73*
Pitchtchan, S., 100(304), 101(304), 105(304), 123(304), 128(304), *145*, 195(172), 196(172), 197(172), *248*, 284(59), *293*, 1002(85), *1006*
Plachinda, A. S., 664(147), *812*
Planchon, M., 697(91), *811*
Plaogna, G., 861(81*a*), *878*
Plapp, F. W., 949(134*a*, 205*a*), *970, 972*
Plate, N. A., 983(66), *995*
Platt, R. H., 14(182), *77*, 320(144*d*), 325(144*d*), 425(144*d*), 431(144*d*), *500*, 920(183, 184), *929*
Plazzongna, G., 861(106*a*), *879*, 998(62, 76), *1005, 1006*
Plotnikov, M. V., 111(7), *138*
Pneumaticakis, G. A., 896(160), 901(160), *928*
Pocques, J., 90(319), *145*
Pohl, R. L., 895(70, 71), 903(70, 7), *926*

Pohland, R., 86(295, 296), 93(296), 131(296), 133(296), *145*, 196(167), 197(166), 201(166), *248*, 873(51*a*), *877*, 883(156), *928*

Pohlmann, J. L. W., 646(310), 660(310), 671(310), 696(310), 747(310), 766(310), 767(310), 793(310), 796(310), 798(310), *817*

Polak, L. S., 109(5, 6), 111(7), *137*, *138*, 210(3), *243*, 257(2), 277(2), 278(2), *292*, 325(20, 21), 430(20), *495*, 626(4), 664(189, 190), 689(4), *809*, *814*, 921(141), *928*

Poland, J. S., 521(95), 524(11), 525(93*a*, 95, 95*a*, 95*b*), 533(93*a*), 536(11), 537(95*a*), 542(93*a*), 568(95*a*), 574(95), *575*, *577*, *928*

Polis, A., 85(417)k *147*

Pollak, J., 329(150), *501*

Pollard, F. H., 304(151), 309(151), *501*, 640(311, 312, 313), 664(312), 665(312), 677(312), 678(312, 313), 679(312), 681(311), 683(311), 693(311), 694(312), 703(312), 727(312, 313,) 728(312), 735(312), 736(312), 770(312, 313), 771(312), 775(312), 778(312), 804(313) *817*, *818*, 999(63), *1005*

Poller, R. C., 102(150, 418, 419), 126(420), *141*, *147*, 183(244), 197(245), 200(209), 201(245), 203(246), 205(209), 206(209, 201, 245), 208(209, 210, 245), 210(244), *249*, *250*, 261(73), 263(73), *293*, 298(155), 304(158), 306(158), 308(152), 313(152), 316(159), 318(152), 320–322(154, 159), 327–330(69, 153, 156, 157, 158), 357(152), 377(158), 378(158), 425(152), 430(152, 159), 431(159), 433(154), 437(69, 153, 156), 441(153, 156), 442(69, 153, 156), 454–459(69, 153, 156, 157), 461–463(153, 156), *497*, *501*, 510(133), 538(116), 553(116), 570(116), *578*, 634(257), *816*, *818*, 875(61), *877*, *878*, 882(194), *929*, 933(184, 205*b*), 946(106), 947(106), *969*, *971*, *972*, 1000(64), 1001(64), *1015*

Polster, R., 665(315, 316, 317), 783(315, 317, 318), *818*, 987(67), *995*

Pomeroy, R. K., 909(195), 913(195), *929*

Pommier, J. C., 52(21, 186, 234), *72*, *77*, *78*, 157(206), 162(249*a*), 164(51), 165(248), 181(51), 182(51, 248), 186(206), 187(249a), 188(249, 249*a*), 225(249), 227(247), *245* *249*, *250*, 540(217, 218), *580*

Panaras, A. A., 25(252), *79*

Ponomarev, S. V., 158(216, 254), 163(250, 251, 253), 170(253), 174(216), 175(190, 253, 254), 176(253, 254), 178(190, 252, 253, 254), 179(253), 185(250), 224(191), 228(109, 191), 238(190), 239(191, 250), *248*, *249*, *250*, 316(160), 424(160), *501*, 643(277), 645(320), 677(320), 703(320), 704(319), 716(248), 720(320), 722(248), 736(247, 276, 277), *816*, *818*

Pope, W. J., 86(426), 93(423), 134(424, 425), 135(422), 136(421, 422), *148*

Popoff, P., 117(443), 132(443), *148*

Portanova, R., 123(88, 89), *139*, *140*, 539(35), 572(35), *575*

Post, H. W., 86(155), 130(401), 131(401), 132(401), 133(401), *141*, *147*, 197(102), 212(102), 215(236), 216(236), *246*, *249*, 315(211), 318(211), 322(211), 324(211), 425(211), 428(211), 431–433(211), *502*, 646(23), 796(23, 24), *809*

Potschka, V., 303(161), 357(161), 372(161), *501*

Potter, P. E., 69(187), 70(187), 71(187), *77*

Pourcelot, G., 658(321), *818*

Poutsma, M. L., 20(52), *73*

Powell, D. L., 195(328), 196(328), 197(328), *252*

Powell, P., 328(161*a*), 374(161*a*), 437(161*a*), 442(161*a*), *501*, 914(196), *929*

Powick, W. C., 944(119), *969*

Prade, R., 132(415), *149*, 320(148), 325(148), 430(148), *501*

Prater, B. E., 922(6), *924*

Pratt, J. J. Jr., 946(42), *967*

Pratt, L., 69(187), 70(187), 71(187), *77*

Preobrazhenskaya, E. A., 998(5), *1004*

Price, J. W., 998(11), *1004*

Price, S. J. W., 117(428), 130(429), 131(429, 430), 132(427, 430), *148*

Prince, R. H., 856(38), *877*

Proesch, U., 664(172), *813*, 997(32), 999(65), *1005*
Prokofiev, A. K., 107(259), *144*, 515(83), 535(83), 542(83), 548(83), *577*, 540(228), *580*, 637(203), 639(203), 664(193), 675(193, 203, 204), 676(193, 203, 204), 701–704(193, 204), 731(202), *814*
Prokai, B., 258(103), *294*, 298(119), *499*, 512(96), 517(96), 522(96), 533(96), *577*, 582(31), *621*, 675(360), *819*
Proskurnina, M. V., 179(255), *250*, 704(294), 736(294), *817*
Protzenko, N. P., 49(85*a*), *74*
Pryor, W. A., 20(188), *77*
Ptitsyna, O. A., 127(441), 133(383), 134(441), *147*, *148*, 212(256), 257, *250*
Pu, H., 999(66), *1005*
Puchinyan, E. A., 196(258), *250*
Puckett, J. C., 105(77), *139*
Puddephatt, R. J., 313(60*a*), 325(60*a*), 418(60*a*), 419(60*a*), 426(60*a*), 430(60*a*), 433(60*a*), *496*
Pudovic, A. N., 120(16), 130(16), 132(16), *138*, 288(86), 291(86), *294*, 581(7), 586(37), *621*, *622*
Pusyruva, W. P., 869(45*b*), *877*
Putnam, R. C., 678(322, 323, 324), 680(322, 323), 683(322, 323, 324), 697(324), *818*, 999(66), *1005*
Puzyreva, W. P., 89(279), 92(279), 132(279), *144*, *147*
Pyszora, H., 510(97), 537(97), 538(97), *577*

Q

Quattlebaum, W. M., Jr., 934(206), *972*
Queignec, R., 720(446), *822*
Quintin, C., *148*

R

Raab, G., 37(210), 60(210), *77*, 163(286), 179(286), 203(286), 204(286), *251*
Raas, R. G., 100(74), 102(74), *139*
Rabet, F., 540(229), *580*
Rabinovich, I. B., 774(422), 671(422), *821* 826(82*b*, 82*c*), *878*

Racah, E. J., 25(252), *79*
Radbil, B. A., 173(4), 209(259), 221(5, 6), *244*, *250*, 626(7), 664(7), *809*, 855(2), 863(2, 3), *976*
Radecki, A., 155(242), *250*
Rademacher, B., 953(36), *967*
Rahman, W., 25(189), 41(100), 43(100), 44(100), *74*, *77*, 644(208), 678(208), 680(208), 689(208), 691(208), 692(208), *814*
Raitzyn, I., 94(108), *140*
Ramaiah, K., 164(260), *250*
Ramsden, H. E., 131(432), 133(432), 134(432), 135(432, 447), 136(432, 447), *148*, 161(261), *250*, 667(325), 772(325), 785(325), *818*
Ramsey, N. F., 13(190), *77*, 100(67), *1005*
Ranby, P. W., 965(207), *972*
Randall, E. W., 225(345), *252*, 511(135), 516(137), 534(134), 535(136, 137, 138, 139), 536(136), 542–545(134, 136, 137, 138), *578*, *622*
Rao, U. V., 26(178, 178*a*), *77*
Rashkes, A. M., 195(200), *249*
Rathman, H., 957(208), *972*
Rausch, M. D., 646(326), 647(326), 798(326), *818*
Ravner, H., 131(106), *140*
Razuvaev, G. A., 64(248*a*, 248*b*, 249, 250, 250*a*), *79*, 90(437, 438), 131(434, 435), 133(433), 136(433), *148*, 172(263, 264, 320, 321, 323), 173(322), 175(263), 176(264), 187(262), 204(262), 209(262), 224(324), *250*, *252*, 261(87), 263(88), 264(88, 121), *294*, 298(161*c*, 227*f*), 320(65), 317(161*b*), 344(65), 346(65), 426(65), 429(65), 491(65), 494(65), *497*, *501*, *504*, 582(37*b*, 70*c*, 70*d*), 616–619(17, 29, 29*a*, 70*c*, 71, 72), *621–623*, 629(329), 633(327, 328, 329, 438), 664(327, 437, 438), 665(438), *818*, *821*, 826(82*b*, 82*c*), 832(83, 84, 85), 850(82*d*), 858(83, 87), 859(116), 865(86, 116), 867(83, 87), 873(86), *878*, *879*, 881(224), 882(224), 885(224), 886(106), 889(224), 890(221, 223), 896(224), *927*, *930*
Reddy, M. L. N., 304(105*a*), 378(105*a*), *499*, 629(72), 671(72), 672(72), *811*
Redl, G., 107(405), *147*

Redman, H. E., 84(550), 118(550), 130(550), 131(550), 132(550), *151, 151*, 212(341), *252*

Reed, D. K., 949(209), *972*

Rees, G., 960(210), *972*

Rees, R. G., 107(158), *141*, 155(104), 156(48), 161(265) 184–187(48, 104, 265), 189(48, 104), 202(265), *245, 246, 250*, 270(35), 271(35), 273(35), 279(34), 284(15), 286(34), *292*, 1001(9), 1002(10), *1004*

Reeves, L. W., 38(27, 28), *72, 77*, 106(96), 107(220), 108(220), 120(220), *140, 143*, 314(92b), 320(92b), 325(92b), 415(92b), 418(92b), 425(92b), 430(92b), 431(92b), *498*

Reffy, J., 648(267), 684(268), 697(267), *816*

Reich, P., 596(19), 598(19), 605(19), 606(19), *621*

Reichle, W. T., 14(72), *74*, 86(439), 91(439), 93(439), 107(439), 110(209, 439), 111(209, 439), 121(209), 128(209), *142, 148*, 196(267), 210(266), 212(266), *250*, 257(89), 269(38, 39), 275(38, 89), *292, 294*, 314(162, 165), 315(164), 320(89, 162, 163), 321(164), 348(89), 365(162), 424(164), 425(89, 162, 164, 165), 430(162, 164), 431(162, 164), *498, 501*, 535(63), 537(63, 140, 141), 568(63, 140, 141), *576, 578*, 668(330), *813, 818*

Reifenberg, G. H., 8(190c), 39(190b), *77*, 87(440), *149*, 196(268), 205(268), *250*, 265(90), 275(90), *294*, 309(166), 320(166), 404(166), 433(166), *501*, 627(332), 647(331), 664(332), 665(331a), 665(331a), 759(331), *818*

Reiff, H. F., 317(168a), 323(168a), 336(168a), *501*

Reiss, E., 170(312), 180(312), 181(312), 182(312), *251*, 533(183), 544(183), *579*

Reiss, W., 658(160), 695(160), 751(160), 753(160), 754(160), *813*

Renwanz, G., 87(298), 93(298), *145*

Resnick, P., 12(45), 42(45), *93*, 647(90), 760–762(90), *811*

Reuss, U., 960(201), *972*

Reutov, O. A., 127(441), 133(383), 134(441), *147, 148*, 212(256, 257), *250*

Reverchon, R., 998(68), *1005*

Reznikova, E. B., 194(155), 218(155), *247*

Riccoboni, L., 106(442), 117(443), 132(443), *148*

Richardson, B. A., 947(211), 955(211), 956(211a), *972*

Ridder, J. J., 664(93), *811*

Ridenour, R. E., 67(190d), *77*

Rieber, N., 317(181a), *502*

Rieche, A., 190(269, 273), 191(273), 193(269, 170, 273), 194(273), 220(271, 272, 273), 221(273), *250*, 336(167, 168), *501*

Rieger, R., 511(187), 513(187), 514(187), 541(187), 543(187), 545(187), 546(187), 547(187), *579*

Riethmayer, S. A., 298(169, 170), 329(170), 335(170), 450(170), 452(170), 467(170), *501*, 932(212), *972*

Rijkens, F., 90(329), *146*, 510(113), *578*, 631(244), 637(333), 651(333), 703(333), 704(333), 706(333), *815, 818*, 941(147), 942(147), 943(147), *970*

Riley, P. N. K., 536(94), *577*

Rioux, J. A., 946(115), *967, 969*

Risem, W. M., 918(226), *930*

Roberts, R. M. G., 678(335), 710(334), 742(334), *818*

Robinson, G. C., 84(550), 118(550), 130(550), 131(550), 132(550), *151*, 212(341), *252*

Robinson, M., 130(21), *138*

Robinson, R. E., 94(388), *147*

Robinson, S. A., 646(442), 801(442), *821*

Robinson, W. B., 86(70), 131(70), 133(70), *139*

Robinson, W. R., 520(27), 553(27), *575*

Rochev, V. I., 110(180), 112(179), 120(179), *142*, 308(135a), 351(135a), *500*, 887(111), 920(111), *927*, 1004(27), *1005*

Rochow, E. G., 83(483, 484, 529), 84(484), 85(484), 93(469), 95(484), 100(398), 117(532), 122(398), 123(510), 130–136(175, 396, 444, 469, 483, 484, 509, 510, 529, 532), *142, 147, 148, 149, 150*, 204(45, 231, 274), 208(45), 214(45, 231), 215(308), 217(308), *245, 249, 250, 251*, 254(84), 259(84), 263(81), 264(81), 278(91), *293, 294*, 320(82), 324(42), 430(42, 82), *496*,

497, 538(142), 570(142), 571(162),
572(162), 574(35*a*), *575*, *578*, *579*,
821, 998(57), 999(58), 1000(58), *1005*
Rogachev, B. G., 158(254), 175(254),
176(254), 178(254), *250*
Rogoff, W. M., 947(213), *972*
Rogozev, B. I., 625(26), *809*
Rokhlina, E. M., 303(107*a*), 308(135*a*),
351(107*a*, 135*a*), 357(107*a*), *499*,
500
Römer, R., 10(7), *72*
Roncucci, L., 183(275), 189(275), 190(96),
246, *250*, 279(10, 92, 93), 281(29),
286(92), 287(29), *292*, *294*
Ronecker, S., 886(199), 890(199), *929*
Rones, G., 948(25), *966*
Roper, W. R., 128(149), *141*, *926*
Rösch, L., 585(59*a*), 589(59*a*, 69*a*, 69*c*),
592(59*a*), 595(59*a*, 69*a*, 66*c*),
596(59*a*, 69*a*), 597(59*a*), 602(59*a*,
69*a*, 69*c*), 605(59*a*, 69*a*, 69*c*), 606(59*a*,
69*a*, 69*c*), *622*, *623*
Rose, M. S., 951(214), *966*, *972*
Rosenberg, E., 110(119), 112(119), 128(119),
140
Rosenberg, S. D., 8(74), *74*, 82(221),
86(445), 87(445, 446), 90(446),
91(221, 446), 92(221), 93(221),
131–136(174, 221, 445, 446, 447), *142*,
143, *147*, 154(137), 174(137),
176(137), 179(137), 195(137), 196(276),
197(137), 212(137, 276), 215(137),
247, *250*, 253(42), *293*, 298(93), *498*,
581(23), 598(23), *621*, 626(181),
628(181), 629(181), 633(181), 641(181),
664–670(181), 675–679(181), 681(181),
684(181), 685(181), 687–689(181),
701–704(181), 706–709(181),
711–713(181), 725(181), 727–731(181),
734–737(181), 739–744(181), 746(181),
748–755(181), 770–773(181), 775(181),
776(181), 778(181), 780–786(181),
789(181), 791(181), 804(181), 805(191),
813, 824(41), 826(41), 833(41),
834(36*a*), 860(41), 862(41), 863(36*a*),
864(41), 865(41), 869(36), *877*,
881(135), 883(101, 102, 104), 886(104),
888(94, 101, 102), 889(94, 101, 102),
927, *928*, 933(142), 949(142), *970*,
997(32), 998(26), *1005*

Ross, A., 97(158*b*), 137(158*b*), *141*,
161(58), 195(175, 176), 196(59),
197(175), 200(58, 105), 201(105),
202(58, 105), 205(58), 206(58), *245*,
246, 303(47), 315(47), 369(47), *496*,
846(31), 847(31), 850(31), 870(31),
876, 935(215), 963(215), 964(215),
972, 998(40), 1002(40), *1005*
Ross, D. S., 540(205), *580*
Rossetto, F., 987(8), *994*
Roth, A., 316(200), 336(200), 338(200),
425(200), 476(200), *502*, 519(156),
533(156), 535(156), 540(226),
553(156), 566(156), *578*, *580*, 584(60),
590(50), 591(50), 592(50), 594(50, 60),
595(621, 62*a*), 596(50), 598(50, 60),
605(50), 608–613(61–62*a*), *622*
Rothmann, L. A., 27(91, 92), *77*, *148*
Rothstein, E., 133(91), *140*
Roubineau, A., 540(217, 218), *580*
Rubinchik, G. F., 86(448), *148*, 646(337),
752(337), 756(337), 778(336), 780(336),
785(336), 788(336), 790(336, 338),
818
Rübsamen, K., 65(158, 158*a*, 158*b*),
76, 865(77), *878*
Ruddick, J. N. R., 920(124), *927*
Rudner, B., 986(68), *995*
Rudnevskii, N. K., 102(524), *150*,
284(122), *294*, 1002(85), *1006*
Rudolph, R. W., 885(220), 886(220), *930*
Ruf, H., 340(192, 193), 491(192, 193),
502
Ruff, J. K., 307(170*a*), *501*, 904(197),
907(197), *929*
Rugg, F. M., 964(55), *967*
Rugheimer, L., *878*
Ruidisch, I., 106(460), *148*, 219(277),
220(277), *251*, 298(172), 315(171),
317(171, 173), 318(173), 320(171, 173,
188), 341(174), 342(174), 344(171, 174,
188), 424(188), 429(171, 173, 188),
491(174, 188), *501*, *502*, 515(154),
535(154), 555(154), *578*, 582(38), *622*
Rulewicz, G., 627(47*a*), 665(47*a*), *810*
Rundle, R. E., 11(179), *77*, 833(81),
841(81), 843(81), *878*, 1004(55), *1005*
Rupprecht, H., 14(104), 70(104), 71(104),
75
Rush, J. J., 129(449), *148*

Russel, P., 957(216), *972*
Russell, G. A., 22(192*a*), *77*
Rust, J. B., 983(69), 984(69), 991(69), 992(78), *995*
Rutgers, J. J., 131(43), *138*, 824(12), 831(12), 840(12), 846(12), 859(12), *876*
Ryan, G., 27(18, 19), *72*
Ryan, M. T., 104(200), *142*
Rybakova, N. A., 303(175), 366(175), *501*
Rzaev, Z. M., 980(70), *995*

S

Sacco, A., 130(450), 132(335), *145*, *148*, 581(33), 598(33), *621*
Sacher, R. E., 670(339), *818*
Saegusa, T., 65(193), *77*
Saeleva, I. S., 95(376), 133(376), *146*
Safonova, M. K., 173(42), 176(43), 183(43), *245*
Saikina, M. K., 118(512), 130(451, 512), 131(451), 132(451, 512), 134(451), *148*, *150*
Saito, T., 16(84), 17(84), 61(84), *74*, 104(241), 107(241), *143*, 1001(35), 1003(35), *1005*
Sajus, L., 87(235), *143*, 630(186), 665(186), *814*
Sakai, S., 8(75*a*), *74*, 169(138), 174(138), 176(138), 224(138), *247*, 298(95), 303(175*a*), 311(175*a*), 315(94, 175*a*) 424(94), *498*, *501*, 533(68, 69), 539(68), 543(69), 553(68), *576*, 582(25), *621*
Sakanaka, Y., 744(261), *816*
Salazar, R. W., 614(2, 3), 616(2, 3), *620*
Salquain, J., 956(217), *972*
Sams, J. R., 904(67), 921(161), 922(161), *926*, *928*
Sandler, S. R., 966(72), *968*, 982(71, 72), *995*
Sanford, E., 22(254), *79*
Sanger, G., 960(135, 136), *970*
Sanina, L. P., 63(15*a*, 247), 64(15*a*, 246*a*, 246*c*, 247), 65(246*b*), *72*, *79*, 315–317(36*b*, 225, 226, 227, 227*a*, 227*b*, 227*c*, 227*d*), 320(36*b*), 336(227), 341(225, 226, 227, 227*b*, 227*g*), 342(36*b*, 227*a*, 227*b*, 227*g*),

345(36*b*, 225, 226, 227*c*, 227*g*), 346(227*a*, 227*b*, 227*g*), 424(36*b*, 225, 227, 227*a*, 227*b*), 429(226, 227*c*, 227*d*), 474(227), 491(36*b*, 225, 227, 227*a*, 227*b*), 492(226, 227), 494(36*b*, 225, 226, 227, 227*a*, 227*b*, 222*c*, 227*g*), *496*, *503*, *504*, 615(73), *623*, 864(113), *879*
Sano, H., 110(495, 496), 111(495), 112(496), *149*, 649(413), 664(413), 695(413), *821*, 921(182), *929*
Sarafidis, C., *819*
Sasaki, A., 298(175*c*), 303(175*b*, 175*c*), *501*, *502*
Sasaki, Y., 921(182), *929*
Sasin, G. S., 128(452), 130(452), *148*, 159(278), 176(278, 279), 179(279), *251*, 303(176, 177, 178, 179), 304(176, 177), 306(177), 314(176), 351(176, 177, 179), 353(177, 178), 366(177), 424(176), *502*
Sasin, R., 176(279), 179(279), *251*, 303(177, 178, 179), 304(177), 306(177), 351(177, 179), 353(177, 178), 366(177), *502*
Sasse, K., 303(180), 327(180), 344(180), 350(180), 352(180), 353(180), 355–357(180), 442(180), *502*
Sata, Y., 63(211), *78*
Satchell, D. P. N., 127(361), *146*, 290(72), *293*
Satchell, R. S., 290(72), *293*
Sato, H., 202(234), 204(234), 205(234), 216(234), 217(234), *249*, 256(95), 259(95), 274(95), 277(82), *293*, *294*
Sato, R., 35(179*a*), *77*, 739(296), *817*
Saunders, A. E., 960(220), 963(220), 965(219), *972*
Saunders, B. C., 132(206), *142*, 952(178), *971*
Savidan, L., 102(453), 132(453), *148*
Savitskii, A. V., 632(339*a*), *818*
Sawodny, W., 535(28), 547(28), *575*
Sawyer, A. K., 10(198), 11(101), 15(196, 197, 199, 201, 203), 16(197, 198, 201), 17(197, 200), 54(194), 57(197), 58(199, 202, 203), 60(194), 61(195, 196, 197, 199, 201, 203, 204), 62(195), 63(195, 196), 69(198), 70(195, 196, 197, 198), 71(196, 198), *74*, *77*, 97(158*b*, 456*a*), 107(454, 455,

456), 137 (158*b*, 455 456*a*), *141*, *148*, 200(105), 201(105), 202(105), *246*, *251*, 262(97), 263(96, 97, 98, 99), 264(96, 99), 267(96, 98, 99), *294*, 520(85), *577*, 828(89, 90), 832–837(54, 89, 90, 90*a*), 842(93), 846–850(31, 54, 92, 93, 95, 96, 97, 98), 853(54), 854(96), 859(97), 860(97), 864(91, 94, 95, 97), 866(54), 868(96), 870(31, 91, 96, 98), 875(93), *876–878*, 1001(69, 70), *1005*, *1006*

Sayre, R., 117(457), *148*, 308(181), 329(181), 350(181), 351(181), *502*

Schaeffer, H., 885(181), 886(181), 889(181), 892(181), *929*

Schauer, E., 316(200), 336(200), 338(200), 425(200), 476(200), *502*, 590–592(50), 594(50), 596(50), 598(50), 605(50), *622*

Scheer, H., 16(59, 60), *73*, 834(30), 853(30), *876*, 998(23), *1004*

Scherer, H., 325(63*a*), 434(63*a*), *497*

Scherer, P. C., 8(24), *72*, 100(94), 131(94), *140*, 200(52), 201(52), *245*, 887(49), *925*

Scherer, O. J., 513–515(143–150), 523(145), 528(148), 535(145, 147, 148, 149), 539(219), 540(220), 542(148), 545(147), 553(146), 555–558(143–150), *578*, *580*, 589(41*b*, 42), 599(42, 43), *622*

Schieder, G., 589(42, 43), 599(42), *622*

Schiffner, H., 130(27), 131(27), *138*

Schik, R., 128(387), *147*

Schindlbauer, H., 583(44), 597(44), 600(44), *622*

Schlemper, E. D., 279(100), *294*

Schlemper, E. O., 112(458, 459), 129(459), *148*, 537(150*a*), *578*, 649(340), 695(340), *818*

Schlesinger, H. J., 8(53), *73*

Schlötting, O., *145*

Schmid, D., 526(151), 544(151), 546(151), *578*

Schmid, G., 885(181), 886(181), 889(181), 892(181), *929*

Schmidbaur, H., 106(460), *148*, 215–220(281–284), 227(282), *251*, 298(172), 320(188), 344(188), 424(188), 429(188), 491(188), *501*, *502*, 515(152), 535(152), 537(153), 555(152), 568(152, 153), 569(153), *578*, *580*, 582(38), *622*, 677(341), 679(341), *818*

Schmidt, D., 857(99), *879*

Schmidt, H., 265(101), *294*

Schmidt, J. F., 514(146), 515(147), 528(146), 535(147), 542(146), 545(147), 553(146), 555(146), 557(147), *578*

Schmidt, M., 219(277), 220(277), *251*, 298(189, 190, 203), 303–307(191, 201, 202), 311–313(191*a*, 196*a*, 201, 205, 206, 207), 315(205, 206, 209, 210), 316(202), 317(173, 174), 318(173, 204, 206), 319(204), 320(173), 321(191, 202), 323(194), 324(196), 326–328(194, 230, 231), 330(229, 230, 231), 336(194, 202), 337(205, 206, 207), 340(192, 193, 205, 208), 341(174, 191, 195, 209, 210), 342(174), 343(204), 344(174), 345(205, 208, 209), 346(204), 347(204), 357(191), 358(201), 362(202), 373(191, 203), 413(205, 206), 415(203, 207), 416(191*a*, 196*a*), 417(191*a*, 196*a*), 421(201), 425(194, 203, 204, 206), 426(202), 429(173, 190, 203, 204, 205, 206, 209, 210), 430(191, 196, 203), 431(191, 194, 196, 203), 433(202), 434(194), 436(229), 441(231), 442(230), 470(194, 202), 474(203, 205, 206, 207), 491–494(174, 192, 193, 195, 203, 204, 205, 208, 209, 210), *501*, *502*, *504*, 514(146, 148, 149, 150), 515(147, 154), 528(146), 535(147–150, 154), 542(146), 545(147), 553(146), 555–557(146–150, 154), *578*, 582–584(53, 56, 57, 63, 64, 65, 66), 587(53, 54, 55, 64), 590(55, 56, 57, 65, 66), 592–602(51, 52, 56, 57, 64, 65, 66), 605–608(58, 63, 65, 66), 612–618(58, 59, 63, 64, 65), *522*, 634(342, 343, 344), 659(342, 343, 344), *818*

Schmidt, U., 12(205), *77*

Schmitz-Dumont, O., 540(221, 222), *580*

Schneider, B., 18(222), 36(151, 152, 206), 39(160), 60(159, 161, 221, 222), 61(161), *76*, *77*, *78*, 97(489*a*), 137(489*a*), *149*, 180(222), 197(222), 223(221, 222), *249*, 315(139), 317(139), 340(139), 342(139), 424(139), 491(139), *500*, 526(124, 125, 167, 168), 527(125, 167, 168), 547–547(124, 125, 167, 168), 553(125), *578*, *579*, 585(36),

593(36), 597(36), *622*, 665(285),
704(287), 706(287, 345), 707(287, 288),
709(287), 710(287), 720(285), 728(345),
737(345), 742(287, 345), 743(287),
748(345), 749(345), 783–785(287, 288,
345), 788(287, 288), *817*, *818*,
828(78, 104), 829(78, 103, 104),
834–838(78, 79, 103, 104), 846(104),
849(104), 850(104), 855(104), 868(104),
878, 890(179, 202), *929*, 986(62, 63), *995*
Schnurmann, K., 320(148), 325(148),
430(148), *501*
Schöllkopf, O., 664(346), *818*
Schöllkopf, U., 317(181*a*), *502*
Schrauzer, G. N., 905(198), 907(198), *929*
Schreiber, K. C., 22(258), *79*
Schroeder, H., *818*
Schroth, W., 329(92), 330(92), 336(92),
460(92), 464(92), 470(92), *498*
Schulz-Utermöhl, H., 961(22), *972*
Schumann, Chr., 14(48*a*), *73*
Schumann, H., 298(172, 198*a*, 203),
303–308(181*b*, 191, 197, 199, 201, 202),
311(196*a*, 199, 201, 205, 206),
312(199), 313(196*a*, 197, 199, 201,
206), 315(205, 206, 209, 210),
316(200, 202), 317(194, 197, 204*a*),
318(181*b*, 197, 204, 206), 319(204),
321(191, 202), 323(194, 198),
324(196, 198), 326(194), 336(194, 200,
202), 337(205, 206, 207), 338(200),
340–347(191, 195, 197, 204, 205, 208,
209, 210, 210*a*), 357(191), 358(199, 201),
362(202), 373(191, 203), 413(205, 206),
415(203, 207), 416(196*a*), 417(196*a*),
421(199, 201), 425(194, 200, 203,
204, 205, 206), 426(202), 429(181*b*, 203,
204, 205, 206, 209, 210), 430(191, 196,
198, 203), 431(191, 194, 196, 198, 203),
433(202), 434(194), 470(194, 202),
474(203, 205, 206, 207), 476(200),
491–494(195, 203, 204, 205, 208, 209,
210, 210*a*), *501*, *502*, 517(155),
519(156), 533(156), 535(156),
540(226), 566(155, 156), *578*, *580*
582–587(38, 45–48*c*, 53–57, 59*a*, 60,
63–66*a*), 589–602(19, 45–57, 59*a*, 60,
62, 62*a*, 64–70), 605–618(19, 45, 46,
46*a*, 48*a*, 48*b*, 50, 58, 59, 59*a*, 61–69*c*),
621, *622*, *623*, 634(342, 343, 344),

659(342, 343, 344), *818*, 886(199),
890(199), *929*
Schumann–Ruidisch, I., 317(204*a*), *502*,
513(157, 158), 515(157, 158),
535(157, 158), 555(157, 158), 556(158),
578, *579*
Schunn, R. A., 900(207), 902(207),
923(207), *929*
Schurmann, K., 93(416), 132(415), *147*
Schurter, J. J., 659(271), 660(271),
698(271), 699(271), 733(271), 734(271),
816
Schwabe, P., 316(200), 336(200), 338(200),
425(200), 476(200), *502*, 584(66, 66*a*),
586(65, 66*a*), 590–593(50, 65, 66, 66*a*),
596–599(50, 65, 66, 66*a*), 605(50, 65,
66, 66*a*), 606(66*a*), *622*
Schwartz, W. T., 315(211), 318(211),
322(211), 324(211), 425(211),
428(211), 431–433(211), *502*, 634(349),
705(349), 706(349), 737(349), 739(349),
775(349), 781(349), 783(349), *818*
Schwarz, R., 513(159), *579*
Sciot, M. T., 737(349*a*), 741(349*a*),
804(349*a*), 805(349*a*), 807(349*a*), *818*
Scofield, R. E., 61(204), *77*
Sealey, N. J., 110(151), 112(151), 126(151),
141
Seguin, H., 665(298), *817*
Seidler, H., 310(211*a*), 402(211*a*), *503*
Seidlitz, H. J., 310(80), *497*, 998(25), *1004*
Seifert, B., 510(82), 539(82), 573(82),
574(82), *577*
Selivokhin, P. I., *496*, 665(350), *819*
Seltzer, R., 327(211*b*), 423–425(211*b*),
435(211*b*), *503*
Selwood, P. W., 834(63), 856(62, 63),
868(62), *877*
Semchikova, G. S., 64(250*a*), *79*, 345(64*a*),
346(64*a*), 494(64*a*), *497*, 614–618(71,
72), *623*
Semin, G. K., 109(62, 461), *139*, *148*,
918(174), *929*
Semkina, E. P., 288(86), 291(86), *294*
Semlana, E. P., 586(37), *622*
Senior, B. J., 920(11), 922(11), *924*
Sequeira, R. M., 26(41), *73*
Sessions, W. V., 85(290), 130(290), *144*,
316(106), 424(106), *499*, 824(49),
856(49), 863(49), 864(49), 867(49),

870(49), *877*, 882(153), 887(153), 888(153), *928*

Seyferth, D., 8(209), 25(107, 212, 215), 27(208), 37(210), 60(210), 63(211), 68(209), *77*, *78*, 85–91(463, 464, 465, 466, 467, 471), 93(469), 119(468), 125(468), 127(468), 131–136(175, 444, 462–467, 469, 471, 472), *142*, *148*, *149*, 163(286), 179(286), 203(286), 204(274, 285), 212(284*a*, 287), 216(285), 217(284*a*, 285), 218(285), *250*, *251*, 258(103), 277(102), 278(91, 102), *294*, 298(184*a*, 185, 186, 187), 304(182), 309(183), 320(82, 184), 322(184), 336(184), 380(183), 430(82), 433(184), 471(184), *497*, *502*, 521(161), 548(142), 539(160), 570–573(142, 160, 161, 162, 163), *578*, *579*, 582(39, 40, 41), *622*, 636(359, 366, 369, 371), 638(362), 639(364), 340(362), 642(362, 369), 651(366), 357(352, 354), 359(364), 665(367*a*), 669(355, 358, 429), 675(356, 360, 362, 365, 366, 367, 368), 678(369), 679(359, 361, 369), 680(366), 681(369), 682(366), 685(364), 686(364), 689(351, 355, 358, 363*a*), 693(108, 363, 364, 370, 429), 694(364), 697(364), 698(108), 699(108), 705(366), 734(367*a*), 739(369), 770(359), 771(359), 782(367*a*), 797(364), *811*, *819*, 872(100, 101), *879*

Shamagina, O. P., 155(107), 157(107), 188(107), 208–210(337, 338), *246*, *252*, 264(132), *295*

Shames, M., 707(143), 708(142), *812*

Shapiro, H., 886(200), *929*

Shapiro, P., 9(132), 27(132), 28(132), 57(216), *75*, *78*, 269(104), 271(104), *294*

Sharanina, L. G., 638(456), 695(456), 720(372, 456), 721(372, 456), 723(456), 732(456), 744(456), *819*, *822*

Sharma, K. K., 648(183), 733(183), *813*

Sharp, D. W. A., 89(472a), 102(55), *139*, *149*

Shcheptkova, O. A., 173(264, 322), 176(264), 187(262), 204(262), 209(262), *250*, *252*, 261(87), 263(88), 264(88, 121), *294*, 633(327), 664(327),

818, 832(85), 858(87), 865(86), 867(87), 873(86), *878*

Sheaffer, B. L., 965(223), *973*

Sheldrick, G. M., 540(198, 199, 200, 223, 224), 573(199), *579*, *580*

Sheldrick, W. S., 540(223, 224), *580*

Sheline, R. K., 919(204), *929*

Sheppard, N., 512(56), *576*

Shergina, N. I., 720–722(373, 387), 724(373), 725(387), 746(373), 777(387), *819*, *820*

Sheverdina, N. J., 83(2, 3, 4, 280), 92(280), 132(2), *137*, *144*, 298(100*a*), *499*, 582(28*a*), *621*

Sheyanov, N. G., 664(6), *809*

Shi, Y., 8(75*a*), *74*

Shigorin, D. N., *812*

Shiihara, I., 10(67), 15(67), *74*, 216(128), 217(128), 227(128), *247*, 629(164), 677(164), *813*

Shiina, K., 646(374), 698(374), *819*

Shindo, M., 130(525), *150*, 262(124), 263(124), *295*, 315(212), 321(212), 324(212, 213), 325(212), 336(212), 338(212, 213), 425(212), 430(212, 213), 480(212, 213), *503*, 100(86), *1006*

Shiryaev, V. I., 664(375), *819*

Shlikhter, E. B., 664(189, 190), *814*

Shmidt, H. W., 94(227), *143*

Shorygin, P. P., 664(375), 678(308), 689(308), *817*, *819*

Shostakovskii, M. F., 84(312), 145, 155(291), 157(292), 159(295), 168(290), 175(288–292, 295), 176(288, 291, 292, 295), 178(156, 288), 180(288), 181(288), 223(293, 294), 225(290), *247*, *251*, 317(213*a*), 321(213*a*), *503*, 637(689), 640(390), 664(384, 390), 695(385), 706(390), 714(380*a*), 716(380*a*), 720–722(195, 377–380, 382, 383, 385, 387, 387*a*, 389, 391, 392, 393, 394), 724(379, 383, 385, 389), 725(383, 386, 387, 388, 389*a*, 390), 732(376, 385, 388, 389*a*, 393), 746(376, 385, 393, 394), 777(384, 387), 779(384), 787(384), *814*, *819*, *820*, 977(75), 979(73, 74), 983(76), *995*

Shpinel, V. S., 109(5, 6, 63), 111(7), *137*, *138*, 210(3), *243*, 257(2, 14), 277(2), 278(2), *292*, 325(105*b*),

430(105*b*), *499*, 626(4), 664(189), 689(4), *809*, *814*, 921(141), *928*

Shtyrkov, J. G., 664(147), *812*

Shukoff, J., 134(473), *149*

Shushunov, V. A., 132(369), *146*, 173(42, 296), 192(8), 203(296), 220(7, 8), 221(5, 6, 44), *244*, *245*, *251*, 626(7, 50), 664(7), *809*, *810*, 863(1, 3), *876*

Sichel, J. M., 664(395), 669(395), *820*

Sicree, A. J., 513(182), 533(182), 539(182), 553(182), 571(182), *579*

Siebert, H., 91(474), 103(475), *149*, 606(41*a*), *622*

Sieckhaus, J. F., *818*

Sijpesteijn, A. Kaars, 941–943(145, 146, 147, 149), *970*

Silk, T. A. G., 216(78), 217(78, 86), 219(78), 220(78), *245*, *246*

Sim, S-Y., 646(145), 671(145), 767(145), 799(145), *812*, 868(35), *877*, 882(105), 883(105), 889(95), *927*

Simmons, D. E., 130(127), 132(127), 134(127), *140*

Simmons, H. D., Jr., 25(207, 212), *77*

Simmons, I., 195(176), *248*

Simms, B. B., 217(91), *246*, 966(76), *968*

Simonnin, M. P., 648(397), 695(396, 397), *820*

Simons, P. B., 256(105), 257(106), *294*, 898(136), 899(136), 918(136), *928*

Simpson, W. B., 57(217), *78*, 269–271(1, 107), 273(1, 107), *292*, *294*

Singh, G., 689(363*a*), *819*

Sink, C. W., 102(135), *141*

Sisido, K., 20(218), *78*, 83(476, 479, 480), 92(478), 107(477), *149*, 511(164), 513(165), 514(164, 165), 522(164), 523(164, 165), 534(165), 542(165), 543(164), 544(164), 553(165), *579*, 628(401, 402), 640(401), 647(400), 649(400), 652(398), 656(398), 664(401), 665(402), 677(400), 679(400), 684(400), 688(398), 697(400), 701(400), 726(400), 728(399), 735(400), 754(400), 758(400), 770–772(400), 779(399), 793(400), 795(400), 806(400), *820*, 859(101*a*), 873(101*a*, 101*b*), 874(101*a*, 101*b*), *879*, 999(71, 72), *1006*

Sisler, H. H., 540(203, 204), *579*, *580*

Sjoeberg, B., 303(30*a*), 354(30*a*), *495*

Skeel, R. T., 998(73), *1006*

Skinner, H. A., 57(223), *78*, 91(407), 113(481), 117(406, 407), 130(481), 132(481), 133(481), *147*, *149*, 664(269, 403), 665(73, 269), 669(269), 678(73), 680(73), *811*, *816*, *820*, 833(29), 839(29), 852(29), 860(29), *876*

Sklyanova, A. M., 175(288), 176(288), 178(288), 180(288), 181(288), *251*, 640(390), 664(384, 390), 695(385), 702(390), 721(385), 722(392, 393), 724(385), 725(385, 390), 732(385, 393), 746(385, 393), 777(384), 779(384), 787(384), *820*

Skoldinov, A. P., 90(482), 132(482), 133(482), *149*

Skripkin, V. V., 304(24*a*), 305(135), 374(24*a*, 135), 433(135), *495*, *500*, 887(110), 900(171), 902(171), 911(171), 916(175), 917(175), 921(110), 923(12, 13, 14), *925*, *927*, *928*, *929*

Sladkov, A. M., 635(246*a*), 770(404), 773(246*a*), 774(245*a*, 246*a*), 781(152), 787(151, 246*a*), *813*, *815*, *820*, 987(51), *995*

Slovokhotova, N. A., 127(181), *142*, 155(107), 157(107), 188(107), 209(338), *246*, *252*, 261(108), 263(133), 264(132, 133), *294*, *295*

Smedal, H. S., 539(15), 573(15), *575*

Smirnov, Yu. D., 835(111), *879*

Smith, A., 132(175), *142*

Smith, A. C., Jr., 83(483, 484), 84(484), 85(484), 95(484), 130(484), 134(483, 484), 133(484), *149*, 204(274), *250*, 278(91), *294*, 380(82), 430(82), *497*, 538(142), 570(142), *578*

Smith, A. L., 102(485), *149*

Smith, A. W., 110(151), 112(151), 126(151), *141*

Smith, G. W., 664(405, 406), *820*

Smith, J. J., 964(55), *967*

Smith, P. J., *246*, 920(201), *929*

Smith, T. D., 853(102), *879*

Smith, T. A., 86(486), 90(486), 136(486), *149*, *251*

Smolyan, Z. S., 84(18), 120(18), *138*

Smyth, C. P., 114(394, 488, 489), 130(488), 131(488), 132(488), *147*, *149*

Soborovskii, L. Z., 304(43), 351(43), *496*, 514(26), *575*, 584(8, 9, 10), 598(8, 9, 10), *621*
Sokoloski, E. I., 94(501), *149*
Sokolov, N. A., 176(43), *245*
Sokolski, E. J., 868(107, 109), *879*, 882–884(209, 210, 211, 212), 889(210, 211, 212), *929*
Sokrio, A., 134(490), *149*, 212(298), 215(299), *251*
Solodovnikov, S. P., 684(407), *820*
Soloski, E. J., 9(227, 228, 229), *78*, 628(419), 661(419), 671(419), *821*
Sommer, L., 825(76), 835(76), 856(76), 858(76), 865(76), *878*
Sommer, R., 9(162), 18(157, 222), 35(153, 154), 36(102, 154, 219), 38(154), 39(137*a*, 163, 165, 167), 41(137*a*, 220), 42(164), 43(102, 219), 52(153, 167), 60(157, 161, 221, 222), 61(161, 162), 65(158, 158*a*, 158*b*), 67(166), 71(154, 157), *75*, *76*, *78*, 97(489*a*), 137(489*a*), *149*, 167(223), 180(222), 197(222), 223(222), *249*, 315(139), 317(139), 340(139), 342(139), 424(139), 491(139), *500*, 513(126), 515(126), 518(122, 127), 519(126), 523(166), 526(123, 125, 167, 168), 527(125, 167, 168), 529(166), 537(127), 540(215, 225), 543(123, 125, 167, 168), 544(122, 125, 167, 168), 545(125, 167, 168), 546(167), 547(168), 553(125), 573(126, 127, 166), *578*, *579*, *580*, 585(36), 593(36), 597(36), *622*, 634(286), 638(286), 642(286, 409), 665(285), 679–684(210, 409), 687(409), 706–709(284, 286), 711(286), 720(284, 285), 723(284), 741(286), 748(286), 752(286), 784(286), *814*, *817*, *821*, 828(104), 829(103, 104), 834–841(75, 79, 103, 104), 846(104), 849(104), 850(104), 855(104), 868(104), *878*, *879*, 890(179, 202), *929*
Sosnovsky, G., 220(300), *251*
Souchay, P., 118(124), *140*
Sowerby, D. B., 572(62), *576*
Spaght, M. E., 114(491), *149*
Spalding, T. R., 629(2), 630(2), 652(2), 653(2), 664(2), 665(2), *809*, 920(40), *925*

Sparman, H. W., 88(553), 131(553), *151*, 661(459), *822*
Spencer, D. D., 919(203), *929*
Spielman, R., 678(409*a*), 804(409*a*), 807(409*a*), *820*
Spielman, T. R., 869(16), *876*
Spies, H. W., 919(204), *929*
Spijkerman, J. J., 15(135*b*), *75*, 649(410), *821*
Spillman, J. A., 203(246), *250*, 304(158), 306(158), 316(159), 320–322(159), 327–330(156, 157, 158), 377(158), 378(158), 430(159), 431(159), 437(156), 441(156), 442(156), 454–459(156, 157), *501*
Spilners, I. J., 647(299), 747(299), *817*
Spinel, K. S., 325(20, 21), 430(20), *495*
Spiro, T. G., 882(205), *929*
Sprague, M. J., 539(9), 573(9), *575*
Sprecher, N., 110(367), 112(367), 119(492) 121(367), 124(367), 128(367), *146*, *149*, 298(81), *497*, *812*
Sproul, E. E., 960(135, 136), *970*
Sreenatham, B. R., 914(23), *925*
Srivastava, G., 530(98), 547(98), 574(98), *577*
Srivastava, O. P., 314(213*b*), 425(213*b*), *503*
Srivastava, R. C., 311(96*b*), *498*, 517(99), 522(99), 524(70*a*), 525(70*a*), 528(38*a*, 99), 532(38*a*, 99), 533(38*a*), 542(38*a*, 70*a*), *576*, *577*
Srivastava, T. N., 269(109), 273(109), 276(109), 277(109), 278(109), *294*, 314(213*b*, 214), 425(213*b*, 214), *503*, 537(169), 539(170, 171), 569–571(169, 170, 171), *579*, *973*
Srivastava, T. S., 102(293), 108(293), 109(293), 125(294), *149*
Srp, L., 308(44*a*), *496*
Stacey, G. J., 132(206), *142*
Stack, W. F., 57(223), *78*, 664(269), 665(269), 669(269), *816*
Stadnichuk, M. D., 304(215*b*), *503*
Stamm, W., 538(172), 570(172), *579*
Stapfer, C. H., 303(214*a*), 317(214*c*, 214*d*), 322(214*b*), 354(214*a*), 424(214*d*), *503*
Stark, K., 108(58), 117(58), *139*, 668(51) 664(51), *810*

Starkovsky, N. A., 50(77a), *74*
Staude, E., 885(229), 890(229), *930*
Staudinger, J. J. P., 180(60), 183(60), *245*
Stecher, O., 885(229), 890(229), *930*
Stecker, H., 957(226), *973*
Steele, D., 102(50), *141*, 330(69), 437(69), 442(69), 454(69), 457(69), *497*
Stein, A. A., 217(91), *246*, 966(76), *968*
Steingross, W., 658(411), 695(411), *821*
Steinmeyer, R. D., 664(412), 679(412), 771(412), *821*, 999(74), *1006*
Stelzer, O., 304(181b), 318(181b), 429(181b) *502*, 584–586(59a, 66a), 589(59a, 67–69c), 590(66a), 592(59a, 66a), 593(66a), 595(59a, 62, 62a, 67–69c), 596(59a, 66a, 67–69b), 598(66a), 597(59a, 66a), 599(66a), 602(59a, 67, 68, 69a, 69c), 605(59a, 66a, 67–69c), 606(59a, 66a, 67–69c), 610(62, 62a), *622, 623*
Stepanovich, A. M., 722(394), 746(394), *820*
Stern, A., 9(132, 225), 11(224), 27(132), 28(132), 37(224), *75, 78, 879*
Stiddard, M. H. B., 898(24), 899(24), 901(24), *925*
Stienstra, F., 303(30), 308(30), 376(30), 377(30), 378(30), *495*
Stöckler, H. A., 14(72), *74*, 110(208, 209, 495, 496), 111(209, 495), 112(496), 121(208, 209), 128(208, 209), *142, 149*, 269(38), 275(38), *292*, 320(89), 348(89), 425(89), *498*, 535(63), 537(63), 568(63), *576*, 649(413), 664(414), 666(167), 668(167), 695(413), *813, 821*
Stokely, P. F., 922(32), 923(32), *925*
Stone, F. G. A., 90(471), 131(471), 133(471), 134(471), 135(471), *149*, 212(287), *251*, 277(102), 278(102), *294*, 572(163), *579*, 872(44a), *876, 877*, 887(16), 896(206), 899(59), 900(57–59, 87, 148), 903(148), 904(16), 906(16), 908(57, 58), 910(60), 911(16, 147, 148), 913(60, 147, 148), 918(67, 87), 923(60), *925, 926, 929, 928*, 978(77), *995*
Stoneberg, R. L., 28(253a), *79*
Stoner, H. B., 930(30), 950(30, 227, 228), 951(30, 176, 228), 952(30, 31, 227, 228), *967, 971, 973*
Storey, I. F., 953(132), 954(132), *970*

Stork, G., 597(32), 598(32), 600(32), 612(32), *621*
Stotskaya, L. L., 964(229), *973*
Straner, G., 174(99), 182(99), 183(99), 189(99), 190(99), *246*, 287(31), *292*, 942(100), *969*
Straub, D. K., 334(67), 436(67), 437(67), 441(67), 454(67), 455(67), 457(67), 462(67), 463(67), *497*
Strecker, A., 132(497), *149*, 200(302), 204(301), *251*
Street, B. W., 951(4), *966*
Streitwieser, A., 525(174), *579*
Strommen, D. P., 537(176), 538(176), 568(176), 570(176), 571(176), *579*
Struchkov, Yu. T., 923(12–15), *925*
Strunin, B. N., *151*
Strunk, R. J., 21(255), 36(255), *79*
Stukan, R. A., 210(106), *246*, 308(83c), 314(83c), 320(83c, 83d), 325(83c), *498, 812*, 887(110), 921(110), *927*
Sturis, A., 303(214e), *503*
Sturrock, R. F., 943(133), 945(133), *970*
Styan, G. E., 23(44), 37(44), 46(43), 52(42), *73*, 165(63), 166(63), 174(63), 184(63), 186(63), *245*, 678(76), 689(76), 690(76), 691(76), 692(75), 718(76), 745(76), 787(75, 76), *811*, 871(24), *876*
Sugita, K., 185(232), 216(232), 217(232), 218(232), *249*
Sukhani, D., 223(303), *251*, 298(128a), 303(128, 128b, 215), 304(128, 215), 306(215), 327(215a), 354(128b), 359(215), 366–369(128b, 215), 377(128), 449(215a), 450(215a), 457(215a), *500, 503*
Suldin, B. A., *876*
Sul'din, B. V., 192(9, 11), 193(10), *244*
Sulimov, I. G., 304(215b), *503*
Sumakarova, T. N., 320(83d), *498*
Sundermeyer, W., 627(415), 628(416), 664(415), *821*
Sutcliffe, L. H., 649(112), 799(112), *812*
Sutton, L. E., 113(481), 130(481), 132(481), 133(481), *149*
Suvorora, A. V., 640(390), 664(390), 706(390), 722(392), 725(390), *820*
Suzdalev, I. P., 109(63), *139*, 257(14), *292*, 664(147), *812*

Suzuki, R., 636(366), 651(366), 669(358), 675(366), 680(366), 682(366), 689(358, 363a), 705(366), *819*
Suzuki, Y., 744(261), *816*
Swaddle, T. W., 637(39), 653(37), 655(37), 676(39), 684(37), 685(39), 712(37), *810*
Sweet, R. M., 900(207), 902(207), 923(208), *929*
Swiger, E. D., 108(498), 109(498), *149*
Symes, W. R., 167(89), 168(88, 89), 179(89), 180(89), 181(89), 182(89), 222(83), 232(83), 241(89), 242(89), *246*, 317(61), *496*, 520(55), 538(55), 552(55), 559–561(55), 563(55), 564(55), 570(55), 571(55), *576*, 643(86), 675(86), 735(87), *811*
Syrkin, Ya, K., 114(238), 130(238), 132(238), *143*, 632(339a), *818*
Syutkina, O. P., 119(183), 122(183), *142*, 263(133), 264(133), *295*, 308(83a, 83b), 309(83a, 83b), 324(83a, 83b), 354(83a, 83b), 362(83a, 83b), 366(83a, 83b), 430(83a, 83b), *497*
Szwarc, M., 23(51, 57), *73*

T

Taeymans, J. R., 708(142), *812*
Taft, R. W., Jr., 13(226), *78*
Tagliavini, G., 123(499, 500, 546), 128(499), *149*, *151*, 629(417), 701(109), 734(109), 736(109), *812*, *821*, 857(26, 27, 106); 861(81a, 104b, 106a), 867(104b), 870(104b), *876*, *878*, *879*, 987(8), *994*, 998(75, 76), *1006*
Taikova, N. K., 303(175), 366(175), *501*
Taimsalu, P., 100(502), 103(502), 105(503), 128(502), *149*, 1000(77), 1001(77), *1006*
Takahashi, Y., 303(134a), 481(134a), *500*
Takami, Y., 665(418), *821*
Takamizawa, M., 63(211), *78*
Takeda, Y., 83(479, 480), 129(504), *149*, 176(304), 178(304), *251*
Takimoto, H. H., 992(78), *995*
Takizawa, K., 20(218), *78*, 652(398), 658(398), 688(398), *820*
Talalaeva, T. V., 93(408), 133(408), 134(408), *147*, 212(243, 305), 215(243),

250, *251*, 320(149, 216), 325(149), 431(149, 216), 432(216), *501*, *503*
Talukdar, P. B., 515(57), *576*
Tamborski, C., 9(227, 228, 229), *78*, 94(501), 104(200), *142*, *149*, 513(14), 514(14), *575*, 628(419), 661(419), 671(419), *821*, 868(107, 109), *879*, 882–884(209, 210, 211, 212), 889(210, 211, 212), *929*
Tanaka, T., 12(85), 69(85), 70(85), 71(85), *74*, 100(542), 101(542), 108(244, 245, 247, 248, 349), 119(348), 120(349), 125(507), 126(281, 349, 505, 506), 128(542), 129(244–248, 400), 132(247), *143*, *144*, *146*, *147*, *149*, *150*, 184(148, 306, 313), 185(306, 313), 187(306), 189(313), 190(313), 208(307), 212(307), *247*, *251*, *252*, 279(113), 281–289(50–53, 57, 58, 69, 85, 110, 111, 112, 113, 117), 291(69, 110, 112), *293*, *294*, 298(216a), 313(90c, 91), 341(98a), 418–420(90c, 91), 493(98a), *498*, *503*, 582(70a), *623*, 1001(35), 1002(36, 37, 78, 79), 1003(35, 46), *1005*, *1006*
Tanberger, G., 278(114), *294*
Tandon, S. K., 269(109), 273(109), 276(109), 277(109), 278(109), *294*, 314(213b, 214), 425(213b, 214), *503*, 538(171), 570(171), 571(171), *579*, *973*
Taransenko, N. A., 540(228), *580*
Tarpishchev, Sh. I., 168(290), 175(290), 225(290), *251*, 637(389), 721(389), 722(389), 724(389), *820*
Tate, J. M., 125(41), *138*, 187(29), 189(29), *244*, 279(12), 286(12), *292*, 303(32), 304(32), 357(32), 373(32), *495*, 883(17), 887(17), 888(17), *925*
Tatlow, J. C., 91(214), 94(215), 131(214), 133(215), *142*, 196(132), 197(132), *247*, 279(40), 286(40), *293*, 628(171), 633(171), *813*
Tatlow, W. S., 215(308), 217(308), *251*
Tatrina, N. D., 127(441), 134(441), *148*
Taylor, J. M., 947(27), 955(277), *967*
Tchakirian, A., 95(508), 134(508), *150*
Teer, P. A., 132(136), *141*
Telnoi, V. I., 664(422), 671(422), *821*, 826(82b, 82c), *878*
Temkin, A. Ya., 111(7), *138*

Ter–Sarkisyan, E. M., 186(340), 209(340), 210(340), *252*, 261(134), 264(134), *295*

Tesi, G., 646(310), 660(310), 671(310), 696(310), 747(310), 766(310), 767(310), 769(310), 793(310), 796(310), 798(310), *817*

Testa, A. C., 67(231), *78*

Thacker, G. A., 308(227*k*), *504*

Thayer, J. S., 510(175, 180), 537(176, 177, 178, 179, 180), 538(176), 568(176, 177, 178), 569(179), 570(176), 571(176), 573(180), *579*

Theden, G., 955(61*b*), *968*

Thevarasa, M., 634(257), *816*, 875(61), *877*

Theisen, C. T., *499*

Thies, C., 205(309), 215(309), 216(309), 217(309), *251*

Thom, K. F., 311(205, 206, 207), 313(206), 315(205, 206, 209, 210), 318(206), 337(205, 206, 207), 340(205, 208), 341(209, 210), 345(205, 208, 209), 413(205, 206), 415(207), 425(205, 206), 429(205, 206, 209, 210), 474(205, 206, 207), 491–494(205, 208, 209, 210), *502*

Thomas, A. B., 123(510), 130(509, 510), 131(509, 510), 132(509, 510), *150*

Thomas, C. M., 937(177), 938(177), 939(177), *961*

Thomas, D. H., 660(28*a*), *809*

Thomas, I. M., 162(310), 200(310), *251*, 511(181), 513(181), 523(181), 547(181), *579*

Thomas, L. H., 90(232), 93(232), 130–134(232), *143*

Thompson, A. J., 328(217), 330(217), 437(217), *503*

Thompson, A. R., 64(50), *73*, 638(102), 646(102), 699(102), *811*

Thompson, J. A. J., 308(90*a*), 357(90*a*), *498*, 898(136, 213, 214), 899(136, 213, 214), 900(214), 901(214), 904(67), 918(136), *926*, *928*, *929*, *930*

Thompson, L. K., 909(75, 215), 912(75, 215), *926*, *930*

Thust, V., 627(47*a*), 665(47*a*), *810*

Tiger, R. P., 963(91), *968*

Tigner, J. R., 960(17, 230), *966*, *973*

Tillyaev, K. S., 748(423), 751(423), 754(423), 788(423), *821*

Tisdale, W. H., 959(87), *968*

Tobe, M. L., 896(160), 901(160), *928*

Tobias, R. S., 105(145, 356), 108(145, 356), 121(511), 123(145), *141*, *146*, *150*, 184(193), 189(193), 194(311), *248*, *251*, 270(70), 275(115), 279(71), 282(71), 287(71), *293*, *294*, 1000(49), *1005*

Tobin, M. C., 100(320), 117(321), 130(320), 132(320), *145*, 999(41), *1005*

Todd, L. J., 25(212), *78*

Toley, D. L. B., 126(420), *147*

Tolkmith, H., *252*

Tolstaya, T. P., 133(383), *147*

Tombe, F. J. A., 854(110), *879*

Tomilov, A. P., 86(236), *143*, 265(45), *293*, 628(187), 664(46, 187), 665(187), *810*, *814*, 835(111), *879*

Topart, J., 634(144*a*), 659(144*a*), 808(144*a*), *812*

Topchiev, A. V., 962(229), *973*

Torack, R. M., 951(231), *973*

Toropova, V. F., 118(512), 130(512), 132(512), *150*

Tränckner, H. J., 664(346), *818*

Travers, N. F., 64(111*a*), *75*

Travis, J. C., 920(55), *926*

Tredre, R. Ford, 945(101), *969*

Treichel, P. M., 89(512*a*), *150*, 629(424), *821*

Tremper, H. S., 48(21*a*), *72*

Treverton, J. A., 524(11), 536(10, 11), *575*, 646(103), 661(103), 697(103), *811*

Tricker, M. J., 920(11), 922(11), *924*

Trofimov, B. A., 721(391), *820*

Trotman–Dickenson, A. F., 117(428), 132(427), *148*

Trotter, J., 97(101), 101(101), 112(101, 102), 128(101, 102), *140*, 1000(16), *1004*

Trotter, W., 67(231), *78*

Trukhtanov, V. A., 210(106), *246*, 320(83*d*), *498*

Truskier, P., 132(415), *147*, 320(148), 325(148), 430(148), *501*

Tsai, J. H., 642(68), 643(69), 677–679(68, 69), 682(68), 689(68), *810*, *811*, 871(18, 19), 876, 898(50, 51), 915(50, 51), 917(50, 51), *925*, 1003(14), *1004*

Tsai, T. T., 57(232), 65(232*a*), *78*, 91(513), 92(513), *150*, 269(116),

271(116), 273(116), *294*, 513(182), 533(182), 539(182), 540(227), 553(182), 571(182), *579, 580*, 863(112), 865(112), 870(112), *879*

Tschakirian, A., 339(218), 493(218), *503*

Tseng, C. L., 65(233), *78*, 636(425), 642(425), 701(425), 735(425), 737(425), *820*

Tsou, K. C., 982(71, 72), *995*

Tucker, P. M., 900(87), 918(87), *926*

Tucker, W. P., 665(426), *821*

Tuong, T., 998(39), *1005*

Tuony, T., 132(260), *144*

Turchinskii, M. F., 133(383), *147*, 212(256, 257), *250*

Turler, M., 998(80), 999(80), *1006*

Turner, J. A., 329(70), 330(70), 463(70), *497*

Tuzi, T., 83(476), *149*

Twitchett, H. J., 161(135, 136), 188(136), 215(135), *247*

Tyfield, S. P., 308(5), 320(5), 347(5), 424(5), *495*

Tyminski, I. J., 39(54), 40(54), 42(54), 43(54), *73*, 679(114), 681(114), 682(114), 683(114), 685(114), 686(114), 687(114), *812*

Tzschach, A., 170(312), 180(312), 181(312), 182(312), *251*, 533(183), 544(183), *579*

U

Uden, P., 640(312), 664(312), 665(312), 677(312), 678(312), 679(312), 694(312), 701(312), 703(312), 727(312), 728(312), 735(312), 736(312), 770 (312), 771(312), 775(312), 778(312), *817*

Ueeda, R., 108(248), 129(248), *143*, 184(313), 185(313), 189(313), 190(313), 208(307), 212(307), *251, 252*, 281(117), 283(117), 287(117), *294*, 1002(79), *1006*

Uenaka, K., 284(49), 288(49), 290(49), 291(49), *293*, 1001(34), 1002(34), *1005*

Ugo, R., 311(39), 313(39), 337(37, 39), 338(38), 418(39), 419(39), 420(39), 421(39), 425(39), 475(37, 38), 476(37, 38), *496*, 887(19), 901(18),

906–908(18, 22), 911(18), 917(18), 918(216), *925, 930*

Uguagliati, P., 882(7), *924*

Uhde, W. J., 310(211*a*, 232*a*), 402(211*a*), *503, 504*

Ulbricht, K., 14(90*a*), 25(90*a*), *74*

Ulmer, S. W., 898(37), 904(37), *925*

Unterstenhöfer, G., 303(180), 327(180), 344(180), 350(180), 352(180), 353(180), 355–357(180), 442(180), *502*

Urch, D. S., 304(105*a*), 378(105a), *499*

Ursino, J. A., 628(214), 633(214), 646(214), 661(214), 672(214), 794(214), 801(214), *814*

V

Vahrenkamp, H., 107(325), *145*, 629(293), 648(242), 664(242), *815, 817*

Valade, J., 10(10*a*, 110*a*), 51(183, 185, 234), 52(21, 182*a*, 182*b*, 184, 186), 53(184), *72, 75, 77, 78*, 157(206, 238), 158(237, 314), 162–165(51, 248, 249*a*, 315), 167(239, 240), 179–182(51, 205, 237, 238, 239, 240, 248, 314), 186(205, 206), 187(249*a*), 188(249, 249*a*), 216(27), 217(27), 225(249), 227(27, 247), *244, 245, 249, 250, 252*, 640(303), 642(300), 643(305), 647(304), 654(302), 665(258), 736–738(302, 303, 305), 740(301, 302, 304, 305), 741(300, 302, 305), 742(305), *816, 817*, 884(158), *928*

Van Bost, J., 653(141), 678(141), *812*

Van de Vondel, D. F., 18(235), *78*, 303(219), 308(219, 221*a*), 365(219), 374(219), *503*

Van den Berghe, E. V., 90(36), 91(36), 99(38), 106(37), 107(37, 40), 108(34, 35, 36, 38, 39, 40), 115(37), 116(37), 122(34), 123(33, 34, 39, 40), 124(40), 125(39, 40), 127(34), *138*, 303(219), 308(219, 221*a*), 365(219), 374(219), *503*, 1003(4), *1004*

Van den Bulck, E., 729(427), *812, 821*

Vandendunghen, G., 659(271), 660(271), 698(271), 699(271), 733(271), 734(271), *816*

Van den Hurt, J. W. G., 634(92), *811*, 964(75), *968*

Van der Beek, G. F., 986(22), *994*

Van der Heide, R. F., 310(220, 221), *503*, 936(234, 235), *973*

Van der Kelen, G. P., 13(244), 18(235), *78, 79*, 90(36), 91(36), 99(38), 106(37, 249), 107(37, 40, 249, 514–519), 108(34, 35, 36, 38, 39, 40), 115(37, 249), 116(37), 122(34), 123(33, 34, 39, 40), 124(40), 125(39, 40), 127(34), *138, 143, 150*, 303(219), 308(219, 221a), 365(219), 374(219), *503*, 647(433), 648(431, 432, 433), 649(433), 664(430, 431, 433), 665(433), 667(431), 728(433), 729(433), 736(433), 758(433), 759(433), 778(433), *821*, 1003(4, 38, 81, 82), *1004, 1005, 1006*

Van der Kerk, G. J. M., 8(236, 238), 9(241, 242), 11(243), 19(172), 27(172), 34(174, 237, 239, 240), 35(240), 36(172), 37(172, 239, 240, 243), 38(174, 239), 39(128, 129, 173, 174, 175), 45(239), 46(124), 47(124), 48(121), 49(128, 129, 175), 50(172), 51(239), 52(239), 60(36), 63(31), 64(37, 230), *72, 75, 77, 78*, 82(328), 84(251), 86(254, 328), 87(254, 255, 257), 88(257), 91(250), 93(328), 94(138), 104(254, 255), 130–136(250, 251, 253–256, 328, 390), *141, 143, 144, 145, 147*, 171(225), 175–178(225, 316), 180(225), 182(225), 194(188), 195(188), 196(188, 189), 197(188, 189, 316, 317), 212(318), 223(225), *248, 249, 252*, 254(44), 257(118), 258(65), 265(119), *293, 294*, 298(125, 222a, 222b), 309(222), 314(126), 315(143), 424(126), 425(143), *500, 503*, 510(113), 514(77, 78, 109, 110), 520(70, 77, 78, 109, 110, 111), 521(112), 523(109), 526(46), 528(110), 529(70), 533(78, 109), 537(112), 443–551(78, 109, 110, 111, 112), 559(46), 564(77), 565(77, 110), 568(109, 112), *576–578, 582(70b), 623*, 634(92), 637(292, 333), 643(243), 645(243), 651(333), 654(292), 669(233), 678(227), 689–691(227), 695(243), 703(292, 333), 704(227, 292,

333), 706(333), 714–716(227), 720(243), 721(227), 728(22), 729(428), 730(227), 732(243), 746(243), 773(226), 776(226), 777(226), *811, 815, 817, 818, 821*, 831(23, 119, 120), 834(45a), 836–838(23), 840(119, 120), 854(110), 855(80), 862(45a), *876–879*, 884(65), 888(65), 892(74), *926*, 933(172), 935(237), 940(236), 941(173, 192, 238, 239), 942(146, 192), 943(146), 964(75), 966(168), *968, 970, 971, 973, 986*(65, 80), *995, 996, 1005*

Van der Want, G. M., 94(138), *141*

Van Egmond, J. C., *503*, 941(239), 952(239), *973*

Van Esch, G. J., 950(247), *973*

Vangindertaelen, A., 298(233), 304(233), 305(233), 306(233), 377(233), 378(233), *504*

Van Hooydonck, G., 116(216), *143*

Van Kien, L. K., 132(260), *144*, 998(39), *1005*

Van Lier, K. L., 953(255), *974*

Van Schoor, A., 181(139), *247*

Van Wazer, J. R., 90(184), 91(184), 108(184, 360), *142, 146*, 323(132), 325(132), 336(132), 430(132), *500*, 631(155), 651(155), 664(155), *813*

Varshavskii, S. L., 835(111), *879*

Vashkov, V. I., 197(157), *247*, 946(161), *971*

Vasil'ev, N. P., 175(24), *244*

Vasishtha, S. C., 159(85), 160(39, 85, 90), 162(85, 90), 168(85), 170(90), 179(85, 90), 180(90), 181(85, 90), 182(85), 183(85), 187(90), 223(85), 224(90), 228(39), 232(39, 85), 233(40, 90), 237(39, 90), 241(39), 243(40), *244, 246*, 311(36, 36a), 313(36), 315(36), 417(36), 422(36), 424(36, 36a), *496*, 518(25), 524(25), 531(25), 534(25), 538(25), 540(192), 561(25), 563(25), 573(25), *575, 579*

Vaska, L., 905(217, 218), *930*

Vasta, J. A., 254(8a), *292*, 303(24), 317(24), 424(24), *495*, 539(8), 570(8), 571(8), *575*

Vastine, F. D., 901(56), *926*

Vaughan, L. G., *78*, 657(354), 669(358, 429), 689(351, 358), 693(429), *819, 821*

Venezky, D. L., 298(223a), *503*

Ventura, J. J., *72*, 168(58), 186(57), 196(59), 200(58), 202(58), 205(58), 206(58), *245*, 303(47), 315(47), 369(47), *496*

Venturii, M. T., 905(38), *925*

Verbeek, F., 54(38), 60(38), 61(38), 62(38), 64(39), *73*, 306(50), *496*, 526(47), 527(47), 543(47), 552(47), 559(47), *576*, 593(14), *621*, 895(62), 908(62), 912(62), *926*

Verbeek, W., 627(415), 628(416), 664(415), *821*

Verdonck, L., 13(244), 18(235), *78, 79*, 107(40, 514–519), 108(40), 123(40), 124(40), 125(40), *138, 150*, 647(433), 648(431, 432, 433), 649(433), 664(430, 431, 433), 665(433), 667(431), 728(433), 729(433), 736(433), 758(433), 759(433), 778(433), *821*, 1003(81, 82), *1006*

Verdone, J. A., 118(305), *145*, 655(207), 679(207), *814*

Verity–Smith, H., 298(224), *503*, 933(244), 935(240–243, 245, 246), 936(241, 246), *973*

Verschuren, H. G., 950(247), *973*

Vidal, A., *967*

Viktorova, J. M., 127(181), *142*

Vilarem, M., 257(120), *294*

Vilkov, L. V., 540(228), *580*

Vind, H. P., 955(248), 973

Vingee, R. A., 8(20), *72*, 86(71), 135(71), *139*, 196(47), *245*

Vink, H. H., 950(247), *973*

Visifin, B., 999(83), *1006*

Vladimiroff, E., 14(245), *79*

Vladimiroff, T., 106(520), *150*

Vladimirov, T., 664(434), *821*

Vlasov, V. M., 49(245a), *79*, 155(291), 157(292), 159(295), 168(290), 170(208), 175(290, 292, 295, 319), 176(291, 292, 295), 178(208), 223(293, 294), 225(207, 290), *249, 251, 252*, 317(213a), 321(213a), *503*, 637(389), 644(435), 658(435), 714(380a, 435), 716(380a, 435), 419(435), 721(263, 373, 377, 379, 380, 382, 383, 387a, 389), 722(263, 377, 379, 387a, 389, 435), 724(373, 379, 383, 389),

725(264, 383, 386), 746(373), *816, 819, 820, 821*

Vliegenthart, J. A., 892(74), *926*

Vogel, A. I., 320(53, 54), 348(53, 54), 424(53), *496*, 665(79), *811, 821*

Vogel, A. J., 117(521), 130(521), 131(521), 134(521), 135(521), 136(521), *150*

Vogel, E., 26(246), *79*

Vogel, J., 998(84), *1006*

Volpin, M. E., 904(219), *930*

Von Grosse, A., 82(294), 133(294), *145*, 298(107), 491(107), *499*, 823(51), *877*

Von Hösslin, R., 953(249), *973*

Voronkov, M. G., 8(133), *75*

Voorhees, R. L., 885(220), 886(220), *930*

Vucelic, M., 110(109), *140*

Vucelik, M., 664(74), *811*

Vyalykh, E. P., 721(391), *820*

Vyayraghavan, K. V., 86(523), 93(523), 131(523), 135(523), *150*

Vyazankin, N. S., 63(15a, 247), 64(15a, 246a, 246c, 247, 248a, 248b, 249, 250, 250a), 65(246b, 248), *72, 79*, 90(437, 438), 92(522), *148, 150*, 172(263, 320, 321, 323), 173(322), 175(263, 264), 176(264), 187(262), 204(262), 209(262), 224(324), *250, 252*, 261(87), 263(88), 264(88, 121), *294*, 298(161c), 227e, 227f, 314–317(36b, 64b, 64c, 225, 226, 227, 227a, 227b, 227c, 227d), 320(36b, 65), 336(227), 341–346(36b, 64a, 64b, 64c, 65, 225, 226, 227, 227a, 227b, 227c, 227g), 424(36b, 64c, 225, 227, 227a, 227b), 426(65), 429(65, 226, 227c, 227d), 474(227), 491(36b, 64c, 65, 225, 227, 227a, 227b), 492(226, 227), 494(36b, 64a, 64c, 65, 225, 226, 227, 227a, 227b, 227c, 227g), *496, 497, 501, 503, 504*, 582(37b, 70c, 70d), 616–619(17, 29, 29a, 70c, 71, 72, 73), *621, 622, 623*, 629(329), 633(327, 328, 329, 437, 438), 664(327), 665(438), *818, 821*, 832(83, 84, 85), 848(114), 858(83, 87), 859(116), 864(113), 865(86, 115, 116), 867(83, 87), 870(115), 873(86), *878, 879*, 881(224), 882(224), 885(224), 886(106), 889(224), 890(79, 221, 222, 223), 896(224), *926, 927, 930*

Vyshinskii, N. N., 102(524), *150*, 284(122), *294*, 832(23), 858(83), 867(83), *876*, *878*, 1002(85), *1006*

W

Waack, R., 786(439), *821*
Wada, M., 129(526), 130(525), 137(397), *147*, *150*, 204(233, 325), 205(233, 325), 207(233), 208(233, 307, 325), 212(307), *249*, *251*, *252*, 254(83), 262(124), 263(124), 279(123), 287(123), *293*, *295*, 298(227h), *504*, 539(184, 185), 571(185), 572(185), *579*, 1000(86), 1002(79), *1006*
Wade, K., 298(46), *496*, 510(43), *576*, 895(54), *926*
Wade, R. H., 939(32), *967*
Wagner, D., 65(58), 67(57a), *73*, 202(100), 204(100), 206(100), *246*, 259(32), *292*
Wagner, P. J., 67(250b), *79*
Wagner, W. E., 965(219), *972*
Wahren, M., 26(251), *79*
Waites, P. C., 896(61), 897(61), *926*
Walborsky, H. M., 22(258), *79*
Waldman, M. C., 636(77), 690(77), 695(77), 773(77), 774(77), *811*
Waldmann, S., 677(341), 679(341), *818*
Walling, C., 25(252), *79*, 191(326), *252*
Walker, A., 270(1), 273(1), *292*
Walsh, E. J., Jr., 28(103, 253, 253a), 29(103, 253), 30(103), 31(253), 33(103), *75*, *79*
Walters, K. L., 918(226), *930*
Walther, B., 11(75), *74*, 276(43), *293*, 585(24), 591(24), 597(24), 598(24), *621*
Walton, D. R. M., 64(50), *73*, 638(102), 646(38, 99, 102, 103), 659(38), 661(100, 103), 684(38), 697(99, 100, 103), 698(38, 99, 100), 699(38, 99, 100, 102), 734(99), 768(99), 769(99), *810*, *811*
Walton, R. D., 118(345, 346), *146*, 661(254, 255), *816*
Wang, S. H., 49(137e), *76*, 730(281), *817*
Wannagat, U., 540(229), *580*
Ward, C. H., 100(137), *141*, 999(19, 20), *1004*

Wardell, J. L., 119(527, 528), 120(528), 127(527, 528), *150*, 307(227i), 353(227i), 354(227i), 357(227i), *504*, 634(440, 441), *821*
Ware, M. J., 918(90), *927*
Warkentin, J., 22(254), *79*
Warner, C. R., 19(99), 20(99), 21(255), 36(255), *74*, *79*
Wartman, L. H., 964(55), *967*
Washburn, R. M., 537(186), 572(186), *579*, 990(81, 82, 83), *996*
Washburne, W. S., 636(359), 679(359), 770(359), 771(359), *819*
Wasserman, D., 646(442), 801(442), *821*
Waters, J. A., 87(50), *139*, 659(36a, 103a), 660(36a), 671(36a), 697(36a, 103a), 698(36a, 103a), 726(36a, 756(36a, 103a), 757(36a), 767(36a, 103a), *810*, *811*
Watkins, S. F., 923(225), *930*
Watt, R., 824(60), *877*, 882(162), 889(162), 890(162), *928*
Webb, A. F., 161(265), 186(265), 187(265), 202(265), *250*
Webel, I. U., 936(159), 951(159), *971*
Weber, H. P., 923(227), *930*
Weber, S., 50(256), 57(256), *79*, 846(117), 848(117), *879*
Webley, D. J., 943(133), 945(133), *970*
Webster, D. E., 100(398), 107(59), 113(201, 395), 122(398), *139*, *142*, *147*, 254(84), 259(84), 268(78), 277(78), *293*, *294*, 661(10, 12), 700(10, 12), *809*, 999(58), 1000(58), *1005*
Wegler, R., 303(180), 327(180), 344(180), 350(180), 352(180), 353(180), 355–357(180), 442(180), *502*
Weinberg, E. L., 83(529, 530), 86(445), 132(529), 136(445), *148*, *150*, 935(252), 940(251), 957(250), *973*
Weinberg, K., 86(299), 93(299, 300), 131(299, 300), 133(300), *145*, 195(168), 196(168), 200(168), 201(168), *248*
Weiner, M. A., 131(472), *149*
Weisfeld, L. B., 308(227k), *504*
Weiss, R., 343(210a), 346(210a), 493(210a), 494(210a), *502*
Weiss, R. W., 626(443), 628(443), 633(443), 634(443), 637–639(443), 662(443), 664–671(443), 673–679(443),

681–685(443), 687–689(443), 693(443), 695–714(443), 716–793(443), 795–799(443), 802(443), 803–806(443), *821*, 824(28), *876*

Weissman, P. M., 895(70), 898(72), 903(70), *926*

Wells, E. J., 38(27, 28), *72*, 106(96), *140*, 1003(15), *1004*

Wells, W. L., 838(117a), *879*, 887(228), *930*

Werner, A., 125(531), 130(531), 132(531), *150*

West, R., 320(82), 430(82), *497*, 510(180), 537(177, 178, 179, 180), 568(177, 178), 569(179), 573(180), *579*, *821*

West, R. C., 117(532), 130(532), 131(532), 132(175), 134(532), 135(532), 136(532), *142*, *150*, 195(327, 328), 196(327, 328), 197(327, 328), *252*

Westlake, A. H., 108(523), 129(523), *150*, 182(329), 184(329), 185(329), 189(329), *252*, 279(125), 285(125), 286(125), 287(125), *295*

Westson, M., 664(59, 60), *810*

Wetroff, G., 94(108), *140*

Wheatley, P. J., 156(330), 176(330), *252*

Wheeler, J. W., 26(136), *75*

White, D. G., 202(234), 204(234), 205(234), 216(234), 217(234), *249*

White, P. J., 943(129), 945(129), *970*

White, R. F. M., 122(11), 137(11), *138*, 201(17), 203(17), 204(17), 205(17), 206(17), *244*, 264(4), *292*

Whitehead, M. A., 664(395), 669(395), *820*

Whiteley, P., 958(253), *973*

Whitney, W. K., 949(49), *966*

Wiberg, E., 18(257), *79*, 254(126), 266(126), *295*, 511(187), 513(187), 514(187), 541(187), 543(187), 545(187), 548(187), 549(187), *579*, 646(445), *822*, 855(118), 870(118), *879*, 885(229), 890(229), 893(230), 894(230), 895(230), *930*

Wick, M., 963(190), *971*

Wickham, A. J., 918(125), *927*

Wieber, M., 327(231), 328(230), 330(228, 229, 230), 436(229), 442(230), *504*

Wiegleb, H., 999(31), *1005*

Wiernick, M., 82(193), 86(193), 135(193), *142*, 775(158), *813*

Wihksne, K. J., 572(62), *576*

Wild, S. B., *925*

Wilkins, C. J., 100(534), 101(534), 125(103), 127(103, 534), 128(149), 129(534), *140*, *141*, *150*, 284(23, 127), 288(23, 24), 290(23, 24), 291(23, 24), *292*, *295*

Wilkinson, G., 69(187), 70(187), 71(187), *77*, 776(36), *810*, 906(20), 909(20), 913(20), *925*

Williams, A. A., 130(94a), *140*, 661(63), 698(63), 726(63), *810*

Williams, C. S., 125(104), *140*

Williamsen, L. C., 831(119, 120), 840(119, 120), *879*, 886(231), *930*, 941(147), 942(147), 943(147), *970*

Willis, C. F., 873(17a, 19a), 875(19a), *876*

Willis, C. J., 107(93), *140*, 675(61), *810*

Willis, H. A., 100(74), 102(74), *139*, 156(48), 184(48), 185(48), 186(48), 189(48), *245*, 284(15), *292*, 1001(9), 1002(10), *1004*

Wilmet–Devos, B., 88(66), *139*, 659(54), 660(54), 734(54), 747(54), *810*

Wilputte–Steinert, L., *879*

Wilson, G. R., 988(84), 989(84), *996*

Wilson, H. R., 954(104, 254), *969*, *973*

Wilzbach, K. E., 8(53), *73*

Wimmer, J., 311(92a), *498*

Winfield, J. M., 89(472a), *149*

Wingfield, J. N., 307(17a), *495*, 602(1c), 609(1c), *620*

Winstein, S., 22(258), *79*

Winters, L. J., 514(188), 520(188), 528(188), 530(188), 534(188), 567(188), *579*

Wit, S. L., 953(255), *974*

Wittenberg, D., 94(535), *150*

Wittig, G., 8(259), *79*, 131(536), 137(536), *150*, 883(232, 233), 887(232), *930*

Woggon, H., 310(211a, 232a), 402(211a), *503*, *504*

Woitkowiak, B., 720(446), *822*

Wolfsberger, W., 537(153), 568(153), 569(153), *578*, *580*

Wood, J. L., 100(502), 103(502), 105(503), 128(502), *149*, 1000(77), 1001(77), *1006*

Woods, W. G., 63(168), *76*

Woodward, L. A., 515(56), *576*

Woodward, P., 306(232), 307(232), 402(232), *504*
Work, A., 744(447), 786(447), *822*
Wright, A. N., 65(88), *74*
Wright, B., 134(143), *141*
Wright, C. M., 283(74), 287(74), *293*, 513(189), 542(189), *579*
Wright, N., 648(206), *814*
Wu, T. C., 131(537), 133(537), 134(537), *150*, 890(97), *927*
Wuyts, H., 298(233), 304(233), 305(233), 306(233), 377(233), 378(233), *504*
Wyant, R. E., 83(147, 148, 538), *141*, *150*, 628(111), *812*
Wyatt, P. A., 122(234), 125(234), *143*
Wynter, C., 921(234), *930*

Yernaux, R., 122(167), *141*
Yngve, V., 933(257, 258), *974*
Yoder, C. H., 225(345), *252*, 511(135, 136, 137), 516(137), 535(190), 536(136), 540(213), 542–545(136, 137), *578–580*
Yokoo, M., 264(130), *295*
Yorke, M., 28(253a), *79*
Yoshida, Z., 940(260), *974*
Youinou, M. T., 540(216), *580*
Young, D. M., 963(261), *974*
Young, J. F., 896(235), *930*
Yount, J. B., 22(76b, 76c), *74*
Yu, C. F., 942(65), *968*
Yu, Z. F., 418(235), *504*
Yukubova, F. A., 195(200), *248*

X

Xu, H. S., 418(235), *504*

Y

Yaghmai, A., 595(70), *623*
Yakubov, R. D., 721(391), *820*
Yakubovich, A. Y. 94(540, 541), 131(539, 541), 132(539, 540, 541), 134(539, 541), *150*, 203(332), 212(332), *252*, 693(22), *809*
Yamanaka, H., 26(8), *72*
Yamazaki, H., 25(215), *78*
Yamazaki, J., 665(448), 742(448), 776(448), *822*
Yarosh, O. G., 666(199), 670(199), 720(196), 768(199), *814*
Yasuda, K., 100(542), 101(542), 104(543), 128(542), *150*, 195(235), 200(333, 334), 201(333, 334), 204(333), 205(333), 208(333), *249*, *252*, 268(128), 270–275(128, 129), *295*, 323(234), *504*, 1000(59, 87), 1002(59), *1005*, *1006*
Yasuda, N., 65(193), *77*
Yeldell, J. B., 130(127), 132(127), 134(127), *140*
Yergey, A. L., 117(544), *150*, 649(216, 449), 664(449), 677(449), 680(170, 216), 684(449), *813*, *815*, *822*

Z

Zainchkovskaya, M. K., 722(378), *819*
Zaitseva, N. A., 212(305), *251*, 320(216), 431(216), 432(216), *503*
Zakharkin, L. I., *151*, 197(335, 336), *252*, 645(156), 647(450), 724(156), 725(156), *813*, *822*
Zakharkin, P. I., *809*
Zakharova, M. Y., 305(136a), 376(136a), *500*, 897(170), 898(170), 911(172), 914(170, 172), *928*
Zanella, P., 123(499, 500, 546), 128(499), *149*, *151*
Zanzottera, C., 905(38), *925*
Zavgorodnii, V. S., 45(135, 135a, 260), *75*, *79*, 637(454), 638(455, 456), 658(455), 695(307, 452, 453, 454, 456), 703(307), 716(307, 453), 719–724(306, 307, 372, 451, 453, 454, 455, 456), 732(453, 456), 744(456), *817*, *819*, *822*, 868(121), *879*
Zavistoski, J. G., 647(457), 659(457), *822*
Zedler, R., 943(264), 955–959(38, 262, 263), 961(262), *967*, *974*
Zeil, W., 658(411), 695(411), *821*
Zeman, W., 950(265), 951(265), *974*
Zelmlyanskii, N. N., 119(183), 122(183), *142*, 155(107), 157(107), 188(107), 208–210(337, 338), *246*, *252*, 254(131), 261(108), 263(133), 264(55, 132, 133), *293*, *294*, *295*, 298(100a),

308(83*a*, 83*b*), 309(83*a*, 83*b*),
324(83*a*, 83*b*), 354(83*a*, 83*b*), 362(83*a*,
83*b*), 366(83*a*, 83*b*), 430(83*a*, 83*b*),
497, *499*, 582(28*a*), *621*, 849(122),
879, 993(85), *995*
Zhivukhin, S. M., 186(340), 209(339, 340),
210(340), *252*, 261(134), 264(134), *295*,
993(86), 847(123), 852(123), *879*, *996*
Zhuo, R. X., 418(235), *504*
Ziegler, H., 628(458), 664(458), *822*
Ziegler, K., 94(547, 548, 549), *151*
Zietz, J. R., 84(550), 118(550), 130(550),
131(550), 132(550), *151*, 212(341), *252*
Zilberman, E. N., 303(175), 366(175), *501*
Zilkha, A., 65(58), 67(57*a*), *73*, 202(100),
204(100), 206(100), *246*, 259(32), *292*,
314(129), 316(129), 317(129), 320(129),
321(129), 335(129), 424(129), 426(129),
428–431(129), 467(129), 468(129),
500, 988(52), *995*
Zima, O., 181(139), *247*
Zimmer, H., 87(551), 88(553), 91(551),
131(115, 551, 552, 553), 133(115, 551),
134(115), 135(551), 136(551) *140*, *151*,

197(342), *252*, 257(135), *295*, 661(459),
666(461, 462), 667(462), 668(462),
750(461), 776(461), 784(461), 789(462),
822, 834(124), *879*, 884(236), *930*
Zisman, W. A., 131(106), *140*
Zobel, T., 118(1), *137*, 309(10), 350(10),
365(10), *495*
Zoche, G., 93(25), *138*, 197(25), *244*
Zoepfi, H. J., 664(172), *813*, 999(65), *1005*
Zschunke, A., 329(92), 330(92), 336(92),
460(92), 464(92), 470(92), *498*
Zuckerman, J. J., 110(119, 554), 112(119),
128(119), *140*, *151*, 161(94), 184(94),
188(94), 225(345), *246*, *252*, 325(236),
430(236), *504*, 511(135), 516(137),
534(134), 535(136–139, 190), 536(136),
540(202), 542–545(134, 136, 137, 139),
578, *579*, *622*, 647(457), 649(463),
659(457), 665(463), *822*, 920(237),
921(85), *920*, *926*
Zuech, E. A., 646(145*a*), 672(145*a*),
801(145*a*), *812*
Zweigle, M. L., 205(343), 206(343),
208(343), *252*

CUMULATIVE SUBJECT INDEX

A

Acid halides, scope and mechanism of the reactions with organotin hydrides, 28-33

Aldehydes
addition of the tin-carbon bond to, 171
addition of the tin-hydrogen bond to, 49-54, 164-167
addition of the tin-nitrogen bond to, 170
addition of the tin-oxygen bond to, 167-170

Alkanestannonic acids, 213-215

Alkenes, organotin hydride addition to, 34-45
mechanism of, 42-45
scope of, 34-42

Alkenyltins, symmetrical, 628, 633

Alkenyltins, unsymmetrical (mixed)
mechanisms of bimolecular electrophilic substitution, 657-658
physical constants and spectral properties of, by individual compounds, 662-808
physical properties of, 648-649
preparation, 644-645
preparation by addition-elimination reactions, 645
preparation by hydrostannation, 644
preparation by metal-halogen exchange, 644
preparation by metal-metal exchange, 644
preparation by other addition-elimination reactions, 644-645
reactions of, 657-658
reactions of electrophilic substitution at an olefinic carbon atom, 657-658

stereochemistry of bimolecular electrophilic substitution, 657

Alkoxides and phenoxides (organotin), preparation, structure and physical properties of, 154-190
miscellaneous preparations, mainly involving peroxides, 171-173
preparation by addition to carbonyl compounds, 161-171
preparation by addition of compounds with tin-carbon bonds to carbonyl compounds, 171
preparation by addition of organotin amines (and related compounds with Sn-N bonds) to carbonyl compounds, 170
preparation by addition of organotin hydrides to carbonyl compounds, 164-167
preparation by addition of organotin oxides and alkoxides to carbonyl compounds, 170
preparation by nucleophilic displacement of alkoxide, 157-159
preparation by nucleophilic displacement of amine, 162-163
preparation by nucleophilic displacement of halide, 155-157
preparation by nucleophilic displacement of hydroxide or stannyloxide, 159-162
preparation by nucleophilic displacement of groups bonded through carbon, 163-164
table of dialkyltin alkoxides, 184-189
table of monoalkyltin alkoxides, 190
table of trialkyltin alkoxides, 174-183

Alkoxides, oxides and related compounds (organotin), reactions of the Sn-O bond, 221-243
addition reactions followed by addi-

tion, 241-243

addition reactions followed by substitution, 240-241

addition reactions of dialkyltin compounds, 239-240

addition reactions of trialkyltin compounds with carbodiimides, 232

addition reactions of trialkyltin compounds to a variety of multiple bond acceptors (A = B), 227-232

addition reactions of trialkyltin compounds with carbon dioxide, 231

addition reactions of trialkyltin compounds with carbon disulfide and isothiocyanates, 236

addition reactions of trialkyltin compounds with imines and nitriles, 237

addition reactions of trialkyltin compounds with isothiocyanates, 232-235

addition reactions of trialkyltin compounds with ketene and acetylenedicarboxylic esters, 238-239

addition reactions of trialkyltin compounds with sulfur dioxide, sulfodiimides and sulfinylamines, 235-236

adducts formed from dibutyltin dimethoxide (table of), 240

substitution reactions with derivatives of other metals, 226-227

substitution reactions with organotin compounds, 225-226

substitution reactions with polar organic compounds, 223-225

substitution reactions with protic reagents, 222-223

Alkyl peroxides (organotin), 190-192

Alkyltins, see Tetraalkyltins, symmetrical and Tetraalkyltins, unsymmetrical (mixed)

Alkynes
  addition of organotin hydrides to, 45-49

Alkynyltins, symmetrical, 628, 633

Alkynyltins, unsymmetrical (mixed)

physical constants and spectral properties of, by individual compounds, 662-808

physical properties of, 648-649

preparation by metal-halogen exchange, 645

preparation by metal-hydrogen exchange, 645

preparation by metal-metal exchange, 645

preparation by thermal decomposition, 645

reactions of electrophilic substitution at an acetylenic carbon atom, 658

Allyltin compounds

Aluminum-tin bonds, compounds with, 887

Amines (organotin), and related compounds with Sn-N bonds, (also named stannylamines, aminostannanes, or organotin amides), 510-574

  general introduction, 510-512

  metathetical exchange reactions—tin amides as aminating reagents, 528-529

  miscellaneous pseudohalides, 539-540

  organotin azides, 537

  organotin isocyanates, 538

  organotin isocyanides, 537

  organotin isothiocyanates, 538

  physical properties of, 534-537

  preparation of, 512-521

  preparation of, by addition reactions, 516-519

  preparation of, by metathetical reactions from Sn-O compounds, 519-520

  preparation of, by miscellaneous methods, 520-521

  preparation of, by transamination reactions, 515-516

  preparation of, by transmetallation reactions, 513-515

  pseudohalides with Sn-N bonds, 537-539

  reactions of, 521-534

  reactions of, as dehydrohalogenating reagents, 530-531

  reactions of, as Lewis acids and bases, 529-530

reactions of, with 1,2-dipoles and their retrogressions, 531-534

reactions of, with metal hydrides, 526-528

reaction of, with protic species, 522-526

tables of compounds, 540-574

Analysis of organotin compounds, 997-1006

analysis for specific compounds by spectrophotometry, 998

infrared spectroscopy, 999-1001

infrared spectroscopy, tin-carbon vibrations, 999-1000

infrared spectroscopy, tin-halogen vibrations, 1001

infrared spectroscopy, tin-hydrogen vibrations, 1000-1001

infrared spectroscopy, tin-oxygen vibrations, 1001-1002

Mössbauer spectroscopy, 1004

nuclear magnetic resonance spectroscopy, 1001-1003

thin layer and gas chromatography, 998-999

wet analyses, 997-998

Applications and biological effects of organotin compounds, 5, 931-974

Arsines (organotin), 607-613

chemical properties and reactions of, 608-610

infrared spectra of (table), 610

physical properties of, 610

preparation of, 607-608

proton nmr data of (table), 611

reaction with azides, 609

reaction with carbon disulfide, 609

reaction with halogens and covalent halides, 609

reaction with hydrogen sulfide and thiols, 609

reaction with methyl iodide, 609

reactions with organophosphorus or organoarsenic halides, 609-610

reaction with oxygen, 608-609

reaction with transition metal carbonyls, 610

table of, 612-613

Aryltins, symmetrical, 628, 633-634, see Tetraaryltins, symmetrical

Aryltins, unsymmetrical (mixed)

electrophilic substitution at an aromatic carbon atom, 659-661

nucleophilic displacement at a tin atom, 661

photochemistry, 661

physical constants and spectral properties of, by individual compounds, 662-808

physical properties of, 648-649

preparation of, 646-648

preparation of, by addition reactions, 647

preparation of, by insertion reactions, 648

preparation of, by metal-metal exchange, 646

reactions of, 658-662

B

Biocidal uses of organotin compounds, 953-961

agricultural fungicidal uses, 953-954

anthelmintic use for poultry, 954

antifouling, 958-959

industrial uses, 954-960

medical use as disinfectants, 960-961

paint preservation, 957-958

protection of cables from rodent attack, 960

sanitizing of textiles, 956-957

slime control in paper mills, 957

textile preservation, 956

water treatment, 957

wood preservation, 954-956

Biological effects of organotin compounds, 940-952

anthelmintic activity, 943-945

antbacterial activity, 942-943

antifungal activity, 940-942

herbicidal activity, 943

insecticidal activity, 945-949

mammalian toxicity, 949-952

molluscicidal activity, 945

Bismuthines (organotin), 617-619

chemical properties and reactions of, 617

oxidation of, 617

preparation of, 617

table of, 618
thermal or catalytic decomposition of, 617
reaction with benzoyl peroxide, 617
Bis(triorganotins) oxides, 196-197
complexes with trialkyltin halides, 197-198
table of, 197
Bis(triorganotin) sulfides, 314-320
Boron-tin bonds, organotin compounds with, 885-886, 889
Butyltin $(BuSn)_n$, 832-833

C

Carboxylates (organotin), 253-268
diorganotin dicarboxylates, 259-261
diorganotin monocarboxylates, 262
general preparative methods, 253-254
hexaacetoxyditin, 266
inner salts, 265
organotin tricarboxylates, 261-262
1,1,2,2-tetraorgano-1,2-diacyloxy-ditins, 267-268
tin tetracarboxylates, 265-266
triorganotin carboxylates, 254-259
with Sn-O-Sn bonds, 264-265
Carboxylic acids
reactions with organotin hydrides, 56-58
Catalytic uses of organotin compounds, 961-964
epoxy curing, 964
esterification, 963-964
olefin polymerization, 964
polyurethane formation, 961-963
silicone curing, 963
Catenated organotin compounds, 823-879
preparation and properties of, 824-854
reactions of, 854-875
Chromatography, 90, 998-999
Complexes (organotin)
of organotin halides, 118-130
of tin-nitrogen bonded compounds, 529-530
of tin-oxygen bonded compounds, 197-198, 279-291
Complexes (organotin) with Sn-O bonds,

197-198, 279-291
adducts of organotin cations, 290-291
adducts of organotin halides, 288-291
dimethylsulfoxide adducts of organotin halides, 288-289
diorganotin bisoxinates, 279-280
diorganotin halide oxinates and other salt oxinates, 280-281
diphenylselenoxide adducts of organotin halides, 288-289
mixed organotin chelates, 285-287
monoorganotin chloride bisoxinates, 281
monoorganotin trisoxinates, 281
organotin acetylacetoneates and other β-diketonates, 281-283
organotin kojates, 284
organotin tropolonates, 283
pyridine N-oxide adducts of organotin halides, 288
trialkylarsine oxide adducts of organotin halides, 288
trialkylphosphine oxide adducts of organotin halides, 288
triorganotin oxinates, 279
weak carbonyl donor adducts of organotin halides, 289-290
Coordination compounds
of organotin halides, 118-130
of tin-nitrogen bonded compounds, 529-530
of tin-oxygen bonded compounds, 279-291
Cyclic organopolytins, 833-845

D

Dialkyltin oxides (polymeric), 209-211
Dibutyltin dilaurate, 5, 944
Diethyltin, 1, 824, 833
Diorganotin alkoxide carboxylates, 263-264
Diorganotin halide alkoxides, 155-156
Diorganotin halide carboxylates, 262-264
Diorganotin hydride carboxylates, 263-264, 845-847
Diorganotin hydride halides, 15-17, 849

Diorganotin sulfides, 320-325
Diphenyltin, 833, 843-844
Dipole moments of organotin compounds, 114-117, 119, 125, 309, 313-314, 338, 536, 648
Disinfectant uses of organotin compounds, 960-961
Distannane, 18
Distannoxanes and related compounds, 199-211
    alkanestannonic acids, 213-214
    dialkyldistannoxanes, 213-215
    1,1-dialkyldistannoxanes, 213
    1,3-dialkyldistannoxanes, 213-214
    dialkyltin hydroxides, 200-201
    hexaalkyldistannoxanes, 196-197
    monoalkyltin hydroxides, 213-214
    oligomeric dialkylstannoxanes, 209-210
    pentaalkyldistannoxanes, 199
    polymeric dialkyldistannoxanes, 209-211
    stannoxonium salts, 197-198
    1,1,3-trialkyldistannoxanes and related oligomers, 211-213
    trialkyltin hydroxides, 194-196
    1,1,3,3 - tetraalkylalkoxydistannoxanes, 207-208
    1, 1, 3, 3 - tetraalkyldistannoxanes, 199-207
    1, 1, 3, 3 - tetraalkylhydroxydistannoxanes, 207-208
Ditin hexacetate, 266-267, 855
Ditin hexachloride, 266, 855
    preparation, 826-827, 834-835, 845-851
    reactions, 854-875

E

Electron diffraction, 113,114
Electron spin resonance spectroscopy, 12, 856, 857, 920
Esters, reductions by organotin hydrides, 59

F

Fungicidal uses of organotin compounds, 953

G

Germanium-tin bondsm organotin compounds with, 889-895
Grignard reagents, 1,5, 93-94, 638, 644-645

H

Halides (organotin), 81-151
    acceptor strength of, 118-120
    auto complexation, 128-130
    coordination compounds of, 118-130
    diamagnetic susceptibility of, 118
    dipole moments of, 114-117
    halogen exchange (redistribution) reactions, 98-99
    infrared and Raman spectroscopy of, 99-105
    mass spectrometry of, 117
    Mössbauer spectroscopy of, 109-112
    nuclear magnetic resonance spectroscopy of, 106-108
    nuclear quadrupole resonance spectroscopy of, 108-109
    physical and chemical properties of, 99-118
    polarography of, 117-118
    preparation by alkylation and arylation of tin halides, 93-95
    preparation by halogenation of diorganodistannanes, 91-92
    preparation by halogenation of hexaorganodistannanes 91-92
    preparation by halogenation of tetraorganostannanes through redistribution reactions, 90-91
    preparation by halogenation of tetraorganostannanes with free halogen, 85-97
    preparation by halogenation of tetraorganostannanes with halogen acids, 87-88
    preparation by halogenation of tetraorganostannanes with metal halides, alkyl halides and acyl halides, 89-90
    preparation by halogenation of organotin hydroxides and oxides, 92-93

reactions of, 95-99

reactions with alkali and alkaline earth metals, 96

reactions with the formation of organotin salts, 99

reactions with the formation of tin-Group IV element bonds, 96-97

reactions with the formation of tin-Group V element bonds, 97

reactions with the formation of tin-Group VI element bonds, 97-98

reactions with the formation of tin-transition metal bonds, 98

reductions to organotin hydrides, 96

relative donor strength toward, 120-121

solvolysis, hydrolysis, and complex ion formation in solution of, 121-123

structural analysis by electron diffraction of, 113-114

structural analysis by x-ray diffraction of, 112-113

structure of coordination compounds with R₃SnX, 123-125

structure of coordination compounds with R₂SnX₂ and RSnX₃, 125-128

synthesis from tin and alkyl or aryl halides, 82-84

synthesis of, 82-95

tables of, 130-137

thermochemistry of, 117

ultraviolet spectroscopy of, 105-105

Historical beginnings and development of organotin chemistry, 1-4

Hydrides (organotin), 7-79

addition to alkenes, 34-45

addition to alkynes, 45-49

addition to unsaturated nitrogen compounds, 54-56

colorimetric determination of, 67

diorganotin dihydrides, 8-14

miscellaneous reactions, 63-69

monoorganotin trihydrides, 8-14

pentaorganoditin monohydrides, 18-19

preparation and properties, 8-19

reactions of, 19-67

reaction with acid halides, 28-34

reaction with inorganic and organic acids, 56-58

reaction with aldehydes and ketones, 49-54, 164-167

reaction with tin-element bonds, 60-63

reduction of alkyl halides, 19-27

reduction of aryl halides, 27-28

reduction of sulfur-containing functional groups, 65-66

stepwise reduction of geminal polyhalides, 25

summary, 67-68

tetraorganoditin dihydrides, 17-18

triorganotin hydrides, 8-14

with negative substituents (halide or carboxylate), 15-17

Hydroperoxides (organotin), 219-221

Hydrostannation, 2-3

of aldehydes and ketones, mechanistic aspects of, 49-54, 164-167

of alkenes, scope of, 34-42

of alkenes, mechanism of, 42-45

of alkynes, 45-49

of isocyanates, 54-55

Hydrostannolysis, 60-63

scope and mechanism, 60-61

exchange accompanying, 61-63

of carbon-metal bonds, 64

I

Infrared spectroscopy

general survey of, 999-1002

involving organotin alkoxides, oxides and related compounds, 156-158, 162-163, 169, 191-192, 195-200, 209-211, 218, 234-235, 237, 239

involving organotin amines and related compounds, 530, 534-535, 541-574

involving organotin arsines, 605, 610

involving organotin carboxylates, salts and complexes (with Sn-O bonds), 254-257, 259-260, 262-266, 268-270, 272, 274-279, 281-285, 288-289, 849

involving organotin halides, 99-105. 122-129

involving organotin hydrides, 12, 14,

16-18, 69-71, 875
involving organotin phosphines, 596
involving organotin selenides, 343,
involving organotin sulfides, 302,
    308, 313, 318-319, 324-325,
    326, 330-333, 338, 347
involving organotin tellurides, 346
involving organotin compounds with
    tin-carbon bonds, 648, 662-808
involving organotin compounds with
    tin-metal bonds, 890-892, 918, 920
Isocyanates, 54-55, 232-235, 516-519

J

K

Karl Fisher titration, 195
Ketones
    addition of the tin-carbon bond to,
        171
    addition of the tin-hydrogen bond to,
        49-54, 164-167
    addition of the tin-nitrogen bond to,
        170

L

Lead-tin bonds, organotin compounds with,
        886, 889-890, 892
Lithium-tin bonds, organotin compounds
        with. 882-882, 887-889

M

Magnesium-tin bonds, organotin compounds
        with, 883-885, 887-888
Magnetic susceptibility, 118, 128
Mass spectrometry, 117, 320, 649, 860, 920
Mercury-tin bonds, organotin compounds
        with, 885-886
Metallostannoxanes, 215-220
Monoalkyltin hydroxides, 213-215
Mössbauer spectroscopy, 14, 109-112, 120-
        121, 126, 128, 156, 206, 210,
        257-258, 275, 302, 308, 314,
        325, 334-335, 348, 530, 535,

649, 887, 892, 920-922, 1004

N

Nuclear magnetic resonance spectroscopy,
        12-14, 16-18, 61-63, 69-71, 90,
        98, 106-108, 120, 122-124, 126-
        127, 129, 156, 158, 206, 218,
        225, 235-236, 282-286, 302,
        320, 313-314, 325, 330, 338,
        344, 346, 535-536, 606, 610-
        611, 617, 619, 648-649, 832-
        833, 843, 887, 891-892, 918-
        919, 1001-1003
Nuclear quadrupole resonance spectros-
        copy, 108-109, 919-920

O

Organoditins and other organopolytins,
        reactions of, 845-875
    general introduction, 823-825
    general survey of reactions of, 854-
        855
    homolytic dissociation of organodi-
        tins (the question of), 856-858
    insertion reactions of dihalocarbenes
        using organomercury com-
        pounds, 872
    insertion reactions with alkynes under
        polar conditions, 872
    insertion reactions with fluorinated
        olefins, 871-872
    insertion reaction with hexafluoro-2-
        butyne, 871-872
    insertion reactions with sulfur diox-
        ide, 872
    preparation and properties of, 826-
        854
    reactions of, 854-875
    reactions of dialkyltins with alkyl
        halides, 873
    reaction with azodicarboxylate, 872
    reaction of diphenyltin with alkyl
        halides, 873
    reaction to form an inclusion com-
        pound from hexaphenylditin
        and tetraphenyltin, 875
    reaction with ethyl magnesium bro-

mide, 869
reaction with halogens, 860-862
reactions of hexaorganoditins with perfluoroalkyl iodides, 872-873
reaction with hydrides, 868-869
reaction with inorganic acids, 869-870
reaction with metals (lithium, sodium, potassium, and magnesium) 867-868
reaction with metal halides, 866-867
reaction with organotin halides, 874-875
reaction with organic acids, 869-870
reactions with organic disulfides, 865-866
reactions with organic halides, 872-873
reaction with organomercury compounds, 869
reaction with organotin hydrides, 875
reaction with other organotin compounds, 874-875
reaction with other oxidizing agents (other than molecular oxygen, sulfur or selenium), 865-867
reactions without cleavage of the tin-tin bond, 854-855
reaction with oxygen, 862-864
reaction with permanganate, 866
reactions with peroxides and hydroperoxides, 865
reaction with phenyllithium, 869
reaction with piperidine, 869
reaction with selenium, 864
reaction with sulfur, 864
reaction with silver nitrate, 866
reaction with sodium amide, 869
reaction with transition metal carbonyls, 875
reaction with triorganostibine sulfides, 866
thermal behavior of, 858-860
Organoditins and other organopolytins with functional substituents, preparation and properties 845-854
compounds of the type (RSnX)n, 853-854
organohexatins, 853
organononatins, 853
organopentatins, 852
organotetratins, 852
organotritins, 852
pentaorganoditin monhydrides and other pentaorganoditin compounds, 850-851
tables of, 846-847
tetraorganoditin 1,2-dicarboxylates, 845-849
tetraorganoditin 1,2-dichlorides, 849-850
tetraorganoditin 1,2-dihydrides, 850
Organoditins and other organopolytins without functional substituents, preparation and properties, 826-845
butyltin (BuSn)n, 832-833
branched, 831-833
cyclic, 833-845
hexaorganoditins, 826-827
linear, 826-831
linear organohexatins, 830-831
linear organopentatins, 830
linear organotetratins, 829-830
octaorganotritins, 827-829
organocyclotetratins, 833, 842
organocycloheptatins, 844-845
organocyclohexatins, 842-844
organocyclononatins, 844-845
organocyclopentatins, 842
table of, 834-841
tetrakis(triphenylstannyl)tin preparation and properties of, 831
tris(trialkyltin)phenyltin compounds, preparation of, 831
Organotin acetylacetonates and other β-diketonates, 281-283
Organotin alkoxides, 154-190
Organotin alkyl peroxides, 190-194
Organotin arsines, 607-613
Organotin azides, 537, 568-569, 609
Organotin bismuthines, 617-619
Organotin chalcogens, 297-508
comparative summary, 346-349
general introduction, 297-298
Organotin compounds with tin-carbon bonds, 625-822
physical constants of, by individual compounds, 662-808
physical properties of, general sur-

vey, 648-649

spectral properties of, by individual
    compounds, 662-808
symmetrical, 626-634
tables of compounds, 662-822
unsymmetrical (mixed), 634-662
Organotin compounds with tin-tin bonds,
    823-879
Organotin deuterides, 27
Organotin halides, 81-151, see Halides,
    (organotin)
Organotin hydrides, 7-79, see Hydrides
    (organotin)
Organotin hydroxides, preparation struc-
    ture, and physical properties
alkanestannonic acids and related
    compounds, 213-215
dialkyltin dihydroxides, 200-201
monoalkyltin hydroxides, 213
1,1,3,3-tetraalkylhydroxydistan-
    noxanes, 207-208
Organotin hydroperoxides, 219-221
Organotin isocyanates, 538, 570
Organotin isocycnides, 537
Organotin isothiocyanates, 538, 571-572
Organotin kojates, 284
Organotin mercaptides, 320-309
Organotin mercaptoesters, 309-314
Organotin nitramines, 567
Organotin nitrates, 268-274
Organotin oxinates, 279-281
Organotin oxides, preparation, structure
    and physical properties of,
    192-219
Organotin perchlorates, 274-275
Organotin peroxides, 219-221
Organotin phenoxides, 154-190
Organotin phospates and phosphinates,
    276
Organotin phosphines, 581-606
Organotin pseudohalides, 517-539, 567-
    572
Organotin selenides, 339-344
Organotin stibines, 614-617
Organotin sulfates and sulfonates, 277-
    278
Organotin sulfides, 297-339
Organotin-sulfur heterocycles, 327-335
Organotin tellurides, 345-346
Organotin tropolonates, 283

P

Peroxides (organotin), 219-221
Pentaorganoditin monohydrides, 18-19,
    850-851
Phosphines (organotin), 582-606
addition to alkenes, alkynes and
    carbonyl groups, 594-595
chemical properties and reactions of,
    590-596
hydrolysis of, 592
infrared and Raman frequencies of
    (table), 605
physical properties of, 596-606
preparation of, 582-590
reaction with azides, 594
reaction with butyl lithium, 592
reaction with 1,2-dipoles, 593-594
reaction with methyl iodide, 592
reaction with organophosphorus hal-
    ides, 595
reaction with organoarsenic halides
    or with arsenic trifluoride, 595
reaction with organotin hydrides, 593
reaction with oxygen, 591-592
reaction with sodium in liquid am-
    monia, 592
reaction with sulfur, 592
reaction with transition metal car-
    bonyls, 595-596
table of, 597-604
Polarography of organotin compounds,
    117-118, 320, 344, 848, 857,
    895
Polymers (organotin), 975-996
general introduction, 975-977
with tin atoms in the polymer back-
    bone, 984-993
with tin atoms pendent to the poly-
    mer chain, 977-984
Polymer stabilizers, 933-940
mechanism of stabilizing action for
    poly(vinyl chloride), 937-939
stabilization of polymers other than
    poly(vinyl chloride), 939-940
Polymers with tin atoms in the polymer
    backbone, 984-993
organotin chelate polymers, 989
organotin polyesters, 985
organotin polyolefins, 985-987
polyfunctional tin-containing poly-

mers, monomer and polymers synthesis of, 987-989

polymeric organotin arsonates, 991

polymeric stannoxanes, 993

polyorganotin acetates, 991

polystannanes, 991

stannoxy-siloxane polymers, 991

stannoxy-titanoxane polymers, 991

stannylimidophosphines, -arsines, and -stibines, 990

Polymers with tin atoms pendent to the polymer chain, 977-984

organotin aluminoxanes, 983

organotin polybutadiene, 982

organotin polymers, monomer synthesis and polymerization of, 977-981

organotin polyolefins, 981-982

organotin polystyrenes, 982-983

organotin polyvinyls, 983

organotin titanoxanes, 984

Polytins (organo)

preparation of, with functional substituents, 845-854

preparation of, without functional substituents, 826-845

reactions of, 854-875

Polyurethane formation 961-964

Poly(vinyl chloride), 2,5, 933-939

mechanism of stabilizing action, 936-939

stabilization of, 933-936

synergistic effects, 936

Potassium-tin bonds, organotin compounds with, 883

Q

R

Raman spectroscopy, 98-105, 123, 128, 198-199, 282, 302, 318-319, 343-344, 347, 534-535, 596, 605, 610, 648

Redistribution reactions (also called exchange reactions), 1-2, 15-16, 90-91, 98-99, 155-156, 225-226

S

Salts (organotin) with Sn-O bonds, 268-279

diorganotin dinitrates, 269-271

diorganotin hydroxide nitrates, 271-272

miscellaneous salts, 278-279

organotin carbonates, 274

organotin nitrates with Sn-O-Sn bonds, 272-274

organotin perchlorates, 274-275

organotin phosphates and phosphinates, 276

organotin sulfates and sulfonates, 277-278

triorganotin nitrates, 268-269

Selenides (organotin), 339-344

chemical properties and reactions of, 342-343

physical properties of, 343-344

preparation of, 339-341

tables of compounds, 491-493

Silastannoxanes, 215-219

Silicon-tin bonds, organotin compounds with, 886, 889-895

Sodium-tin bonds, organotin compounds with, 882-883, 887-889

Stabilizers in polymers, 933-940

Stannane, 8

Stannylamines, 509-580, see Amines (organotin)

Stibines (organotin), 614-617

chemical properties and reactions of, 615-617

physical properties of, 615-617

preparation of, 614

reaction with aluminum bromide, 615

reaction with benzoyl peroxide, 615

reactions with benzyl bromide or cyclopentyl bromide, 615

reaction with bromine, 615

reaction with oxygen, 615

table of, 616

Sulfides (organotin), 298-339

bis(triorganotin) sulfides, 314-320

chemical properties and reactions of, 300-301

compounds of the type $R_nSn(SR')_{4-n}$. 302-309

compounds of the type (RSnS)₂S, 325-327

diorganotin sulfides, 320-325

heterocycles containing ring tin-sulfur bonds, 327-335

miscellaneous compounds, 336-339

organotin mercaptoesters, 309-310

organotin thiocarboxylates, thiocarbonate esters and related compounds, 310-314

physical properties of, 301-302

physical constants of individual compounds, 350-490

polymers containing tin-sulfur bonds, 335-336

preparation of, 298-300

T

Tellurides (organotin), 345-346

tables of compounds, 494

Tetraalkenyltins, symmetrical

chemical properties of, 633

preparation of, 628

Tetraalkyltins, symmetrical

addition to unsaturated compounds, 628

chemical properties of, 629-633

conversion of alkyltin halides to tetraalkyltins, 628

mechanism of electrophilic substitution, 629-632

physical constants and spectral roperties of, by individual compounds, 662-808

preparation by electrolytic syntheses, 628

preparation by metal-metal exchange reactions, 627

preparation by tin-alloy syntheses, 627

reactions with electrophiles, 629-632

reactions with radicals, 632-633

redistribution reactions, 630-631

Tetraalkyltins, unsymmetrical (mixed)

light induced reactions of halogens with, 655-656

physical constants and spectral prop-

erties of, by individual compounds, 662-808

physical properties of, 648-649

photochemistry of, 656-657

preparation, 634-643

preparation by addition-elimination on enol acetates, 643

preparation by addition of organotin hydrides to alkenes, 641-642

preparation by metal-halogen exchange, 641

preparation by metal-hydrogen exchange, 641

preparation by metal-metal exchange 639-641

preparation by other addition reactions, 642-643

preparation by thermal decompositions, 643

reaction by electrophilic substitution at a saturated carbon atom, 650-655

reaction by radical substitution at a saturated carbon atom, 655-657

reaction of allyl derivatives—the S_E2 mechanism, 654-655

reactivity sequency and the S_E1 mechanism in electrophilic substitution, 653-654

selectivity in electrophilic substitution, 650-652

stereochemistry of bimolecular electrophilic substitutions, 652-650

stereochemistry of radical substitutions, 656

Tetraaryltins, symmetrical

an inclusion compound of tetraphenyl tin with hexaphenylditin, 633

chemical properties of, 633-634

physical constants and spectral properties of, by individual compounds, 662-808

preparation of, 628

reaction with halogens, 632

reaction with sulfur or selenium, 633

redistribution reaction with stannic

chloride, 632-633

Tetraaryltins, unsymmetrical (mixed) see Aryltins, unsymmetrical (mixed)

Tetrakis (triphenylstannyl) tin, 824, 831

Tetraorganoditin dicarboxylates, 267-268, 845-849

Tetraorganoditin dihalides, 16-18, 849-850 854-855

Tetraorganoditin dihydrides, 17-18, 850, 854-855

Thermochemistry, 91, 117, 263-264, 536, 826

Tin tetracarboxylates, 265-266

Toxicity of organotin compounds, 949-952

Transition metal-tin bonds, compounds with, 895-924

Trialkyltin hydroxides, 194-196
    complexes with trialkyltin halides, 197-198
    table of, 196

Triorganotin radicals by photolysis of organotin hydrides, 12

Transition metal- tin bonds, compounds with, 894-924
    crystallographic structure determination of, 924
    insertion reactions, 915-917
    methods of preparation, 896-911
    miscellaneous reactions, 917
    Mössbauer spectra, 920-922
    nucleophilic displacement at tin, 911, 914
    physical properties of, 918-924
    preparation by condensation reactions, 908-913
    preparation by insertion reactions, 904-908
    preparation by metathetical reactions involving alkali metal derivatives, 896-904
    preparation by oxidative addition reactions, 905-908
    reactions of, 911-918
    reaction with boron trifluoride, 914
    reaction with halogens, 914-915
    reaction with hydrogen, 914-915
    reaction with hydrogen halides, 914-915
    reaction with iodotrifluoromethane, 914
    spectra other than Mössbauer (ir,

nmr, esr, etc.) 918-920

Typical element-tin bonds, compounds with, 881-895
    of tin with Group IA, IIA, IIB, and IIIA elements, preparation of, 882-887
    of tin with Group IA, IIA. IIB, and IIIA elements, physical properties of, 887
    of tin with Group IA, IIA, IIB, and IIIA, elements, reactions of, 887-889
    of tin with other Group IVA elements, preparation of, 889-890
    of tin with other Group IVA elements, physical properties of, 890-893
    of tin with other Group IVA elements, reactions of, 893-895
    conductivity properties of triphenyltin sodium and trimethyltin sodium, 887
    electrochemistry of compounds with $Sn-M_{IV}$ bonds, 895
    infrared data of compounds with $Sn-M_{IV}$ bonds, 890-892
    Mössbauer spectra of compounds with $Sn-M_{IV}$ bonds, 892
    Mössbauer spectra of triphenyltin lithium, 887
    preparation of organotin compounds with tin-germanium bonds, 886, 889-890
    preparation of organotin compounds with tin-lead bonds, 886, 889-890
    preparation of organotin compounds with tin-silicon bonds, 886, 889-890
    preparation (attempted) of organotin compounds with tin-aluminum bonds, 887
    preparation of organotin compounds with tin-boron bonds, 885-886
    preparation of organotin compounds with tin-lithium bonds, 882-883
    preparation of organotin compounds with tin-magnesium bonds, 883-885
    preparation of organotin compounds

with tin-mercury bonds, 885-886

preparation of organotin compounds with tin-potassium bonds, 883

preparation of organotin compounds with tin-sodium bonds, 882-883

preparation of organotin compounds with tin-tin bonds, 823-879

proton nmr data for organotin compounds with tin-silicon bonds, 891-892

proton nmr spectra fo trimethyltin lithium and dimethyl tin dilithium, 887

reaction of tin-boron bonds, 889

reactions of Sn-M bonds with alkli metals, 895

reactions of Sn-M bonds with halogens, 895

reactions of Sn-M bonds with hydroxide, 895

reactions of Sn-M bonds with organolithium reagents, 895

reactions of Sn-M bonds with oxygen, 894

reactions with retention of the Sn-·M bond, 893-894

reactions with scission of the Sn-M bond, 894-895

reductions with triphenyltin sodim, 888-889

relative stabilities of Group IV organometallic lithium compounds in THF, 889

table of, 886

ultraviolet spectra of compounds with Sn-M bonds, 892-893

X

X-ray structural analysis, 11, 112-113, 128-129, 156, 207, 210, 279, 301-302, 308, 318-319 323-324, 326-327, 343, 347, 833, 842-843

Y

Z

U

Ultraviolet spectroscopy, 105-106, 125-127, 158, 279, 302, 309, 313, 320, 330, 596, 606, 648, 892-893

V

W